ISBN 978-1-332-30337-3
PIBN 10311499

1 MONTH OF
FREE
READING

at

www.ForgottenBooks.com

By purchasing this book you are eligible for one month membership to ForgottenBooks.com, giving you unlimited access to our entire collection of over 700,000 titles via our web site and mobile apps.

To claim your free month visit:

www.forgottenbooks.com/free311499

English
Français
Deutsche
Italiano
Español
Português

www.forgottenbooks.com

Mythology Photography **Fiction**
Fishing Christianity **Art** Cooking
Essays Buddhism Freemasonry
Medicine **Biology** Music **Ancient**
Egypt Evolution Carpentry Physics
Dance Geology **Mathematics** Fitness
Shakespeare **Folklore** Yoga Marketing
Confidence Immortality Biographies
Poetry **Psychology** Witchcraft
Electronics Chemistry History **Law**
Accounting **Philosophy** Anthropology
Alchemy Drama Quantum Mechanics
Atheism Sexual Health **Ancient History**
Entrepreneurship Languages Sport
Paleontology Needlework Islam
Metaphysics Investment Archaeology
Parenting Statistics Criminology
Motivational

JOURNAL

OF THE

WASHINGTON ACADEMY

OF SCIENCES

VOLUME V, 1915

PUBLISHED SEMI-MONTHLY
EXCEPT IN JULY, AUGUST, AND SEPTEMBER, WHEN MONTHLY

BY THE

WASHINGTON ACADEMY OF SCIENCES

OFFICE OF PUBLICATION
THE WAVERLY PRESS
BALTIMORE, MD.

Nph (1)

JOURNAL

OF THE

WASHINGTON ACADEMY OF SCIENCES

Vol. V   JANUARY 4, 1915   No. 1

PHYSICS.—*The total emissivity of platinum and the relation between total emissivity and resistivity.* PAUL D. FOOTE. Communicated by C. W. WAIDNER.

On the basis of the Maxwell theory, Planck[1] has derived the following equation representing the relation between the reflection coefficient of a metallic surface, the volume resistivity of the metal, and the wave length of the incident radiation:

$$R_\lambda = \frac{\sqrt{3600\ \lambda^2/r^2 + 1} + 1 - \sqrt{2(\sqrt{3600\ \lambda^2/r^2 + 1} - 1)}}{\sqrt{3600\ \lambda^2/r^2 + 1} + 1 + \sqrt{2(\sqrt{3600\ \lambda^2/r^2 + 1} - 1)}} \quad . \ . \ (1)$$

where R_λ is the ratio of the intensities of the reflected to the incident radiation, r the volume resistivity of the metal in ohms cm, and λ the wave length of the radiation in cm. Defining the monochromatic emissivity as $E_\lambda = 1 - R_\lambda$ and expanding the above expression into a series of ascending powers of $\sqrt{r/\lambda}$, Hagen and Rubens[2] have obtained the following equation in which the terms of higher order than those indicated are negligible:

$$E_\lambda = 0.365 \sqrt{\frac{r}{\lambda}} - 0.0667 \left(\frac{r}{\lambda}\right) + \ \ . \ . \ . \ . \ . \ (2)$$

The spectral distribution of the energy radiated by a black body may be expressed by the Planck equation:

[1] Planck, Sitz. Königl. Ak. Wiss. Berlin, p. 278. 1903.
[2] Hagen and Rubens, Königl. Ak. Wiss. Berlin, p. 468. 1910.

$$J_\lambda = C_1\lambda^{-5} \left[e^{\frac{c_2}{\lambda T}} - 1 \right]^{-1} \quad \ldots \ldots \ldots \quad (3)$$

where T is the absolute temperature and $c_2 = 1.4450$ cm. deg. The total energy (any arbitrary unit) radiated by a black body is given by the integral of equation (3):

$$J = \int^\infty J_\lambda\, d\lambda \quad \ldots \ldots \ldots \ldots \quad (4)$$

The total energy radiated by a nonblack metal may be expressed as the integral of the Planck relation multiplied by the monochromatic emissivity:

$$J' = \int_0^\infty J_\lambda\, E_\lambda\, d\lambda \quad \ldots \ldots \ldots \ldots \quad (5)$$

If the total emissivity E of a metal is defined as the ratio of the energy emitted by the metal at an absolute temperature T to that emitted by a black body at the same temperature, one obtains the following relation:

$$E = \frac{J'}{J} = \frac{\int_0^\infty J_\lambda E_\lambda d\lambda}{\int_0^\infty J_\lambda d\lambda} \quad \ldots \ldots \ldots \quad (6)$$

Equation (6) may be converted to the gamma function form and is hence readily integrable. One thus obtains the following expression for the total emissivity of a metal:

$$E = 0.5736 \sqrt{rT} - 0.1769\, rT \quad \ldots \ldots \quad (7)$$

where T is the absolute temperature of the radiating metal and r the volume resistivity in ohms cm at this temperature.

It is therefore apparent that the total emissivity of most pure metals should increase with increasing temperature both because of the increasing value of T in equation (7) and because of, in general, the increasing volume resistivity. The increase in total emissivity with increasing temperature has been observed in nearly all of the extremely few instances where this quantity has been measured.[3]

[3] Langmuir, Trans. Am. Elec. Chem. Soc., **23**: 321. 1913; Randolph and Overholser, Phys. R., **2** (2): 144. 1913; Burgess and Foote, Bureau of Standards Scientific Paper **224**.

The above derivation is essentially that of Aschkinass,[4] who, in an extensive paper, has discussed the energy emission of metals, the value of λT_m of the displacement law for metals, and the relation of various properties of the radiation from metals to similar properties of black body radiation. He used for the value of E_λ the first term only of equation (2), the one term formula having been derived by Planck;[1] but inasmuch as Hagen and Rubens[2] have since found that the one term relation was insufficient, it appeared of interest to derive the somewhat general relation (7) for total emissivity from the more accurate relation (2) for monochromatic emissivity. The first term of equation (7) may be obtained directly from Aschkinass' work by dividing his equation (10) by the integral of Planck's spectral equation and correcting the value of c_2 in (10) to the present accepted value of 1.445. The second term of equation (7) becomes equal to 11 per cent of the first term at 1700°C. and hence is of considerable importance, especially at the higher temperatures.

In order to check formula (7) quantitatively, measurements have been made, with Mr. Kellberg's assistance, upon the total emissivity of platinum. The apparent temperatures of thin platinum strips were measured by three radiation pyrometers of the Féry mirror type and the apparent temperatures for a wave length $\lambda = 0.65\mu$ were obtained with a Holborn Kurlbaum optical pyrometer. The apparent temperatures measured by the optical pyrometer were converted in the usual manner to true temperatures using the value of $E_{0.65} = 0.33$. The emissivity of this metal for $\lambda = 0.65\mu$ is independent of the temperature.[5] This is of course in contradiction to the Maxwell relation (2) above. But it must be noted that, for metals, the visible spectrum is usually the region where resonance phenomena are taking place, and hence one would here expect that the general theoretical deductions might fail to apply, as is experimentally found to be the case. This fact does not materially

[4] Aschkinass, Ann. d. Physik., (4) 17: 960. 1905.

[5] Waidner and Burgess, Bureau of Standards Scientific Paper 55; Mendenhall, Astrophys. J., 33: 91. 1911; Spence, Astrophys. J., 37: 194. 1913.

alter the validity of the expression (7) for the total emissivity, since by far the greater part of the radiant energy of glowing metals at temperature below 1500°C. is confined to a spectral region where resonance phenomena do not exist.

The relation between the true absolute temperature T of a material, the apparent absolute temperature, S, measured by a total radiation pyrometer, and the total emissivity is given by the following expression:

$$E = \frac{S^4 - T_0^4}{T^4 - T_0^4} \quad \cdots \cdots \cdots \cdots \quad (8)$$

where T_o is the temperature of the receiver. The temperature coefficient of mass resistivity of pure platinum from 0 to 1100°C. is very accurately given by the Callendar[6] parabolic equation where $\delta = 1.49$ and C the fundamental coefficient is 0.0039.

It does not appear likely that serious error is introduced by the extrapolation of this equation to the melting point of platinum. Observations by Pirani,[7] Holborn and Wien,[8] and Langmuir[9] above 1100°C. do not deviate seriously from the parabolic relation. Langmuir concluded from his determinations that the relation was linear above 1200° but he uses the value 1710° instead of 1755° for the melting point of platinum. If his data are corrected for the error in the temperature scale the observations follow the Callendar formula quite satisfactorily. The mass resistivity of a 0.6 mm. × 100 cm. wire of Heraeus platinum, presumably of the same degree of purity as that of the strips used in the emissivity determinations, was very kindly measured by Mr. C. F. Hanson of this Bureau, with an accuracy of about 0.1 per cent. Reduction to the volume resistivity at 0°C. gave the value of 9.77 × 10⁻⁶ ohms cm, with possibly an error as great as 1 per cent. The ratio r_t/r_o, determined by resistances at constant mass, is equal to the ratio determined at constant volume within the accuracy of the present work.

[6] Waidner and Burgess, Bureau of Standards Scientific Paper **124**: 151.
[7] Pirani. Verh. d. Phys. Ges., **12**: 315. 1910.
[8] Holborn and Wien, Ann. d. Physik, **59**: 360. 1896.
[9] Langmuir, J. Am. Chem. Soc., **28**: 1357. 1906.

Figure 1 represents the total emissivity of platinum as a function of the temperature in the range 0° to 1700°C.

The computed points are represented by crosses. Preliminary observations made with radiation pyrometers which were later found to be somewhat defective are shown by small dots and the final observations made with an instrument comparatively free from these defects are plotted as circles. The large dot at 15°C. was obtained from the work of Hagen and Rubens on the reflection coefficients of platinum. These investigators have determined the dispersion of the reflection coefficient to

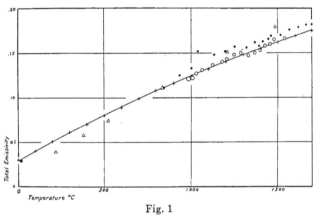

Fig. 1

25μ. If the values of $E_\lambda = 1 - R_\lambda$ are substituted in equation (6) the total emissivity may be btained. The integration was performed graphically. The triangles represent the observations of Lummer and Kurlbaum.[10]

The agreement between the theoretical and experimental values is excellent, when one considers the difficulties involved in an accurate determination of total emissivity. The deviations of the computed values from the observed values are in general much less than ± 0.01, which is about the limit of accuracy of the experimental determinations.

Table I presents a summary of the values of the total emissivity of pure platinum for the temperature range 0° to 1700°C.

[10] Lummer and Kurlbaum, Verh. d. Phys. Ges., **17**: 106. 1898.

Table II shows the corrections which must be applied to the
temperature observed with a radiation pyrometer, when sighted
upon pure platinum, in order to obtain the true temperature of
the radiating platinum.   The temperature of the receiver is considered as 300° abs. .

TABLE I

TOTAL EMISSIVITY VS. TEMPERATURE

DEGREES CENTIGRADE	EMISSIVITY	DEGREES CENTIGRADE	EMISSIVITY
0	0.030	900	0.116
100	0.040	1000	0.124
200	0.051	1100	0.132
300	0.061	1200	0.140
400	0.070	1300	0.148
500	0.080	1400	0.155
600	0.089	1500	0.162
700	0.099	1600	0.169
800	0.108	1700	0.175

TABLE II

TOTAL RADIATION PYROMETER SIGHTED ON PLATINUM
(RECEIVER = 300° ABS.)

OBSERVED TEMPERATURE	CORRECTION TO ADD	TRUE TEMPERATURE
200° C.	365° C.	565° C.
300	425	725
400	475	875
500	520	1020
600	560	1160
700	595	1295
800	630	1430
900	660	1560
1000	695	1695

In a subsequent paper the emissivity of other metals will be
discussed.   Approximate measurements have already indicated
that equation (7) is a general relation, and is by no means restricted to the example cited in the present paper.

SUMMARY

A definite relation has been found to exist between the total
emissivity and the volume resistivity of a metal.   This relation

follows directly from the Maxwell theory of reflection and absorption. Experimental determinations of the total emissivity of platinum have verified the derived relation.

MINERALOGY.—*Four new minerals.* WALDEMAR T. SCHALLER, Geological Survey.

The following very brief notes of four new minerals are given in order to secure priority, as it is desired to extend further the optical determinations before the detailed papers are published. The formulas given have all been derived from the completed chemical analyses.

Minasragrite is a blue hydrous vanadium sulphate from Minasragra, Peru. The monoclinic crystals dissolve readily in cold water. The vanadium is quadrivalent and the mineral is a hydrous acid vanadyl sulphate with the formula $V_2O_4 \cdot 3SO_3 \cdot 16H_2O$, which is interpreted as $(V_2O_2)H_2(SO_4)_3 \cdot 15H_2O$.

Fernandinite is a green hydrous calcium vanadyl vanadate from Minasragra, Peru. The analysis yields the formula $CaO \cdot V_2O_4 \cdot 5V_2O_5 \cdot 14H_2O$, which may be written, as a metavanadate as follows: $[H_4Ca(V_2O_2)][VO_3]_{10} \cdot 12H_2O$.

Shattuckite is a blue hydrous copper silicate from the Shattuck Arizona Copper Company's mine at Bisbee, Arizona. Its formula is $2CuO \cdot 2SiO_2 \cdot H_2O$ and it is close to plancheite in composition but differs considerably therefrom in its optical properties. Shattuckite forms pseudomorphs after malachite and also occurs as small spherulites.

Bisbeeite is found with the shattuckite and forms pseudomorphs after the shattuckite pseudomorphs of malachite. In composition bisbeeite is identical with dioptase, $CuO \cdot SiO_2 \cdot H_2O$, but is orthorhombic, pale blue to nearly white in color, and has distinct optical properties.

ZOOLOGY.—*The geographical divisions of the recent crinoid fauna.* AUSTIN H. CLARK, National Museum.

The division of the present crinoid fauna as a whole into satisfactory zoögeographic regions has proved to be a task of no little difficulty, chiefly because of the almost complete absence of these animals from littoral waters having a seasonal fluctuation of temperature and salinity, and because of the complete intergraduation of the littoral and the abyssal types.

Yet the very features which place the greatest obstacles in the way of outlining the zoögeographic divisions indicated by the crinoids at the same time suggest that these divisions are of more than usual significance, and are more fundamental in character, especially in their relation to the zoögeographic divisions of the past, than those of the other groups of marine organisms.

In the construction of the scheme outlined below, instead of following the usual method of subordinating the biological to the geographical aspect of the problem, I have examined all the known species of recent crinoids from the point of view of their systematic affinities and their obvious relationships, later assigning them to the various zoögeographic divisions in which they appear naturally to group themselves, so that these divisions are outlined purely from the biological viewpoint, and follow, if it may be so expressed, the phylogenetic rather than the geographical migrations of the class.

The crinoid fauna of the present seas is found to be divisible into two main sections, which, though faunally equivalent, are different in size and range. These two zoögeographic units are:

I. The Australian Fauna: Occurring all around the coasts of Australia, and including the Aru Islands and southern New Guinea (Papua).

The Australian fauna, which is littoral and sublittoral only, is characterized by certain very distinctive, primitive and aberrant specific types. Three genera, *Comatulella*, *Oligometrides* and *Ptilometra* are confined to it, while *Zygometra* and *Petasometra* are here very highly developed. It is related to the Indo-Pacific-Atlantic fauna, though it cannot be considered as a part of it, or as a derivative from it. Of the several divisions of the Indo-Pacific-Atlantic fauna it is most closely allied with the Caribbean, and two of the three peculiar genera are, outside of the Australian region, most closely related to Caribbean types, *Comatulella* to the genus *Comactinia*, and *Oligometrides* to the genus *Analcidometra;* it is interesting to note that neither *Comactinia* nor *Analcidometra* occur on the eastern shores of the Atlantic. The Australian and the Indo-Pacific-Atlantic faunas over-lap more or less in the Moluccas and in the Lesser Sunda Islands, and at the present time the entity of the former has become clouded and largely masked through the intrusion of numerous alien types from the Malayan region, particularly on the east Australian coast. The Australian fauna appears to be the last remnant of a once dominant fauna which, overwhelmed by a more vigorous fauna of subsequent origin, now persists only in the Australian littoral, and, almost entirely submerged, in the littoral and sublittoral zones of the Caribbean Sea.

II. THE INDO-PACIFIC-ATLANTIC FAUNA: Primarily character-istic of the region from Formosa to the Korean Straits, and eastward to Tokyo Bay, the Hawaiian Islands, the Kermadec Islands, the Admiralty Islands, the Meangis Islands, the Moluc-cas, the Lesser Sunda Islands, thence westward and northward along the southern shores of Java and Sumatra to the Nicobar and Andaman Islands, Ceylon and southwestward to Madagas-car and southeastern Africa, northwestern Africa and south-western Europe, and the Caribbean Sea. From this primary region, which falls into numerous subdivisions, faunal units, more or less differentiated from the original unit, have been and are being evolved (the "derived" faunas mentioned beyond) which occupy the entire area of the present seas at all depths, excepting only the Australian littoral.

The Indo-Pacific-Atlantic fauna, chiefly developed between the temperature of 10° and 18°.33C. (50° and 65° Fahrenheit), and composed entirely of species of moderate size, none very large and none very small, appears to represent the dominant, conservative, and homogeneous widely spread fauna of the more recent geological past, and to be the original homogeneous unit from which the recent faunal units are being evolved (1) by disruption of the ancient land continuity and consequent geo-graphical differentiation, (2) by migration of certain virile types into the cold abysses where, becoming modified, they undergo redistribution as abyssal types, and (3) by migration of other virile types into the purely recent hot tropical littoral where, becoming modified, they are redistributed as a tropical littoral fauna.

The geographical divisions of the Indo-Pacific-Atlantic fauna are the following:

1. *Southern Japanese-Hawaiian:* Formosa to the Korean Straits, and eastward to Tokyo Bay; the Hawaiian Islands.

a. Southern Japanese: Formosa to southern Japan, from the Korean Straits to Tokyo Bay. *b.* Hawaiian: Hawaiian Islands.

2. *Kermadec Island:* Kermadec Islands.

3. *East Indian-Australian:* Andaman Islands southward and eastward to the Lesser Sunda Islands, the Moluccas, Celebes and the Meangis Islands, and southward (in deeper water than that in which the Australian fauna occurs) to southwestern Australia and Tasmania.

4. *Ceylon-East African:* Ceylon westward and southwestward to Madagascar and southeastern Africa.

5. *Atlantic:* Northwestern Africa and southwestern Europe, and the Caribbean Sea.

a. East Atlantic: Northwestern Africa and southwestern Europe. *b.* Caribbean: Caribbean Sea.

The derived faunas originating from the Indo-Pacific-Atlantic which include chiefly or entirely littoral and shallow water types are the following:

1. *Malayan:* The region westward and northward of the Andaman, Nicobar and Lesser Sunda Islands, and east of the Moluccas and Celebes, as far as the Philippine Islands and Hong Kong.

2. *Littoral Atlantic:* Norway to the Gulf of Guinea, including the Mediterranean Sea; Caribbean Sea to Rio de Janeiro, Brazil.

a. Afro-European: Norway to the Gulf of Guinea, including the Mediterranean Sea.

b. American: Caribbean Sea to Rio de Janeiro, Brazil.

3. *Red Sea:* Red Sea, and eastward to the Persian Gulf.

The derived faunas originating from the Indo-Pacific-Atlantic which include exclusively primarily deep water types are the following:

1. *Arctic:* Arctic Ocean and north Atlantic, south to Nova Scotia and the extreme north of Europe; the western shores of the Seas of Okhotsk and Japan.

a. Arctic Ocean: Arctic Ocean, and the extreme north Atlantic.

b. East Asiatic: Western shores of the Seas of Okhotsk and Japan.

2. *Antarctic:* Antarctic regions, and the west coast of South and North America to Alaska, westward to the western Aleutian Islands, and southward to southern Japan.

a. Continental Antarctic: Coasts of the Antarctic continent, Kerguelen, and Heard Island.

b. Megellanic: Cape Horn northward to Alaska, westward to the western Aleutian Islands, thence southward to Tokyo and Sagami Bays, Japan.

c. Abyssal: The abysses in the extreme south, and in the eastern and northern portions of the Pacific and Atlantic Oceans; probably also the abysses in the eastern part of the Indian Ocean.

The various geographical divisions of the Indo-Pacific-Atlantic fauna occupy each a relatively circumscribed area, supporting distinctive species; but the derived faunas, while characteristic of the area as delimited above, have ill-defined borders and encroach more or less upon the surrounding faunas.

Thus the Malayan fauna, especially characteristic of, and apparently originating in, the very warm water of the Malayan littoral, is very widely spread wherever very warm water occurs; a few of its distinctive species reach southwestern Japan, one reaches the Hawaiian Islands, and several reach Australia, where they overlie the species of the Australian fauna proper, especially on the northeastern and eastern coasts, reaching as far south as Perth and Sydney; Ceylon also supports a few representatives of this fauna. The Littoral Atlantic fauna, excepting in the Mediterranean Sea, overlies the true Atlantic fauna. The other derived faunas similarly have extended their ranges more or less into territory occupied originally by other faunal units.

The derived faunas appear to be the dominant faunas of the present seas, composed of the most vigourous and most adaptable elements in the original Indo-Pacific-Atlantic stock. This latter now appears to be on the road to complete submergence, owing to its inability to adapt itself as a whole to the increasingly diverse oceanographical conditions.

ABSTRACTS

Authors of scientific papers are requested to see that abstracts, preferably prepared and signed by themselves, are forwarded promptly to the editors. Each of the scientific bureaus in Washington has a representative authorized to forward such material to this journal and abstracts of official publications should be transmitted through the representative of the bureau in which they originate. The abstracts should conform in length and general style to those appearing in this issue.

ATMOSPHERIC ELECTRICITY.—*On certain new atmospheric-electric instruments and methods.* W. F. G. SWANN. Terr. Mag., **19**: 171–185. 1914.

The first instrument described is a modification of the Ebert ion-counter, designed with a view to securing greatly increased sensitiveness. There are two concentric cylinders, as in the Ebert apparatus, but instead of the central one being connected to an electroscope reading up to 200 volts, as in that instrument, it is connected to the fiber of a single-fiber electroscope of the Einthoven type adjusted to a sensitivity of about 20 or 30 divisions per volt. The potential of the fiber is never allowed to depart far from zero potential and the necessary field is obtained by insulating and charging the outer cylinder to about 200 volts. On releasing the fiber from earth it, of course, starts to move, and the rate of movement can be noted. In order to prevent the charge on the outer cylinder affecting the number of ions coming to the apparatus, it is shielded by another cylinder which is earthed. In order to insure that the charge on the upper edge of the shielding cylinder does not rob the air of ions which should go to the central rod, a special attachment is made to the latter which renders this impossible.

The second portion of the paper describes a modification of Elster and Geitel's apparatus for determining the radio-active content of the atmosphere. Instead of the collecting wire being charged to −2000 volts below the potential of the earth, as in Elster and Geitel's method, it is charged to −2000 volts below the potential which the air in its vicinity would have if it were absent. In this way the charge on the wire, which is shown to determine the amount of active deposit collected, is independent of the potential gradient. A more fundamental unit of activity is suggested than that used by Elster and Geitel. It is based on the initial rate of production of ions in the ionization chamber, corresponding to unit charge on the collecting wire when exposed. The employment of an Einthoven electrometer in a manner analogous to that adopted in the case of the ion-counter described above renders it possible greatly to increase the convenience, rapidity, and accuracy of the measurements.

The third portion of the paper describes a piece of apparatus suitable for obtaining relative values of the potential gradient. Its action is based on recording the change of potential which a metal disc undergoes when, after being earthed and insulated, it is caused to alter its position in the Earth's field. The chief advantage of the method is that high insulation is not necessary, since it is only while the disc is changing its position that leakage is operative. In view of the slow action of the usual forms of collectors, leakage usually becomes a serious consideration in determining the final potential obtained, especially at sea. Another advantage of the present method is that it enables the potential-gradient to be obtained at any instant.

W. F. G. S.

ATMOSPHERIC ELECTRICITY.—*On certain matters relating to the theory of atmospheric electric measurements.* W. F. G. SWANN. Terr. Mag., **19**: 205–218. 1914.

The earthed portions of pieces of apparatus exposed to the atmospheric potential gradient have to take a negative charge in order that their potential may remain zero. The effect of the charge in modifying the measurements is discussed for various cases. In the Ebert ion-counter the effect is to decrease the measured ionic density in the case of the negative ions, while in the case of the positive ions the results are unaffected, though the paths of the ions are of course influenced by the charge. It is shown that the effect is expressible very simply in terms of the charge induced by the potential gradient on the *inside* of the opening where the air enters. By measuring this charge it is possible (knowing the rate of the air flow) to estimate the order of magnitude of the effect. The effect is greatest of course when the apparatus is mounted on a tall slender support. It was found by measurement that it might easily amount to 20 per cent of the value of the quantity measured. The analogous effect is discussed for the case of the Gerdien conductivity apparatus, and it is shown that even in the case of the negative ions no error is introduced, provided that the potential of the central conductor is not too high. In fact the effect of the potential gradient is simply to lower the value of the maximum potential to which it is allowable to charge the central system. In the case of the conductivity of the positive ions, while the ionic paths are influenced, neither the conductivity nor the maximum potential allowable are influenced on the whole.

The effect of making measurements of conductivity on the top of a high tower is discussed in the above light and it is shown that, if suitable precautions are taken, the proper conductivity will be obtained for the air at that altitude, in spite of the influence of the charge on the tower. There is an advantage in making measurements on the air far removed from the ground, since the number of ions present are then uninfluenced by the effects due to the potential gradient referred to in the first abstract. The question of shielding the instruments to protect them from the potential gradient is discussed. It is only in the case of the Ebert apparatus that shielding of this kind is necessary. It is important to ascertain, however, whether the avoidance of charge on the earthed portions of the apparatus by shielding is not counteracted by the effect of the charge on the shield. It is shown that a properly arranged shield is on the whole effective.

W. F. G. S.

ATMOSPHERIC ELECTRICITY.—*The atmospheric-electric observations made on the second cruise of the Carnegie, 1909–1913.* C. W. HEWLETT. Terr. Mag., **19**: 127–170. 1914.

The atmospheric-electric work on board the *Carnegie* has been confined entirely to observations of the specific conductivity, the potential-gradient, and the radioactivity of the atmosphere, the greater part of the observations consisting of the first two quantities named. The observations are divided naturally into three principal groups, according to the observer who made them. From New York to Colombo, E. Kidson conducted the observations; for the route from Colombo to Manila, owing to breakage in the instruments and the impossibility of having the requisite repairs made, there are no observations; from Manila to Tahiti, H. F. Johnston conducted the observations, and from Tahiti to New York, the work was carried on by C. W. Hewlett. For an account of the instruments and methods used, as well as for the detailed results obtained, reference must be made to the original article.

From a summary of the various results thus far obtained at sea, the following deductions in regard to the mean values of the elements may be drawn: The potential-gradient is of the same order of magnitude over the sea as over the land; the radioactivity of the air over ocean-areas far removed from land is small, compared to that found over land; and the ionization over the ocean is at least as large as that found over land.

C. W. H.

ATMOSPHERIC ELECTRICITY.—*Investigation of certain causes responsible for uncertainty in the measurement of atmospheric conductivity by the Gerdien conductivity apparatus.* C. W. HEWLETT. Terr. Mag., **19**: 219–233. 1914.

The object of the writer was to test experimentally the behavior of the apparatus under various conditions. It was shown theoretically by Dr. Swann that the theory of the apparatus does not necessitate a constancy of the velocity over a cross section of the air current, and that, if the potential is below a certain minimum value depending on the total air flow, the correct value of the conductivity is obtained. By covering up half of the space opposite the fan, a considerable irregularity was produced in the air flow. For low charging voltages, however, the conductivity was practically the same as without the obstruction. As the voltage is increased beyond a certain point, the measured conductivity, without the obstruction, becomes less than that with it, but this is due to the fact that the critical voltage is less with the obstruction than without it, owing to the smaller air flow in the former case.

As the measured conductivity was found to depend upon the presence or absence of the funnel, it was thought advisable to investigate the exact effect of the latter. Certain theoretical considerations point to the conclusion that, in the absence of the funnel, the maximum allowable voltage is reduced, owing to the fact that the stream lines of the air which enter the funnel near the edges suffer sharp bends in that vicinity. Experiments were consequently made to determine whether the effect of the funnel was less important for low charging voltages. It was found that for charging voltages of 10, 30, 50, 70, 100, the relation of the conductivity without the funnel to that with the funnel was 0.98, 0.96, 0.98. 0.94, 0.89; hence the theoretical conclusion that the ratio is practically unity for low voltages, and less than unity for higher voltages, is borne out. Experiments have also been made to determine the effect of the charge induced on the earthed portions of the apparatus owing to the existence of the potential gradient. It is found that under certain conditions this effect may be considerable. The usual theory of the Gerdien apparatus neglects the effect of the charge collected by the rod which supports the central cylinder. Experiments were made to measure directly this charge, and it was found to be far from negligible in comparison with that collected by the central cylinder. In the use of the Gerdien apparatus it is important that the charging potential shall always be sufficiently low. The most sensitive region of the electroscope supplied with the instruments is usually in the neighborhood of 150 to 200 volts. It has been found, however, that the maximum allowable voltage varies considerably from day to day, presumably owing to variations in the specific ionic velocities. Usually a charging potential of 150 volts is far too high.

C. W. H.

TERRESTRIAL MAGNETISM.—*The local magnetic constant and its variations.* L. A. BAUER. Terr. Mag., **19**: 113–125. 1914.

Good progress has been made by various investigators in establishing the relationship between fluctuations of the Earth's magnetism and those of the Sun's activity during the Sun-spot cycle. The magnetic quantity most frequently used for this purpose has been the range of the diurnal variation—generally of the magnetic declination. In connection with a preliminary examination of this relationship, made in 1909, occasion was found to employ various other magnetic quantities. One of these was what is here termed the "local magnetic constant," which, under certain assumptions, is proportional to the magnetic moment of the Earth, or to the intensity of magnetization; it is thus a quantity which lends itself readily to physical interpretation. The result of chief interest obtained from the 1909 investigation was that an increase in solar activity was accompanied, in general, during 1906 to 1909, by a decrease in the local magnetic constant. Since this investigation, Abbot's extensive observations at Mt. Wilson, California, and Bassour, Algiers, showing the fluctuations in the values of the solar constant of radiation for various years, have become available. The question arises whether any changes in the Earth's magnetism follow the same course as that of the solar constant.

As a provisional result, subject to modification when the final computations have been made, it was found that for a change of 10 per cent observed in the solar-constant values, there is apparently a change in the local magnetic-constant of about 0.03 per cent of its value, *i.e.*, about 10×10^{-5} C.G.S., decreased magnetic constant corresponding to increased solar constant. The effect appears to be most pronounced for the observatories in the Sun-lit portion of the globe, and seems to be reversed for the observatories in the night portion, judging from the place where the corresponding solar observations are made. This is being looked into further.

In the discussion of magnetic disturbances we may have to distinguish between two broad classes:

(1) The *curvilinear*, the more prominent as far as general magnitude is concerned, occurring practically over the whole Earth at the same time, seemingly initiated by such radiations or streams of charged particles which are deflected from a straight path, when they come under the influence of the Earth's magnetic field, as to pass around and behind the Sun-lit portion of the Earth.

(2) The *rectilinear*, occurring practically only over the portions of the Earth reached by the straight-line, or ordinary, radiations from the Sun.   L. A. B.

TERRESTRIAL MAGNETISM.—*Regarding improvement of appliances for measurement of the Earth's magnetic elements by magnetic and electric methods.* (Progress Report.)   L. A. BAUER, Terr. Mag., **19**: 1–18. 1914.

The instruments for magnetic measurements, employing distinctively magnetic methods, have now reached the requisite stage of perfection for meeting the practical requirements, both on land and at sea. However, the desire is to devise and try out new methods, as, for example, those based on electrodynamic or electric principles, with a two-fold object in view: (1) to obtain, more expeditiously than is possible with the type of magnetometer now in general use, a magnetic measurement within the relative accuracy required for a successful study of the magnetic variations; (2) to obtain, another control, by means of a distinctively different method, on the absolute accuracy of the present magnetic standards. The present report summarizes what has been done thus far with respect to improvement of the appliances and methods for the measurement of the terrestrial-magnetic elements and what is still further to be undertaken.

In all of the Department's types of magnetometers, the magnet house is of wood. Furthermore, every instrument is as nearly as possible an independent or absolute one, *i.e.*, all the various constants can be absolutely determined. It is shown that, as the result of numerous comparisons, it would seem safe to conclude that the H, or horizontal-intensity, standards of Kew, Potsdam, and Washington (Department of Terrestrial Magnetism) give an absolute accuracy within one part in 10,000, except for some possible error which may be inherent in the magnetometer-method but not yet disclosed.

When the ocean work of the Department was begun in 1905, it was necessary either to design entirely new, or to modify considerably, existing devices. There have resulted thus new magnetic instruments, for use at sea, designed, as well as chiefly constructed, by the Department. With these instrumental devices, an accuracy in ocean magnetic work has been secured which, under favorable conditions and devoting the same time as in land work, does not fall much short of the general accuracy of land field work.   '   L. A. B.

TERRESTRIAL MAGNETISM.—*Results of magnetic observations made by the U. S. Coast and Geodetic Survey in 1913.* R. L. FARIS. U. S. Coast and Geodetic Survey Special Publication No. 20. Pp. 52. 1914.

In 1882 the results of field magnetic observations made by the Coast and Geodetic Survey prior to 1881, together with descriptions of stations, were published as Appendix 9, Report for 1881. In "Magnetic Declination Tables and Isogonic Charts for 1902" declination results were given for all stations occupied up to that time and descriptions were given of stations established subsequent to 1881. From 1903 to 1911 there was published annually an appendix to the Superintendent's report giving the results of the magnetic observations made during the fiscal year (July to June) covered by the report. Special Publication No. 15 contained the results of magnetic observations made between July 1, 1911 and December 31, 1912.

The present publication contains the results of observations made on land and at sea during the calendar year 1913, and in the Philippine Islands in 1912, together with descriptions of the stations occupied. Results are given for 282 stations in 245 localities including a general magnetic survey of the Philippine Islands, a detailed survey of the crater of Kilauea, Hawaii, and an investigation of the area of local disturbance in the vicinity of Wilmington, Delaware. A table is given presenting a comparison of the declination results at 69 repeat stations with the results of earlier observations in the same localities. The results have been corrected to reduce them to the International Standard of the Department of Terrestrial Magnetism of the Carnegie Institution of Washington. Horizontal Intensity results heretofore published must be diminished by 1 part in 1000 to reduce them to that standard.   D. L. HAZARD.

GEOLOGY.—*The transportation of debris by running water.* GROVE KARL GILBERT. Based on experiments made with the assistance of EDW. CHAS. MURPHY. U. S. Geological Survey Professional Paper 86. Pp. 263. 1914.

For original brief statement of results see this JOURNAL, **4:** 154–158. 1914.

GEOLOGY.—*The Montana group of Northwestern Montana.* EUGENE STEBINGER. U. S. Geological Survey Professional Paper 90-G. Pp. 68. 1914.

For original brief statement of results see this JOURNAL, **4:** 383–384. 1914.

GEOLOGY.—*A reconnaissance in the Canyon Range, west-central Utah.* G. F. LOUGHLIN. U. S. Geological Survey Professional Paper 90-F. Pp. 10. 1914.

The formations studied are all of sedimentary origin and include limestone of lower Mississippian (Madison) age, quartzite of probable upper Mississippian age, Eocene conglomerates and sandstones, and the Pleistocene Lake Bonneville beds. The principal structural features are a series of folds, some open and others close, one of the latter being accompanied by a strike fault of probable reverse character. Evidence of "basin range" faulting is also present. The contact between Eocene and Carboniferous strata indicates that the former were deposited on an erosion surface of considerable irregularity.

The folding of the Carboniferous rocks is believed to have taken place in late Jurassic or post-Jurassic time. This was followed by an erosion period, in Cretaceous time, and by deposition of the Eocene strata, which probably once covered the entire area of the present range. The volcanic eruptions took place in late Eocene or post-Eocene time. The volcanic period was followed by profound faulting and uplift of the range. Sevier River maintained its course during the uplift, cutting through the Eocene beds and following a probable pre-Eocene synclinal valley in the quartzite. Pleistocene time was marked by the deposition of the Lake Bonneville beds and subsequent erosion of them along the present course of Sevier River.

The ore deposits of the range, which is included in the Leamington mining district, include small replacement bodies of oxidized and sulphide lead-zinc ore, with low silver values, and also small showings of oxidized copper minerals in quartz veins, which have been only superficially prospected.   The deposits resemble in general character several deposits, low in silver, in neighboring mining districts.   G. F. L.

GEOLOGY.—*Reconaissance of oil and gas fields in Wayne and McCreary counties, Kentucky.* M. J. MUNN.   U. S. Geological Survey Bulletin No. 579. Pp. 105. 1914. (Prepared in cooperation with the Kentucky Geological Survey.)

The strata which outcrop in Wayne County have a maximum thickness ranging between 1200 and 1500 feet.   The upper part of the series consists of sandstone, shale, conglomerate, clay, and coal belonging to the Pennsylvania series ("Coal Measures") of the Carboniferous system.   These beds are underlain by about 1000 feet of limestone, shale, and thin sandstone, belonging to the Mississippian series ("sub-Carboniferous").   Pennsylvanian rocks are absent over the northern part of the county and along the principal streams, having been removed by erosion.   The maximum thickness, probably 400 or 500 feet, of Pennsylvanian rocks is found in the high hills along the southern border of the county.   The limestones and the red and green shales of the upper part of the Mississippian series are exposed along the valleys and hillsides of the mountainous region, and the limestones of the middle and lower part form the surface of the rolling plain in the northern and western portions of the county.   These older beds consist of 20 to 40 feet of Devonian shale at the top, underlain unconformably by Silurian or Ordovician limestones down to water level.   Over 1500 feet of rocks, mostly limestones, which are not exposed at the surface, are known to have been pierced by a few deep wells.

Most of the oil in this district is found in a cherty geode-bearing limestone called by drillers the Beaver Creek "sand."   In well records the Beaver Creek "sand" is shown to vary considerably in distance above the top of the Chattanooga ("Black") shale.   In many wells it is as much as 60 feet above the Chattanooga shale, but in most places where productive it appears to be only a few feet above that shale, from which it is separated by light-green and blue clay shales. The writer suspects that in many places where the Beaver Creek "sand" is reported by producers to be "high" above the Chattanooga shale, the true Beaver Creek "sand" may be absent, as in the Beaver Creek mill section, and that certain limestones may have been mistaken for it.

The geologic structure of this region is that of a broad, comparatively shallow trough in which occur many minor anticlines and synclines. The axis of this great trough or synclinorium trends generally northeast and southwest. The general dip of the rocks in Wayne County is toward the southeast and amounts to about 20 feet to the mile. There is, however, considerable difference in the degree and direction of dip from place to place, due partly perhaps to unconformities in the rocks of the different series and systems and to unequal deposition of sediments, but mainly to warping in the process of folding, which caused the minor folds and wrinkles that seem to be so intimately associated with the origin of the oil pools.

ALFRED H. BROOKS.

GEOLOGY.—*The Iditarod-Ruby region, Alaska.* H. M. EAKIN. U. S. Geological Survey Bulletin No. 578. Pp. 45. 1914.

The province treated extends from Yukon River at Ruby to Iditarod River and includes the Ruby, Innoko, and Iditarod mining districts. The hard rocks of the Ruby district belong to an older complex of more or less altered sedimentary and volcanic rocks which can be provisionally correlated with the metamorphic Paleozoic and possibly older rocks of the Yukon-Tanana region. The Innoko and Iditarod districts are underlain by a younger series, predominantly of sedimentary and subordinately of volcanic rocks, in part at least of Cretaceous and probably all of Mesozoic age. Intrusive rocks occur in all the districts. They include granitic batholiths, stocks, dikes and sills, that range widely in lithologic character. In most of the region the hard rocks are heavily mantled by alluvial and possibly lacustrine deposits in the lowlands, by residual clays and fragmental deposits on the slopes and lower ridges, and locally near the higher mountain groups by morainic and glacial outwash deposits.

Auriferous deposits occur in both the Paleozoic and Mesozoic areas, and they are probably related genetically to certain of the younger intrusive rocks. This relation is especially clear in the cases of the monzonites of the Iditarod district and the altered rhyolite porphyry dikes of the Innoko district. H. M. E.

GEOLOGY.—*The ore deposits of northeastern Washington.* HOWLAND BANCROFT; *including a section on the Republic mining district.* WALDEMAR LINDGREN and HOWLAND BANCROFT. U. S. Geological Survey Bulletin No. 550. Pp. 215. 1914.

The area investigated in the reconnaissance whose results are here set forth is situated in the extreme northeastern part of the State of

Washington, containing within its boundaries the whole of Stevens and Ferry counties.

The rocks of this region are referred to the Proterozoic, Paleozoic, Mesozoic, and Cenozoic eras. The rocks classified provisionally as pre-Cambrian are the crystalline schists and metamorphosed limestones and quartzites found between Laurier and Orient. The larger part of the region is occupied by an extensive series of more or less dynamo-metamorphosed argillites, lime shales, limestones, and quartzites. Because of its general similarity to rocks farther west in Washington, which in places are fossiliferous, this series has been referred to the Paleozoic era. In places these rocks were intruded by diabase or it flowed out over their surfaces and was metamorphosed along with the rest of the series, so that it is now represented by greenstone. In part of the district greenstones are prominent. One of the most conspicuous rocks of northeastern Washington is intrusive granite. It is thought that large batholiths intruded the sedimentary series during Mesozoic time, parts of the batholiths having been subsequently exposed by erosion. The presence of monzonite porphyry in most of the mining districts is believed to be due to later eruptions of the granitic magma, and these may have taken place at intervals from late Mesozoic to early Tertiary time. Lava flows of various types fill many of the erosion depressions in the older rocks, and in places form high mountains. Their eruption is thought to have taken place during Tertiary time. Still later flows of basalt are prominent in the extreme southern part of the area investigated, although some were seen in the Republic district. The gold-quartz veins of the Republic (Eureka) district and the First Thought gold deposits, in the Orient district, are of late Tertiary age and are seliniferous.

The period in which the granite, quartz diorite, quartz monzonite porphyry, and monzonite porphyry and the accompanying dikes were intruded was that of the most extensive mineralization. The major part of the ore deposits are believed to be of Mesozoic age, and they owe their origin to the after effects of igneous intrusion. During the Paleozoic period of dynamometamorphism, while the greenstones were being formed, some of the metallic ores may have been concentrated from the basic rocks, so that a few of the ore deposits in the area may be of Paleozoic age. However, intrusive rocks thought to be of Mesozoic age were found in the vicinity of the greenstones, and it is more likely that the deposits associated with the greenstones are due to the Mesozoic intrusions.   ALFRED H. BROOKS.

GEOLOGY.—*Mining districts of the Dillon quadrangle, Montana, and adjacent areas.* ALEXANDER N. WINCHELL. U. S. Geological Survey Bulletin No. 574. Pp. 191. 1914.

The Dillon quadrangle lies in southwestern Montana and is in general mountainous, but it contains one large valley, that of Beaverhead and Jefferson rivers, and numerous smaller valleys. Sedimentary rocks ranging in age from Algonkian, possibly Archaean, to Quaternary, are represented in this province. Igneous rocks include quartz monzonite, occurring in a large batholith, together with various other types of intrusives; volcanics also occur.

The geologic structure was determined largely by the intrusion of the great Boulder batholith, which seems to have penetrated by faulting or thrusting, or by assimilation of material, or by updoming important areas in the quadrangle in Tertiary time, or, more probably by a combination of all these processes.

The principal mineral resources of this area and those adjacent include gold, silver, copper, and lead, and smaller quantities of zinc, iron, manganese, tungsten, antimony, arsenic, bismuth, vanadium, tellurium, and sulphur.

The Boulder batholith in a large sense seems to be in whole or in part the source of many of the ore deposits of the Dillon quadrangle. The ore deposits occur chiefly in fissure veins or in irregular bodies produced by contact metamorphism in limestone or dolomite. Some of the ore deposits are in the form of fissure veins. Others belong to the type of ore disseminated in the country rock.

ALFRED H. BROOKS.

GEOLOGY.—*Electric activity in ore deposits.* ROGER C. WELLS. U. S. Geological Survey Bulletin No. 548. Pp. 1–78. 1914.

Many of the chemical reactions that occur in ore deposits involve oxidation and reduction, and with electrolytes the phenomena of oxidation and reduction are closely linked with electric activity. Many ores are also conductors of electricity. It is therefore possible, and necessary to consider, that balanced chemical action may occur in ore deposits at two points somewhat removed from each other. Such activity would produce different mineral associations than would result from a direct admixture of the chemical agents. One of the simplest possible combinations by which electric action could occur would consist in the presence of two different active solutions in contact with a single body of ore, the two active solutions being united by any "indifferent" electrolyte. Pyrite is so inert to many solutions as to function like an "unattackable" electrode, thus making oxidizing and reducing solutions available for producing electric currents in ore deposits. Differences in polarization were detected, however, and measured when different minerals were employed as anodes and cathodes.   R. C. W.

GEOLOGY.—*Geology of the phosphate deposits northeast of Georgetown, Idaho.* R. W. RICHARDS and G. R. MANSFIELD, with preface by H. S. GALE. U. S. Geological Survey Bulletin No. 577. Pp. 74. 1914.

The area discussed lies in southeast Idaho and includes many formations ranging in age from lower Carboniferous (Madison limestone) to Quarternary (chiefly alluvium and basalt). It is traversed by the great Bannock Overthrust, the plane of which is warped and partially eroded. The older rocks constituting the upper block are folded into a series of anticlines and synclines with axes trending slightly west of north. Large bodies of phosphate rock occur in the synclines. The younger rocks of the lower block are also underlain by phosphate. Salt deposits occur along the line of the Bannock Overthrust.

                                                                R. W. R.

GEOLOGY AND PALEONTOLOGY.—*Cretaceous deposits of the eastern Gulf region, and species of Exogyra from the eastern Gulf region and the Carolinas.* LLOYD WILLIAM STEPHENSON. U. S. Geological Survey Professional Paper No. 81. Pp. 71. 1914.

The paper is a preliminary general account of the character, distribution, and age relations of the Cretaceous deposits of the eastern Gulf region, followed by detailed descriptions of the species of Exogyra from this region and the Carolinas. It is shown that marine Upper Cretaceous deposits composing certain great formations merge along the strike into marine deposits of different character in such a manner that the relative ages of the deposits in different parts of the area can not be determined by stratigraphic sequence alone. Two major faunal zones characterized respectively by *Exogyra ponderosa* Roemer and *Exogyra costata* Say, and two sub-zones characterized respectively by the genus Mortoniceras and the species *Liopistha protexta* Conrad, are recognized; an unnamed zone in the lower part of the Eutaw formation in the Chattahoochee region is also indicated. Within each of these zones and subzones are found many other species of restricted range. Paleontologic means is thus afforded of establishing the age relations of the deposits.

Included in the paper are tables showing the occurrence and geologic range of Upper Cretaceous fossils, a table indicating graphically lithologic variations and age relations of the Cretaceous deposits, and a geologic map on a scale of 1:2,500,000.

The value of the genus Exogyra in correlation rests on the fact of its extended geographic distribution and the restricted stratigraphic range of its principal species, *Exogyra costata* and *Exogyra ponderosa*.

L. W. S.

GEOLOGY.—*Slate in the United States.* T. Nelson Dale and others. U. S. Geological Survey Bulletin No. 586. Pp. 220. 1914.[1]

Slate, in ordinary usage, denotes a rock with more or less perfect cleavage adapting it to various commercial uses, and in which the particles with few exceptions can not be distinguished except in thin section under a microscope. Slates are classified, according to genesis, into (1) sedimentary and (2) igneous; group (1) being by far the most important and subdivided into:

A. Clay slates: Matrix without any or with very faint aggregate polarization.

B. Mica slates: Matrix with marked aggregate polarization.

A further subdivision of each group is based upon mineral character. Igneous slates are divided into (A) ash slates and (B) dike slates.

The slates of group (A) originate in marine deposits of clay and sand. The angular grains of feldspar and quartz in slate imply the nearness of masses of granitic rocks. The alternation of slate beds with quartzite or grit corresponds to the alternation of extremely fine clayey with sandy sediments from such land masses. These sediments consisted largely of quartz, feldspar and mica, with zircon and other silicates, various compounds of iron, lime and magnesia, together with kaolin from the decomposition of the feldspar.

The next stage in the formation of slate is attributed ultimately to the radiation of the earth's internal heat and the consequent corrugation of its outer portion. One effect of this compression was to metamorphose the shale into slate. This included two processes of uncertain priority. Under the combined presence of moisture and the effect of pressure and heat, both the heat generated by the pressure and that which pervaded the strata at the depth at which they were buried,

[1] This is a revised edition of Bulletin 275 of 1906. The coworkers include: W F. Hillebrand (analyses), E. C. Eckel, A. F. Purdue, L. M. Prindle, F. H. Moffit, C. A. Bonine (geology), M. Merriman (tests), Miss A. T. Coons (statistics).

there occurred such a chemical recombination of the silica, alumina, potash, iron and water of the feldspar, kaolin and iron of the shale, as to generate new potash mica in amount sufficient to constitute, in the mica slates, over 33 per cent of the resulting slate. This muscovite was of infinitesimal thinness and other dimensions and mostly of longish, tapering or ribbonlike outline. Most of these scales arranged themselves with their flat sides parallel to, or overlapping, one another but facing the direction from which the pressure came and also with an angle of inclination governed by that pressure. A small but variable proportion, however, of these scales took such a position that their flat sides became parallel to the direction of the pressure thus giving rise to the "grain."

As mica crystallizes in columnar crystals and as the plates or scales due to its molecular structure are transverse to the crystal column, and as a slab of slate consists largely of parallel scales of mica it may be said to correspond, when held horizontally, to such a crystal held vertically. When a mica slate is cut in thin section across the cleavage its optical behavior under polarized light is like that of a mica crystal cut across its crystal cleavage. Yet as not only a considerable number of the mica scales in slate lie across the cleavage, but as some scales of chlorite and crystals of other minerals do also, the texture of a mica slate combines some of the features of a crystal with some of those of a tissue.

This crystalline fabric may inclose in its meshes any sedimentary particles of quartz, zircon, feldspar, kaolin, or other minerals which were not or could not be made over into mica or secondary quartz but whose alignment became more or less parallel to that of the major part of the new mica. During this metamorphism other chemical combinations were formed by the constituents of the shale, resulting in isolated scales or crystals of chlorite, biotite, various carbonates, pyrite, magnetite, graphite, tourmaline, andalusite, etc. These arranged themselves variously—some in the cleavage direction, some in the grain direction. Lenses consisting of one mineral surrounded by one or two others were also formed and concentrically or radiately arranged. The subjects of slip cleavage, shear-zones, cleavage banding, slate discoloration and weathering are considered in some detail.

T. N. D.

PROCEEDINGS OF THE ACADEMY AND AFFILIATED SOCIETIES

THE CHEMICAL SOCIETY

The 241st meeting was held at the Bureau of Standards on Thursday, October 8, 1914.

The Secretary read the announcement of the action of the Directors in establishing the Maryland Section, whose territory covers all that part of the previous territory of the Washington Section lying north of a parallel of latitude through Laurel, Md., including the city of Laurel.

Director S. W. STRATTON outlined the work of the Bureau of Standards, discussing the different kinds of work done and the general plan of organization. Dr. W. F. Hillebrand described, more in particular, the chemical work of the Bureau. He gave statistics to show the variety and magnitude of the regular testing work, and then took up individually the various lines of research which have been carried forward during the past years. The meeting then adjourned for an inspection of some of the laboratories.

The 242d meeting was held at the Cosmos Club on Thursday, November 12, 1914.

The meeting was devoted to the election of officers for 1915. The election resulted as follows: *President:* C. L. ALSBERG, of the Bureau of Chemistry; *First Vice-Pres.:* R. B. SOSMAN, of the Geophysical Laboratory; *Second Vice-Pres.:* H. M. LOOMIS, of the Bureau of Chemistry; *Secretary:* E. C. McKELVY, of the Bureau of Standards; *Treasurer:* F. P. DEWEY, of the Bureau of the Mint; *Councilors:* J. A. LeCLERC, Bureau of Chemistry, P. H. WALKER, Bureau of Standards, J. JOHNSTON, Geophysical Laboratory, F. P. DUNNINGTON, University of Virginia; *Executive Committee,* E. W. BOUGHTON, Bureau of Standards, R. C. WELLS, Geological Survey, A. N. FINN, Bureau of Standards, O. F. BLACK, Bureau of Plant Industry.

The 243d Meeting was held at the Cosmos Club on Thursday, December 10, 1914. The amendments proposed at the last meeting, providing for the separation of the Maryland Section, were passed unanimously. The President called attention to the recent death (on December 5) of DR. A. C. PEALE, one of the first members of the Society, and its Secretary for ten years or more. Dr. Bigelow and Dr. Dewey spoke briefly upon the work of Dr. Peale.   Dr. Le Clerc moved that a committee of three who had been personally acquainted with Dr. Peale be appointed to draw up suitable resolutions.   Messrs. F. W. Clarke, W. F. Hillebrand, and F. P. Dewey were appointed.

The following papers were read:

F. P. DEWEY, of the Bureau of the Mint: *The recovery of osmiridium in the electrolytic refining of gold.*   Practically all bullion refining in the Mint service is now done by the electrolytic process.   After suitable selection, gold anodes containing osmiridium are specially treated. By hanging a beaker under the anode the slime is collected, and from it the grains of osmiridium are washed out.   Details of the older and newer procedures were given by the speaker.

Discussion: WELLS spoke of the need for more thorough work on the chemical reactions of the platinum metals.   FITZGERALD inquired about the form in which the osmiridium separates, and about the percentages of metals found therein.   The iridium varies from 43 to 77 per cent of the alloy.   SOSMAN compared the platinum content of the Ural deposits with that of some ores discussed by Dewey, and mentioned that the recently advertised discovery of platinum in Westphalia had turned out to be a fraud.   FOSTER inquired about the settling of osmiridium from a silver melt, and also about a reported discovery of platinum at the Katahdin Iron Works in Maine.   DEWEY stated that no information about this discovery had been published.

E. H. WALTERS, of the Bureau of Soils: *The presence of primary cleavage products of protein in soils.*   In an investigation of a water extract and a dilute alkali (2 per cent sodium hydroxide) extract of a sample of Norfolk sandy loam soil from Virginia, substances were obtained which responded to the characteristic reactions of proteoses and peptones. The color reactions obtained and the methods employed in making a partial separation of these bodies showed that a complex mixture of the various proteoses and peptones was present and persisted in the soil for a considerable period.   The experiments described show that proteins undergo hydrolytic decomposition in soil in much the same way as in digestion by enzymes, acids, or alkalines in the laboratory. (Author's abstract.)

Discussion: WELLS inquired about the precipitation of barium carbonate by carbon dioxide.   WALTERS stated that the barium is held in solution by carbamino compounds.

A. SEIDELL: *The excretion of thymol in the urine.*   Thymol has been widely used in the treatment of the hookworm disease.   Being a protoplasmic poison, and its absorption being promoted by the presence of fats and oils, its use is somewhat dangerous.   In order to find a safer substitute, experiments have been made to determine the manner of action of thymol in eliminating hookworm.   Methods for the elimination of thymol in excreta were studied, and it was found that it can be recovered by two steam distillations, one acid and one alkaline, and then determined in the neutral water solution.   Using this method, it was found that no thymol is excreted in feces.   It does pass out, how-

ever, in the urine, but in combination as glycuronate. It can be separated therefrom by steam distillation from sulfuric acid solution, followed by an alkaline solution containing certain salts which hold back
substances which might interfere with the subsequent bromine titration.
Experiments on dogs showed that the thymol excretion ends before 15
hours, but only about one half of the original thymol can be found by
the analyses. The remainder may escape in part through the lungs;
part of the loss may also be due to the first sulfuric acid distillation.

Discussion: LUBS inquired whether the glycuronate could be separated from urine directly and afterwards decomposed. ALSBERG suggested that part of the thymol might be eliminated either in the
form of a decomposition product or as some other compound than the
glycuronate, and might not afterwards appear as thymol. SEIDELL
stated that the glycuronate is a very stable compound, and doubted
whether any other compound was formed. ALSBERG also inquired
whether the product obtained and titrated might not be a derivative
and not thymol itself. SEIDELL replied that all the properties indicated
thymol and not a derivative. Studies of the excretion of phenol suggest by analogy that the explanations advanced are correct. MENGE
inquired what confirmatory tests had been made on the recovered
thymol; SEIDELL stated that no specific chemical tests were made, but
that dependence was placed upon its characteristic odor and physical
properties.

ROBERT B. SOSMAN, *Secretary.*

THE GEOLOGICAL SOCIETY OF WASHINGTON

The 286th meeting was held in the lecture room of the Cosmos Club,
November 11, 1914.

Informal communications:

CLARENCE N. FENNER on *Babingtonite from Passaic County, New
Jersey* (See this Journal **4**: 552-558, 1914).

F. C. SCHRADER: *Mountain leather from Rawhide, Nevada.*

T. WAYLAND VAUGHAN: *Tectonic features of certain volcanic islands
in the West Indies.*

Regular program:

N. L. BOWEN: *The importance of crystallization in the differentiation
of igneous rocks.* Some experiments were described in which the sinking
of olivine and pyroxene crystals was obtained in certain artificial silicate
melts. The importance of this process as a means of differentiation of
igneous rocks was pointed out. The results were discussed especially
in connection with the Palisade diabase still of New Jersey. Reasons
were given for considering Prof. J. Volney Lewis correct in his explanation of the olivine-diabase ledge and also the general richness in heavier
minerals toward the base as due to the sinking of crystals.

WILLIS T. LEE: *Relation of cretaceous formations to the Rocky Mountains.* This paper is a continuation of one presented a year ago under the
title, *Use of physiography in the study of Rocky Mountain stratigraphy,*

in which evidence was presented that seemed to prove that the Dakota sandstone originally extended uninterruptedly over the area now occupied by the Rocky Mountains in Colorado and New Mexico. The present paper presents evidence that the marine Upper Cretaceous formations also originally covered this area, and that the Cretaceous sediments of the Rocky Mountain region came mainly from the continental land mass that lay west of the interior sea during Cretaceous time. That this was the course of the sediments is indicated by the prevalence of sandstone, some of which is conglomerate near the shores of this western continent and by the prevalence of marine shale farther east; and also by the thinning eastward toward the present Rocky Mountains, of sandstones such as the Mesaverde in the San Juan Basin and the Ferron sandstone of Utah and western Colorado, and by the corresponding thickening of the marine shales in the same direction.

Comparison of published sections viewed in the light of personal observation in the field indicates that the Cretaceous formations on opposite sides of the mountains and in the intermontane basins are comparable in thickness, character and stratigraphic succession. The thickness of the Pierre shale, however, as reported from various localities, especially east of the mountains, varies by some thousands of feet. This has been interpreted as due to local down-warps of the Cretaceous floor with assumed corresponding up-warps in the present mountainous area. But it is possible that these great differences in thickness may be due in large part to crushing and other rock movements following deposition rather than to original differences.

It seems probable that the interior Cretaceous Basin which includes the present Rocky Mountain areas was a great geosyncline in which, until near the close of the Cretaceous the main movement was downward, with minor warpings. It also seems probable that there was no effective barrier in the relatively small area now occupied by the mountains to prevent the uniform spread of sediments derived from the continental mass west of the Cretaceous sea. If this hypothesis endures the test of future investigation it should lead to a readjustment of certain correlations that now seem discordant and should indicate definitely that the Cretaceous-Tertiary unconformity represents a clearly defined period of erosion, for the Cretaceous sedimentary rocks must have been removed before the pre-Cretaceous rocks could supply the pebbles found in the basal conglomerates of the Tertiary.

E. W. SHAW: *A study of the Lafayette at and near the type locality.* Although the surface of Lafayette County, Miss., and much adjoining territory is immediately underlain by a thin wash-creep-residuum mantle made up principally of material derived from underlying strata but containing certain elements not found in them, it is concluded from recent studies that no formation such as the Lafayette is conceived and described to be is present in the county from which it was named. On the other hand, such a formation is present in the county just west of Lafayette and in other places in the Coastal Plain, and it therefore appears probable that the concept Lafayette, with certain modifications, will be retained.

At the 287th meeting, November 25, 1914, informal communications were presented by W. T. SCHALLER on:

1. *So-called vanadic ocher.*
2. *The minerals of northern New Jersey which are now represented by casts.*

Regular program:

EDGAR T. WHERRY: *A peculiar oolite from Bethlehem, Pa.* The grains in an oolite limestone show a division, parallel to the bedding, into a light and a dark portion, the latter being the lower. Chemical analysis showed the grains to be higher in dolomite, quartz, kaolin, limonite, and carbon, and lower in calcite and siderite, than the matrix. Microscopic study shows the nuclei to be imbedded in the dark material, which is heaped up around them. It is concluded that the original grains consisted of concentric layers of aragonite, containing more or less carbon, and that, after solidification of the sediment, circulating waters dissolved away the former, the carbon and the nuclei falling to the bottom of the cavities. These were later filled up again by secondary dolomite, the coarse crystallization of which is evident in the sections. The carbon precipitated pyrite from iron sulphate-bearing waters, and, finally, this was changed to limonite by weathering.

J. S. DILLER: *The recent eruptions of Lassen Peak.* Although eruptions have occurred at Mt. Baker and St. Helens as late as 1842 and 1843 the great volcanoes of the Cascade Range are generally regarded as extinct. Lassen Peak, the southern terminus of the Cascade Range, has long been noted for its fumaroles and solfataras, but until recently there has been no explosive action. On May 30, 1914, a series of explosive eruptions began, and up to the middle of November of the same year more than 60 eruptions had occurred.

Some of the various forms of ejected dust-laden vapors, rise more than 10,000 feet above the mountain summit, and the progress of the development of the new crater, from its starting point within the old crater of Lassen Peak up to the western side, where it has broken through the old rim, was illustrated by lantern slides.

Fine dust was scattered over the country in various directions for nearly a dozen miles, and close to the crater the large rock fragments ejected form a stratified rim 25 feet or more in thickness about the new crater. So far as known none of the material was molten at the time of its ejection. The ejected vapors which were almost wholly steam, were slightly acid, with sulphurous odors. W. C. WHEELER treated the ejected dust with water and found both sulphur and chlorine in the resulting acid solution, showing that the ejected vapors were similar to those of the solfataras in the region.

There was once vigorous solfataric action in the old crater, but it had entirely ceased. Its rejuvenation and extension is a matter of special interest. Flashes of light and flying luminous fragments have been reported on good authority, and as the crater gets larger and deeper hotter material is ejected.

That there has been an influx of heat along the throat of the old volcano is highly probable, but the limit is not yet evident.

H. S. WASHINGTON: *The condition of the southern Italian volcanoes.* The speaker gave an account of the conditions of volcanic activity at Vesuvius, Etna, Vulcano and Stromboli as observed by Dr. A. L. Day and himself during the summer of 1914. The talk was illustrated by lantern slides.

Vesuvius was in a fairly active, solfataric condition, with numerous fumaroles. A descent into the crater permitted observation of the mouth formed in May, 1910, in the southwestern part of the crater floor. Two separate columns of brown and white smoke were issuing continuously from an orifice near the bottom of this. No liquid lava was seen, but there was recent pumiceous scoria, which analysis shows to be like the recent Vesuvian lavas. The crater was filled with acid vapors, chiefly SO_3, SO_2 and HCl.

Etna was in a state of mixed solfataric and strombolian activity, though not violent. There was a constant emission of acid smoke, and occasional outbursts from one or more of the five mouths seen at the bottom of the crater, which sent up tall columns of dark smoke to a considerable height. There was no emission of lava, but a constant, though slight, fall of fine ash. The *"bocca"* of 1911 on the northeast flank of the cone had increased in size and was fairly active, emitting much smoke and some ash, but no lava.

At Vulcano the solfataric condition since the eruption of 1888–9 still persists—fumaroles of two distinct types being abundant both within the crater and in the outer slopes of the cone. Many samples of gas were collected, as well as specimens of the very abundant salts covering the upper parts of the cone. These are mostly sulphates of potash and alumina, with some boric acid, for the most part quite free from chlorides.

At Stromboli five distinct small vents in the crater floor were emitting smoke and lapilli, though the mode of activity of each was different. The volcano seemed to be in a state of moderate and normal activity.

At the 288th meeting, December 9, 1914, the presidential address was delivered by the retiring president:

ARTHUR KEITH: *Main features of Appalachian structure* (illustrated). The address will be published on a later date.

At the twenty-second business meeting, which followed the address, the following officers were elected for the ensuing year:

President, T. WAYLAND VAUGHAN; *Vice-Presidents,* ARTHUR C. SPENCER, W. C. MENDENHALL; *Secretaries,* CLARENCE N. FENNER, C. H. WEGEMANN; *Treasurer,* C. A. LESHER; *Members-at-large-of-the-Council,* R. S. BASSLER, G. F. LOUGHLIN, G. C. MARTIN, EUGENE STEBINGER, J. B. UMPLEBY.

FRANK L. HESS, *Secretary.*

JOURNAL

OF THE

WASHINGTON ACADEMY OF SCIENCES

Vol. V JANUARY 19, 1915 No. 2

ASTROPHYSICS.—*A comparison of stellar radiometers and radiometric measurements on 110 stars.*[1] W. W. Coblentz, Bureau of Standards.

In this paper experiments are described showing that there is but little difference in the radiation sensitivity of stellar thermocouples constructed of bismuth-platinum, and thermocouples of bismuth-bismuth + tin alloy, which have a 50 per cent higher thermoelectric power. Improvements in the method of maintaining a vacuum by means of metallic calcium are described whereby it will be possible to go to the remotest stations for making radiation measurements without carrying an expensive vacuum pump. With this outfit measurements were made on the radiation from 112 celestial objects, including 105 stars. This includes measurements on the bright and the dark bands of Jupiter (also a pair of his satellites), the rings of Saturn, and a planetary nebula. Quantitative measurements were made on stars down to the 5.3 magnitude; and high grade qualitative measurements were made on stars down to the 6.7 magnitude. It was found that red stars emit from 2 to 3 times as much total radiation as blue stars of the same photometric magnitude.

Measurements were made on the transmission of the radiations from stars and planets through an absorption cell of water. By this means it was shown that, of the total radiation emitted, the

[1] Detailed paper to appear in the Bulletin of the Bureau of Standards.

blue stars have about two times as much radiation as the yellow stars, and about three times as much radiation as the red stars, in the spectral region to which the eye is sensitive.

A stellar thermocouple and a bolometer were compared and the former was found to be the more sensitive. The conclusion arrived at is that, from the appearance of the data at hand, greater improvements are to be expected in stellar thermocouples than in stellar bolometers.

The object of the investigation was to obtain some estimate of the sensitivity required in order to be able to observe spectral energy curves of stars. The radiation sensitivity of the present apparatus was such that, when combined with a 3-foot reflecting telescope, a deflection of 1 mm. would have resulted when exposed to a candle placed at a distance of 53 miles. In order, however, to do much successful work on stellar spectral energy curves, a sensitivity one hundred times this value is desirable. In other words, assuming that the rays are not absorbed in passing through the intervening space, the radiometric equipment (radiometer and mirror) must be sufficiently sensitive to detect the radiation from a candle removed to a distance of five hundred miles. This can be accomplished by using a 7-foot mirror and by increasing the sensitivity of the present radiometer (thermocouple and galvanometer) twenty times. This increase in sensitivity is possible.

Measurements were made to determine the amount of stellar radiation falling upon 1 cm² of the earth's surface. It was found that the quantity is so small that it would require the radiations from *Polaris* falling upon 1 cm² to be absorbed and conserved continuously for a period of one million years in order to raise the temperature of 1 gram of water 1°C. If the total radiation from all the stars falling upon 1 cm² were thus collected and conserved it would require from 100 to 200 years to raise the temperature of 1 gram of water 1°C. In marked contrast with this value, the solar rays can produce the same effect in about one minute.

CRYSTALLOGRAPHY.—*A new crystal-grinding goniometer.*
FRED. E. WRIGHT,   Geophysical Laboratory.

In the measurement of the change of crystallographical and optical properties of crystals with change of temperature or of pressure it is essential that the crystal faces be flat and correctly located; also that the optical sections and prisms be accurately oriented and ground.   Natural crystals with faces sufficiently perfect for such work are exceedingly rare and the observer is

Fig. 1

usually forced to regrind and polish certain of the faces and often to add new faces of definite orientation.   This postulates an instrument of precision for the purpose.   Several crystal-grinding goniometers have been described heretofore,[1] and of these the

[1] Wolz, M., Jahrb. f. Min., **2**: 243–246. 1888.

Fuess, R., Jahrb. f. Min., **2**: 181–185. 1889.

Wülfing, E. A., Zeitschr. f. Kryst., **17**: 445–459. 1890; Jahrb. f. Min., **2**: 1–22. 1901.

Tutton, A. E. H., Crystalline Structure and Chemical Constitution, **25–35**: 1910; Phil. Trans., *A*, **185**: 887. 1895; **192**: 457.   1899; Proc. Roy. Soc. **57**: 324. 1895.

Stöber, F., Bull. Ac. Belge, (3) **33**: 843–858. 1897.

Goldschmidt, V., Zeitschr. Kryst., **51**: 358. 1912.

Wulff, G., Zeitschr. Kryst., **36**: 22. 1902; **50**: 14–16. 1913.

Goldschmidt, two-circle type is the latest and best in principle. The present instrument is also based on the theodolite principle, but it is essentially different in design and construction from its predecessors; certain features of the Goldschmidt design have, however, been incorporated in it.   With the new grinding goniometer crystal faces can be ground with a precision of 1′ or greater, and flat within a wave length of light; plane-parallel crystal plates can

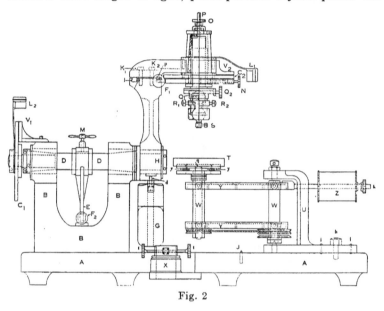

Fig. 2

also be ground normal to any given optical direction, as an ellipsoidal axis (α, β, or γ) or an optic axis.   The instrument has been in use for over half a year and has proved so satisfactory in routine work that a brief description may be of interest.

The grinding goniometer was designed and constructed[2] with special reference to adjustment facilities and to precision.   All of the working parts are heavy and all bearing surfaces are wide

[2] The instrument was built in the instrument shop of this Laboratory by Mr. J. Jost, to whose skill and ingenuity much of its success is due.   The writer is also indebted to Dr. C. N. Fenner and Mr. J. H. Snapp for a thorough test of the grinding and polishing devices and materials which are used on the goniometer.

and accurately fitted.   There are four essential parts, as indicated
in figures 1, 2, and 3: (a) telescope (fig. 3a); (b) two-circle theodolite arrangement for holding and measuring crystals (fig. 2);
(c) grinding plate (fig. 2); (d) optical system of an axial angle
apparatus mounted on a special tripod (fig. 3b).   A brief description of these parts will now be given.

The telescope (fig. 3a) is fitted with an autocollimating device[3]
which consists of a strip of thin cover-glass of the shape indicated
in figure 3e; this is placed
in the rear focal plane of
the telescope objective O.
Light from a small tung-
sten lamp is sent through
the plate to the inclined
edge of the cover-glass,
where it is totally reflected and passes thence
through the objective
and prism to the crystal
plate, whence it is re-
flected back through the
lens system and appears
then, when viewed
through the eyepiece, as
a sharp bright line in the
dark field.   Settings are

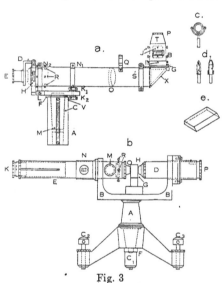

Fig. 3

made by covering the bright line by the reflecting edge of the glass
slip, so that the field becomes practically dark.   A transverse
etched line across the center of the reflecting edge serves as
reference point for the setting.   In place of the transverse line two
short cover glasses, separated slightly and so mounted that their
reflecting edges form a straight line, have been used to advantage.
The images due to reflection from the faces of the telescope prism
(X, fig. 3a) are easily eliminated by mounting the prism in slightly
tilted position so that the rays reflected from its faces reach the
image plane outside the field of the positive eyepiece E.   The

[3] F. E. Wright, this Journal, 4: 235. 1913.

intensity of illumination secured by this device is similar to that of the Abbe refractometer slit, while the accuracy of settings is considerably better than that of the angular readings, namely, $\frac{1}{4}'$. The telescope is mounted on a vertical rotating axis and can be raised by means of a pin and ratchet movement. (X, fig. 2, M, fig. 3a.)   Enlarged signals are obtained by means of objective O with eyepiece E; reduced signals, by objective P and objective O; images of the crystal surface, by means of objective O alone, or by objective P + objective O + eyepiece E.   This telecentric arrangement of the optical system has been found well suited to the purpose.   The mounted crystal is held by the clamp S (fig. 2), is adjusted by the ball and socket device R, is centered by the sliding carriages Q, and is moved up and down by the screw P which operates the triangular steel stem indicated in the figure. The theodolite position-angles can be read directly to $\frac{1}{4}'$ on the circles C_1 and C_2.[4]

The grinding wheel (fig. 2) is driven slowly (200 r.p.m.) by a small low speed $\frac{1}{4}$ h.p. motor (400 r.p.m.), and is mounted on a rotating axis W, supported between arms Y which allow the wheel to be raised and lowered without tilting.   The grinding wheel itself is supported on an adjustable steel block.   Experience has shown that for grinding and polishing purposes block-tin wheels are the most satisfactory.   Three or more such wheels are in constant use and are kept flat by grinding them, the one against the other, in rotation.   Pitch wheels have also been used for polishing purposes but they are apparently not greatly superior to the tin disks and are more troublesome to prepare.   The grinding disk is adjusted normal to its axis of rotation by means of light rays reflected either from the upper surface of the wheel itself or from a plane-parallel optical glass plate 3 inches in diameter placed on top of the grinding disk.   Only the finest abrasives are used, crystolon or alundum 65 F of the Norton Company, or washed emery M 303 of the American Optical Company. Polishing powders are: washed rouge, putty powder, and chromium oxide.   These polishing powders are not equally good for

---

[4] These circles were specially graduated by Bausch & Lomb Optical Company; no error approaching $\frac{1}{4}'$ in magnitude has been detected in the graduations.

a given crystal and only an actual test can show which powder is the best for a particular crystal. By use of the counter weight Z (fig. 2) the pressure of the grinding disk against the crystal can be regulated.

(d) The attachment for the orientation of optical sections is the optical system of Wülfing's axial angle apparatus mounted on a tripod (fig. 3b) which fits in place on three hardened steel points. The crystal or fragment from which a plane-parallel, optically oriented plate is to be ground is mounted on a special holder (fig. 3d) by means of which the fragment is first strapped into place by a copper wire or belt and then cemented. On the goniometer the crystal is immersed in a liquid of its refractive index β; this eliminates in large measure the disturbing reflections at the irregular surfaces of the crystal grain. In this form the grinding goniometer serves all the functions of an axial angle apparatus and has the additional advantage that on it the angle which a given optical direction includes with a given crystallographical direction can be obtained directly from the position-angles of the two directions. After the crystal has been properly set so that the desired optical direction is observed, the axial angle apparatus is removed, the arm of the goniometer is rotated 90° on the horizontal axis D, and the grinding disk is swung into place.

Adjustment of the goniometer. The goniometer is in adjustment when: (1) the horizontal and vertical axes of rotation ($D\ D$ and $P\ S$, fig. 2) are at right angles and intersect at a point; (2) the axis of the telescope is vertical and intersects the above point; (3) the axis of the grinding plate is vertical; (4) the axis of the optical system of the axial angle attachment is horizontal, but normal to the horizontal axis of the goniometer, and intersects the above point.

In the adjustment of the goniometer it is essential that a definite plan, like that outlined below, be followed so that each successive adjustment does not interfere with those preceding. The adjustment is facilitated by the use of two small attachments: (a) a mounted minute glass bead obtained by melting the end of a fine glass thread, and (b) a plane parallel plate mounted so that it can be rotated about a horizontal axis (fig. 3c).[5]   The different possible lens combinations are: (A) *For viewing crystal surfaces:* (1) Objective O alone; (2) objective P+ objective O+ eyepiece E. (B) *For viewing reflection signals:* (1) Objective O+ eyepiece E; (2) objective P+ objective O.

SYSTEMATIC ADJUSTMENT

(a) Adjustment of telescope. (Fig. 3a)

(1) Use lens combination B1.   Illuminate reflecting edge of cover glass prism at H (fig. 3a) and center same by placing a flat glass plate on telescope-mount above prism X and then bringing reflected image of edge to coincidence with edge itself.

(2) Mount reflecting glass plate (fig. 3c) in S (fig. 2) so that edge of plate is normal to axis D D.   Adjust telescope axis normal to axis D D by means of adjustment screws K and I and test adjustment by noting that the image obtained by reflection from either side of the glass plate coincides with the reflecting cover-glass edge.   This is accomplished by rotating the glass plate about the horizontal axis D D.

(3) Center telescope by means of eccentric stop screw at H.

(4) Center and adjust in similar manner the reducing attachment P to the positions just obtained.   Use adjustment screws, Q, R, S for the purpose.

(b) Adjustment of axis P S

(1) Adjust axis P S (fig. 2) normal to axis D D by means of mounted glass plate (fig. 3c) so turned that its reflecting surface is normal to axis P S.   Axis is adjusted when signal observed in telescope (lens combination B1) remains stationary during rotation of glass plate about axis P and coincides with reflecting edge of cover-glass prism.   Adjustment screws are K_1, K_2 in conjunction with wedge shaped, hardened steel bar I which is moved forward by means of the flanged screw f. The tilting is done on the steel axis at p.   (2) Center axis P S to intersection of axis D D by means of minute glass bead mounted on pin inserted in S (fig. 2).   Use lens combination A1.   When properly centered by means of eccentric fitting on axis D D (clamped by screw d, fig. 2) the centered glass bead remains stationary on rotation about axis D D or axis P S.

(c) Adjustment of grinding plate

(1) Adjust grinding plate T normal to axis of rotation W by means of screws y, figure 2.   Adjustment is attained when a distant object, as seen by reflection from the top surface of the plate, remains stationary on rotation of the plate about axis W.   In case the surface of the tin grinding disk does not reflect light adequately, an optically plane-parallel glass plate, 3 inches in diameter, is placed on top of the grinding disk and furnishes a satisfactory reflection of the distant object.

[5] Goldschmidt, V., Zeitschr. Krist., **29**: 342.   1898.

(2) Adjust axis W of grinding plate by means of three screws i in the base-plate support (fig. 2). Adjustment is accomplished when a crystal face ground and polished by the wheel is in the position indicated by the telescope. This part of the adjustment usually involves the grinding and polishing of several crystal faces before the correct position is attained, but, as the grinding and polishing of each face takes less than 10 minutes' time, the time loss is not serious.

(d) Adjustment of the axial angle apparatus

(1) Use glass plate (fig. 3c) so mounted that its edge is parallel to axis $P\ S$ and is vertical. The correct horizontal position is first ascertained by means of telescope and lens combination $B1$ after which axis $P\ S$ of goniometer is turned through 90° to vertical position.

(2) Place axial angle apparatus (fig. 3b) in position and test direction of axes by use of autocollimation at M. Adjust by means of screws C and clamping screw F until axis of telescope is normal to glass plate. Cross-hairs should be vertical and horizontal. Test by rotating glass plate about vertical axis $P\ S$ and horizontal axis $D\ D$.

(3) Center if necessary by means of mounted glass bead and screws C. Retest adjustment after centering.

FORESTRY.—*The place of forestry among natural sciences.*[1]
HENRY S. GRAVES, Forest Service.

In an old forest magazine, *Sylvan,* is a story about Germany's great poet, Karl von Schiller. Schiller, taking rest at Illmenau, Thuringen, met by chance a forester who was preparing a plan of management for the Illmenau forest. A map of the forest was spread out on which the cuttings for the next 220 years were projected and noted with their year number. By its side lay the plan of an ideal coniferous forest which was to have materialized in the year 2050. Attentively and quietly the poet contemplated the telling means of forest organization, and especially the plans for far distant years. He quickly realized, after a short explanation, the object of the work and gave vent to his astonishment:

> I had considered you foresters a very common people who did little else than cut down trees and kill game, but you are far from that. You work unknown, unrecompensed, free from the tyranny of egotism, and the fruit of your quiet work ripens for a late posterity. Hero and poet attain vain glory; I would like to be a forester.

[1] Paper delivered before the Washington Academy of Sciences on December 3, 1914.

An opinion not unlike that held by Schiller before meeting with the forester still commonly prevails in scientific circles in this country. It is quite generally believed that foresters are pure empiricists; something on the order of gardeners who plant trees, of range-riders who fight forest fires, or lumbermen who cruise timber, carry on logging operations or manufacture lumber and other forest products; that for whatever little knowledge of a scientific character the forester may need in his work, he depends on experts in other branches of science; on the botanists for the taxonomy of the trees, on physicists, chemists, and engineers for the proper understanding of the physical, chemical, and mechanical properties of the wood; on the geologist and soil physicist for the knowledge of sites suitable for the growth of different kinds of trees; upon the plant pathologist for the diseases of trees; upon the entomologist for the insect enemies of the forest, and so on.

Such an impression is undoubtedly strengthened when the activities of such an organization as the Forest Service are considered. The placing under management of about 165 million acres of forest land has been an administrative problem of enormous magnitude. The administration of this vast public property involves many large industrial and economic questions, and affects intimately a number of varied and important interests: the lumber industry, the grazing industry, water power development, navigation, municipal water supplies, agricultural settlement, mining development, and the railroads. In launching this great public enterprise, undertaken in the face of strong opposition, administrative activities appeared to overshadow research work. In this way doubtless many scientific men have gained the impression that forestry has little to do with science, which seeks for the causal relationship of things and for the establishment of laws and principles; that forestry is rather a patch work of miscellaneous knowledge borrowed from other sciences and assembled without particular system to help the practical administrator of forest property.

My endeavor in this paper will be to show that this impression is erroneous. While it is true that forestry as an art, as an applied science, utilizes results furnished by the natural and engineering sciences; while it is also true that the forester's activities—particularly during the pioneer period of establishing forest practice—may be largely administrative in character; there is nevertheless a fundamental forest science which has a distinctive place. As with all others, the science of forestry owes its distinctive character to its correlation, from a certain point of view, of parts of certain other sciences, such as mathematics, botany, entomology, civil engineering, and chemistry. But these are only auxiliary to the resultant science—forestry—which rests upon a knowledge of the life of the forest as such, and which therefore depends upon the discovery of laws governing the forest's growth and development.

It is in this field chiefly that foresters may claim some scientific achievement, some contribution to general science. Sciences do not develop out of curiosity; they appear first of all because there are practical problems that need to be solved, and only later become an aim in themselves. This has been equally true of the science of forestry. The object of forestry as an art is to produce timber of high technical quality. In pursuing this object, the forester very early observed that tall, cylindrical timber, comparatively free of knots, is produced only in dense stands, in forests in which the trees exert an influence upon each other as well as upon the soil and climate of the area occupied by them. He further discovered that the social environment produced by trees in a forest is an absolutely essential condition for the continuous natural existence of the forest itself. If the forester had not found forests in nature, he would have had to create forests artificially in order to accomplish his practical purpose, since it is only through the control and regulation of the natural struggle for existence between trees in the forest that the forester is capable of managing it for the practical needs of man. Thus from the very nature of his dealings with the forest, the forester was forced from the beginning to consider the forest not merely as an aggregation of individual trees but as communities of trees—tree societies—and first from purely utilitarian reasons, developed a science upon which the practice of silviculture now rests.

Forestry as a natural science, therefore, deals with the forest as a community in which the individual trees influence one another and also influence the character and life of the community itself. As a community the forest has individual character and form. It has a definite life history; it grows, develops, matures, and propagates itself. Its form, development and final total product may be modified by external influences. By abuse it may be greatly injured and the forest as a living entity may even be destroyed. It responds equally to care and may be so molded by skillful treatment as to produce a high quality of product, and in greater amount and in a shorter time than if left to nature. The life history of this forest community varies according to the species composing it, the density of the stand, the manner in which the trees of different ages are grouped, the climatic and soil factors which affect the vigor and growth of the individual trees. The simplest form of a forest community is that composed of trees of one species and all of the same age. When several species and trees of different ages occupy the same ground, the form is more complex, the crowns overlapping and the roots occupying different layers of the soil. Thus, for instance, when the ground is occupied with a mixed stand of Douglas fir and hemlock, the former requiring more light, occupies the upper story, and because of its deeper root system extends to the lower lying strata of the soil. The hemlock, on the other hand, which is capable of growing under shade, occupies the under story, and having shallow roots utilizes largely the top soil.

These are forest communities, such for instance as those typical of northwestern Idaho, where western larch, Douglas fir, western white pine, white fir, western red cedar, and hemlock all grow together. Such a forest is evidently a very complex organism, the stability of which is based on a very nice adjustment between the different classes and groups occupying the same ground. Any change in one of these classes or groups must necessarily affect the other. If, for instance, in the Douglas fir-hemlock forest, the Douglas fir is cut out, the remaining hemlock trees are likely to die out because their shallow roots are left exposed to the drying effect of the sun and wind. It is only by a thorough understanding of such mutual adjustments that the forester is capable of intelligently handling the forest. With the great number of species that are found in this country, with the great variety in climatic and other physical factors which influence the form of the forest, it is self-evident that there are many forest communities, each with distinctive biological characteristics, which offer a wide field for scientific inquiry. Amid the great volume of administrative phases of the work in the Forest Service this main objective has never been lost sight of in handling the National Forests. The Forest Service is now spending nearly $300,000 annually for research work; it maintains eight forest experiment stations and one thoroughly equipped forest products laboratory, and is doing this work solely to study the fundamental laws governing the life of the forest and their effect upon the final product—wood.

Forestry may be called tree sociology and occupies among natural sciences the same position as sociology among human- istic sciences. Sociology may be based upon the physiological functions of man as a biological individual. A physician, how- ever, is not a sociologist, and social phenomena can be understood and interpreted only in the light of sociological knowledge. So also with forestry. Forestry depends upon the anatomy and physiology of plants, but it is not applied anatomy and physiology of plants. With foresters, anatomy and physiology of plants is not the immediate end but enters only as one of the essential parts without which it is impossible to grasp the processes that take place in the forest.

As the science of tree societies, forestry really is a part of the larger science dealing with plant associations, yet its develop- ment was entirely independent of botanical geography. When the need arose for the rational handling of timberlands, no science of plant association was in existence. Foresters were compelled to study the biology of the forest by the best methods available; they used the general scientific methods of investiga- tion and developed their own methods when the former proved inadequate. I am frank to admit that the present knowledge of plant associations in botany has not yet reached a point where

foresters could leave wholly to botanists the working out of the
basic facts about the life of the forest which are needed in the
practice of forestry.   When the general science of plant associations has reached a higher state of development, the two may
possibly merge, but not until then.

In developing the science of tree associations, the forester has
been unquestionably favored by the fact that the forests, being
the highest expression of social plant life, afford the best opportunity for observing it.

The reason for the ability of forest trees to form most highly
organized plant societies lies in their mode of growth.   Each
annual ring of growth, together with the new leaves that appear
every year, is in reality new colonies of cells.   Some of the cells
die toward the end of the vegetative season; others continue to
live for a number of years.   When the conditions of life in a
forest have changed for a certain tree, when, for instance, from a
dominant tree it became a suppressed one, the new colonies of
cells formed during that year, and which sustain the life of that
tree, are naturally adapted to these new conditions.   The same
is true when a suppressed tree, through some accident to its
neighbors comes into full enjoyment of light.   The last annual
growth is at once capable of taking advantage of the new situation created in the forest.   Therefore, as long as a tree can form
annual rings, it possesses the elasticity and adaptability essential
for trees living in dense stands.   It is only when a tree is suppressed to a point when it can not form new growth that it dies
and is eliminated from a stand.

Because of the fact that the forest is the highest expression of
social plant life, the foresters occupy the stragetic position from
which they command vistas accessible only with difficulty to other
naturalists.   In this lies the strength of forestry, its peculiar
beauty, and the debt which natural science owes to it.   It is a
significant fact, although, of course, only of historic importance,
that, according to Charles Darwin[2] himself, it was "an obscure
writer on forest trees who, in 1830, in Scotland (that is, 29 years
before the *Origin of Species* was published), most expressly and

[2] Origin of species.

clearly anticipated his views on natural selection in a book on Naval Timber and Arboriculture." For the same reason it was foresters, who, long before the word "ecology" was coined, had assembled a vast amount of material on the life of the forest as a plant association—the basis of their silvicultural practice. Warming, Schimper, and other early writers on ecology, borrowed most of their proofs and examples from the facts established by the foresters, and the forest literature of today is still practically the only one which contains striking examples of the application of ecology to the solution of practical problems.

One discovery recently made at the Wind River Forest Experiment Station in Oregon comes particularly to my mind. In northwestern Idaho where the western white pine is at its optimum growth and is greatly in demand by the lumberman; our former method of cutting was to remove the main stand and leave seed trees for the restocking of the ground. In order to protect the seed trees from windfall, they were left not singly but in blocks, each covering several acres. The trees left amounted often to from 10 to 15 per cent in volume of the total stand, and since they could not be utilized later they formed a fairly heavy investment for reforesting the cutover land. A study of the effect of these blocks of seed trees upon natural reforestation has proved that they can not be depended upon, at least within a reasonable time, to restock naturally the cutover land. The distance to which the seed is scattered from these seed trees is insignificant compared with the area to be reforested. Splendid young growth, however, is found here and there on cutover land, away from any seed trees, where the leaf litter is not completely burned. It is evident, therefore, that the seed from which this young growth originates must have come from a source other than the seed trees. The study of the leaf litter in a virgin stand showed that the latter contained on the average from one to two germinable seed per square foot. Some of the seed found was so discolored that it must have been in the litter for a long time. Thus it was discovered that the seed of the western white pine retains its vitality for years while lying in the duff and litter beneath the mature stands, and then germinates when the ground is exposed to direct light by cutting. It was found similarly that in old Douglas fir burns, where the leaf litter was not completely destroyed, the young growth invariably sprung up from seed that had escaped fire and had been lying dormant in the ground. Should a second fire go through the young stand before it reaches the bearing stage, the land may become a complete waste, at least for hundreds of years, although there may be seed trees left on the ground. This conclusively proves that the young growth comes from the seed stored in the ground before cutting took place and not from the seed scattered after cutting by the seed trees left.

The wonderful capacity of the leaf litter and duff of the cool, dark forests of the Northwest to act as a storage medium for the seed until favorable conditions for its germination occur is confined not only to the Douglas fir and western white pine but to the seed of other species which often grow together with them, such as Noble fir, amabilis fir, western red cedar, and hemlock. The subsequent appearance of other species in a Douglas fir or western white pine stand depends apparently to a large extent upon the seed stored in the ground at a time when the original forest still existed. This discovery revolutionizes our conception of the succession of forest stands, since it shows that the future composition of the forest is determined by the seed stored in the leaf litter; and the appearance of seedlings first of one species and then of another results simply from the differences in the relative endurance of seed of the different species that are lying in the ground. Besides being of scientific importance this discovery has also a great practical significance. It accentuates the disastrous consequence of a second fire in an old burn because no more seed remains in the ground while the capacity of the few seed trees that may be on the burn is very limited in restocking the ground. This discovery enabled the Service to change materially the present methods of cutting in the white pine and Douglas fir forests, to the mutual advantage of the Government and of the logging operators.

I shall give briefly a few other illustrations of the life of the forest which stamp it as a distinct plant society.

The first social phenomenon in a stand of trees is the differentiation of individuals of the same age on the basis of differences in height, crown development, and growth, the result of the struggle for light and nourishment between the members of the stand. A forest at maturity contains scarcely 5 per cent of all the trees that have started life there. Yet the death of the 95 per cent is a necessary condition to the development of the others. The process of differentiation into dominant and suppressed trees takes place particularly in youth and gradually slows down toward maturity. Thus, in some natural pine forests, during the age between 20 to 80 years, over 4,000 trees on an acre die; whereas at the age between 80 to 100 only 300 trees die. With some trees this natural dying out with age proceeds faster than with others. Thus in pine, birch, aspen, and all other species which demand a great deal of light, the death rate is enormous. With spruce, beech, fir, and species which are satisfied with less light, this process is less energetic. The growing demand for space with age by individual trees in a spruce forest may be expressed in the following figures:

At	20 years of age	4 sq. ft.
"	40 " " "	34 " "
"	60 " " "	70 " "
"	80 " " "	110 "
"	100 " " "	150 "

If we take the space required by a pine at the age between 40 and 50 years as 100: then for spruce at the same age it will be 87; for beech 79; and for fir 63. This process of differentiation is universal in forests everywhere.

Another peculiarity that marks a tree community is the difference in seed production of trees which occupy different positions in the stand. Thus if the trees in a forest are divided into five classes according to their height and crown development, and if the seed production of the most dominant class is designated as 100, the seed production for trees of the second class will be 88; for the third class, 33; for the fourth class only 0.5 per cent, while the trees of the fifth class will not produce a single seed, although the age of all these trees may be practically the same. The same struggle for existence, therefore, which produced the dominant and suppressed trees works toward a natural selection, since only those which have conquered in the struggle for existence, and are endowed with the greatest individual energy of growth, reproduce themselves.

In a forest there is altogether a different climate, a different soil, and a different ground cover than outside of it. A forest cover does not allow all the precipitation that falls over it to reach the ground. Part of the precipitation remains on the crowns and is later evaporated back into the air. Another part, through openings in the cover, reaches the ground, while a third part runs down along the trunks to the base of the tree. Many and exact measurements have demonstrated that a forest cover intercepts from 15 to 80 per cent of precipitation, according to the species of trees, density of the stand, age of the forest, and other factors. Thus pine forests of the north intercept only about 20 per cent, spruce about 40 per cent, and fir nearly 60 per cent of the total precipitation that falls in the open. The amount that runs off along the trunks in some species is very small—less than 1 per cent. In others, for instance beech, it is 5 per cent. Thus if a certain locality receives 50 inches of rain, the ground under the forest will receive only 40, 30, or 20 inches. Thus 10, 20, and 30 inches will be withdrawn from the total circulation of moisture over the area occupied by the forest. The forest cover, besides preventing all of the precipitation from reaching the ground, similarly keeps out light, heat, and wind. Under a forest cover, therefore, there is altogether a different heat and light climate, and a different relative humidity than in the open.

The foliage that falls year after year upon the ground creates deep modification in the forest soil. The changes which the accumulation of leaf litter and the roots of the trees produce in the soil and subsoil are so fundamental that it is often possible to determine centuries after a forest has been destroyed, whether the ground was ever occupied by one.

The effect which trees in a stand have upon each other is not confined merely to changes in their external form and growth; it extends also to their internal structure. The specific gravity of the wood, its composition, and the anatomical structure which determines its specific gravity differ in the same species, and on the same soil, and in the same climate, according to the position which the tree occupies in the stand. Thus in a 100-year-old stand of spruce and fir the specific gravity of wood is greatest in trees of the third crown class (intermediate trees). The ratio of the thick wall portion of the annual ring to the thin wall of the spring wood is also different in trees of different crown classes. The difference in the size of the tracheids in trees of different crown classes may be so great that in one tracheid of a dominant tree there may be placed three tracheids cells of a suppressed tree. The amount of lignin per unit of weight is greater in dominant trees than in suppressed trees.

Forest trees in a stand are thus influenced not only by the external physical geographical environment, but also by the new social environment which they themselves create. For this reason forest trees assimilate, grow, and bear fruit differently and have a different external appearance and internal structure than trees not grown in a forest.

Forestry, unlike horticulture or agriculture, deals with wild plants scarcely modified by cultivation. Trees are also long-lived plants; from the origin of a forest stand to its maturity there may pass more than a century. Foresters, therefore, operate over long periods of time. They must also deal with vast areas; the soil under the forest is as a rule unchanged by cultivation and most of the cultural operations applicable in arboriculture or agriculture are entirely impracticable in forestry. Forests, therefore, are largely the product of nature, the result of the free play of natural forces. Since the foresters had to deal with natural plants which grew under natural conditions, they early learned to study and use the natural forces affecting forest growth. In nature the least change in the topography, exposure or depth of soil, etc., means a change in the composition of the forest, in its density, in the character of the ground cover, and so on. As a result of his observations, the forester has developed definite laws of forest distribution. The forests in the different regions of the country have been divided into natural types with corresponding types of climate and site. These natural forest types, which, by the way, were also developed long before the modern conception of plant formations came to light, have been laid at the foundation of nearly all of the practical work in the woods. A forest type became the silvicultural unit which has the same physical conditions of growth throughout and therefore requires the same method of treatment. The manner of growth and the method of natural regeneration, once developed for a forest type, hold true for the same type, no matter where it occurs. After the relation between a certain natural type of forest and the climate and topography of a region has been established, the forest growth becomes the living expression of the climatic and physical factors of the locality. Similarly, with a given type of climate and locality it is possible for the forester to conceive the type of forest which would grow there naturally. The forester, therefore, may speak of the climate of the beech forest, of the Engelmann spruce forest, of the yellow pine forest. Thus, if in China, which may lack weather observations, we find a beech forest similar to one found in northern New York, we can be fairly certain of the climatic similarities of the two regions. More than that, a type of virgin forest growth may serve as a better indication of the climate of a particular locality than meteorological records covering a short number of years. A forest which has grown on the same ground for many generations is the result not of any exceptional climatic cycle, but is the product of the average climatic conditions that have prevailed in that region for a long time. It expresses not only the result of one single climatic factor, but is the product of all the climatic and physical factors together. Similarly, the use of the natural forest types for determining the potential capacity of the land occupied by them for different purposes is becoming more and more appreciated. When the climatic characteristics of a certain type of forest, for instance those of Engelmann spruce in the Rocky Mountains, is thoroughly established, the potential capacity of the land occupied by it for agriculture, grazing, or other purposes is also largely determined.

Observations of the effect of climate upon forest growth naturally brought out facts with regard to the effect of forests upon
climate, soil and other physical factors and led to the development of a special branch of meteorology, known as forest meteorology, in which the foresters have taken a prominent part.
While there are some phases in forest meteorology which still
allow room for disagreement, some relationships established by
foresters are widely accepted.   One of these is the effect which
forests have upon local climate, especially that of the area they
occupy and of contiguous areas.   Every farmer who plants a
windbreak knows and takes advantage of this influence.   Another
relation is that between the forest and the circulation of water on
and in the ground, a relation which plays such an important part
in the regimen of streams.   Still a third one, as yet beyond the
possibility of absolute proof, is the effect of forests in level countries, in the path of prevailing winds, upon the humidity and
temperature of far-distant regions lying in their lee.

If in the field of botany the forester has contributed to the
progress of botanical geography and in the realm of meteorology
has opened new fields of investigation, his influence in wood
technology has been in changing entirely the attitude of engineers,
physicists and chemists in handling wood products.   The methods
of studying the physical, mechanical and chemical properties of
wood were, of course, those used in engineering by chemists and
physicists; but the forester has shown that wood, unlike steel,
concrete, or other structural material, is subject to altogether
different laws.   Wood, he has shown, is not a homogeneous
product, but is greatly influenced by the conditions in the stand
from which it comes.   Were it not, therefore, that mechanical
properties can be tied up with some definite forest conditions and
correlated with some readily visible expression of tree growth,
such as the number of rings per inch or the specific gravity of the
wood, timber would be too much of an indefinite quantity for
architects and other users of wood to handle with perfect safety.
To find such a relation is just what the foresters have been attempting to do, and most of the studies of the strength of wood
have been with the view of establishing certain relations between

the mechanical, physical, and amatomical properties of the wood. Some of these relations I may mention here.

One of the earliest relations which foresters have established with a fair certainty is that between the specific gravity of the wood and its technical qualities. Some of the foresters even go so far as to claim that the specific gravity of wood is an indicator of all other mechanical properties and that the strength of wood increases with the specific gravity, irrespective of the species and genus. In other words, the heavier the wood, all other conditions being equal, the greater its strength. Even oak, which formed apparently an exception, has been recently shown to follow the same law. If there is still some doubt that the specific gravity of wood can be made a criterion of all mechanical and technical properties of wood, the correlation between the specific gravity and the resistance to compression end-wise (parallel to the grain) is apparently beyond question. Thus by the specific gravity the resistance to compression end-wise can be readily determined. The compression end-wise equals 1000 times the specific gravity minus 70, when the moisture content of the wood is 15 per cent, or $C = 1000\ S - 70$.

Since in construction work the most desirable wood is the one which possesses the highest strength at a given weight, the ratio between the compression strength and the specific gravity was found to express most clearly the strength of wood. This ratio, however, increases with the increase in the specific gravity, a fact which further substantiates the law that the specific gravity of wood determines its mechanical properties.

Another relation which has been fairly established is that between the resistance to compression end-wise and the bending strength of timber. By the resistance compression end-wise, therefore, the bending strength of timber can be determined.

One of the other properties of wood, namely hardness, was found to have a definite relation to the bending and compression strength of wood and this fact tempts the conclusion that by hardness alone all other mechanical properties can be determined. The test for hardness is very simple: it can be made even by a small manufacturer and therefore the whole problem of wood testing would be greatly simplified. Hardness was also found to have a definite relation to the proportion of the summer wood in the annual ring, and consequently to the specific gravity of the wood. The specific gravity of wood is determined by its anatomical structure, by the proportion of fibro-vascular bundles, their thickness and length, the proportion of thick-walled cells, medullary rays, etc. The anatomical structure in its turn is probably determined by the combination of two factors,—the amount of nourishment in the soil and the intensity of transpiration. The mechanical properties of wood come, therefore, within the control of the forester who raises and cares for the forest.

There is another field of scientific endeavor in which foresters in this country may claim some credit. This is in the field of forest mathematics. One unfamiliar with forest growth can hardly realize the difficulties in the way of measuring the forest crop, the amount of wood produced in a forest composed, for instance, of many different species, sizes, and ages. If a tree resembled any geometric body, such as a truncated cone, or an Appolonian paraboloid, it would be a simple matter to determine its contents by applying the formula for such body. But a tree's form does not coincide with that of any known geometric body, so that it would seem that the only possible way of determining the contents of the trees forming a forest would be by measuring each single tree. Evidently this would be an entirely impracticable task.

The common practice of determining the contents of trees either in board measure or in cubic feet is to measure a large number of trees of a given species in a given locality and apply the average figures to the trees of the same diameters and heights within that locality. Since there are, however, a great many species of trees in this country, some of which have a very wide geographic range, this method necessarily involves the preparation of a large number of local volume tables and hence the measurement of hundreds of thousands of trees. The measurement of the taper of a larger number of trees has shown that there are certain critical points along the stem of a tree, the ratio between which expresses the form of the tree in a sufficiently accurate manner. It was found that trees having the same total height, the same diameter breasthigh ($4\frac{1}{2}$ feet from the ground) and the same ratio between the diameter at half the height of the tree and the diameter breasthigh, must invariably have the same cubic contents irrespective of the species of the tree or the region in which it grows.   Thus whether it be a Scotch pine of northern Sweden, a yellow pine of Arizona, a mahogany of the tropics, or a scrubby birch of the Arctic Circle, the volume of the tree may be expressed by means of one simple relationship.   The discovery of this very simple relation provides, for the first time, a basis for the construction of a universal volume table.   The mathematicians of the earlier period sought in vain to find a formula by which the cubic contents of a tree could be expressed.   What the mathematicians failed to develop by the deductive method, foresters have found by the inductive method. With a reliable table for converting cubic measure into board measure for trees of different sizes, the universal volume table expressed in cubic feet could be translated into a universal table expressed in board feet, which is the measure peculiar to this country.

There is another contribution of which I am somewhat hesitant to speak, for it is not a contribution to pure science, if by science is meant only the physical or natural sciences.   Since, however, it touches the interests of a large number of people, I may be forgiven if I say a few words about it.   It is a contribution to what one economist has aptly called the "science of social engineering."   The transfer of the forest reserves in 1905 to the Department of Agriculture marked a new departure in the national economic life.   It recognized the new principle that the Nation's resources should be managed by the Nation and directly in the interests of the whole people; it recognized that these resources should be developed collectively rather than individually and indirectly.   Nearly ten years have now passed since the inauguration of this policy.   The record of what has been accomplished and the manner in which many of the problems have been approached and solved must unquestionably be considered a contribution to the methods by which similar problems may be handled by the Nation in the future. In the administration of the National Forests there is being developed gradually what I believe to be a truly scientific system for attaining a concrete economic end, a system of controlling certain correlated industries with a single purpose in view—the maximum of the welfare of the Nation as a whole. In spite of many mistakes which we have undoubtedly made and which we have attempted to correct as we went along, in spite of the lack of practice and experience in solving the problems at hand, this new policy, it seems to me, has already proved to be entirely safe and workable.

BOTANY.—*A new genus of Chenopodiaceae*,[1] *from Arizona.* PAUL C. STANDLEY, National Museum.

While examining some sheets of Chenopodiaceae from the herbarium of the Missouri Botanical Garden not long ago the writer came upon one consisting of specimens of a low shrub, from northern Arizona, which in general appearance were exactly like *Grayia brandegei*; and being only in flower they were so labeled, although that species was not otherwise known from Arizona. The specimens were associated with this rare species quite naturally, for the writer knew there was no other described member of the Chenopodiaceae in the Southwest that was similar in general aspect.

More recently Mrs. Walter Hough has generously presented to the U. S. National Museum an interesting collection of plants, gathered chiefly in northern Arizona in 1896 and 1897. While inspecting the sheets of this accession the writer's attention was drawn to one which at once recalled the specimen just mentioned. This second one, however, was in mature fruit and showed clearly that the plant was no Grayia. Careful examination definitely placed it as a member of the Atripliceae, but as scarcely referable to any known genus. While, unfortunately, this curious shrub is known only from pistillate branches, the staminate flowers

---

[1] Published by permission of the Secretary of the Smithsonian Institution.

in this group of the Chenopodiaceae are of so little taxonomic importance—being singularly uniform through all the genera of the tribe—that the writer has no hesitation in making it the basis of a new genus, named in honor of the discoverer. Its characters are discussed below.

ZUCKIA Standley, gen. nov.

Low erect shrubs, with a copious covering of whitish inflated trichomes. Leaves numerous, alternate, petiolate, the blades flat, entire. Flowers dioecious, the pistillate ones sessile, solitary or in small glomerules forming short interrupted naked paniculate spikes, each flower bibracteolate, the bractlets accrescent in age, united except for a small aperture at the depressed apex, slightly inflated, thin, depressed vertically, 6-carinate vertically, 2 of the keels broader than the others and winglike; perianth none. Ovary depressed-globose; stigmas 2, filiform, exserted, connate at the base. Utricle included in the bracts, the pericarp membranaceous. Seed horizontal, the testa membranaceous; embryo annular, surrounding the copious endosperm; radicle centrifugal.

Type species, *Zuckia arizonica* Standley.

Zuckia arizonica Standley, sp. nov.

Plants 1.5–4 dm. high, fruticose nearly throughout, copiously branched, the branches slender, erect, striate, the older ones gray or brown, the younger ones stramineous and densely furfuraceous; leaf blades oblong-oblanceolate or spatulate-oblanceolate, or the uppermost linear-oblanceolate, 10–20 mm. long, 1.5–7 mm. wide, obtuse to acutish at the apex, attenuate at the base to a short stout petiole, thick and somewhat coriaceous, grayish-furfuraceous; pistillate spikes much interrupted, divaricate, forming nearly naked panicles 5–12 cm. long and 2–6 cm. wide; fruiting bractlets 4–5 mm. broad, densely furfuraceous, the 6 keels acute, two of them usually 1–1.5 mm. wide and winglike; utricle furfuraceous; seed orbicular, compressed, 2 mm. in diameter, yellowish brown, dull.

Type in the U. S. National Herbarium, no. 694799, collected at Chalcedony Park (the Petrified Forest), eighteen miles southeast of Holbrook, Arizona, October 15, 1897, by Miss Myrtle Zuck (Mrs. Walter Hough). Also collected at Adamana, Arizona, in early August, 1903, by Dr. David Griffiths, no. 5085 (Mo. Bot. Gard. no. 46127). The type is in mature fruit and the second specimen in flower.

The genus Zuckia is a member of the tribe Atripliceae, subtribe Atriplicinae, as defined by Volkens.[2] It is difficult to tell to which of the included genera it is most closely related. In the key given by Volkens it would run to either Spinacia or Suckleya. Certainly

[2] In Engl. and Prantl, Nat. Pflanzenfam. 3[1a]: 62. 1893.

Zuckia is not very closely related to the species of Spinacia, which are glabrous annuals with indurated bracts, 4 or 5 stigmas, and vertical seeds. Suckleya, too, is an herbaceous plant with strongly obcompressed bracts and vertical seeds. Only two other genera are included in the subtribe Atriplicinae: Endolepis and Atriplex. Endolepis has been included in Atriplex by most authors, but it seems to the writer sufficiently distinct in having a perianth in the pistillate flowers, a character which, along with its vertical seeds, also separates it from Zuckia.

Apparently this new genus is most closely related to Atriplex, but in the latter the bracts are never. wholly united; at least the tips are always free, and commonly the bracts are distinct at least to the middle, often nearly or quite to the base. In Zuckia they are wholly united, and at the depressed apex there is only a very small aperture through which the styles are exserted. In only a small group of Atriplex species—the subgenus Dichospermum Dum., which contains the type of the genus, *A. hortensis*—are horizontal seeds found. In these species there are two kinds of pistillate flowers on each plant: some with vertical seeds inclosed by two distinct bracts, and others with horizontal seeds inclosed in a regular herbaceous calyx. In Zuckia all the pistillate flowers are alike, having the horizontal seed included in the somewhat inflated bracts, with no calyx present. As already noted, Zuckia bears a superficial resemblance to *Grayia brandegei*, the two being almost exactly alike in habit and leaf form; but the species of Grayia have a copious pubescence of small branched hairs, and, of course, the structure of the pistillate flowers and the fruit is very different.

Zuckia is evidently a very distinct genus and one of the most remarkable members of the whole tribe. That it was not found by some of the earlier collectors who visited this region is rather strange, but doubtless attributable to the circumstance that the two localities whence it now comes are in a part of Arizona in which comparatively little collecting has been carried on. This and the fact that so much critical attention has been given recently to the Chenopodiaceae, without the discovery of this new generic type, lead to the belief that Zuckia is generally wanting in herbaria. Its rediscovery and collection in adequate amount for distribution will be a matter of much interest; for, while many new genera have been proposed in recent years for United States plants removed from well known genera, the opportunity rarely arises of establishing a genus of phanerogams upon a plant previously quite unknown.

ABSTRACTS

Authors of scientific papers are requested to see that abstracts, preferably prepared and signed by themselves, are forwarded promptly to the editors. Each of the scientific bureaus in Washington has a representative authorized to forward such material to this journal and abstracts of official publications should be transmitted through the representative of the bureau in which they originate. The abstracts should conform in length and general style to those appearing in this issue.

GEOLOGY.—*Carnotite near Mauch Chunk, Pennsylvania.* EDGAR T. WHERRY. U. S. Geological Survey Bulletin 580-F. Pp. 147–151. 1914.

The location, history, geology, composition, origin, and commercial value of the deposit are briefly discussed. The results of a new analysis are given, the potassium being much higher than the calcium and the usual carnotite ratio of $V:U = 1:1$ being shown.

E. T. W.

MINERALOGY.—*Notes on wolframite, beraunite, and axinite.* EDGAR T. WHERRY. Proceedings of the U. S. National Museum, **47**: 501. 1914.

Analyses of two specimens of wolframite and the calculated mineral compositions are given. The convenience of chemical prefixes for the end members of isomorphous series is illustrated by the adoption of the following nomenclature: Ferrowolframite, $FeWO_4$; manganowolframite, $MnWO_4$; calcioscheelite, $CaWO_4$; magnesioscheelite, $MgWO_4$; cuproscheelite, $CuWO_4$; ferrotantalite, $Fe(TaO_3)_2$; manganotantalite, $Mn(TaO_3)_2$; ferrocolumbite, $Fe(CbO_3)_2$; and manganocolumbite, $Mn(CbO_3)_2$.

A ferric phosphate from Hellertown, Pennsylvania, showed wide variations in composition, although it agreed in physical features with beraunite. The variations may be explained by considering the material a meta-colloid: In the original colloid condition it was an adsorption compound of the constituent oxides and water; but, when it attained its present form, the adsorbed constituents united as well as they could into definite compounds, which formed mix-crystals.

A supposed new mineral from Avondale, Pennsylvania, proved to be axinite containing intergrown zoisite.

E. T. W.

JOURNAL

OF THE

WASHINGTON ACADEMY OF SCIENCES

VOL. V FEBRUARY 4, 1915 No. 3

PHYSICS.—*Characteristic equations of tungsten filament lamps and their application in heterochromatic photometry.*[1] G. W. MIDDLEKAUFF AND J. E. SKOGLAND. Communicated by the Bureau of Standards.

The most difficult problem in ordinary photometry is the comparison of the intensity of light sources differing widely in color. In such comparisons it is practically impossible, even for the most experienced observers, to agree in their measurements, this disagreement being due principally to difference in color vision and to difference in judgment as to when two colors viewed in the photometer are of equal intensity. Hence, especially, to establish standards, a large number of observations by different experienced observers must be taken to average out the personal errors.

One of the most convenient methods of avoiding color difference in practical photometry is by the use of colored glasses to bring the lamps to a color match; but by this method the principal difficulties are merely shifted to the problem of calibrating the glasses, a large number of which are necessary to meet the present requirements of colored light photometry.

By the method described in this paper, color differences are avoided by the use of tungsten standard lamps which are adjusted in voltage to color match the light source to be measured, and the candlepower values of the standards at the voltage

[1] To be published in full as Scientific Paper No. 238 of the Bureau of Standards.

corresponding to that color are computed from the voltage at which the candlepower is known, this computation being made by the use of the voltage-candlepower equation of the standards.

In order fully to realize the advantages of this method in practice, it was necessary, first, to measure a large variety of tungsten lamps to find the relation of candlepower to voltage, and then to calculate the equation which would express this relation over a wide range of voltage or efficiency. The results were far more satisfactory than was at first anticipated.

It was found that all vacuum tungsten lamps, within a wide range of wattage, have the same voltage-current-candlepower characteristics regardless of the make or method of manufacture. It was found also that, not only the voltage-candlepower relation, but also the voltage-current, voltage-wattage, and voltage-watts per candle, relations could be accurately expressed by one general equation of the form $y = Ax^2 + Bx + C$. In this equation $x = $ log voltage, $y = $ log candlepower, log wattage, log current, or log watts per candle, and A, B, and C are constants, the values of which depend upon the significance of y. It is found most convenient to express all these variables, except watts per candle, in terms of the respective values of each at a chosen normal efficiency. In this way the constant C disappears from the equation except when y represents the watts per candle, in which case C is the logarithm of the watts per candle chosen as normal.

The above general equation applies very exactly over the whole range investigated, namely, from 0.7-*wpc* to 3.3-*wpc*, the latter limit extending somewhat beyond the watts per candle corresponding to color match with 4-*wpc* carbon lamps.

These equations are useful for two purposes. The international candle is maintained at the Bureau of Standards by means of 4-*wpc* carbon standard lamps. If for example it were desired to establish a group of tungsten standards operating at 1.5 *wpc*. these tungsten standards would be measured directly in terms of the primary 4-*wpc* carbon standards with the voltage on the tungsten lamps so adjusted as to bring them into color match with the primary standards. Then, from the voltage and corresponding efficiency of the tungsten lamps at this color, the voltage, current, watts, and candlepower corresponding to an efficiency of 1.5 *wpc* are computed by means of the above characteristic equations.

Another use of these equations is in connection with tungsten standards the values of which are known at some particular efficiency (or color). In standardizing other lamps these standards are adjusted to a color match with the lamps to be measured and the values of candlepower, current, etc., for each standard, at the voltage corresponding to that particular color, are determined by means of the characteristic equations.

Although these equations are simple and easy to handle, their use involves comparatively long and tedious computations. To avoid the necessity of making such computations, there has been computed a set of tables from which, with the aid of an ordinary slide rule, correction factors to reduce values of candlepower, current, etc., from one efficiency to another can be read directly.

By the method described above, the photometric difficulties due to color difference are dealt with, once for all, in determining the characteristics of the tungsten lamp, and thereafter all measurements are reduced to the photometry of lights of the same color.

PHYSICS.—*The temperature coefficient of magnetic permeability within the working range.*[1] RAYMOND L. SANFORD. Communicated by the Bureau of Standards.

Magnetic measurements at different temperatures within the atmospheric range were made on wrought iron, cast iron, and low carbon steel with different heat treatments. The results of these measurements seem to warrant the following conclusions:

I. The temperature coefficient of magnetic permeability though small can not be neglected in magnetic measurements of high accuracy.

II. On account of the wide variation in temperature coefficient, not only for different materials but also for the same

---

[1] To appear in full in the Bulletin of the Bureau of Standards.

material with different heat treatments, correction cannot be made to standard temperature from data obtained from other materials.

III. Unless the temperature coefficient is known for the particular material under test, temperature control offers the only means of avoiding the error due to temperature changes, at least where errors as great as 1 per cent are to be avoided.

GEOCHEMISTRY.—*Experiments with colloidal gold and silver.* EDSON S. BASTIN,[1] Geological Survey.

GOLD

In a series of preliminary experiments on the precipitative action of metallic sulphides, arsenides, etc. on gold held in dilute solutions, the results of which were published in 1913,[2] it was noted that chalcocite (Cu_2S) precipitated gold from a dilute aqueous solution of auric chloride ($AuCl_3$) as a dark brown dull coating sometimes exhibiting moss-like protuberances, whereas most other common metallic minerals precipitated it as a thin lustrous yellow or orange coating. The brown gold coating chalcocite when touched with the blowpipe flame becomes orange-yellow and lustrous.

As the brown gold showed no indication of being anything but pure gold and as brown gold of somewhat similar appearance is known to occur in nature the suggestion presented itself that the brown color was largely due to a very fine state of division of the gold, its condition possibly approaching that of a coagulated colloid. To test the accuracy of this supposition advantage was taken of certain well known properties of colloidal solutions.

Colloidal solutions may be conveniently divided into two classes according as the "dissolved" substance is solid or liquid. If the "dissolved" substance is solid, as in the case of a colloidal solution of gold in water, the solution is termed a *suspensoid.* If the "dissolved" phase is liquid, as in a solution of gelatine in water, the solution, is termed an *emulsoid.* Even very small amounts

[1] Published with the permission of the Director of the U. S. Geological Survey.
[2] Palmer, Chase, and Bastin, Edson S., Metallic minerals as precipitants of silver and gold. Economic Geology, 8: 140–170. 1913.

of electrolytes added to suspensoids will cause the suspended solid particles to coagulate, i.e. to assemble into larger groups which settle out of the solution. Resolution after coagulation is impossible without introducing entirely new conditions. If on the other hand small amounts of an emulsoid (such as a gelatine solution) are mixed with a suspensoid, coagulation may be much delayed in spite of the presence of electrolytes in the solution.

It seemed possible therefore that if the brown gold developed on chalcocite was colloidal in character, its deposition might be delayed by mixing an emulsoid with the gold chloride solution before inserting the piece of chalcocite and that by this means some of the gold might be obtained in colloidal suspension. This was readily accomplished.

In the experiments first to be reported the solutions were heated to boiling, since it has been determined that in reactions of metallic minerals on gold chloride solutions, heating increases the rate without as a rule greatly affecting the character of the reactions. Much time was thereby saved. In the first experiment a solution of gelatine in water and a $\frac{N}{20}$ solution of auric chloride were employed. Two solutions of equal strength as regards gold were prepared by adding to one volume of $AuCl_3$ solution (1) in one case one volume of gelatine solution, and (2) in the other case one volume of water. The solutions therefore differed only in the presence in one of an emulsoid solution of gelatine. Into each were introduced a few small pieces of chalcocite and both were then heated to boiling and kept there until the reactions were complete. The solution without gelatine rapidly changed from clear yellow to clear pale green-blue in color as the auric chloride was replaced by cupric chloride. At the same time a coating of brown gold formed on the chalcocite. Upon further heating, after the yellow color had wholly disappeared, the solution again changed color becoming deeper blue by transmitted and pale reddish by reflected light. After cooling and standing for about an hour this pseudo-fluorescent coloration disappeared, the solution again showing the pale green-blue of cupric chloride. With the gelatine-bearing solution the reaction proceeded similarly until the yellow color of the solution gave way to pale green-blue; upon further heating, however, *the solution became deep blue by transmitted and bright brick red by reflected light*, due, as later proven, to the presence of gold in colloidal solution.   This solution remained unchanged for days. To exclude the possibility of this very intense coloration being due to the action of the copper salt formed, on the gelatine, gelatine solution was added to the solution resulting from the action of $AuCl_3$ solution alone on chalcocite; even in prolonged boiling there was no intensification of the pale coloration of this solution   To determine whether the brown gold once precipitated can be "dissolved" in an emulsoid, the piece of gold-coated chalcocite obtained from the action of $AuCl_3$ solution alone was boiled in a gelatine solution.   There was no noticeable change.

Although some metallic minerals such as smaltite precipitate lustrous bronze-colored gold from auric chloride solution under the conditions of these experiments, none known to the writer precipitate dull reddish-brown gold, except chalcocite.   It is well known, however, that many *metals* precipitate dull brown to black gold from $AuCl_3$ solutions, and it was desirable to determine whether colloidal gold solutions could be obtained by the aid of these metals.   One part of $\frac{N}{20}$ $AuCl_3$ solution was mixed with one part of dilute gelatine solution and to equal parts of this solution in four test-tubes were added small amounts of metallic zinc, copper, cadmium and tin.   The solutions were then boiled.   In each case dark-brown to nearly black gold was precipitated on the metal.   With zinc and copper colloidal gold solutions were obtained which were identical in appearance with that obtained with chalcocite.   Cadmium yielded a colloidal gold solution that was dark brick-red by reflected and purple by transmitted light.[3]   Tin yielded the well-known "purple of Cassius" solution.

[3] The appearance of colloidal gold solutions is so characteristic that there could be no reasonable doubt upon this ground alone of the nature of the solutions obtained.   Several of them were, however, through the courtesy of Mr. George Vinal of the Bureau of Standards, examined under the ultra-microscope and found to show all the characteristics of colloidal suspensoids.   Moreover they deposit films of gold upon standing for several days.

To determine whether colloidal gold solutions could be obtained with the aid of substances known to precipitate lustrous yellow or orange gold from AuCl$_3$ solutions, fragments of pyrite, chalcopyrite, enargite, and galena were boiled with the same gelatine-bearing solution of AuCl$_3$ used in the previous experiments. In each case lustrous yellow gold was deposited on the mineral, the solution at the same time losing its yellow color; but *gold was not obtained in colloidal solution even on prolonged boiling.* Metallic bismuth, which unlike zinc, copper, and cadmium precipitates lustrous yellow gold from a gelatine-bearing AuCl$_3$ solution, also failed to yield a colloidal gold solution.

The experiments that have been described were conducted at temperatures at or near 100° C. to speed the reactions, but beautifully colored solutions of colloidal gold were also obtained at ordinary room temperatures by the action of metallic copper and of chalcocite on gelatine-bearing AuCl$_3$ solutions. The finely-divided gold first appears as a cloud over the surface of the copper or chalcocite; this cloud, when the dish is jarred, detaches itself in streamer-like forms and finally becomes wholly dispersed in the solution. The color of the solution gradually changes from yellow to purplish red as these gold clouds disperse through it. The facility with which the colloidal solutions can be obtained at room temperatures is markedly dependent upon the strength of the solutions and the most favorable conditions have not been accurately determined by the writer.

A colloidal silica solution was prepared by dialysis of an aqueous sol of sodium silicate that had been neutralized by sulphuric acid. This sol was used instead of gelatine sol in experiments similar to those previously described and yielded colloidal gold solutions with chalcocite and copper, and purple of Cassius with tin.

It is well known that ferrous sulphate readily precipitates gold from solutions of auric chloride. When dilute solutions of these two compounds are mixed there results a solution that is blue by transmitted light and brick-red by reflected light, due to the presence of gold in very fine suspension. From the particular solution prepared by the writer all of the suspended gold settled after standing 1½ hours. If either gelatinous silica or gelatine is present in the solutions similar gold suspensions result, *but from these the gold settles only very slowly.*

Summary for gold. From the foregoing results it is evident that the readiness with which colloidal gold solutions may be obtained under the conditions of these experiments bears a close relation to the nature of the gold deposited. The dull brown or black condition of gold is favorable and the lustrous yellow condition unfavorable to their formation. In the experiments conducted at room temperatures the colloidal gold appeared to originate on the surface of the metal or sulphide, and to slowly diffuse out into the liquid. These phenomena suggest that the dull brown or black gold may be in a finely divided condition approaching that of a coagulated colloid.

Brown gold occurs occasionally in nature usually if not always in the oxidized zone. Lindgren[4] states that the gold derived from the oxidation of tellurides is commonly dull brown in color. While it is very probable that the brown color of some natural gold is due to impurity or to coatings, the possibility that some of it is in a condition approaching the colloidal should not be overlooked.

In the experiments with chalcocite and with ferrous sulphate colloidal silica appeared to function similarly to gelatine in delaying the complete precipitation of gold, some being retained in colloidal suspension. The possibility of gold being taken into colloidal solution in the oxidized zone of ore deposits in the presence of such emulsoids as colloidal silica appears to be worthy of further investigation.

SILVER

In the preliminary paper by Palmer and Bastin already referred to, attention was called to the fact that certain metallic minerals are capable of reducing silver sulphate in dilute aqueous solutions. With some minerals the only silver mineral formed was metallic silver, in other cases native silver and a compound of silver formed, and in still other cases only a silver compound.

[4] Lindgren, W., Mineral Deposits, 434. 1913.

Some differences were noted in the crystal forms of the silver developed on different minerals, but all was silver-white, lustrous and metallic in appearance.

Following the experiments with gold, similar experiments were conducted with silver using a solution composed of equal parts of $\frac{N}{40}$ Ag$_2$SO$_4$ and a dilute aqueous sol of gelatine.

In the first experiment small pieces of chalcocite were boiled: (1) with gelatine-bearing Ag$_2$SO$_4$ solution, and (2) with the same strength Ag$_2$SO$_4$ solution without gelatine. The gelatine-bearing solution yielded a brown colloidal solution of petroleum-like appearance evidently containing silver and possibly silver sulphide;[5] only a slight precipitate of metallic silver formed on the chalcocite. The solution without gelatine yielded no colloidal solution of silver but became pale blue from copper sulphate formed, metallic silver being deposited in abundance on the chalcocite.

Colloidal solutions similar in general appearance to those obtained with chalcocite were obtained from gelatine-bearing Ag$_2$SO$_4$ solutions with enargite, smaltite, maucherite (Ni$_4$As$_3$) and niccolite. Some of the solutions carried presumably not only silver but compounds of silver in colloidal suspension, but the writer has had no opportunity to determine their composition. In each case some metallic silver was precipitated on the mineral, though in notably lesser abundance than when gelatine was not present.

From chalcopyrite, a mineral which does not precipitate metallic silver from neutral Ag$_2$SO$_4$ solution,[6] there was obtained upon boiling with gelatine sol and dilute Ag$_2$SO$_4$ a yellowish-brown colloidal solution, probably of a sulphide of silver and copper. This solution was quite different in appearance from the petroleum-like solutions obtained with minerals that precipitate metallic silver. During the reaction the chalcocite becomes

[5] Palmer has demonstrated the reaction Cu$_2$S + 2 Ag$_2$SO$_4$ = 2 CuSO$_4$ + Ag$_2$S + 2 Ag, for a neutral electrolytic solution.

[6] In the preliminary paper already referred to some precipitation of metallic silver by chalcopyrite was reported but it was subsequently learned that tarnishes on the fragment used produced this effect and that the perfectly clean mineral precipitated no metallic silver from a dilute Ag$_2$ SO$_4$ solution.

covered with peacock tarnish, due presumably to the formation of some double sulphide of silver and copper.

When a colloidal silica sol prepared by dialysis was substituted for the gelatine solution under the conditions of the experiments described above colloidal solutions were obtained upon boiling, with chalcopyrite and metallic tin. With metallic copper and with chalcocite, and enargite, only fine suspensions of silver were obtained with the comparatively dilute silica solution used, but with a solution of sodium silicate[7] much richer in silica true colloidal solutions of silver were readily obtained with all these substances.

Hydrogen sulphide gives with a dilute Ag_2SO_4 solution a black precipitate of Ag_2S, the solution becoming very pale yellowish, probably from the presence of minute amounts of Ag_2S in colloidal solution. In the presence of gelatine, however, no Ag_2S is precipitated, but the solution becomes deep brownish-yellow, all the Ag_2S presumably going into colloidal solution. Entirely analogous results were obtained with cupric sulphate solutions, the gelatine-bearing solution yielding no precipitate, but a yellowish-brown colloidal solution (presumably of sulphides of copper). When a colloidal silica sol was substituted for the gelatine sol in the above experiments, some sulphide was precipitated, but some also went into colloidal suspension, strongly coloring the solutions.

Summary for silver. The above experiments show that, in the presence of an emulsoid such as gelatine, part of the metallic silver or silver compounds that would otherwise be precipitated from silver sulphate by certain metallic minerals is likely to be retained in colloidal solution. Silica appears to function similarly to gelatine in favoring the entrance of the silver or its compounds into colloidal solution. Because of the fact that basic rocks, particularly those rich in olivine, yield colloidal silica in weathering more readily than acid rocks, it is in ores associated with such rocks that we might expect to find the most evidence of colloidal downward transport of these metals. The writer

[7] Sodium silicate in aqueous solution undergoes partial dissociation, yielding sodium hydroxide and silica.

believes, however, that the transport of silver or gold in colloidal solution is of very much less importance in downward enrichment of ore deposits than their transfer as salts in true (electrolytic) solutions. In primary ore deposition colloidal transport may be of much more importance.

General. The writer regrets that he has been unable to carry out these experiments quantitatively, determining fully the products of the reactions. He has also had no opportunity to make a careful search of the foreign literature to determine how much of originality can be claimed for the results. In this country, however, attention appears not to have been directed to the possible geologic bearing of these phenomena. As the writer will be unable for some time to continue these studies the preliminary data are offered for whatever suggestiveness they may have to those interested in the rôle of colloids in ore deposition.

As evidencing the occasional occurrence of gelatinous silica in considerable amounts in mineral deposits, the following statement by Mr. J. H. Levings[8] may be of interest.

I was surprised to find that members could only instance one case of silicic acid in the gelatinous condition. About four years ago, when the writer was connected with the Great Australia Mine, Cloncurry, Queensland, a drive was beat out under the siliceous copper outcrop. Water was continuously flowing through this ore body, which acted as a drainage conduit for the surrounding country. Numerous vughs were cut into, and silica in all stages of gelatinization was found, varying from a viscous fluid to veins which could be cut with a knife like cheese. The writer de-hydrated many samples; some were practically pure silica, some contained carbonate of lime and carbonates of copper. In other samples, taken from solidified portions, a complete gradation from silica to calcite could be followed. Apparently, silica and calcite can be precipitated from the same solution in any proportions. It may be mentioned that the lode occurs in diorite.

Some years previously, in Tasmania, some jelly-like substance was brought for the writer to determine. It had been obtained from a vugh in a siliceous copper lode, and contained some free slender quartz crystals about 2 inches long, both ends of which terminated in prisms. Some similar but better proportioned crystals about $\frac{1}{2}$ inch long, were also present. On examination the substance was found to be silica in a gelatinous state. The lode occurred in old sedimentary rocks.

[8] Trans., Institution of Mining and Metallurgy, 21: 478. 1911–1912.

BOTANY.—*The application of the generic name Achyranthes.*[1]
Paul C. Standley, National Museum.

The generic name Achyranthes was applied by Linneaus in 1753 to a group of plants now placed in the family Amaranthaceae. Linnaeus' genus included several species which are now referred to three genera, only two of which need receive consideration here. When, in working recently with the Amaranthaceae for the North American Flora, it became necessary to determine the type species of the genus, the writer was much surprised to find it to be *Achyranthes repens* L., a plant usually referred to Alternanthera, a member of the tribe Gomphreneae. Achyranthes has commonly been applied to a quite different group of species, of the tribe Achyrantheae. It thus becomes necessary to reapply it in a sense historically correct, and to substitute another name for the Achyranthes of recent authors.

It is unfortunate that the name Achyranthes must be used in a sense other than that in which it has generally been employed in recent years. The earlier botanists, however, placed most of the species of Alternanthera in Achyranthes, so that at least those botanists who urge the use of generic names according to their original application cannot complain of the changes now introduced. There seems, moreover, to be no doubt as to the type of the genus Achyranthes, under the American Code of nomenclature. Linnaeus' genera of the Species Plantarum are to be typified by the citations in the Genera Plantarum of 1754. In that work we find under the name Achyranthes a single citation,—Achyracantha Dill. Elth. *pl. 7, f. 7.* This illustration is cited by Linnaeus under *Achyranthes repens*, which species thus becomes the type of the genus. Furthermore, the generic description given by Linnaeus applies better to this plant than to those lately referred to Achyranthes. In all the editions of the Genera Plantarum the Dillenian citation is the only one listed. On the other hand, Stachyarpagophora Vaill., which is Achyranthes as recently accepted, is cited by Linnaeus under Celosia.

[1] Published by permission of the Secretary of the Smithsonian Institution.

Linnaeus himself was responsible for the later misinterpretation of Achyranthes, for in 1762 he transferred *A. repens* to the genus Illecebrum, renaming it *Illecebrum achyrantha*; a procedure which, however, does not change the nomenclatorial type of Achyranthes. He was the first, apparently, to apply the name Achyranthes to the group of plants of which *Achyranthes aspera* is typical, a group which other writers had referred to Amaranthus.

Achyranthes, as here delimited, has several synonyms. Alternanthera Forsk. (1775) was the first published. Others are: Allaganthera Mart. (1814), Pityranthus Mart. (1817), Telanthera R. Br. (1818), Brandesia Mart. (1826), Mogiphanes Mart. (1826), Bucholzia Mart. (1826), and Steiremis Raf. (1836). Telanthera was maintained by many authors until recently, being applied to the tall perennial species with pedunculate inflorescence. If maintained at all, it could only be on these habital characters. Some authors have attempted to separate it upon the length of the stamen tube, amending the genus so as to include some of the low annual plants with sessile inflorescence; but when this has been done Telanthera has included just as diverse elements as the genus Achyranthes as here defined. The form of the stamen tube and the length of the pseudostaminodia are not good generic characters, for all intermediate forms can be found in species that are evidently of the closest relationship. The genus Mogiphanes has some claims to generic rank. It includes those species in which the flowers are manifestly pedicellate inside the bractlets; but this character seems only relative, when some of the species of other groups are examined.

The published species of Achyranthes which come within the range of the North American Flora are the following: *Achyranthes axillaris* Hornem. (*Alternanthera spinosa* R. & S.); **A. leiantha** (*Alternanthera pungens* H. B. K., 1817, not *Achyranthes pungens* Lam., 1783; *Alternanthera achyrantha leiantha* Seub., 1875); *A. repens* L.; *A. polygonoides* (L.) Lam.; *A. sessilis* (L.) Steud., 1840, as synonym; **A. martinicensis** (*Telanthera martinicensis* Moq., 1849); **A. portoricensis** (*Alternanthera portoricensis* Kuntze, 1891); **A. watsoni** Standley, nom. nov. (*Telanthera stellata* S. Wats., 1886, not *Achyranthes stellata* Willd., 1797);

A. ficoidea (L.) Lam.; *A. halimifolia* Lam.; **A. maritima** (*Alternanthera maritima* St. Hil., 1823; **A. obovata** (*Bucholzia obovata* Mart. & Gal., 1843); **A. urbani** Standley, nom. nov. (*Alternanthera geniculata* Urban, 1912, not *Telanthera geniculata* S. Moore, 1895); **A. olivacea** (*Telanthera olivacea* Urban, 1899); **A. philoxeroides** (*Bucholzia philoxeroides* Mart., 1826); **A. mexicana** (*Brandesia mexicana* Schlecht. & Cham., 1832); **A. pycnantha** (*Brandesia pycnantha* Benth., 1844); **A. gracilis** (*Gomphrena gracilis* Mart. & Gal., 1843); **A. jacquini** (*Mogiphanes jacquini* Schrad., 1834); **A. ramosissima** (*Mogiphanes ramosissima* Mart., 1826); **A. brasiliana** (*Gomphrena brasiliana* L., 1756); **A. costaricensis** (*Alternanthera costaricensis* Kuntze, 1891).

The following are some of the better known South American species of Achyranthes which have been described under other generic names: **Achyranthes albida** (*Telanthera albida* Moq., 1849); **A. aphylla** (*Alternanthera aphylla* Glaziou, 1911); **A. bangii** (*Telanthera bangii* Rusby, 1896); **A. bastosiana** (*Alternanthera bastosiana* Glaziou, 1911); **A. boliviana** (*Alternanthera boliviana* Rusby, 1895); **A. chacoensis** (*Alternanthera chacoensis* Morong, 1893); **A. cyclophylla** (*Telanthera cyclophylla* Seub., 1875); **A. echinocephala** (*Brandesia echinocephala* Hook. f., 1847); **A. elongata** (*Gomphrena elongata* Willd., 1819); **A. hookeri** Standley, nom. nov. (*Bucholzia filifolia* Hook. f., 1847, not *Achyranthes filifolia* Willd., 1819); **A. flavicoma** (*Telanthera flavicoma* Anderss., 1854); **A. frutescens** (*Illecebrum frutescens* L'Her., 1785); **A. galapagensis** (*Telanthera galapagensis* Stewart, 1911); **A. geniculata** (*Telanthera geniculata* S. Moore, 1895); **A. glaucescens** (*Bucholzia glaucescens* Hook. f., 1847); **A. hassleriana** (*Alternanthera hassleriana* Chod., 1903); **A. helleri** (*Telanthera helleri* Robinson, 1902); **A. lehmannii** (*Alternanthera lehmannii* Hieron, 1895); **A. lorentzii** (*Alternanthera lorentzii* Uline, 1899); **A. martii** (*Telanthera martii* Moq., 1849); **A. microphylla** (*Alternanthera microphylla* R. E. Fries, 1905); **A. minutiflora** (*Telanthera minutiflora* Seub., 1875); **A. morongii** (*Alternanthera morongii* Uline, 1899); **A. nodifera** (*Telanthera nodifera* Moq., 1849); **A. nudicaulis** (*Bucholzia nudicaulis* Hook. f., 1847); **A. pilosa** (*Alternanthera pilosa* Moq., 1849); **A. pinheirensis** (*Alternanthera pinheirensis* Glaziou, 1911); **A. praelonga** (*Alternanthera praelonga* St. Hil., 1823); **A. puberula** (*Brandesia puberula* Mart., 1826); **A. reineckii** (*Alternanthera reineckii* Briq., 1899); **A. rigida** (*Alternanthera rigida* Rob. & Greenm., 1895); **A. paraguayensis** Standley, nom. nov. (*Mogiphanes rosea* Morong, 1893, not *Achyranthes rosea* Spreng., 1827); **A. rufa** (*Brandesia rufa* Mart., 1826); **A. rugelii** (*Telanthera rugelii* Seub., 1875); **A. rugulosa**

(*Telanthera rugulosa* Robinson, 1902); **A. snodgrassii** (*Telanthera snodgrassii* Robinson, 1902); **A. strictiuscula** (*Telanthera strictiuscula* Anderss., 1854); **A. seubertii** Standley, nom. nov. (*Alternanthera tomentella* Seub., 1875, not *Achyranthes tomentella* Zipp., 1841); **A. vestita** (*Telanthera vestita* Anderss., 1854).

Since the generic name Achyranthes is to be used in the sense above indicated, another name must be used for the genus which has been passing under that name. The oldest synonym cited by Dalle Torre and Harms under Achyranthes is Amaranthulus Heist., 1763. This, however, was cited by Fabricius[2] merely as a synonym, hence is not available. Centrostachys was published by Wallich[3] in 1824. The type species is *C. aquatica* Wall. Moquin considered the genus distinct from his Achyranthes, but later authors have merged it in the latter genus. The included species seem to the writer to be congeneric with Achyranthes as defined by Moquin and more recent writers, and the name Centrostachys may, therefore, stand for the genus. Rafinesque subsequently (1836) proposed the name Cadelaria for this group and that name would be a very appropriate one, for it was used in pre-Linnaean botany. Another pre-Linnaean name, Stachyarpagophora of Vaillant, was restored by Dr. Maza in 1897,[4] but fortunately, because of the cumbrousness of the word, it is invalidated by the two earlier names which were properly published.

Two species of Centrostachys occur in North America: **C. indica** (*Achyranthes aspera indica* L., 1753; *A. obtusifolia* Lam., 1783), and **C. aspera** (*Achyranthes aspera* L., 1753).

A large number of other species of Centrostachys occur in the Old World, chiefly in Africa and the East Indies. The following new binomials should be made for some of the better known of these: **Centrostachys abyssinica** (*Achyranthes abyssinica* Nees, 1850); **C. alba** (*Brandesia alba* Mart., 1840); **C. angustifolia** (*Achyranthes angustifolia* Benth., 1849); **C. arborescens** (*Achyranthes arborescens* R. Br., 1810); **C. australis** (*Achyranthes australis* R. Br., 1810); **C. avicularis** (*Achyranthes avicu-*

[2] Enum. Pl. Hort. Helms. ed. 2, 358.
[3] In Roxb. Fl. Ind. **2**: 497.
[4] Fl. Haban. 92.

laris E. Mey., 1849); **C. bidentata** (*Achyranthes bidentata* Blume, 1825); **C. breviflora** (*Achyranthes breviflora* Baker, 1897); **C. canescens** (*Achyranthes canescens* R. Br., 1810); **C. carsoni** (*Achyranthes carsoni* Baker, 1897); **C. conferta** (*Achyranthes conferta* Schinz, 1896); **C. elegantissima** (*Achyranthes elegantissima* Schinz, 1895); **C. fasciculata** (*Achyranthes fasciculata* Schweinf., 1867); **C. flabellifera** (*Achyranthes flabellifera* Boerl., 1891); **C. fruticosa** (*Achyranthes fruticosa* Lam., 1783); **C. grandifolia** (*Achyranthes grandifolia* Moq., 1849); **C. heudelotii** (*Achyranthes heudelotii* Moq., 1849); **C. involucrata** (*Achyranthes involucrata* Moq., 1849); **C. schinzii** Standley, nom. nov. (*Achyranthes lanuginosa* Schinz, 1895, not *A. lanuginosa* Nutt., 1820); **C. mauritiana** (*Achyranthes mauritiana* Moq., 1849); **C. moquini** Standley, nom. nov. (*Achyranthes javanica* Moq., 1849, not *A. javanica* Pers., 1805); **C. oblanceolata** (*Achyranthes oblanceolata* Schinz, 1895); **C. ovata** (*Achyranthes ovata* Ehrenb., 1867); **C. schweinfurthii** (*Achyranthes schweinfurthii* Schinz, 1896); **C. splendens** (*Achyranthes splendens* Mart., 1849); **C. velutina** (*Achyranthes velutina* Hook. & Arn., 1841); **C. welwitschii** (*Achyranthes welwitschii* Schinz, 1895).

ZOOLOGY.—*The bathymetrical distribution of the Arctic and Antarctic crinoids.*[1] AUSTIN H. CLARK, National Museum.

In their bathymetrical distribution the crinoids of the Arctic and Antarctic Oceans are most interesting. I have already[2] presented the reasons for considering the crinoids of the Atlantic, from the standpoint of their systematic interrelationships, and of their geographical distribution, as representing merely the fauna of an inland sea, derived from the fauna of the Indo-Pacific as a parent, the crinoids of the Arctic Ocean representing also an inland sea fauna derived in part from the Bay of Bengal direct, and in part from the adjacent portion of the Atlantic. The fauna of the Antarctic Ocean is merely the southerly extension of the deep water fauna of the Indo-Pacific Ocean.

Examining the diagram (fig. 1), we find that the line representing the Antarctic fauna, and that representing the Antarctic and the Arctic faunas combined, are strikingly similar to the line

[1] Published with the permission of the Secretary of the Smithsonian Institution.

[2] Internationale Revue der gesamten Hydrobiologie und Hydrographie, 1914.

representing the distribution according to depth of the genera confined to the Atlantic (fig. 2). This is the more remarkable when we remember that only one genus (*Hathrometra*) is common to the Atlantic and to the Antarctic, and to the Atlantic and the Arctic, while in the polar seas the temperature is comparatively uniform from the surface to the bottom in contrast to the Middle Atlantic where the surface temperature is very high.

It thus appears that essentially the same selective processes have operated both in the Atlantic and in the Antarctic in weed-

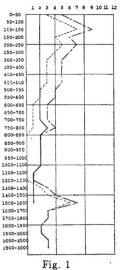 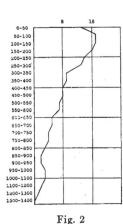

Fig. 1   Fig. 2

Fig. 1. Bathymetrical distribution of the Artic (——) and Antartic (- - - -) crinoids, and of the two combined (— · —).

Fig. 2. The frequency at different depths of the crinoid genera confined to the Atlantic.

ing out the less adaptable of the primarily Indo-Pacific genera; but the results in each case are radically different, showing conclusively that the Atlantic could never have been populated by passage from the Indian Ocean south of Africa, between Africa and Antarctica.

An inland sea, biologically speaking, is a more or less enclosed body of water which, connected with an ocean, has received all of its fauna from that ocean. Its fauna, therefore, is composed of the same types that occur in the ocean with which it is most intimately connected, with the less plastic and adaptable weeded out and the remainder modified in proportion to the difference between the physics and chemistry of the inland sea and that of the parent ocean.

All inland seas necessarily differ physically to a greater or lesser degree from the oceans with which they are connected. Their abyssal water cannot form a part of the general abyssal circulation of the oceans, moving slowly anticlockwise about the oceanic basins, and therefore tends to become more or less stagnant and, under certain conditions, either abnormally cold, as in the Arctic, or abnormally warm, as in the Mediterranean. Their surface water, no longer a part of the general superficial oceanic circulation, unless there be an outlet sufficiently large so that a continuous flow is maintained, increases in salinity through an excess of evaporation, as in the Mediterranean and in the Red Sea, or decreases in salinity through an excess of rainfall in the tributary drainage area as in the Baltic. Either of these changes is fatal to a certain percentage of the organisms which enter inland seas, so that necessarily their fauna is composed only of the more resistant and adaptable organisms of the parent oceans.

On account of the physical alteration of the waters of an inland sea, through which they become less favorable than oceanic waters for the support of marine organisms, inland seas never serve as the cradle for new organic types; their fauna is entirely derived from outside, though the component elements may be forced to undergo a certain amount of modification in order to meet the new conditions imposed.

An inland sea of the present epoch may be a derivative from a much greater sea of the past, as in the case of the Mediterranean.

The restriction in size of any large portion of an ocean immediately alters and restricts the circulation of the enclosed water, bringing it more and more under the influence of the local meteorological conditions; the effect upon the fauna is therefore exactly the same as though the sea arose through a sinking of the land resulting in an inflow of oceanic water. The biological conditions in an inland sea are not in any way concerned with the question whether the sea originated by a sinking of the land, or whether it arose by a restriction of a previously much larger body of water. Both processes lead to a mean which is physically and oceanographically the same, and therefore biologically the same.

A number of curious types occur in enclosed seas which are quite different from any types inhabiting the oceans with which these enclosed seas were once connected. These types are mainly to be interpreted as relics of a once generally distributed fauna which, able to survive the changing conditions, have been preserved from extermination by the fact that none of the economically more efficient types of later origin, through competition with which they have been extirpated from the oceans, have been able to enter the enclosed basins, for the reason that these basins became cut off from the oceans before the appearance of these later types.

Such types are found in enclosed seas, but almost never in inland seas, for the reason that all types of later origin are excluded from the former; an animal type efficient and vigorous enough to overcome and to exterminate competing types in the oceans would, other things being equal, also be efficient enough to extirpate them from all the inland seas.

Among the crinoids two such types occur in the Caribbean Sea, *Isocrinus* and *Holopus*. These persist here not for the reason that they originated here, but because the disruption of the connection between the Caribbean region and the East Indies took place before the evolution of the more efficient and vigorous types now dominant in the Indo-Pacific littoral, through competition with which they have there been extirpated.

It is a curious fact that the sea about the Antarctic continent is more in agreement physically, chemically and biologically with an inland sea than with an ocean or broad embayment like the Arabian Sea or the Bay of Bengal. It might aptly be described as a combination of the Arctic Ocean and the Mediterranean, that is, a chilled Mediterranean; for the temperature is low, varying little from the surface to the bottom, as in the more typical parts of the Arctic, or, farther from shore, with an intermediate warmer layer, also as in certain parts of the Arctic; while the salinity is high, varying but little from the surface to the bottom, as in the Mediterranean.

The Arctic and the Mediterranean are connected with the Atlantic through geographically and bathymetrically restricted channels. The Antarctic is connected with the oceans north of it by a bathymetrically narrowly restricted thermal zone; for the difference in temperature in the upper layers between the Antarctic and the South Pacific, Indian and South Atlantic Oceans is such as to preclude the entrance from any of the latter into the former of all organisms excepting only those of the cold abysses.

The Antarctic, therefore, is a great thermally isolated sea, directly connected with the oceans to the north only through the abysses, corresponding very closely in its physical, chemical and biological characters to a geographically isolated sea which is connected with the adjacent ocean only by a shallow strait.

As the necessary corollary of oceanographic changes, all tending toward oceanographic simplicity, the more restricted an inland, or an isolated, sea becomes, the more featureless and the more nearly vertical becomes the line representing the distribution of its crinoids in their relation to depth. Thus we are prepared to find the line representing the bathymetrical distribution of the Arctic crinoids nearly vertical and almost straight, although species of three quite different genera are involved. Practically the same featureless vertical line represents the bathymetrical distribution of the crinoids of the Mediterranean, and of the Okhotsk and Japanese Seas.

The crinoid fauna of the Arctic Ocean includes two species (*Heliometra glacialis* and *Ilycrinus carpenterii*) apparently derived from the crinoid fauna of the Bay of Bengal, and one (*Hathrometra prolixa*) derived from the Antarctic by way of the Atlantic.

The Arctic fauna of the western part of the Sea of Okhotsk and of the Sea of Japan includes one species (*Heliometra maxima*) derived from the Bay of Bengal, one species (*Thaumatometra tenuis*) derived from the Pacific to the southward of Japan, and one species (*Psathyrometra erythrizon*) derived from the Pacific to the northeastward.

The oceanographic conditions in both of these divisions of the Arctic province are practically identical; but the faunal differences are such as to suggest that they never have been parts of the same fauna since the present distribution of land and sea became established.

Hathrometra prolixa is probably an intruder into the Arctic Ocean from the Atlantic under the present conditions, and the same is undoubtedly true of *Thaumatometra tenuis* and *Psathyrometra erythrizon* in the Okhotsk and Japanese Seas.

Judging from what we know of the fauna of the great Russian lakes, Aral, Balkash and Baikal, as well as of the lesser lakes between them, it appears not improbable that this region was the original home of *Heliometra*, which it reached from the southward, and from which, long ago, it spread both northward and eastward to the Arctic Ocean and to the Seas of Okhotsk and Japan; but there must always be kept in mind the very remote possibility that *Heliometra* reached the Okhotsk and Japanese Seas from the Arctic Ocean by way of the Bering Strait and the coast of Kamchatka, by some means divesting itself on the way of its inseparable Arctic companion, *Hathrometra prolixa*.

The bathymetric range of the three Arctic crinoids:

	fathoms		fathoms
Heliometra glacialis....	2–755	*Ilycrinus carpenterii*...	755–1563
Hathrometra prolixa...	10–1088		

The bathymetric range of the eighteen Antarctic crinoids:

	fathoms		fathoms
Thalassometra bispinosa	1600	*Trichometra remota*....	1600
Psathyrometra antarctica	1430	*Isometra angustipinna*.	56–600
Eumorphometra hirsuta.	140	*Thaumatometra abyssorum*..............	1600
Eumorphometra concinna................	211–222	*Bathymetra carpenteri*..	2600
Promachocrinus kerguelensis..............	10–222	*Thaumatocrinus renovatus*...............	1347–1800
Solanometra antarctica.	75–150	*Ilycrinus australis*.....	1375–2575
Anthometra adriani....	124–500	*Ptilocrinus brucei*......	2485
Florometra magellanica	17–782	*Ptilocrinus antarcticus*.	266
Hathrometra exigua....	50–140	*Hyocrinus bethellianus*.	1600–2575

The frequency of the Arctic and Antarctic crinoids at different depths:

Fathoms	Artic	Ant-arctic	Total	Fathoms	Artic	Ant-arctic	Total
0–50	2	3	5	800–850	2	0	2
50–100	2	5	7	850–900	2	0	2
100–150	2	7	9	900–950	2	0	2
150–200	2	4	6	950–1000	2	0	2
200–250	2	5	7	1000–1100	2	0	2
250–300	2	4	6	1100–1200	1	0	1
300–350	2	3	5	1200–1300	1	0	1
350–400	2	3	5	1300–1400	1	2	3
400–450	2	3	5	1400–1500	1	3	4
450–500	2	3	5	1500–1600	1	6	7
500–550	2	2	4	1600–1700	0	3	3
550–600	2	2	4	1700–1800	0	3	3
600–650	2	1	3	1800–1900	0	2	2
650–700	2	1	3	1900–2000	0	2	2
700–750	2	1	3	2000–2500	0	3	3
750–800	3	1	4	2500–3000	0	3	3

ABSTRACTS

Authors of scientific papers are requested to see that abstracts, preferably prepared and signed by themselves, are forwarded promptly to the editors. Each of the scientific bureaus in Washington has a representative authorized to forward such material to this journal and abstracts of official publications should be transmitted through the representative of the bureau in which they originate. The abstracts should conform in length and general style to those appearing in this issue.

GEODESY.—*Precise leveling from Brigham, Utah, to San Francisco, Cal.* WILLIAM BOWIE. U. S. Coast and Geodetic Survey. Special Publication No. 22. Pp. 67. 1914.

This publication gives the results of a line of precise levels run along the Southern Pacific Railway, from Brigham, Utah, to San Francisco, California, in 1911 and 1912. The line is 891 miles long and fixes the elevations of 315 permanent bench marks. The elevation of the top of rail in front of each of the railway stations along the line was also determined. The elevations of the bench marks and of the top of rail in front of the railway stations are given in meters and feet. As in all precise leveling in the United States the datum used is mean sea level. This line was fitted or adjusted to the elevations resulting from the 1912 adjustment of the precise level net of the country (Special Publication No. 18), hence the elevations given are standard, that is, they will not be changed as the net is further extended. Included in this report are discussions of the methods used and the accuracy attained in precise leveling.

The result of a study of the errors of leveling is also reported on. The basis for this study is the data for five level lines, giving the times of the runnings of the different sections, with the weather conditions prevailing at the time the observations were made. The data are arranged in eight tables in such a manner as to set forth various relations between the errors of leveling and the conditions of weather, the time of the observations and the grade. It is believed that, other things being equal, the running in the afternoon gives, on an average, more accurate results than the forenoon leveling; also that, other things being equal, a running in wind is more accurate, on an average, than one in calm; and that, other things being equal, a running with a cloudy sky will be more accurate, on an average, than one in sunshine.   Hence, the ideal condition would be an afternoon with a moderate wind and a cloudy sky.

The line divides the long circuit between San Diego, California, and Seattle, Washington, and completes another direct connection between sea level on the Atlantic and Pacific coasts.   H. G. AVERS.

PHYSICS.—*Calibration tables for copper-constantan and platinum-plantinrhodium thermo-elements.* L. H. ADAMS.   J. Am. Chem. Soc., **36:** 65–72.   1914.

Thermo-elements, if they are to yield accurate readings of temperature, must frequently be recalibrated by determination of their electromotive force at a series of fixed points and subsequent interpolation. The labor of interpolation is minimized by the aid of the tables presented in this paper, which give temperatures and temperature differences for each 100 microvolts up to the limit of usefulness of each thermo-element, and are used in combination with the appropriate derivation curve deduced for each element from the observations at the fixed points.

L. H. A.

PHYSICS.—*Thermo-element installations, especially for calorimetry.* WALTER P. WHITE.   J. Am. Chem. Soc., **36:** 1856–1868.   1914. *Potentiometers for thermo-electric measurements, especially in calorimetry.* WALTER P. WHITE.   J. Am. Chem. Soc., **36:** 1868–1885. 1914.

These two papers describe a type of auxiliary installation for thermo-elements which in high-temperature measurement and other work of moderate precision is valuable for its convenience, quickness, and comprehensiveness, and which is also capable of the very high precision often desired for calorimetry.

When a thermo-element is used with its two ends at nearly the same temperature, a condition easily provided in calorimetry, the relative precision required in the electrical measurement falls to a value no greater than that desired in the temperature reading, and the most serious errors ordinarily affecting the electrical thermometer practically disappear.

The absolute electrical precision required is also comparatively low. With a convenient and easily made copper-constantan multiple thermo-element of 24 couples, 0.0001°C. corresponds to 0.1 microvolt.

The satisfactory attainment of a precision of 0.1 microvolt demands two, and only two, special electrical instruments. ` The first is an arrangement for eliminating the effect of parasitic thermal electromotive forces. A common copper knife-switch will perform this service admirably. The second special requirement is an appropriate potentiometer, that is, one reliable to 0.1 microvolt.

The slide-wire and Feussner potentiometers of 1 volt range or more now in common use are not thus reliable, and are otherwise unsuited for thermo-element work. Split-circuit potentiometers are satisfactory in this and all other important respects, and so are combination potentiometers, or potentiometers having two otherwise separate, very simple instruments in series in the same galvanometer circuit. A very low-priced split-circuit potentiometer is on the market; and the combination potentiometer, on account of its mechanical and electrical simplicity, is an easy instrument to build to order.

The potentiometer system, either with or without the thermo-element, is especially suited to simultaneous measurements of different and differently varying electromotive forces. Its convenience for such measurements can be increased by using a few pieces of hard-rubber sheet as stops for the dial switches, and still further increased by arranging a double potentiometer, with duplicate dials. One effective form of double potentiometer, which employs a master-switch, can be arranged at the cost of a few knife-switches and very little labor. An especially suitable instrument to arrange in this way is the combination potentiometer, all of whose dial switches are single, and free from contact resistance error.

Another convenience especially easy to obtain with the thermo-element-potentiometer system is the power to take the last two figures of any reading directly from the galvanometer scale. It increases speed, simplifies manipulation, diminishes errors, and gives calorimetric data in a form specially convenient for further treatment.

For high-temperature measurements and much other thermo-element work not calorimetric, though the required precision may often be less, most of the features above described are desirable, especially the facility for simultaneous and direct readings.   W. P. W.

PHYSICS.—*Leakage prevention by shielding, especially in potentiometer systems.* WALTER P. WHITE. J. Am. Chem. Soc., **36:** 2011–2020. 1914.

An insulation resistance of 5,000 megohms or more is often necessary to prevent serious disturbance of thermo-electric measuring systems from stray portions of power or lighting currents, and the frequently more sensitive resistance-measuring system is of course in greater danger still. All such trouble is absolutely prevented by an equipotential shield, which is merely a connected system of metal plates, wires, etc., which interposes itself at every point of solid contact between the measuring system and external bodies. This shield need not be, and preferably should not be, "earthed."

Slight modifications of this shield are also useful in electric furnaces, in the measurements upon power circuits, and within the potentiometer circuit itself.

These arrangements are easy to install, most of them require no subsequent attention, and all are easily tested.   W. P. W.

PHYSICS.—*Thermo-elements of precision, especially for calorimetry.* WALTER P. WHITE.   J. Am. Chem. Soc., **36**: 2292–2313.   1914.

Inhomogeneity, once a serious foe to precision in thermo-elements, and still often supposed to be such, can without difficulty be rendered practically negligible in copper-constantan thermo-elements used for any precision up to 50 parts per million.   Such thermo-elements, accordingly, may, except for imperfect insulation, easily preventable, be free from all appreciable errors other than those (such as incomplete depth of immersion) which are possible with all thermometers.   To attain this freedom from error the wire used must be tested, and the essential though easily satisfied requirements peculiar to a thermo-electric system must be observed.   These requirements this paper attempts to consider in detail, and it also describes simple but important details regarding the operations of construction, insulation, inclosure, calibration, etc., of the thermo-elements.

Constantan wire for thermo-elements has been so far improved that continuous lengths are frequently obtainable which vary (in electromotive force against copper) less than 0.0002, making sensitive thermo-elements with errors usually less than 20 per million.

The testing of wire enough for a thermo-element of maximum sensitiveness takes but an hour or two, with simple apparatus.

On account of the ease with which thermo-elements can be constructed, the more sensitive combination of several couples is generally preferable to a single couple, even for cruder measurements.   W. P. W.

PHYSICS.—*Easy calorimetric methods of high precision.* WALTER P. WHITE. J. Am. Chem. Soc., **36**: 2313–2333. 1914.

In the calorimetric method of mixtures, a precision approaching or reaching 0.1 per mille, though somewhat unusual, is often desirable, and is ordinarily not difficult to attain with appropriate apparatus. Its attainment is especially easy˙with a two-calorimeter installation, which secures the convenience and high precision of differential thermo-electric temperature measurement. This is the only advantage of the two-calorimeter arrangement; the diminution of heat-loss error, often counted an advantage, turns out upon examination to be largely illusory. By abandoning the twin calorimeters previously used to get this supposed advantage, and using for the comparison calorimeter a vacuum-jacketed flask, there is a gain in convenience and precision. A special thermo-element combination renders the necessary temperature observations as simple as with the twin arrangement. A completely inclosing jacket of uniform temperature is necessary for this method, but this is no loss, for such a jacket proves to be necessary for highest precision with any other method. This method is quite as effective with two jackets, one around each calorimeter, and therefore with adiabatic methods.

Efficient complete jackets can be very easily realized according to several methods, which are described.

As compared with others, the present method is specially advantageous for observations of great absolute precision and wherever it is desirable to secure the advantages which the thermo-electric system possesses in the way of rapidity and of facility in making varied observations.   W. P. W.

PHYSICS.—*A significant instance of galvanometer instability.* WALTER P. WHITE. Phys. Rev. (2), **3**: 491–492. 1914.

A radial-field moving coil galvanometer, very free from ordinary tremors, was much deflected by various shocks occurring within the building, and this effect disappeared whenever the supporting shelf was fastened to the wall with sufficient firmness. Apparently, a slight tipping of the shelf was to blame. At any rate, if there had also been any visible tremors of the galvanometer coil, these would have been supposed to be responsible for the trouble. It follows that in other cases where tremors *are* present, and are supposed to cause troublesome deflections, the real trouble may be due to some other, more easily removable cause.   W. P. W.

PHYSICS.—*Einige neue Doppelkompensatoren*. WALTER P. WHITE. Z. Instrumentenkunde, **34**: 71–82; 107–113; 142–151. 1914.

This paper deals with the construction of potentiometers possessing the high precision needed for accurate work with thermo-elements. Two general features of value are: (1) The use of the *partial deflection* method, where the quantity to be measured is largely compensated or balanced, and the outstanding small difference read directly by some deflection instrument. Such methods usually combine all the precision of null methods with almost the quickness of straight deflection methods. (2) The use of neutral ("anti-thermoelectric") contacts, especially in the switches. This renders it possible to dispense with the very low contact resistance required in many existing instruments, and also brings other advantages. Neutral contacts are easily secured by simply using thin leaves of metal, adding blocks of the same metal in dial switches.

Various electrical arrangements for high-precision potentiometers, suggested by Wolff, Waidner, Hausrath, Diesselhorst, Wenner, and the present writer, are examined in detail. The preference is given to a "split-circuit" potentiometer (embodying features due to Wenner and White) somewhat different from previous split-circuit designs, and to a new type, the "combination potentiometer" (features due to Hausrath, Diesselhorst, White), which requires two batteries, but is otherwise remarkably simple and free from sources of error.

One advantage of the potentiometer is the ease with which it can be adapted to almost simultaneous readings of different electrical quantities. A potentiometer with two sets of switches is especially effective in this respect, and practically does the work of two instruments. The two sets of dials are controlled either by a master switch or by sliding two sets of switch arms over a single set of central blocks. This latter arrangement is easily secured in the "gridiron" potentiometer, by means of a new and simple type of switch construction.

Instruments now in use in the Geophysical Laboratory are described which illustrate the above types of design and construction.

W. P. W.

PHYSICAL CHEMISTRY.—*The ternary system $CaO–Al_2O_3–SiO_2$*. G. A. RANKIN; with optical study by FRED. E. WRIGHT. Am. Jour. Sci. (4), **39**: 1–79. 1915.

The purpose of this investigation was to ascertain the stability relations in the ternary system $CaO–Al_2O_3–SiO_2$, not only from a purely scientific point of view, but also from the bearing of the facts thus discovered upon a number of geological inquiries and upon the problem of the nature of portland-cement clinker. Many papers on this general topic have, of course, already been published, but the work recorded is in the main fragmentary and of little avail in settling the large general questions involved. The present investigation aims to treat the system rather completely, to ascertain the equilibrium relations in the system. To this end all the possible compounds which are found in dry melts of the three oxides CaO, Al_2O_3, SiO_2 have been determined, especially those which are stable at the liquidus; this involves measurements of the respective melting-points or dissociation temperatures, and the determination of the invariant points, boundary curves (monovariant systems), and fields of stability (divariant systems) of the various compounds.

This paper contains a summary record of the work performed; it is the first thoroughgoing attempt, so far as known, to determine all the compounds, both binary and ternary, of CaO, Al_2O_3, SiO_2, and the mutual relations of these compounds, many of which have, of course, previously been made synthetically by others. The data obtained are made use of in a discussion of the nature and constitution of portland-cement clinker and of the formation of certain natural minerals from the magma.

Three papers dealing with this system have already appeared from the Geophysical Laboratory. The first two dealt with the binary systems,[1] while in the third[2] provisional locations were assigned to ternary quintuple points and boundary curves and the new relations applied in a discussion of the constitution of portland-cement clinker. In the present paper a more exact location is given for the eutectics, quintuple points, and boundary curves, together with the corresponding temperatures. Because of the large amount of data it has not been possible to give in a paper of this nature more than the mean values obtained from a large number of determinations of the various points. But complete tables of data and a much more complete discussion of methods and apparatus and of the results obtained will be given in a later monograph.   F. E. W.

[1] The lime-silica series of minerals. A. L. Day, E. S. Shepherd, and F. E. Wright. Am. Jour. Sci. (4), 22: 265. 1906. The binary systems of alumina, with silica, lime, and magnesie. E. S. Shepherd, G. A. Rankin, and F. E. Wright. Amer. Jour. Sci. (4), 28: 293. 1909.

[2] Preliminary report on the ternary system $CaO-Al_2O_3-SiO_2$. A study of the constitution of portland-cement clinker. E. S. Shepherd, G. A. Rankin, and F. E. Wright. Jour. Ind. Eng. Chem., 3: 1–43. 1911.

PHYSICAL CHEMISTRY.—*The utilization of diffusion processes in the preparation of pure substances.* JOHN JOHNSTON. J. Am. Chem. Soc., **36:** 16–19. 1914.

Many slightly soluble substances, when formed by precipitation in the ordinary way, are very fine-grained and consequently contain occluded impurities which are not easy to get rid of; but by taking advantage of the slowness of diffusion in liquids, one can secure very slow precipitation, and in this way prepare such substances in relatively large crystals free from impurity. By this means, for instance, one can readily obtain crystals of calcium hydroxide $(Ca(OH)_2)$ in the form of hexagonal prisms 3 mm. long with the base 1 mm. thick, or crystals of barium sulphate as much as 2 mm. long.   J. J.

PHYSICAL CHEMISTRY.—*The binary system MgO–SiO₂.* N. L. BOWEN and OLAF ANDERSEN. Am. Jour. Sci. (4), **37:** 487–500. 1914.

Equilibrium in the binary system $MgO–SiO_2$ was studied by applying the method of quenching.

There are two compounds, the orthosilicate Mg_2SiO_4 and the metasilicate $MgSiO_3$, capable of existing in contact with liquid in the binary system. The former crystallizes in a form corresponding with the mineral forsterite and the latter forms crystals similar to enstatite in most properties, but of monoclinic symmetry, clino-enstatite.

Clino-enstatite is the only stable form of $MgSiO_3$ encountered. It has no true melting-point, but breaks up at 1557° C. (formerly considered the melting-point) into forsterite and liquid, and the temperature must be raised to 1577° C. before complete solution of the forsterite takes place.

In an earlier Geophysical Laboratory publication, crystals termed α-$MgSiO_3$ were described as a high-temperature form of magnesium metasilicate. They were considered to be the product of inversion of clino-enstatite (β-$MgSiO_3$), but the crystals described have now been proved to be a product of the dissociation at 1557° C. and to be the orthosilicate forsterite, not a form of the metasilicate.

On account of the break-up of clino-enstatite into forsterite and liquid there is no eutectic between the two compounds, and the liquids show, on cooling, the partial or complete re-solution of forsterite at the reaction-point, 1557° C., the liquid reacting with the forsterite crystals to give clino-enstatite.

A discussion is given of the geological significance of this resorption of the olivine forsterite, by reaction with the liquid to give the pyroxene clino-enstatite.

Summary of invariant points[1]

SOLID PHASE	LIQUID PHASE	TEMPERATURE
Periclase (MgO)	MgO, 100%	2800° (Kanolt)
Periclase (MgO) Forsterite (Mg₂SiO₄)	} MgO, 14% Mg₂SiO₄, 86%	1850° ± 20°
Forsterite (Mg₂SiO₄)	Mg₂SiO₄, 100%	1890° ± 20°
Forsterite (Mg₂SiO₄) Clino-enstatite (MgSiO₃)	} MgSiO₃, 97.5%; SiO₂, 2.5%	1557° ± 2°
Clino-enstatite (MgSiO₃) Cristobalite (SiO₂)	} MgSiO₃, 87.5%; SiO₂, 12.5%	1543° ± 2°
Cristobalite (SiO₂)	SiO₂, 100%	1625° (Fenner)

[1] These points are, of course, invariant only when the system is considered as a condensed system.

N. L. B.

CHEMISTRY.—*Determination of cuprous and cupric sulphide in mixtures of one another.* EUGEN POSNJAK. J. Am. Chem. Soc., **36:** 2475–2479. 1914.

The reaction between cuprous sulphide and silver nitrate was confirmed in accordance with the equation

$$Cu_2S + 4AgNO_3 = Ag_2S + 2Ag + 2Cu(NO_3)_2$$

It was found that silver sulphide only, and no metallic silver, is formed by the reaction between cupric sulphide and silver nitrate, the equation for this reaction being

$$CuS + 2AgNO_3 = Ag_2 + Cu(NO_3)_2$$

Based on the difference between these reactions, a method is given in this paper for the determination of cuprous and cupric sulphide in mixtures of the two. The mixture is treated with silver nitrate and from the product the metallic silver is extracted by means of ferric nitrate. The amount of cuprous sulphide is calculated from the metallic silver, while the cupric sulphide is calculated from the difference between the silver in the silver sulphide and the metallic silver.

In mixtures containing the constituents in any proportion whatever, the method was shown to be accurate within 1.5 per cent. E. P.

CHEMISTRY.—*A method for determining magnesium in calcium salts.* J. C. HOSTETTER. Jour. Ind. Eng. Chem., **6:** 392–396. 1914.

The usual methods for the determination of magnesium in the presence of calcium are not applicable when the latter element amounts to as much as 1,000 times that of the magnesium.   The essential feature of the method here presented is the concentrating of the magnesium into a precipitate containing but a small amount of calcium.   This concentrating is effected by precipitating $Mg(OH)_2$ with a slight excess of solid $Ca(OH)_2$.   The magnesium in this precipitate is determined as pyrophosphate after removal of the calcium by two oxalate precipitations.   Determinations in some 30 highest-grade calcium salts show, generally, far more magnesium than reported by the makers.   J. C. H.

MINERALOGY.—*Das Studium der Mineralschmelzpunkte.* ARTHUR
    L. DAY. Fortschritte der Mineralogie, **4**: 115–160· 1914.

A critical review of the work of recent years in the determination of the melting temperatures of the minerals, in which an effort has been made to clear up some of the confusion which now prevails in this field of research.   Some attention has been given to the applicability of the laws of solutions to the change of state of minerals and to the criteria available for the definition and experimental measurement of those changes of state which can be competently studied with the methods and apparatus thus far developed.   The effect of disturbing factors, such as viscosity and inertia, which frequently intervene to delay or prevent the establishment of equilibrium in the system, and so compel the use of methods of approximation, has also been considered, together with the effect of admixtures of minor mineral components in natural mineral types.   A sharp distinction is drawn between the characteristic properties of single minerals and of groups of two or more in solid solution.   The failure to recognize and properly to appraise this distinction appears to have been the cause of a considerable part of the confusion alluded to above.

Following these general considerations, several pages are devoted to the description of the apparatus now in use in the various laboratories for the determination of mineral melting-points, together with the limitations encountered in its application to such studies and to the interpretation of the results obtained with it.   The effect of pressure upon the change of state in minerals is also considered.   The closing chapter contains a table of all the melting temperatures of record, in which appropriate attention has been given to the chemical purity of the specimen studied.   A. L. D.

MINERALOGY.—*The Stokes method for the determination of pyrite and marcasite.* E. T. ALLEN and J. L. CRENSHAW. Am. Jour. Sci. (4), **38**: 371–392. 1914.

The Stokes method for determining pyrite and marcasite, alone or in mixtures, depends on the estimation of the iron dissolved when the finely ground and purified sulphide is treated with a boiling standard solution of ferric alum, The *same* pyrite or marcasite gives very constant values and the influence of each in mixtures is additive, *i.e.*, there exists a linear relation between the iron dissolved and the composition of the mixture. The sum of the errors usually amounts to about 1 per cent, reaching a maximum of 2 per cent. There are two important sources of error. First, there must be a sufficient excess of the sulphide, which is many times greater (7 to 15) than the amount required by theory. With such an excess the percentage of the surfaces remains on the average nearly the same as the percentage by weight, the basis on which the mixtures are made up. About 1 gram is sufficient for 250 cc. of the standard solution. Secondly, the marcasite has a characteristic tendency to flocculate and thus reduce its reacting surface. This difficulty may be avoided by shaking the reacting mixture with pure quartz and beads until the lumps of the powder are thoroughly disintegrated. *Different specimens* of pyrite and marcasite give with the Stokes reaction values which differ somewhat. The differences are due in some cases, if not in all, to the presence of impurities. It is unfortunate that small quantities of impurities which will reduce ferric ron or give up iron to the solution exercise a serious influence. It is therefore not always possible to decide between a natural pyrite and a pyrite containing several per cent of marcasite by the Stokes reaction alone, nor to determine accurately the percentage of each in a natural mixture. In an investigation on the conditions of formation of pyrite and marcasite, this method has been very useful.

The results with the Stokes method plainly indicate that each mineral behaves in a mixture of the two just as it does alone; each appears to reduce a quantity of solution which is proportional to its surface; and each appears to reduce the solution at practically the same rate. The rates at which the sulphides are decomposed are quite different for the two minerals, because more of marcasite than of pyrite is required to reduce a given quantity of ferric iron. The ratio of these rates is not far from 1:2.5.

That ferric sulphate dissolves from pyrite a smaller quantity of iron than it does from marcasite means simply that more reduction is effected by sulphur in the case of pyrite; in other words, that more of the sulphur in pyrite is oxidized. Stokes considered only the relation of p, the percentage of sulphur oxidized, to y, the percentage of pyrite in the sulphide mixture. We have shown that this curve is a hyperbola. This characteristic behavior of pyrite and marcasite towards oxidizing agents is probably general. It has been found by other observers that nitric acid and hydrogen peroxide both oxidize more of the sulphur in pyrite under the same conditions.

E. T. A.

MINERALOGY.—*Effect of temperature and acidity in the formation of marcasite (FeS_2) and wurtzite (ZnS); a contribution to the genesis of unstable forms.* E. T. ALLEN and J. L. CRENSHAW. Microscopic study by H. E. MERWIN. Am. Jour. Sci. (4), **38**: 393–431. 1914.

Our former results on the genesis of marcasite and wurtzite have been reinvestigated, the former conclusions have been confirmed, and new data determined. The specific influence of acidity and alkalinity on the crystal form of the sulphides investigated has been much more rigorously demonstrated. Only from acid solutions were the unstable forms obtained. The sulphides were prepared by the action of hydrogen sulphide on acidic solutions of zinc salts and by hydrogen sulphide and sulphur on acidic solutions of ferrous salts. The unstable forms were usually mixed with the corresponding stable forms, viz., sphalerite and pyrite, and the composition of the mixtures was determined, approximately for the zinc sulphides, by microscopic estimation; and within 1 to 2 per cent by the Stokes method for the iron disulphides.

As previously found, the higher the maximum temperature of experiment, other conditions remaining unchanged, the greater the quantity of the stable form, pyrite or sphalerite, obtained in the product.

As previously concluded, the higher the percentage of acid in the solution, other conditions remaining unchanged, the greater in general the quantity of the unstable sulphide, marcasite or wurtzite. The relation between the percentage of marcasite and the average acidity was practically linear for maximum temperatures of 200° and 300°C. There are also indications of a similar relation in the case of wurtzite. In the case of wurtzite, however, the final acid was found to be the determining factor, since at 300° and 325°C. wurtzite appears to change into sphalerite when heated with sufficiently dilute acid. The temperature-acid field in the case of zinc salts may be divided by two boundary curves into three subfields: a high-acid field in which only wurtzite is obtained, a low-acid field where only sphalerite is obtained, and an intermediate field where mixtures of the two are obtained.

No crystalline zinc sulphide could be obtained from the hydrochloric-acid solutions, but the iron disulphides were crystallized from them, and always contained much more marcasite for an equivalent quantity of acid, *i.e.*, hydrochloric acid has a much greater influence on the crystal form than an equivalent quantity of sulphuric acid, which should be the case if the hydrogen ion concentration were the real determining factor.

The acid concentration required to give rise to pure marcasite or pure wurtzite falls with the temperature and is close to neutrality for marcasite at ordinary temperature, and probably so for wurtzite.

Several conditions other than acidity and temperature were varied in the formation of wurtzite, where the process was necessarily more complicated; these were zinc concentration, addition of sodium sulphate to the solutions, and hydrogen-sulphide pressure. None of these had any influence, except as they affected the acidity.

At temperatures of 25° and 200°C. from sulphuric-acid solutions and at 300°C. from hydrochloric-acid solutions we obtained a product containing 95 per cent of marcasite comparable with the purest natural marcasite we have had in our hands. Since this determination depends on the quantity of iron dissolved from the mineral under definite conditions, and different natural specimens vary somewhat, it may be that this product is pure synthetic marcasite.

Some new data on the genesis of the natural minerals are cited.

E. T. A.

MINERALOGY.—*The simultaneous crystallization of calcite and certain sulphides of iron, copper, and zinc. A crystallographic study.* H. E. MERWIN. Am. Jour. Sci. (4), **38**: 355–359. 1914.

The study of three occurrences of the sulphides of iron and zinc has established with certainty the deposition of marcasite, and with strong probability the deposition of wurtzite contemporaneously with calcite. The marcasite is definitely oriented with regard to the calcite and also the accompanying pyrite. A close similarity between the crystallographic elements of pyrite and marcasite is shown.   H. E. M.

MINERALOGY.—*The optical properties of roscoelite.* FRED. E. WRIGHT. Am. Jour. Sci. (4), **38**:, 305–308. 1914.

The optical data were obtained on unusually good material, kindly loaned by Dr. W. F. Hillebrand for the purpose. Color, olive green.

Luster, splendid, almost submetallic and bronze-like. Cleavage, 001, perfect; 010, good. Hardness between 2.5 and 3. Pleochroism, γ = green brown, β = olive green, α = olive green. Absorption, fairly strong, $\gamma > \beta > \alpha$. Refractive indices, γ = 1.704 $\pm$ 0.003, β = 1.685 $\pm$ 0.003, α = 1.610 $\pm$ 0.003. Birefringence strong. $2E_{Na}$ = 42 to 69°; $2E_{Li}$ = 34 to 60°. Axial dispersion strong, $2Ev > 2E_r$. Optical orientation, $b = \gamma, a : \beta = 0°$ or a small angle not over 4°.   F. E. W.

PETROLOGY.—*The composition of rockallite.* HENRY S. WASHINGTON. Quart. J. Geol. Soc., **70:** 294–302. 1914.

The paper is a chemical study of a unique aegirite granite from the islet of Rockall, north of Ireland. Only three small specimens are known, and that examined was generously given through Prof. J. W. Judd by the Governors of the Imperial College of Science. A very complete chemical analysis was made, which confirms in the general features one made some years ago in England. It shows, in addition, the presence of large amounts of zirconia and ceria—the amount of the latter being next to the highest yet known for igneous rocks. By comparison with the minerals present in the rock, it is shown that these two oxides belong to the pyroxenes, and the probability is pointed out that the presence of these two oxides is characteristic of acmite as contrasted with their absence in the closely related aegirite. Further study of this point will be undertaken when material from Norway, to be furnished through the kindness of Professor Brögger, is received.   H. S. W.

PETROLOGY.—*The occurrence of molybdenum in rocks, with special reference to those of Hawaii.* JOHN B. FERGUSON. Am. Jour. Sci., (4), **37:** 399–402. 1914.

This article deals with the unexpected discovery of traces of molybdenum in two basaltic lavas from Hawaii and the question of the distribution of this element in igneous rocks. Its presence in the two basalts reopens the question of its occurrence, since it was thought to be confined entirely to the more siliceous rocks. Tests were accordingly made on a trachyte obsidian from Hawaii, on some sodic, and especially on some nephelite-bearing igneous rocks from other localities. From these it would appear that the presence of molybdenum is not correlated with high soda or potash content. Except for its well-known tendency to occur in the more siliceous rocks, it therefore seems to be influenced by regional rather than by general chemical characters.   J. B. F.

PETROLOGY.—*The analcite basalts of Sardinia.* HENRY S. WASHING-
TON. Jour. Geology, **22**: 742–753. 1914.

At Monte Ferru and elsewhere in Sardinia lavas occur which show
in thin section small round isotropic areas, resembling sections of leucite, so that the rocks have been commonly held to be leucite basalts.
A careful study and three chemical analyses of these rocks, collected
during the author's trip to Sardinia in 1905 for the Carnegie Institution
of Washington, show that the supposed leucite is in reality the hydrous
soda mineral analcite, and that it is of primary origin. Comparison
with similar rocks from other regions indicates that some so-called leu-
citic rocks are in fact analcite-bearing, and that rocks containing primary analcite in well-developed crystals are much more abundant than
has been supposed. Analyses are also given of the augite and olivine
which form nodules in one of the lavas, the optical study of which is
to be taken up later. H. S. W.

PETROLOGY.—*I Basalti Analcitici della Sardegna.* HENRY S. WASH-
INGTON. Boll. Soc. Geol. Ital., **33**: 147–167. 1914.

An Italian translation of "The analcite basalts of Sardinia" (J. Geol.,
22: 742–753. 1914); abstracted above. An appendix is added which
gives a brief outline of the quantitative classification of igneous rocks.
H. S. W.

BOTANY.—*Mutation in Egyptian cotton.* T. H. KEARNEY. Journal
of Agricultural Research, **2**: 287–302, pls. 17–25. July, 1914.

Four varieties of Egyptian cotton, each distinguished by numerous
well marked characters, have been developed during the last ten years
in Arizona. Two of the new varieties are here described for the first
time. Evidence is brought forward to show that these varieties, as
well as the numerous varieties of this type of cotton which have been
developed in Egypt, have arisen by mutation, their mode of origin presenting many analogies to that of mutants of *Oenothera Lamarckiana*
described by DeVries.

Mutation among higher plants is defined in this paper as "a type
of variation manifesting itself in the sudden appearance of a distinctly
different individual, the characters of which are uniformly expressed by
its descendants when self-pollinated or cross-pollinated only among
themselves."

In the case of Egyptian cotton, a type supposed to be of hybrid origin, there is a strong presumption that the mutative tendency is due to complex or remote hybridization, although the evidence is against the conclusion that the mutants are immediate products of hybridization between different types of cotton.   T. H. K.

FORESTRY.—*Yields from the destructive distillation of certain hardwoods.* L. F. HAWLEY and R. C. PALMER. Bulletin of the U. S. Department of Agriculture 129. Pp. 16, with text figures. 1914.

The chief hardwoods used for distillation in this country are beech, birch, and maple. Tests were made to determine the relative value of these three species, as well as the amount of various products which could be obtained from such southern woods as the oaks, red gum, tupelo, and hickory. Various woods were distilled under similar conditions and their products analyzed by the same methods. It was found that the yields of alcohol and acetic acid vary a great deal among the different species, more so for the former than for the latter. A given species may rank low in its yield of alcohol and high in its yield of acid. Thus, chestnut, which gives the lowest yield of alcohol, is among the highest in the yield of acid; and hickory, which is among the highest in alcohol yield, is among the lowest in acid yield.

The average yield from beech, birch, and maple wood grown in Wisconsin and Indiana is somewhat higher for acid and considerably lower for alcohol than for the same species grown in Pennsylvania. The relative yield of the three species in either product does not change with the locality. The order of yield for alcohol is beech, maple, birch; for acid, birch, beech, maple.

Although slabs with a large amount of bark are usually considered very poor material for distillation, the yields of alcohol and acetic acid from slabs having as high as from 13 to 25 per cent bark by volume were in most cases only slightly lower, and in some cases even higher than from heartwood. This was not due to the bark, however, but to the very high yields from the sapwood.

Assuming that the value of the charcoal and the cost of plant operation per cord of wood is the same for all species, the differences of the value of alcohol and acetic acid produced by the various woods represent the differences of the value of these woods for distillation purposes. The average value of the alcohol and acetate woods from Indiana beech and Wisconsin birch and maple heartwood is $8.06 per cord. The values of these products from the heartwood of chestnut, red gum, tupelo (slabs), and southern and northern oak are less than this amount by $3.78, $1.14, $1.03, $1.30, and $0.54, respectively. From hickory (factory waste) the products are $1.55 greater in value. Since the average price paid for wood used in distillation is only about $3.50 per cord, the use of chestnut for this purpose is out of the question. Oak, tupelo, and red gum, under favorable conditions of supply and cost, might be used profitably, while hickory should command a very good price.

FINDLEY BURNS.

ZOOLOGY.—*The Atlantic Ocean biologically an inland sea.* AUSTIN H. CLARK. Internationale Revue der gesamten Hydrobiologie und Hydrographie, Suppl. z., **6:** 1–18. 1914.

An inland sea is defined in biological terms, and the faunal difference between an inland sea and a true ocean is explained. A list is given of all the genera of recent crinoids found in the Atlantic with their geographical ranges, together with a list of the corresponding Indo-Pacific genera also with their geographical ranges.

There are no Atlantic genera which are not represented in the Indo-Pacific basin, or as fossils about the shores of that basin. But in addition to representatives of all the Atlantic genera there are in the Indo-Pacific basin fifty additional genera, and nine families, which do not occur elsewhere. Thus since it possesses no genera which are not derivatives from Indo-Pacific types, and none of the more specialized Indo-Pacific types, the Atlantic fauna is in effect the fauna of an inland sea tributary to the Indo-Pacific. The geographical and thermal distribution of the crinoids found in the Atlantic point to four different paths of migration from the Indo-Pacific, which are explained in detail. The greater antiquity of the Caribbean fauna as compared with the Mediterranean and the east European fauna is pointed out, and its significance indicated.

A. H. C.

ZOOLOGY.—*The porpoise in captivity.* CHAS. HASKINS TOWNSEND. Zoologica, Scientific Contributions of the New York Zoological Society, **1:** 1–22, figs. 1–14. May, 1914.

This is an account of the first successful attempt to keep the porpoise in captivity for any considerable length of time, five individuals having lived in the New York Aquarium seven months. The species obtained was *Tursiops truncatus*, from Cape Hatteras. After two failures a satisfactory method of handling the animals was found.

The paper contains an account of the methods of capture, transportation, and treatment in captivity, with some observations on their habits, and notes on the porpoise fishery.

Among the illustrations are photographs showing porpoises rising to breathe, and foetal porpoises of both sexes.

C. H. T.

BACTERIOLOGY.—*The composition of Roquefort cheese fat.* JAMES N. CURRIE. Journal of Agricultural Research, **2**: 429–434. September 21, 1914.

Fat separated from Roquefort cheese representing four popular brands of imported cheese was studied and compared with the fat from cow's milk. Results are tabulated, together with Browne's[1] figures for the fat of cow's milk, as follows:

ACID	FAT OF ROQUEFORT CHEESE	FAT OF COW'S MILK (BROWNE)
	per cent	*per cent*
Butyric....................	3.48	5.45
Caproic....................	4.73	2.09
Caprylic...................	0.58	0.49
Capric.....................	3.80	0.32
Lauric.....................	5.84	2.57
Myristic...................	11.36	9.89
Palmitic...................	28.53	38.61
Stearic....................	1.71	1.83
Oleic......................	38.10	32.50
Dioxy Stearic..............		1.00

Attention is called to the much higher figures for caproic and capric acids in the fat of Roquefort cheese, which is nearly pure sheep's milk fat. It was shown by the author in a previous publication[2] that these two acids are chiefly responsible for the peppery taste of Roquefort cheese. It is concluded that a Roquefort cheese made from sheep's milk will have more of this hot or peppery taste than one of the same ripeness made from cow's milk.

J. N. C.

[1] Journ. Amer. Chem. Soc., **21**: 807.
[2] Journ. Agric. Research, **2**: 1–14.

JOURNAL

OF THE

WASHINGTON ACADEMY OF SCIENCES

Vol. V   FEBRUARY 19, 1915   No. 4

PHYSICS.—*The accurate measurement of the refractive indices of minute crystal grains under the petrographic microscope.* FRED. E. WRIGHT, Geophysical Laboratory.

The principal refractive indices of fine crystal particles, measuring 0.01 mm. in diameter or larger and of medium refringence and birefringence can be determined by the immersion method with an accuracy of ± 0.001.[1] In strongly birefracting minerals and in deeply colored substances of high refractive index this degree of accuracy is rarely attainable by the im-

[1] For a discussion of the principles and details of practical application of the immersion method to refractive index determinations under the petrographic microscope see: Tschermak's Miner. petrogr. Mitteil., **20**: 239. 1901; Am. Jour. Sci., (4), **17**: 385–387. 1904; (4), **35**: 63–82. 1913; Carnegie Institution of Washington, Pub. **158**: 93. 1911; Jour. Wash. Acad. Sci., **4**: 270, 389. 1914. Since the publication of these papers a new procedure for the measurement of the refractive indices of immersion liquids on the total refractometer has been adopted by the writer and has proved so satisfactory that it may be described briefly. Plane parallel disks (2 cm. in diameter, 2 to 3 mm. thick) of high refracting glass ($n > 1.74$) serve in place of ordinary object glasses. The refringence tests between mineral grain and immersion liquid are made in the usual way under the microscope. The glass disk is then mounted directly on the glass hemisphere of the total refractometer with a drop of highly refractive liquid intervening (methylene iodide or Rohrbach solution), and the refractive index of the liquid is measured through the glass disk. By this method, it is possible to measure the three principal refractive indices of a biaxial mineral grain without removing it from the liquid, the refractive index of the liquid itself being raised or lowered the proper amount to match the different refractive indices of the mineral by the addition of a small drop of a suitable refractive liquid. The danger of scratching the surface of the glass hemisphere by mineral grains embedded in the refractive liquid is also eliminated.

mersion method and can only be approached by a careful observance of certain favorable conditions of observation. It is the purpose of the present paper to consider these conditions briefly and to ascertain their relative importance in accurate work.

The methods for the detection of differences in refractive index between crystal grain and immersion liquid are based primarily on differences in intensity of illumination in different parts of the grain. In order that these differences be readily visible even for slight changes in refractive index it is essential that attention be given to the following factors: (a) the source of light; (b) the optical condenser system of the microscope for producing the different types of illumination—central or oblique—of the crystal grain; (c) the optical system for observing the differences in illumination thus produced.

(a) For accurate measurements intense, uniform, monochromatic light is essential. The most satisfactory light source is the mercury lamp used in conjunction with either a dispersion prism or the Wratten ray filters. It furnishes a very intense green light (546.1 $\mu\mu$) and an intense orange-yellow light (576.9 and 579 $\mu\mu$). The ordinary sodium, thallium, lithium, and calcium flames, the helium and hydrogen tubes, and the cadmium and iron arcs are also useful. The light source is placed in the focus of a condenser lens, and either the light itself or the illuminated condenser lens is imaged in the object plane of the microscope by means of the substage condenser. In case still more uniform, but less intense, illumination is desired a finely ground glass disk may be placed in the lower focal plane of the substage condenser.

(b) Two types of illumination, central and oblique, are employed in refractive index determinations by the immersion method. In *central illumination* a narrow cone of light whose axis coincides with that of the optical system, is used and is obtained either by closing the iris diaphragm below the substage condenser or by lowering the condenser. The angle which the marginal rays of the central cone include with the axis can be measured by means of a graduated apertometer scale located in the lower focal plane of the condenser and imaged in the eye-circle of the ocular. The angle ordinarily employed with a 16 mm. objective (Zeiss apochromatic; N. A. = 0.30) is 8° to 10°; under these conditions the diameter of the eye-circle (compensating eyepiece 4) is 1.3 mm. This angle can be reduced to 4° by closing the iris diaphragm as far as possible; but the diameter of the eye-circle is then only 0.6 mm., the illumination of the field is weak and dust particles are troublesome. In a high power objective (Zeiss apochromatic, E. F. = 4 mm.; N. A. = 0.95) the angular aperture usually employed in central illumination is about 15°; for this aperture the diameter of the eye-circle is 0.5 mm. In case the smallest possible aperture, 4°, be used, the diameter of the eye-circle is reduced to 0.15 mm.; the field illumination is then so weak that a strong light source is necessary; all lenses and also object cover glass must be thoroughly cleaned to reduce, as far as possible, the disturbing effects resulting from dust particles and from diffraction. In *oblique illumination* a narrow pencil of obliquely incident light is employed and is best obtained by means either of a movable iris diaphragm or of a sliding metal strip in the lower focal plane of the substage condenser. Experience has shown that in the case of the sliding substage-stop the best effects are produced when the stop is inserted past the axis to a point midway between the center and the margin of the condenser opening. Under these conditions the inclination of the incident rays in the 16 mm. objective ranges from 9° to 18°, with an average inclination of 12.5°. This angle can be decreased by closing the substage iris diaphragm and withdrawing the sliding stop a short distance; but then the intensity of field illumination decreases rapidly and the disturbing effects of dust particles become serious. With a 32 mm. objective (N. A. = 0.10) the angular field measures 6° on a side and the best results in oblique illumination are obtained for rays of an average angular inclination of 4° (3° to 6°). With the 4 mm. objective it is difficult to obtain proper illumination by this method because of the rapid decrease in definition of image with oblique, one sided illumination.

(c) Experience has proved that the effects produced by central illumination are best observed under relatively high magnifications (300 to 75 diameters; 4 mm. or 16 mm. objective) while in oblique illumination lower magnifications are more favorable (75 to 30 diameters; 16 mm. or 32 mm. objective).

Refractive index · measurements on birefracting grains. The phenomena obtained by central illumination are different from those resulting from oblique illumination; but the principle underlying both types of illumination, namely that of the deviation of transmitted light waves by prismatic refraction,[2] is the same. It is of interest to compare the results obtained by the two kinds of illumination on irregular, birefracting crystal particles. In a birefracting mineral the refractive indices of the transmitted light waves vary with the direction of transmission; the two methods of illumination are therefore subject to correction factors because in both methods more or less obliquely incident light is employed. In crystals of medium to weak birefringence these factors are practically negligible and experience has shown that the degree of accuracy attainable by either method is about the same. But in strongly birefracting minerals a slight change in the direction of transmission of the · light waves may produce a decided change in refractive index, and then the actual angle of inclination and the direction of the waves may become an important factor in the accuracy

[2] The method of central illumination is frequently called the Becke-line method while that of oblique illumination is designated the Schroeder van der Kolk method. The papers by Becke and Schroeder van der Kolk were of great importance in emphasizing the significance of these methods in microscopical petrography; but in view of the fact that both methods had been described and applied by Maschke and Thoulet one or two decades earlier and also that in ordinary microscope work (biological, etc.) these methods have long been used and called by the above descriptive terms—central and oblique illumination— it would seem better than these terms be employed in preference to the above. The term Becke-line should be retained, however, for some of the relative refringence determinations in rock thin sections; but in refractive index determinations of crystal grains by central illumination the Becke-line constitutes only part of the phenomena observed, the determination being based primarily on the relative convergence or divergence of the light transmitted through the mineral grain.

attained. This is well illustrated on plates of calcite which is
very strongly birefracting ($\omega - \epsilon = 0.172$).

In Table 1 are listed the computed extraordinary refractive
indices (ϵ') for light waves entering a calcite plate under different angles of incidence. In columns 1 and 2 the values
are given for a plate cut normal to the principal axis; in columns 3 and 4 ,the values for a plate cut parallel with the principal axis; in columns 5, 6, and 7, the values for a cleavage
plate of calcite. Each of the above plates is considered to be
so placed that its principal section is parallel to the plane of
vibration of the incident waves. In columns 1, 3 and 5 are
listed the refractive indices for extraordinary waves transmitted along directions contained in the plane normal to the

·TABLE 1.

i	1	2	3	4	5	6	7
0°	1.658	1.658	1.486	1.486	1.564	1.564	1.564
5	1.658	1.657	1.486	1.487	1.564	1.573	1.555
10	1.658	1.656	1.486	1.488	1.564	1.582	1.547
15	1.658	1.653	1.486	1.491	1.564	1.592	1.539
20	1.658	1.649	1.486	1.494	1.564	1.601	1.528

principal section; it may be noted that the refractive index for
each of these columns remains constant for the different directions of transmission. In columns 2, 4, 6, and 7 the refractive
indices are given for light waves whose lines of propagation
are contained in the principal section. In these columns the
refractive indices vary noticeably with change in direction of
transmission. In column 6 the refractive indices ϵ' are listed
for different angles of incidence i in the principal section of
the cleavage rhombohedron on the side toward the emergent
optic axis; in column 7 the refractive indices are given for light
waves incident also in the principal section but on the side
away from the optic axis.

From this table it is evident that if a calcite cleavage flake
be immersed in a liquid of refractive index about 1.564, the
plate will appear to have approximately the same refractive

index for oblique waves transmitted in the vertical plane normal to the principal section (column 5); but a noticeably higher refractive index than the liquid for light waves incident under conditions of column 6, and a much lower refractive index for conditions of column 7; also that the refractive index of a basal section of calcite will appear, if observed under the conditions of oblique illumination of column 2, to have a lower refractive index than the maximum refractive index ω; under similar conditions (column 4) a section parallel to the principal axis will appear to have a higher refractive index than the minimum refractive index ϵ which it might be expected to show. It may be noted, however, that, even under the most favorable conditions, the rays incident on the mineral grain are not all contained in the diametral plane normal to the principal section. Of the cone of rays emerging from the condenser all but a small segment is eliminated by the sliding-stop; the marginal rays of this segment include an appreciable angle with the diametral plane, and are accordingly transmitted through the mineral grain under conditions different from those in the diametral plane; the phenomena which we observe are the result of the aggregate action of all the rays and not solely of those of the diametral plane, on which the determinations are based. This defect can be remedied to a large extent by the use either of small circular holes[3] or of a narrow slit opening in the sliding-stop. Disregard of this factor may affect the accuracy of measurements on strongly birefracting minerals. These relations serve also to explain the long-continued appearance of colored fringes on the margins of such crystal grains when observed in white light, these fringes persisting over a much greater range of refractive indices than might be expected were they due solely to the difference in dispersion between mineral and liquid.

In central illumination the inclination of the transmitted rays is, in general, less than that in oblique illumination with the result that the error introduced because of this factor is proportionately less. Offsetting this advantage in part, however, is the sensitiveness of central illumination to the character,

[3] Tscherm. Miner. petrogr. Mitteil., 20: 240. 1901.

shape, and size of the grain and its edges. In many grains, especially cleavage flakes, the phenomena are so masked by local irregularities that it is difficult to determine whether the grain has a slightly higher or slightly lower refractive index than the immersion liquid. With central illumination the differences, noted above, in refractive indices of the light waves which emerge in the different quadrants find expression in a noticeable difference in the behavior of the different sides of the grain on raising the objective.

Experience has proved that the two methods furnish, in general, results which are of the same order of exactness; in special instances, however, central illumination is superior to oblique illumination because of the smaller angle of inclination of the cone of its incident rays; in other cases oblique illumination is preferable because the phenomena, which it produces, are then more distinct. As a rule it is good practice to use both methods and to verify the results of the one by those of the second.

Summary. In the exact measurement of refractive indices of minute crystal particles by the immersion method it is essential: (a) that correctly oriented sections be selected which are normal to at least one principal optic section; (b) that in case oblique illumination be used, only those pencils of light be employed whose direction of propagation is included in the plane normal to the principal optical section; in other words, the metal sliding-stop should be so inserted that its front edge is parallel to a principal section; (c) that with central illumination special weight be given to the effects along those edges of the grain, which trend approximately parallel to the principal section. If these conditions be disregarded the value obtained for the maximum refractive index will be too low, the value for the minimum refractive index, too high, while that of any intermediate refractive index, as β, may be too high or too low. Failure to recognize these factors may lead, especially in the case of strongly birefracting crystal particles, to refractive index determinations which are appreciably in error.

GEOLOGY.—*An estimate of the age of the last great glaciation in Alaska.* STEPHEN R. CAPPS, Geological Survey.

For many years certain Alaska glaciers have been under observation, and considerable material dealing solely with glaciation in Alaska has been published. A large amount of data on glacial conditions throughout the territory has also accumulated incident to general geologic investigations, and has been published in the reports which treat of the geology of the different districts. The published literature on glaciation in Alaska is, therefore, so extensive that it can not be discussed in this paper.

It is a generally recognized fact that the present glaciers of Alaska are but the shrunken descendants of vastly greater glaciers which at some former time reached a much more extensive development than they now have. Yet notwithstanding the amount of attention which has been given to the subject by many observers, practically no attempt, based on trustworthy evidence, has been made to date the age of this last great ice advance in Alaska, or to correlate it with any of the glacial stages which have been so well established in the Mississippi Basin.

Quantitative studies of the variations of certain coastal glaciers of Alaska, some of which have advanced or retreated long distances within a comparatively short term of years, have established a rather general impression that the greater portion of the retreat of all Alaskan glaciers from the points of greatest advance to their present positions has taken place rather recently. Few men have been willing to hazard a guess as to how many years ago a particular valley was bared of ice; but that the time should be measured in centuries, rather than in thousands of years, would probably have seemed reasonable to most of those who have thought on the subject. The feeling that the time should be measured in hundreds of years, rather than in terms of greater magnitude, has also been strengthened by the small amount of post glacial erosion which can be discovered in many strongly glaciated valleys.

During the progress of a reconnaissance geological survey

in the upper portion of the White River basin in the summer of 1914 some facts were obtained which throw light on the problem of the length of time which has elapsed since Russell Glacier, a large, vigorous glacier in which White River heads, retreated to approximately its present position. Russell Glacier draws its ice-supply from a high, rugged range of mountains near the international boundary. The main body of the glacier lies in a pass and a portion of its drainage goes to the Copper River basin, although the main discharge is to the Yukon. It gives abundant evidence of active movement, and although its lower end is well covered by morainal material, the detritus has a very fresh appearance, and vegetation has secured only a scanty foothold upon it. It may fairly be considered as an average example of the glaciers of the Wrangell Mountains and it may be inferred that the major events of its history have been roughly duplicated by the other similar glaciers in the same general region.

  At a point on the north side of White River about 8 miles below the source of that stream in Russell Glacier, the river has eroded its bank to form a high bluff which for an east and west distance of over a mile shows excellent exposures. Although its height and the thickness of its constituent members vary somewhat from place to place, a single section will serve well to illustrate the conditions found there. The base of the bluff at the point measured (fig. 1) shows 30 feet of typical, unconsolidated and unoxydized glacial till, with an uneven, rolling surface. Above the till and extending to the top of the bluff is 39 feet of fibrous, peaty vegetable material, full of stumps and roots, but probably formed for the most part of the remains of sphagnum moss (figs. 2 and 3). Seven feet below the top of the bluff the peat is interrupted by a two-foot layer of white volcanic ash. The surface of the ground above the bluff is covered by a thick coating of sphagnum moss and supports also a dense forest of spruce, with scanty underbrush. The peat, ash and glacial till are permanently frozen a few inches back from the face of the bluff, even though having a south exposure, and subjected to the long hours of summer sunshine, the light, fluffy waste from the peat acting as an effective insulator. Even the surface moss was solidly frozen at a depth of 6 inches in early July. The cut bank, therefore, shows generally a nearly vertical peat face, and erosion takes place by the formation of great vertical cracks through the peat, and the falling outward of large, tree covered blocks which tumble down to the stream level and are gradually thawed and removed (fig. 4). An examination of this section at once suggested that if the rate of accumulation of the peaty material could be determined, then a fairly accurate estimate could be made of the length of the time period whch has intervened between the final retreat of the ice from this locality and the present.

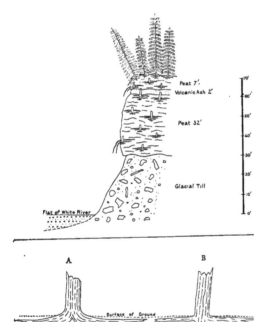

The peculiar appearance of the roots of the spruce trees which grow on the edge of the bluff, as well as of the stumps which make up a considerable portion of the peaty deposit, suggested that it might be possible to determine approximately the rate of

Fig. 1. Diagrammatic section of stream bluff on White River, showing relations of glacial till, peat, and volcanic ash. The process of peat deposition is still going on at the surface. A, a normal spruce stump with flat root base, growing on solid ground. B, a spruce stump growing on rapidly accumulating peat. Below the line of ground frost, which rises with the growth of peaty material, the roots cease to unction, and the tree is forced to throw out additional oots in the unfrozen surface portion of the ground.

accumulation of the peat at this place. The ordinary spruce, growing upon solid ground, either frozen or unfrozen, sends its roots out radially, parallel with the surface, the roots penetrating only a few inches below the surface of the ground (fig. 1A). The uprooted spruce tree, with its flat root base, is a familiar object to all who have travelled through an Alaskan spruce forest. In the White River locality, however, the roots of the spruce trees, both those growing at the edge of the bluff, or recently overturned, and those deeply buried within the peat mass, showed quite different characteristics (fig. 1B). Instead of a single, flat-based set of radial roots, these trees all show a central stem often several feet long, from which roots branch off at irregular intervals, with an upper set of roots near the surface, corresponding to those of the normal tree. An attempt to dig out one living tree for the purpose of examining its roots, resulted in failure, for the ground was found to be solidly frozen 6 inches below the top of the moss, and an excavation 18 inches deep did not reach to the lowest roots. Below the frost line the roots were sound and undecayed, but of a darker color than the live surface roots, and were apparently not functioning.

Fig. 2. Section of bluff, showing glacial till overlain by peat and volcanic ash.

From the above facts it seems evident that a seedling spruce, having established itself on the mossy soil in this area of rapidly accumulating vegetation, sent out radial, flat-based roots in a normal way, but the constantly thickening moss and following it the rising line of frozen ground cut off the food sup-

ply from the lowest roots and caused the tree constantly to
throw out new sets of roots near the surface, in its efforts to
survive. If these premises are correct, then the vertical distance between 'the lowest horizontal roots of a tree and the
surface of the ground represents the thickness of the peaty
accumulation during the growth of the tree, and the rate of
accumulation can be determined by ascertaining the age of the
tree, as shown by the annual rings.

It is readily admitted that any figures for the rate of accumulation of peat, obtained in the way outlined are subject to

Fig. 3. Close view of an overturned block of peat, with included spruce
stumps.

many uncertainties, and before they can be considered final
should be checked by a much larger number of measurements
than could be made in the single day which was available for this
study. Most of the qualifying factors, however, seem to fall
on the side of conservatism, and to give a minimum, rather
than a maximum figure. Among the unweighed factors the
following may be briefly mentioned:

1. The vegetable matter accumulating near the surface is
less compact than that deeper in the section, so that the ma-

terial making up a layer a foot thick around a living tree would be considerably less than that thickness after it became deeply buried.

2. Toward the edge of the bluff, where the roots could be best examined, the accumulation near the surface contains a considerable admixture of wind-blown dust from the bare sand and silt flat below. The deeper portions of the peat bed are comparatively free from such extraneous material, and it is probable that at the time they were laid down they were at some distance from the bare gravel plain of White River.

Fig. 4. Peat bluff, with angular, overturned blocks of peat and volcanic ash. Photograph by F. H. Moffit.

3. A considerable period of time probably elapsed after the retreat of the ice before vegetation had completely established itself upon the bared area of glacial till. Similarly, the ejection of the heavy layer of volcanic ash, while it failed to kill the spruce forest, doubtless destroyed the surface covering of sphagnum moss, and this moss cover may have been a long time in reëstablishing itself. Even now there are on the mountain front to the south large areas of bare ash, on which there is only scanty vegetation.

4. According to F. V. Coville, trees of very slow growth fail during unfavorable years to form distinct annual rings, and therefore the age of the tree, as shown by a count of the rings, may be considerably greater than the figures obtained. From the same authority comes the statement that during the first years after germination the spruce tree grows very slowly, so that a count of the rings made 4 feet above the present surface, or say 6 feet above the lowest horizontal roots, would fail to show the first 20 years or so of the tree's growth.

Sound trees so situated that their roots could be studied, and ring counts made, were not easily found, and in only one instance was the count made on a tree which seemed to have developed under conditions which approached the average. On this tree one count, made 6 feet above the present surface of the ground, where the tree had a diameter of $7\frac{1}{2}$ inches, showed 373 annual rings. At 8 feet above the ground another count was made as a check and gave 362 rings. This tree had an accumulation of 24 inches of vegetable matter above its lowest horizontal roots. With an allowance of 27 years for the growth of the tree up to the point where the count was made, a rate of accumulation of the vegetable material of about 1 foot in 200 years was obtained. In the peaty material around the roots of this tree there was considerably more wind-blown sand and silt than in the peat exposed below. Another count, made on a tree $5\frac{1}{2}$ inches in diameter, gave 133 rings, and the roots had 16 inches of very sandy peat about them. The unusually sandy condition of the peat about this tree must indicate an unusually rapid burial of the tree, and consequently the figures of the rate of accumulation are too small to be generally applied. Emphasis is again placed upon the fact that the surface peat is much less solidly compacted than that more deeply buried, and the figure on which most confidence is placed, namely 200 years to the foot of peat, is doubtless much less than the actual number of years required for the average foot of peat to accumulate at this place.

Disregarding, therefore, many unweighed factors, all of which would tend to give a slower rate of accumulation, and assuming the rate of 200 years to the foot to be correct, we are brought face to face with the conclusion that a period of at least 7800 years or in round numbers 8000 years has been required for the formation of the 39 feet of peat exposed in this section, and that the final retreat of the front of Russell Glacier to within 8 miles of its present position had taken place some 8000 years ago. This figure of 8000 years is by no means to be considered as final, but is merely believed to express the proper order of magnitude of the term of years since the disappearance here of the glacial ice. The writer is inclined to believe that this estimate falls considerably short of the time which has actually elapsed. But if the estimate is within 25, or even 50 per cent correct, it gives one a broader basis from which to consider the geologic and physiographic history of Alaska since the withdrawal of the last great glaciers. At the time of its maximum extension Russell Glacier, according to Brooks, reached as far north as the mouth of Donjek River, about 130 miles beyond its present terminus. Its retreat over 90 per cent of this distance had therefore been completed 8000 years ago.

This retreat of over 90 per cent of the distance must, however, not be considered to represent 90 per cent of the elapsed time since the retreat began. The withdrawal of the ice was probably a comparatively rapid one until the terminus withdrew to somewhere near its present position, and the terminus may have remained nearly stationary for a long while. This glacier was first seen in 1891 and has been visited at intervals since, and during the last 20 years its outer margin has changed but little.

Various estimates have been made of the length of time since the Wisconsin ice sheet began to retreat. Chamberlin and Salisbury, after reviewing the evidence, place the time as somewhere between 20,000 and 60,000 years. The determination made in the White River valley, at a point which was not bared until a large part of the retreat had been completed, is of the same order of magnitude as the figures gained from other widely different sources, and it therefore now for the first time seems safe to say that the last great ice advance in Alaska was contemporaneous with the Wisconsin continental glaciation.

BOTANY.—*A new genus of palms allied to Archontophoenix.*
O. F. COOK, Bureau of Plant Industry.

Apart from the several species of Phoenix and Cocos, only
one pinnate-leaved palm is commonly planted in the open
air in California. This is usually known as *Seaforthia elegans*, but has also been called *Ptychosperma elegans*, *Archontophoenix alexandrae*, and *Archontophoenix cunninghamiana*. As
these names belong to other species they should not be applied
to the palm grown in California. Reference of the plant in
question to Ptychosperma or Seaforthia is excluded because
the seeds are not sulcate. In this respect there is agreement
with Archontophoenix, but other characters are divergent.

One cause of confusion is that characters given by Drude,
in Engler and Prantl's *Natürlichen Pflanzenfamilien*, as diagnostic of Archontophoenix are not found in the type of that
genus, *A. alexandrae*. These discrepancies relate to the form
of the pistillode and the structure of the fruit. Acquaintance
with the true *Archontophoenix alexandrae* was gained by the
writer in 1905, at Cordoba, Mexico, fruit and seed of an individual there studied agreeing closely with Mueller's original
description and figures,[1] but differing from those of the familiar
palm of California. For comparison with the genuine *Seaforthia
elegans* ample material was afforded by palms studied in 1914
at the Belize Botanical Station, British Honduras. The identification of the latter material led to a recognition of the fact
that the California palm was different from all of the species
to which it had been supposed to belong.

Taking into account the original description of Archontophoenix and the characters of the type species, the pistillode
should not be described as short and pyramidal in Archontophoenix, but as having the same slender, elongate form as in
Ptychosperma and Seaforthia. Nor does the seed of the true
Archontophoenix alexandrae have an adherent endocarp, as stated
by Drude. The endocarp is represented in Archontophoenix
by a firm, bony shell, rather thin, but hard and brittle, and

[1] Fragm. Austr. **5**: 47, *pls. 43, 44.*

readily separable from the seed. The raphe, instead of being broad and adherent, is a narrow, superficial strand of fibers, only slightly attached to the seed-coat.

The characters assigned by Drude to Archontophoenix—the short pistillode, the thin adherent endocarp, and the broad, adnate raphe—are in fact possessed by the palm grown in California, and are among the features which interfere with its assignment to Archontophoenix. Although Archontophoenix, as originally described in 1875 by Wendland and Drude,[2] was based upon Mueller's *Ptychosperma alexandrae*, Drude's later diagnosis seems to have been drawn for a different palm, perhaps the very species grown in California. The features of special interest in this comparison are summarized in the following key and diagnoses.

ARCHONTOPHOENIX Wendl. & Drude. Flowers white or greenish; stamens 9–12, the anthers about twice as long as the filaments; pistillode with long slender style exceeding the stamens. Pistillate flowers with petals equal to the sepals and of the same form; staminodes wanting. Fruit elliptical, with a thin fleshy pericarp containing rather narrow needle-like, simple or forked, longitudinal fibers, adherent to the outer surface of a thin endocarp of bony palisade tissue, distinct and readily separable from the seed-coats. Seed erect, oval or elliptic, with pattern of the rumination apparent on the surface of the seed-coats. Raphe represented by a narrow, vertical, superficial strand of fibers, only slightly adherent to the seed-coats.

Loroma Cook, gen. nov.

Flowers purple or lilac, the staminate with strongly carinate sepals and valvate petals; stamens 12–16, with anthers about half as long as the filaments; pistillode conic-pyramidal, deeply trifid at apex, much exceeded by the stamens. Pistillate flowers with sepals broadly rounded, ecarinate; petals exceeding the sepals, very broadly imbricate, unequal, with a broad angular emargination on each side of a broadly triangular apex; staminodes present, represented by a circle of six minute rudimentary filaments. Fruit subglobose, the pericarp supported by a layer of broad, flat, strap-like, slightly anastomosing fibers and an underlying layer of coarse-celled tissue closely adherent to the surface of the seed except at the base and apex, with no indication of a bony endocarp or shell of palisade tissue. Seed somewhat obliquely depressed at apex, the raphe represented by a broad vertical band of strongly adherent fibers, partially embedded in the seed-coats. Albumen rather deeply and coarsely ruminate; embryo erect, basal.

[2] Linnaea **39**: 214.

The derivation of the generic name refers to the strap-like form of the fibers surrounding the seed. In addition to the type, *Loroma amethystina*, known from cultivated plants in California, a second species, **Loroma cunninghamiana** (*Ptychosperma cunninghamiana* Wendl.), from northern Australia, is referable to this genus.

SYNOPTICAL KEY TO LOROMA AND ALLIED GENERA

Pistillode of the staminate flower similar to the fertile pistil, bearing three distinct rudimentary stigmas, these much exceeded by the stamens; seed protected by a layer of broad, strap-like fibers........Loroma.

Pistillode unlike the fertile pistil, bearing a long filiform style, this exceeding the stamens; seed with a coat of slender fibers............1.

1. Seeds oval, the surface even, without longitudinal furrows, enclosed in a thin bony endocarp, readily separable from a distinct woody seed-coat....................................Archontophoenix.

1. Seeds with distinct longitudinal furrows, both endocarp and seed-coats thin and membranous..............................2.

2. Trunk extremely slender; leaves with remote pinnae; filaments shorter than the anthers; fruits oblong-oval, very strongly apiculate ....Ptychosperma.

2. Trunk moderately robust; leaves with crowded pinnae; filaments longer than the anthers; fruit spherical or somewhat depressed, slightly apiculate ....Seaforthia.

The type of the genus Loroma is *L. amethystina*, cultivated in California, probably from Australia; of Archontophoenix, *A. alexandrae* (Mueller) Wendl. & Drude, from Australia, of Ptychosperma, *P. gracilis* Labill., from New Caledonia; of Seaforthia, *S. elegans* R. Br., from Australia.

Loroma amethystina Cook, sp. nov.

Trunk attaining a height of 8–10 meters and upward, the largest trunks about 30 cm. in diameter at the base, tapering above to 15–20 cm. Leaf sheath 96 cm. long, the outer surface reddish, with numerous purplish-brown scales; texture rather thin, but tough and leathery. Petiole 9 cm. long, 4 cm. wide. Blade 2 meters long and more, with 70–80 pinnae on each side, the basal and terminal pinnae much narrower and shorter than the others. Lowest pinnae 24 cm. long, 0.4 cm. wide, or sometimes only 0.2 cm. wide; fifth pinnae 36 cm. long, 1.3 cm. wide; middle pinnae about 80 cm. long, 4.5 cm. wide; subterminal pinnae about 30 cm. long, 1.4 cm. wide; terminal 1 cm. wide. Midribs of pinnae with long coarse scales beneath. Rachis triangular, convex below, sharply carinate above, the insertions of pinnae very deeply folded. Tips of leaves very slender and drooping, usually turned on edge (as in *Attalea cohune* or *Phoenix canariensis*).

Inflorescences developed in the axils of living leaves, but not appearing until the leaves fall, the spathes opening as soon as released by the falling of the leaf, and the flowers soon after. Spathes 2, of nearly equal length, strongly compressed, white and of very thin delicate texture, their protective function being performed by the leaf-sheaths. Newly opened inflorescences deep purple in color, the flower buds much more crowded than in *Seaforthia elegans*, the branches covered with a short close pubescence or scurf, this at first creamy yellow, changing to light sulphur yellow, then fading to white. Flowering branches simple, about 60 cm. long, strictly pendent almost from the first, not erect-spreading or merely drooping from the weight of the fruits as in *Seaforthia elegans* and other allied genera.

Flowers purplish-pink throughout, including the' petals, the filaments and the connective of the anthers, and the pistillodes, but the anthers and pollen uncolored. Sepals broadly imbricate, acutely angled at apex and with a strong median carina, the fleshy basal portion somewhat pinkish. Petals rather stiff and horny, translucent when fresh, and with an abruptly thickened, transverse, fleshy pulvinus at base. Stamens 12–16, usually 13–15, often with some of the filaments double. Pistillode about half the length .of the filaments, not produced into a long filiform style, but with 2 or 3 divergent prongs, these usually unequal (or only one, the others rudimentary), sometimes united with one of the filaments, inserted with the filaments at the apex of a broad, turbinate cushion of loose, spongy texture.

Fruits subglobose, coral pink, 12 mm. long, 11.5 mm. wide; stigma subapical, borne on a slightly elevated rim; epidermis smooth or with slight, scattered, raised points; pericarp fleshy, thin, less than 0.5 mm. thick, supported by a firmer layer containing numerous broad band-like fibers adhering to form a shell-like coat separable with difficulty from a less fibrous layer of marbled white and coarse red cells underneath, this marbled layer strongly adherent to the thick brownish seed-coat and often entering deeply into the ruminations. No layer of bony palisade tissue under the fibers as in Archontophoenix.

Seeds subglobose, 10 mm. in diameter when fresh, somewhat obliquely depressed or flattened above, slightly broader than long, not sulcate; slightly flattened at the base, but not provided with adherent basal and apical cushions as in Seaforthia. Surface of seed with an adherent fibrous layer, the raphe represented by a broad band of vertical embedded fibers. Albumen of rather soft, loose texture, with deep and irregular ruminations, broader and less numerous than those of *Archontophoenix alexandrae*, extending about half way to the center of the seed. Color of ruminations in fresh seeds pale yellowish brown, becoming rusty brown.in dry seeds. Embryo erect, exactly basal.

The type specimen, no. 694813 in the U. S. National Herbarium, was collected at Santa Barbara, California, by the writer, November 11, 1914, the type individual being one of several unusually fine palms in the collection of Mr. C. B. Hale, under the care of Mr. W. H. Morse. The specimen consists of branches of an inflorescence, with unopened flowers and ripe fruits. The characters and measurements of the

trunk, leaves, and the mature flowers were drawn from a palm standing at the side of the Court House in San Diego, California.

This species, or at least a member of this genus, is represented
also in the Economic Herbarium of the U. S. Department of Agriculture by two vials of dried fruits from Australia, one from Baron
von Mueller, formerly director of the Botanical Garden at Melbourne,
and the other from Dr. J. H. Maiden, Director of the Botanical Garden
at Sidney, the latter received as *Ptychosperma elegans* (S. P. I. No.
1329). These two lots, which are very closely alike, differ from the
typical material in having the strap-like fibers somewhat narrower
and more frequently branched. Fruits from the Philippine Islands,
collected by Mr. H. Boyle, are somewhat smaller than those from
Australia.

Nothing has been learned regarding the introduction of Loroma
into California, but its botanical relationships indicate that it is a
native of northern Australia, along with the true *Seaforthia elegans*
and *Archontophoenix alexandrae*. Though both of these palms have
been reported very frequently from California, their existence there is
not certain; the confusion of names would naturally obscure the need
of introducing genuine examples of the species. The newly recognized
type is a distinctly larger and more robust palm than the true *Seaforthia elegans*, but smaller and more slender than the true *Archontophoenix alexandrae*, which is more similar in general appearance to the
royal palms of the American tropics.

The habit of the inflorescences to remain enclosed in the leaf-bases,
and thus secure protection till the time of flowering, may be considered as an adaptive specialization. The very soft thin texture of the
spathes indicates that these have little or no protective function. In
the case in which it was possible to observe the sequence of events the
spathes opened on the same day that the old leaf fell off; the blade
of the leaf was dead, but the tissue of the basal sheath was still rather
fresh.

Flowers in alcohol showed on the next day a notable brown discoloration of the petals and filaments, but the anthers remained white.
The change of color seemed to be dependent on exposure to the light,
or to the air in the bottle. Flowers on the under side of the mass were
scarcely changed, the delicate pink tint still appearing fresh. The name
chosen for the species alludes to the very attractive color of the flowers,
which is rather unusual among palms.

In attempting a specific identification of the cultivated palm just
described almost as many difficulties were encountered as with the

generic designation. Its reference to *Loroma cunninghamiana* would appear to be justified by some descriptions, but the type of this species seems to have been a smaller palm and different in other respects. The case is complicated at the beginning by the fact that the two original accounts of this species, by Hooker and Wendland, do not agree. Hooker's description and plate, published in 1857,[3] under the name *Seaforthia elegans*, indicate a relatively small, slender palm with a broad flat crown of horizontal spreading leaves, and about 30 pinnae on each side of the midrib. The form of the leaves appears to be oblong, with little indication of the extreme reduction of the pinnae at the base and tip, or of the tendency of the leaves to stand erect and turn on edge, as shown in *Loroma amethystina*. This individual had been raised at Kew from seed sent from northern Australia by Allan Cunningham, but no definite locality was given.

The most obvious discrepancy is that Wendland, in proposing the new name *Ptychosperma cunninghamiana*,[4] gives the number of pinnae as 55–65 on each side of the rachis. It appears that Wendland had a palm in his garden in Germany that had been considered as distinct from *Ptychosperma elegans;* but the new species was not named until after Wendland had visited Kew and seen the palm that had been raised from Cunningham's seed—the individual figured by Hooker as *Seaforthia elegans*. In naming the species *Ptychosperma cunninghamiana* and referring to Hooker's plate as the only published illustration, Wendland must be considered to have adopted the Kew palm as the type of his species. Yet it is difficult to believe that a botanical drawing made at Kew would have failed to show an approximation to the correct number of pinnae. The possibility that Wendland studied a different palm in Germany and included some of its characters in the description naturally suggests itself.

A color difference is indicated in Hooker's account of the flowers, which are described as "a pale, dull lilac," instead of a rather bright pinkish purple, as in *L. amethystina*. The staminodes also appear much larger in Hooker's drawing than in the type of *L. amethystina*. Hooker states that the palm was "said to attain a height of 30 feet in its native country," while Wendland and Drude, in transferring the species to Archontophoenix in 1875,[5] give the height as 40–60 feet, and add several other particulars that may not relate to the original

[3] Curtis' Bot. Mag. III. **13:** *pl. 4961.*
[4] Bot. Zeit. **16:** 46.
[5] Linnaea **39:** 214.

cunninghamiana, and yet are not altogether in agreement with *amethystina.* The pinnae are said to attain a length of 80 cm. and a width of 7 cm. The length of the pistillodes is given as 3–4 mm., and the filaments 2–3 mm.; whereas in *amethystina* the filaments are about 4 mm. long and the pistillodes only 2–3 mm. The length of the inflorescence is given as about 60 cm., with the ultimate divisions 30 cm. long; while the inflorescences of *amethystina* are over a meter long, with the flowering branches 60 cm. long. Wendland states that there are 18 stamens in *cunninghamiana* and Hooker's plate shows 18. The flowers of *amethystina* collected at San Diego usually had less than 15; over twenty flowers were examined without finding more than 16 stamens.

In view of these differences it has seemed desirable to recognize the California palm as a distinct species, instead of attempting to base the new genus on a species whose characters are so largely in doubt.

BACTERIOLOGY.—*Bacillus abortus in market milk.* ALICE C. EVANS, Dairy Division, Bureau of Animal Industry. Communicated by L. A. Rogers.

An organism of considerable interest which occurs commonly in milk is that which causes contagious abortion in cattle. In 1911 Schroeder and Cotton[1] reported this organism to be common in milk. They demonstrated its presence by the inoculation of guinea pigs. Whenever *Bacillus abortus* was present in the milk there was a slow development of lesions which resembled those of tuberculosis. This organism has been shown to be pathogenic for all kinds of laboratory and domestic animals. Whatever may be its effect on human health is unknown; but in view of its pathogenicity for animals it will naturally be regarded with some suspicion in its relation to human health until its nonpathogenicity has been demonstrated. Interest in this direction has been stimulated by the work of Larson and Sedgwick,[2] who reported a large percentage of positive results in a

[1] Schroeder, E. C., and Cotton, W. E. The bacillus of infectious abortion found in milk. U. S. Dept. of Agric. Bur. of Animal Industry, 28th Annual Rpt. 1911.

[2] Larson, W. P., and Sedgwick, J. P. Complement deviation reaction in the blood of children using the *Bacillus abortus* as an antigen. Rpt. of the Annual Meeting of the American Association of Medical Milk Commissions. 1913.

series of complement deviation tests with the blood of children in which the abortion bacillus was used as an antigen.

So far as the writer is aware, no bacteriological methods have been described by which *B. abortus* can be demonstrated in milk, and no data have been reported to show the numbers of these organisms which may be present. Therefore, a detailed description of a method by which *B. abortus* may be isolated from milk and identified may be useful at this time.

The milk is plated on ordinary lactose agar, to which there is added just before pouring into the plate, at a temperature of about 50°C., 10 per cent of sterile blood serum. After incubating for four days at 37°C., a certain area of the plate, large enough to include several colonies of *B. abortus*, should they be present, is selected, and the colonies are transferred to a nutrient broth containing 1 per cent of glycerine. Colonies from a similar area are transferred to tubes of whole milk containing litmus. The growth in the glycerine broth is quite characteristic: There is a medium amount of growth in tiny, compact, spherical masses which settles to the bottom of the tube and does not cloud the broth. In litmus whole milk there is an abundant growth in the cream layer, with a gradual development of acid. Cultures in litmus milk from which the cream has been removed grow sparingly, with no apparent effect. On plain infusion agar slopes the growth is in very small, separate colonies, which are scattered over the whole surface of the slope, if it happens to be moist at the time of inoculation; or the colonies are confined to a ribbon-like growth along the line of inoculation, if the agar is comparatively dry when inoculated.

Cultures which were isolated by the above method agreed in all essential points with the descriptions of *B. abortus* found in the literature. This organism is a small rod-shaped bacterium about 0.5 μ in width, and with a length sometimes of 3 μ. But the cells are often so short as to appear almost coccoid in form. Growth in ordinary media is very sparing or may not take place. The carbohydrates and related substances which many bacteria ferment are not attacked, with the exception of glycerine, which serves as a food, but is not broken down with the formation of

appreciable amounts of acid.   Five per cent bile added to ordinary media favors growth.   Several cultures which have been
isolated from milk were sent to Dr. Lothe, of the University of
Wisconsin, who reported positive reactions to the complement
fixation test in the presence of *B. abortus* amboceptor.

In a study of the bacteria of the udder samples of milk which
were drawn aseptically have been examined from four herds.
Out of the samples of milk taken from 14 cows of one herd, *B.
abortus* was shown to be present in the milk from 5 of the cows,
in numbers up to 50,000 per cubic centimeter.   Samples of
milk were taken from 40 cows of another herd.   These cows
are under the constant supervision of a veterinarian, and it is
the aim of the dairyman in charge to supply to the institution
which owns the herd milk equal to that from the best certified
dairies.   *B. abortus* was shown to be present in two out of the 40
samples; in both of which cases there were about 4,000 of these
bacilli per cubic centimeter.   It is almost certain that the
results obtained from the milk from these two herds falls short
of showing the actual number of *B. abortus* present, for this
part of the study was made before the method which favors the
isolation of this organism was perfected, as described above.

Samples of milk from two certified dairies in another region were
studied according to the method given.   Out of 22 samples
taken at one of these dairy farms, 7 were shown to contain *B.
abortus* in numbers ranging from 180 to 800 per cubic centimeter.   Out of 24 samples taken at the other dairy farm, 7 were
shown to contain *B. abortus* in numbers ranging from 110 to
4,300 per cubic centimeter.   Considering together all the samples
taken at these two certified dairies, 14 out of 46, or about 30
per cent, were shown to contain *B. abortus.*

Two bottles of certified milk were purchased in market, kept
at room temperature for about six hours, and then plated on the
serum agar.   About 28,000 of the abortion bacilli were shown
to be present in the cream layer of one sample, and about 1,900
in the cream layer of the other sample.   In both samples the
number of *B. abortus* was about 25 per cent of the whole number
of bacteria.

A simple experiment was planned to show whether the increasing amounts of lactic acid in milk not carefully handled might check the multiplication of *B. abortus*. The results showed that lactic acid added to the milk to bring the acidity to 0.4 per cent had no effect upon the multiplication of these organisms in the cream layer.

Bacillus abortus is characteristically an organism infecting cream. Since glycerine has been shown to be one of a very few food substances which it can utilize, and inasmuch as growth takes place slowly, with no apparent effect in litmus milk from which the cream has been removed, but is abundant in the cream layer of whole milk, with the production of acid, the facts suggest that the butter fat is broken down to obtain the glycerine and that the fatty acids thus liberated increase the acidity of the milk. Chemical determinations will be made to prove or disprove this theory, and the results will be included in a detailed report of the various bacteria occurring in the udder.

ZOOLOGY.—*On certain aspects of the bathymetrical distribution of the recent crinoids.*   AUSTIN H. CLARK, National Museum.[1]

In bridging the gap which lies between the conclusions deduced from the facts gathered through the study of palæontology—which gives us a more or less detached series of instantaneous flat views of local littoral conditions covering an immense period of time—and the conclusions deduced from the facts accumulated through the study of marine zoölogy—which permits a prolonged examination of a single stereoscopic view—the two prime requisites are: (1) to discover some means of adding geographical and bathymetrical perspective to each of the palæontological pictures, and (2) to discover some means of calculating geological time based upon the internal characters of the recent animal groups without reference to their fossil representatives.

The comparison between recent marine types and their fossil representatives, while yielding results of the greatest value, is open to two objections: (1) it necessarily takes no account of the ability of many types to persist in specially restricted localities where they stand little or no chance of preservation, yet where

---

[1] Published with the permission of the Secretary of the Smithsonian Institution.

there is possible an unbroken organic continuity extending through long periods of geological time, as in the case of the elasipod holothurians, certain anemonies, and many annelids, known only from the Cambrian and from the recent seas; and (2) it fails to emphasize the significance of the gradual differentiation in the conditions of marine life as a result of which many organisms, originally living together under the same œcological surroundings, have during geological time travelled gradually, and increasingly, diverging paths, so that now they have become widely separated from their original companions, like the phyllopod crustaceans, certain marine worms, and the elasipod holothurians, all of which lived side by side in the Cambrian seas.

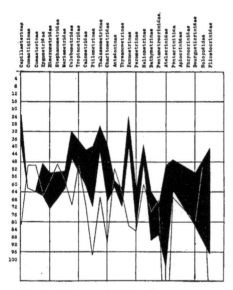

Fig. 1. Difference between the average range in depth, expressed as a percentage of the total range, and the average depth of habitat, expressed as a percentage of the mean depth of habitat, together with the average range in depth expressed as a percentage of the average depth of habitat.

As yet we have not sufficient information at hand to permit us to state with certainty that we shall ever be able to determine time factors of palæontological value from the study of the recent marine animals alone; but we have enough data to be able tentatively to suggest certain lines of procedure by which it may be possible in the future, when our knowledge of the present marine fauna is more detailed, to classify with more or less accuracy the various animal groups according to their comparative geological antiquity.

In the following lists are given for the subfamilies and higher groups of recent crinoids:

(1) The average range in depth expressed as a percentage of the total range in depth.

(2) The average depth of habitat expressed as a percentage of the mean depth of habitat.

(3) The average depth of habitat expressed as a percentage, of the average range in depth.

	Average range in depth expressed in per cent of total range.	Average depth of habitat expressed in per cent of mean depth.	Average depth of habitat expressed in per cent of average range.
	per cent	per cent	per cent
ARTICULATA................	14	41	144
PENTACRINITIDÆ............	15	28	77
Comatulida..............	15	27	90
Oligophreata............	10	15	70
Comasteridæ..........	18	23	63
Capillasterinæ.......	23	37	81
Comactiniinæ.......	62	62	50
Comasterinæ........	64	64	50
Zygometridæ..........	49	66	66
Himerometridæ........	54	73	66
*Stephanometridæ.....	100	100	49
Mariametridæ.........	53	62	58
Colobometridæ........	32	46	71
*Tropiometridæ.......	100	100	50
Calometridæ..........	42	61	72
Thalassometridæ......	25	34	68
Ptilometrinæ........	40	72	98
Thalassometrinæ....	29	42	67
Charitometridæ......	39	69	91
Macrophreata..........	24	46	96
Antedonidæ..........	19	28	71
Antedoninæ........	58	61	52
Thysanometrinæ....	61	72	64
Zenometrinæ.......	24	39	82
Perometrinæ........	63	82	85
Heliometrinæ.......	39	48	60
Bathymetrinæ.......	64	90	75
Pentametrocrinidæ.....	71	87	69
Atelecrinidæ.........	50	125	244
Pentacrinitida............	47	63	67
APIOCRINIDÆ...............	()	()	()
PHRYNOCRINIDÆ............	()	()	()
BOURGUETICRINIDÆ..........	54	82	80
*HOLOPODIDÆ..............	100	100	50
INADUNATA................	41	97	145
PLICATOCRINIDÆ............	41	97	145

It should, perhaps, be emphasized that, strictly speaking, the bathymetrical distribution of any animal type is of itself without biological significance. The only factor correlated directly with ' increase in depth, other than the decrease in illumination in the upper strata, is the increase in pressure, and increase of pressure has never been shown to exert any appreciable influence on the distribution of the higher invertebrate types either directly, or indirectly through the inhibition of the physiological processes.

The determining factor in the bathymetrical distribution of marine animals is the decrease of temperature with depth, and the study of the bathymetric distribution of any large group not directly dependent upon plants for food is in reality the indirect study of its thermal distribution. As our temperature observations in any one group are usually comparatively few, while our bathymetrical records are numerous, we are able to discuss to advantage the bathymetrical distribution of the component types in any unit, while at the same time we are unable to consider similarly the thermal distribution of the same types. But we must always remember that in discussing the bathymetrical distribution of a subfamily or higher group we are really considering its thermal distribution, and our bathymetric records may be readily transposed into thermal records by means of comparisons with tables showing the decrease in the temperature in the sea according to latitude and depth.

The average range in depth of the families of recent crinoids (excluding the Stephanometridæ, Tropiometridæ and Holopodidæ, monotypic, and the Apiocrinidæ and Phrynocrinidæ, insufficiently known), calculated as the average of the ranges of all of the included genera, represents a very varying percentage of their total range—from 23 per cent in the Capillasterinæ to 71 per cent in the Pentametrocrinidæ.

The sequence of the families according to the relation of the average to the total range in depth is as follows:

	per cent		per cent
Capillasterinæ	23	Atelecrinidæ	50
Zenometrinæ	24	Mariametridæ	53
Thalassometrinæ	29	Himerometridæ	54
Colobometridæ	32	Bourgueticrinidæ	54
Charitometridæ	39	Antedoninæ	58
Heliometrinæ	39	Thysanometrinæ	61
Ptilometrinæ	40	Comactiniinæ	62
Plicatocrinidæ	41	Perometrinæ	63
Calometridæ	42	Comasterinæ	64
Pentacrinitida	47	Bathymetrinæ	64
Zygometridæ	49	Pentametrocrinidæ	71

Average for all families 48 per cent.

From this list it is evident that there is no definite correspondence between the relation of the average to the total range and the systematic scheme, for closely related families, such as the Capillasterinæ and the Comasterinæ in the Oligophreata, and the Bathymetrinæ and the Zenometrinæ in the Macrophreata, occur at opposite extremes.

But it is interesting to observe that it is within the interval 41 per cent to 54 per cent, a range of only 27 per cent, or a little more than one-fourth, of the total range, that the families Plicatocrinidæ, Calometridæ, Pentacrinitida, Zygometridæ, Atelecrinidæ, Mariametridæ, Himerometridæ and Bourgueticrinidæ fall, these eight families, the average range of which is 48 per cent, or exactly that of all of the crinoid families together, including not only all of the stalked types, but also the Zygometridæ, the only comatulid family satisfactorily represented as a fossil, and the Atelecrinidæ, the only comatulid family in which the primitive basals persist in the adult. In other words, we find here all of the families of which we possess any definite palæontological history.

This would suggest that in ancient types still persisting the normal condition is for the average range of all the genera in any given family to be about one-half the total range of the same family, while in the later types there is a departure toward both extremes.

Within the first half of the list there are 7 oligophreate, 2 macrophreate and 2 stalked groups; within the second half 4 oligophreate, 6 macrophreate and 1 stalked groups.

The families toward the beginning of the list are chiefly families with a comparatively large temperature range; that is, in which one genus has extended itself into water considerably warmer or (usually) colder than the optimum for the family; while those toward the end of the list are largely families which cover a comparatively small temperature range, but which, however, may be confined either to cold or to warm water.

A family confined either to very cold or to very warm water would be in almost all cases a family of comparatively recent origin, for the coldness of the abysses and the warmth of the tropical littoral are themselves of comparatively recent origin. Also a family with a large temperature range would be of comparatively recent origin (or at least development) for the temperature of the ancient seas was fairly uniform.

Thus we should expect the more ancient types to occur at or near the centre of our series.

If we consider the families which are confined to a depth less than 1000 fathoms in contrast to those which occur below 1000 fathoms we find that the two groups are as follows:

Not occurring below 1000 fathoms.		*Ranging to below 1000 fathoms.*	
	per cent		*per cent*
Capillasterinæ	23	Zenometrinæ	24
Colobometridæ	32	Thalassometrinæ	29
Ptilometrinæ	40	Charitometrinæ	39
Calometridæ	42	Heliometrinæ	39
Zygometridæ	49	Plicatocrinidæ	41
Atelecrinidæ	50	Pentacrinitida	47
Mariametridæ	53	Bourgueticrinidæ	54
Himerometridæ	54	Bathymetrinæ	64
Antedoninæ	58	Pentametrocrinidæ	71
Thysanometrinæ	61		
Comactiniinæ	62		
Perometrinæ	63		
Comasterinæ	64		
Average	50	Average	45

Each group has approximately the same range, and approximately the same average, and neither appears to possess any distinctive characters.

Similarly if we compare the families the total range of which is less than 1000 fathoms with those in which it is greater we find that neither group possesses any marked characteristics.

Ranging more than 1000 fathoms.		Ranging less than 1000 fathoms.	
	per cent		*per cent*
Thalassometrinæ	29	Capillasterinæ	23
Charitometridæ	39	Comactiniinæ	62
Zenometrinæ	24	Comasterinæ	64
Heliometrinæ	39	Zygometridæ	49
Bathymetrinæ	64	Himerometridæ	54
Pentametrocrinidæ	71	Mariametridæ	53
Pentacrinitida	47	Colobometridæ	32
Bourgueticrinidæ	54	Calometridæ	42
Plicatocrinidæ	41	Ptilometrinæ	40
		Antedoninæ	58
		Thysanometrinæ	61
		Perometrinæ	63
		Atelecrinidæ	50
Average	45	Average	50

But if we consider the larger groups we are at once struck by the fact that of two comparable types the more highly specialized always shows a much lower figure than the more primitive, the figure for the former being only from 28 per cent to 41 per cent (with the average 35 per cent, or little more than one-third) of the figure for the latter. In the following list four strictly comparable groups are given:

More specialized		More primitive		
	per cent		*per cent*	*per cent*
Articulata	14	Inadunata	41	(34)
Pentacrinitidæ	15	Bourgueticrinidæ	54	(28)
Comatulida	15	Pentacrinitida	47	(32)
Oligophreata	10	Macrophreata	24	(41)

This is due to the great predominance of the more specialized and more recent types in the warm shallow water, from which they have not as yet spread into the deep sea, but from which, through their superior economic equipment, they have to a greater or lesser extent extirpated the preceding less specialized and more ancient forms which, persisting chiefly, therefore, in the deeper and consequently cooler and more uniform water, naturally show much greater generic ranges, and consequently higher percentages representing the mean range as compared with the total range of any one family.

In this connection it must be borne in mind that the crinoids are confined to clear water of a comparatively slight range in salinity and in composition, and with a very low maximum of silt. They therefore are unable to exist in many of the localities in which other ancient types, such for example as *Artemia*, *Xiphosura* and *Lingula*, find a safe refuge from more efficient competitors, with the result that each succeeding type is necessarily brought into direct and intimate contact with the greater part, or even all, of its predecessors.

A comparison between the average depth inhabited by each group (excluding the Stephanometridæ, Tropiometridæ and Holopodidæ, monotypic, and the Apiocrinidæ and Phrynocrinidæ, imperfectly understood) calculated as the average of the mean depth of all of the component genera (or higher groups), and the mean depth of each group as represented by the mean between its two extremes, expressed as a per cent obtained by dividing the former by the latter, gives the following figures:

	per cent		per cent
Antedonidæ	28	Zygometridæ	66
Capillasterinæ	37	Charitometridæ	69
Zenometrinæ	39	Ptilometrinæ	72
Thalassometrinæ	42	Thysanometrinæ	72
Colobometridæ	46	Himerometridæ	73
Heliometrinæ	48	Perometrinæ	82
Antedoninæ	61	Bourgueticrinidæ	82
Calometridæ	61	Pentametrocrinidæ	87
Mariametridæ	62	Bathymetrinæ	90
Comactiniinæ	62	Plicatocrinidæ	97
Comasterinæ	64	Atelecrinidæ	125

Average.................66 per cent

Contrasting older and less specialized with more recent and more specialized groups, we have:

More specialized		More primitive	
	per cent		per cent
Articulata	41	Inadunata	97
Pentacrinitidæ	28	Bourgueticrinidæ	82
Comatulida	27	Pentacrinitida	63
Oligophreata	15	Macrophreata	46

The groups including stalked species show the following relationship:

per cent

Pentacrinitidæ	28
Pentacrinitida	63
Bourgueticrinidæ	82
Plicatocrinidæ	97

It is evident from the preceding two tables that the average depth of the habitat of all the genera of any group among the more highly specialized types is only a comparatively small fraction of the mean depth of the group as a whole, and that this fraction increases with the age and with the progressive decrease in the specialization of the group, reaching, in the chiefly palæozoic Inadunata, 97 per cent. It is, of course, also high in highly specialized groups confined to a very small range in depth, such as the Perometrinæ, Himerometridæ and Thysanometrinæ.

Any new or very vigorous group continually gives rise to new forms in the region most favourable for their existence, namely the littoral or sublittoral zones. The existence of a number of such juvenile types within a vigourous group therefore lowers the average depth of the group, which is consequently far less than the mean depth. But in the older mature or senile groups the formation of new types in the littoral is inhibited through group senility, and prevented by the occupation of the available economic territory by types derived from more specialized and more efficient stock. Therefore, theoretically, the older and less specialized the group the closer should the average depth approach the mean.

In the Atelecrinidæ the average depth exceeds the mean depth by 25 per cent; but we know only two genera of this family, one merely from a single specimen of a single species taken only once, in 907 fathoms. This family should therefore be disregarded in forming general conclusions.

Putting aside the Atelecrinidæ as insufficiently known, it appears to be demonstrable that no crinoid type ever originated in the deep sea, for if such had ever been the case the primarily abyssal types should be immediately disclosed through showing an average depth of habitat considerably greater than the mean depth.

The approximation of the average to the mean depth in the older types, taken in connection with what we know in regard to the association of genera in the older horizons, suggests that the older types not only possessed a very limited range of possible creative evolution and development, but that, in contrast to the later types, the new forms which they gave off were not adapted to meet special conditions, but rather to exist side by side with the parent types, utilizing the excess of available food.   As would be expected, a small number of the groups of the present day (for instance the Comasteridæ) appear to be giving off, or attempting to give off, new types in this way.

The series of figures showing the average range expressed as a percentage of the average depth suggest that in the older and less specialized groups the tendency is for the average range to equal or to exceed the average depth of habitat, but in the more recent and more specialized types to be less.   The figures (which are given in the following tables) are, however, not conclusive.

	per cent		per cent
Comasterinæ	50	Colobometridæ	71
Comactiniinæ	50	Calometridæ	72
Antedoninæ	52	Bathymetrinæ	75
Mariametridæ	58	Bourgueticrinidæ	80
Heliometrinæ	60	Capillasterinæ	81
Thysanometrinæ	64	Zenometrinæ	82
Himerometridæ	66	Perometrinæ	85
Zygometridæ	66	Charitometridæ	91
Pentacrinitida	67	Ptilometrinæ	98
Thalassometrinæ	67	Plicatocrinidæ	145
Pentametrocrinidæ	69	Atelecrinidæ	244

Average..................68 per cent.

Contrasting the more specialized with the less specialized types:

	per cent		per cent
Articulata	144	Inadunata	145
Pentacrinitidæ	77	Bourgueticrinidæ	80
Comatulida	90	Pentacrinitida	67
Oliophreata	70	Macrophreata	96
Average	95	Average	97

Considering the groups including stalked forms:

	per cent
Pentacrinitidæ	77
Pentacrinitida	67
Bourgueticrinidæ	80
Plicatocrinidæ	145

THE PHILOSOPHICAL SOCIETY OF WASHINGTON

The 746th meeting was held on November 21, 1914, at the Cosmos Club, President FISCHER in the chair; 31 persons present.

Mr. W. P. WHITE presented a paper on *Electric pendulums and pendulum contacts*. Most methods of driving a pendulum can be adequately represented mathematically by supposing that the position of equilibrium is shifted for a longer or shorter time. If the device acts by means of a spring, it may be necessary also to consider that the periodic time of the pendulum is altered through part of its vibration. The resulting effect upon the motion of the pendulum can very readily be handled by means of the circle of reference. A change in the position of equilibrium is then graphically represented by continuing the line along a new circle whose center is shifted accordingly. By the application of this method it is possible to show that, while a strong impulse communicated to the pendulum as it passes through the equilibrium position is a satisfactory method of increasing its energy without affecting its period, yet the variation of the effect upon the period which may occur as a result of varying amplitude is often less when the pressure is changed from an impulsive one to one acting for half the time of the swing. The two best forms of electric drive appear to be: (1) that in which the drive is purely electric and is due to an induced current which can both be made almost strictly impulsive and very constant; and (2) an electrically operated arrangement in which the pendulum, as it swings, raises and lowers a light weight. The paper was discussed by Mr. C. A. BRIGGS.

Mr. E. BUCKINGHAM then spoke on *The principle of dimensional homogeneity and the form of physical equations*. Reasoning based on the consideration of the ratios, in any two stages of a physical phenomenon, of the quantities involved in it as variables, shows that the physical equation which describes the phenomenon by describing the characteristic relation among the quantities, must necessarily have a certain simple general form. This form is dimensionally homogeneous. No use is made of the other known relations among quantities of the kind in question, so that the result does not depend upon the use of an absolute system of units but is true when the units of measurement are all completely arbitrary and independent. If such relations are utilized and all measurements are made in terms of absolute units, the necessary general form of a physical equation may be still further specified, and it reduces to a form given by the speaker at a former meeting of the Society, when the principle of dimensional homogeneity was assumed and used as a starting point. The paper was discussed by Messrs. HANSEN, AGNEW, and DOUGLAS.

The 747th meeting was held on December 5, 1914, at the Cosmos Club, President FISCHER in the chair; 70 persons present.

By invitation, Prof. W. S. FRANKLIN, of Lehigh University, addressed the Society on *Some phenomena of fluid motion and the curved flight of a baseball.* The steady curvature of path of a rapidly spinning baseball was explained on the basis of the principle enunciated by Daniel Bernoulli in 1726, viz., in a stream of water, or air, the pressure is high where the velocity is low, and the pressure is low where the velocity is high. The principle and its application in fluid motion were illustrated both by lantern slide diagrams and experiments. The "spit-ball" was also explained by the same principle. In the course of the lecture the speaker, in an interesting digression, raised question as to the strict validity of the law of cause and effect. The paper was discussed by Mr. WILEY, who cited several phenomena in his own experience during wind storms that could be explained by Bernoulli's principle, and by Mr. HUMPHREYS, who asked as to the explanation of the principle. Professor FRANKLIN then discussed some of the limitations of the principle. The best point of view in explanation is that of conservation of energy.

The chair expressed to the speaker the thanks of the members and guests for his interesting lecture and experiments.

The 748th meeting (44th annual meeting) was held on December 19, 1914, at the Cosmos Club, President FISCHER in the chair; 24 persons present.

The report of the secretaries was read by Mr. AGNEW, showing an active membership of 144. Sixteen regular meetings have been held. The report was ordered accepted. The Treasurer's report, dated December 16, 1914, was read by Mr. SOSMAN. The total receipts for the year were $3078.77, including proceeds from sales of investments; total expenditures, $3151.20, including purchases of bonds of par value $2500; total investments, $11,500; cash in hand, $454.72. The report was ordered accepted. The report of the Auditing Committee, consisting of Messrs. WHITE, KIMBALL, and FERNER, was read by Mr. WHITE. This Committee reported the statements in the Treasurer's report to be correct. The report was ordered accepted. It was moved and passed that the reading of names of members entitled to vote be omitted. Messrs. F. J. BATES and C. A. BRIGGS were appointed tellers. The following officers were duly elected for the ensuing year: President, W. S. EICHELBERGER; Vice-Presidents, L. J. BRIGGS, WM. BOWIE, G. K. BURGESS, and W. J. HUMPHREYS; Secretaries, J. A. FLEMING and P. G. AGNEW; Treasurer, R. B. SOSMAN; General Committee, N. E. DORSÉY, E. BUCKINGHAM, M. D. HERSEY, E. G. FISCHER, R. L. FARIS, H. L. CURTIS, D. L. HAZARD, R. A. HARRIS, W. P. WHITE. It was moved and carried that the Secretary ' communicate to the General Committee that it is the sense of the meeting that the membership list be revised, published, and distributed more frequently. It was moved and carried that the plan of having refreshments at the regular meetings be presented to the General Committee for consideration. There was also informal discussion as to the desirability of a revision of the by-laws and organization. It was suggested that the General Committee empower the Executive Committee to designate other meeting places than the Cosmos Club when desired, and that the General Committee provide for taking of votes by post when specific questions arise requiring prompt action.

The 749th meeting was held on January 2, 1915, at the Cosmos Club, President EICHELBERGER in the chair; 20 persons present.

Mr. F. E. WRIGHT spoke on *The measurement of relative strain in glass.* The history of researches with reference to the optical effects resulting from strain in glass and to the methods suggested for measuring such effects was reviewed. In the method used by the speaker, the glass plate is examined in strong monochromatic light between crossed nicols. The path difference of the emergent light waves at any given point is measured by a bi-quartz compensator of special type. The conversion of the optical retardations thus measured to the corresponding elastic deformation data is accomplished by direct measurements in the glass subjected to a series of mechanical loads of known magnitudes. The paper was illustrated by experiments and projections on the screen. The discussion was participated in by Messrs. BAUER WHITE, C. A. BRIGGS, MARVIN, CURTIS and SOSMAN particular inquiry being made with reference to applications in determining strains in engineering constructions.

Mr. M. D. HERSEY presented a paper on *Some characteristics of aneroid barometers.* The speaker described briefly the general principles and mechanical details of the aneroid barometer. The various types were illustrated by lantern slides and sketches. In the consideration of relative merits and permissible limits of error account must be taken of the proposed use. The different classes of error were discussed. The chief source of error appears to be in the construction of the vacuum box. Mr. MARVIN discussed the paper, stating that his experience confirmed the conclusion of the speaker and that undoubtedly the greatest improvement must be looked for in better material for the vacuum box.

The 750th meeting was held on January 16, 1915, at the Cosmos Club, President EICHELBERGER in the chair; 50 persons present.

The evening was devoted to the address of the retiring President, Mr. L. A. FISCHER, on *Measurement of length.* The speaker briefly sketched the early history of the English yard and the origin of the present metric standards of length. The earliest authentic copies of both the yard and the meter in the United States were brought to this country by Ferdinand Hassler, the first superintendent of the Coast Survey, and when he organized that service later on the meter

was made the basis of that work. The causes which led to the establishment of the International Bureau of Weights and Measures in France,
and the prominent part taken by geodesists in the development and
preservation of standards of length up until very recent times, were
brought out. The progress made in the measurement of primary
base-lines by the U. S. Coast and Geodetic Survey during the period
while the speaker was connected with that service was then briefly
sketched, emphasis being laid upon the important part taken by members of the Philosophical Society in the development of the subject,
not only in the United States, but throughout the world. The compensated base bars of Schott, the simple steel bars used by Tittmann,
the duplex apparatus of Eimbeck, and the methods of Woodward of
measuring with the 5-meter iced bars, and steel tapes, were briefly
discussed and the advantages and the accuracy of the different methods
compared. Mr. Fischer also exhibited some very accurately measured
steel gauges to illustrate the progress in perfecting accurate manufacturers' standards.

The chair expressed to the speaker the thanks of the members and
guests present for his most interesting paper.

The 751st meeting was held on January 30, 1915, at the Cosmos
Club, President EICHELBERGER in the chair; 52 persons present.

Mr. W. F. G. SWANN presented a paper on *The atmospheric-electric
work of the Department of Terrestrial Magnetism*, illustrated with lantern slides. A brief survey of the methods and uncertainties in atmospheric-electric observations was given, and certain new instruments
and methods were described. A short discussion of the observations
made by Messrs. C. W. HEWLETT and H. F. JOHNSTON during the second and last cruises of the *Carnegie* was given. Ocean observations
appear to show a curious diminution in the conductivity followed by
an increase as one passes from mid-ocean to land, and vice versa.
Reasons were given for believing that the specific velocity is the factor
responsible for this phenomenon. The radioactive content was determined by a modification of Elster and Geitel's method. By an
application of theoretical considerations, it has been possible to calculate the approximate absolute radioactive content of the air. The
decay curves correspond to radium emanation, and the average emanation content per cu. cm. is 107 curies, which is as much as is found
on land, and would be more than sufficient to account for the conductivity observed if many of the ions produced were not ions of slow
velocity. In the discussion Mr. HUMPHREYS referred to the chaotic
state of atmospheric-electric work until recent years; the progress being made results first from a thorough discussion of the underlying principles and then a design of apparatus accordingly. Mr.
BAUER referred to his experience in planning for the atmospheric-
electrical work of the Department of Terrestrial Magnetism in 1905,
and of the observational quarters being now provided on the *Carnegie*
for the coming cruise.

Mr. C. R. DUVALL then presented a paper, illustrated by lantern slides, on *The recurring-series method of seeking hidden periodicities with applications*. A generating function in the form of a general rational proper fraction in x may be developed into a power series in two ways. In the first, the coefficients satisfy a scale of relation, and in the second the general coefficient is in the form of a sum of products of polynomials by powers. Both processes being uniquely reversible, a general form is determined of a sequence of numbers satisfying a scale of relation. A sum of sine terms is transformed into a sum of powers; a particular case of a sum of products of polynomials by powers. Hence, any sequence of numbers which may be represented by a sum of sine terms, satisfies a scale of relation, and its general term may be determined and the periods, amplitudes, and phrases. Results of applications to magnetic and sun-spot-number data were given, showing a striking agreement in the two phenomena of three periods of about 11.4, 22, and 70 years, with some indications of a fourth period of 6 to 8 years. Prof. E. W. BROWN's diagram of fluctuations in the longitude of the Moon, Earth, and Mercury, all compared with the sun-spot curve, gave indications of a common period of about 70 years, and suggested a connection between these fluctuations and changes in the Earth's magnetic field, all possibly due to changes in the Sun's magnetic field. The paper was discussed by Mr. BAUER, who gave a brief account of recent work of others, particularly of Schuster and Michelson; Mr. SOSMAN asked whether any groupings had been taken for periods associated with that of the rotation of the Sun; Messrs. HUMPHREYS and ABBOT made reference to the inaccuracy of data sometimes published.

J. A. FLEMING, *Secretary.*

THE GEOLOGICAL SOCIETY OF WASHINGTON

The 289th meeting was held in the lecture room of the Cosmos Club, on January 13, 1915.

INFORMAL COMMUNICATIONS

H. M. EAKIN, *Effect of the earth's rotation as a deflecting force in stream erosion.* In 1909 the speaker gave a paper before the Geological Society of Washington in which rotational deflection was discussed as to its source, its variations with latitude and velocity, and its expression in torsional flow and selective lateral erosion in alluvial streams as compared with that of the more familiar centrifugal force developed on stream bends. It was shown that above latitude 60° N. a straight stream has the same tendency to greater erosion on its right bank due to rotational deflection as that directed to the outer bank by centrifugal force on a bend with a 6-mile radius of curvature. This measure of the erosional effect of rotational deflection lead to the conclusions: That this force is sufficient to cause lateral migration of large streams in high latitudes; that the Yukon River, in Alaska, has thus migrated to the right side of its valley throughout the lower 800 miles of its course; and that large rivers generally in high latitudes, especially those of northern Siberia, should have characteristics similar to those of the Yukon.

The first authentic data regarding the Siberian rivers has just become available in Nansen's new book, *Siberia the Land of the Future*, and both the data and the author's interpretations are in entire harmony with the conclusions cited in the earlier paper by the speaker.

Discussion. S. R. CAPPS and F. C. SCHRADER expressed the opinion that, as regards the Yukon and Tanana, other factors than the earth's rotation were of much importance. Such, for instance, was the formation of delta deposits in streams entering from one side and not from the other. EAKIN agreed that this was a factor of importance but did not believe the whole effect could be ascribed to it.

E. W. SHAW, *A unique coal mine gas explosion.* At the time of the unprecedented high water on the lower Ohio, in the spring of 1913, a gas explosion occurred in a coal mine at Equality, Illinois, which was unique in that the gas was ordinary air. As the water approached the mine efforts were made to prevent ingress by throwing up a low dike about the shaft, but when this dike had been raised to a height of about 5 feet the water broke through and rushed down the shaft. The space in the mine once occupied by the millions of cubic feet of coal which had been mined out was at this time occupied by air, and the water rushed down in such volumes that it allowed no air to escape. After several hours the reaction came with a roar. The water bounced out again, geyser fashion, bringing with it all manner of débris, coal cars, tools, etc., and throwing them high in the air. Perhaps the most important fact concerning this remarkable occurrence is that the owners of this mine, like most coal operators, had no map of their workings, and the site chosen for a new shaft was not sufficiently distant to avoid breaking through into the old mine. An expenditure of thousands of dollars was necessary to pump the water out so that the new shaft could be used.

REGULAR PROGRAM

OLAF ANDERSEN, *Mineral occurrences and associations in southern Norway.* The granitic pegmatite dikes form large bodies injected into various types of pre-Cambrian rocks. The dikes are, as a rule, very coarse-grained, some of the minerals (e.g., feldspars) forming huge crystals. Graphic granites and various other graphic intergrowths are very common. The main feldspar is always a microcline perthite. Plagioclases (commonly oligoclase) are also present in considerable quantities. Micas (biotite and muscovite) are found in most of the dikes. Magnetite is commonly present in small amounts. With respect to the associations of the less common minerals several types may be distinguished: the beryl-bearing dikes, the tourmaline-bearing dikes, the dikes rich in niobates and tantalates, etc. Each type has its characteristic mineral association, but there are no sharp boundaries between the types.

The most interesting rare minerals of the dikes are the niobates, tantalates, and titano-niobates (columbite, fergusonite, euxenite, blomstrandine, etc.) and the silicates containing rare earths (thorite, orthite, gadolinite, hellandite, thortveitite, etc.). The following are some of the rare elements present in these minerals: yttrium, erbium, cerium, scandium, thorium, uranium, tungsten, niobium, tantalum. The cordierite-bearing pegmatites occur in small veins in gneiss, and contain chiefly oligoclase (sunstone), cordierite, and quartz, with small amounts of magnetite, apatite, etc. The epidote-bearing peg- • matites occur as veins in metamorphic rocks (altered quartz-porphyries). They contain microcline and quartz as chief minerals, with considerable quantities of epidote, apatite, and hematite, and some biotite, muscovite, and titanite.

Discussion. E. S. Bastin spoke of the resemblance in structure (rather than in mineralogy) which the Norwegian pegmatites show to those of the United States, especially as regards the graphic intergrowths. He thought that it was difficult to consider these intergrowths as eutectics, because of the variable ratios in which the minerals occur in them. He inquired as to Andersen's views on this matter. Andersen said that he had not yet studied them thoroughly from this standpoint, but he thought that simultaneous crystallization had been a factor, and showed by a diagram that in a three-component system the boundary curves might follow such a course as to give varying proportions of two components which are simultaneously crystallizing out.

E. T. Hancock, *The history of a portion of Yampa River, Colorado, and its possible bearing on that of Green River.* The relation between the main Uinta uplift and two minor uplifts known as Junction Mountain and Juniper Mountain was first pointed out, also the relation in origin of these uplifts to the Axial Basin anticline, which C. A. White called "the inceptive portion of the Uinta fold." The views of some of the earlier geologists regarding the origin of Green and Yampa Rivers were briefly cited. The author of the paper then gave the evidence to show that at one time both the Juniper and Junction Mountain uplifts were covered by the overlapping Browns Park formation, and that Yampa River, instead of being antecedent, as C. A. White and others supposed, is superimposed, and that the entrenched meanders east of the Juniper Mountain uplift are due to the fact that for a time the uplifted Paleozoic rocks of Juniper Mountain acted as a barrier. After the river succeeded in cutting its channels down through the hard rocks it then deepened its channels throughout that part of its course where it had previously established its meanders. (To be published in complete form in U. S. Geological Survey Professional Paper No. 90, Chapter K.)

Discussion. C. W. Cross spoke of the earlier work done by S. F. Emmons in this region and inquired if Emmons' reasons for believing that the Green River had other than an antecedent origin had the same basis as those of Hancock. Hancock replied that Emmons' conclusion

was based on the fact that the antecedent hypothesis presented problems which no one had been able to solve. Probably also Emmons
suspected that the late Tertiary sediments had formerly overlapped
the Uinta Mountains. E. W. SHAW raised the query whether the
present elevated position of the Browns Park beds in certain places
might not be due to subsequent deformation. Hancock gave reasons
for doubting this. B. S. BUTLER spoke of a remnant of a mature
topographic form on the north side of the Uinta Mountains in the
form of a gravel-capped plateau. A similar form occurs on the south
side of the range and one is impressed with the probability that at
one time they were connected and are parts of a mature topography
now dissected, and that a correlation can be made between the physiographic stages represented in the Uinta region and those of the High
Plateau. C. J. HARES drew an analogy with the North Platte and
Sweetwater River systems and thought their history was similar to that
described by Hancock for the Green River-Yampa system.

G. F. LOUGHLIN, *Stratigraphy of the Tintic Mining District, Utah.*
The sedimentary rocks of the Tintic district have a total thickness
of more than 13,000 feet, the lower half consisting of quartzite with
a narrow shale band at its top and the upper half consisting chiefly of
limestone and dolomite. These rocks were first described in 1897 by
TOWER and G. OTIS SMITH, who assigned the quartzite and shale to the
Cambrian, and the limestone-dolomite series tentatively to the Carboniferous. In 1905 WEEKS found Middle and Upper Cambrian
fossils in the lower 2000 feet of limestone. During a recent resurvey
of the district by the U. S. Geological Survey the overlying limestones
were found to include 2000 feet or more of Ordovician, 150 or more of
Devonian, and a minimum of 1800 feet of lower and upper Mississippian. Two unconformities were recognized; one at or near the base
of the Ordovician, and one at the base of the Mississippian. No proof
of an unconformity in the Cambrian quartzite corresponding to that
in the Big Cottonwood Canyon section could be found. The Middle
Cambrian limestones are only about one-third as thick as those in the
House Range and Blacksmith Fork sections, but no evidence indicating
the cause of this difference was found.

Discussion by GEORGE OTIS SMITH and C. W. CROSS.

C. N. FENNER, *Secretary.*

THE ANTHROPOLOGICAL SOCIETY OF WASHINGTON

At a special meeting of the Society held November 3, 1914, at the
Public Library, Dr. J. WALTER FEWKES, of the Bureau of American
Ethnology, read a paper on *Vanished races of the Caribbean,* using lantern slides to show characteristic artifacts found on different islands.
About 235 persons were present. The lecturer said that while it
has been frequently stated that there are races of men without history, by this must be meant that they have no written history; for
every race has had a cultural development worthy of study even if

it has not been recorded in writing. Its earliest steps in culture, those taken before the development of written history, can be traced by a study of its archaeology and are important, even though they represent only a small segment of its evolution. One of the most instructive aboriginal types of man in pre-historic America is that which in pre-Columbian times inhabited the West Indies, extending from Trinidad on the coast of South America to Cuba, a few miles south of the peninsula of Florida. These aborigines may be regarded, from the cultural point of view, as members of a vanished race, for, with the exception of very incomplete historical accounts and a few highly modified living survivors, archaeological remains are all that is left from which to determine its culture. A study of this limited material shows that the Antillean culture belonged to the stone age, and while it had attained a considerable development it · was quite unlike that of any other area in the New World. It is taken for granted that these islands were originally peopled from the neighboring continent, and it is probable, from the peculiar types of stone objects which occur on the islands, that the culture they represent originated where it was found. In other words, the aborigines of the West Indies developed a cultural center distinct from that of any other region in the world. There are archaeological evidences of a division in this culture into two types, one of which existed in the Greater Antilles and the other in the Lesser, or the so-called Carib Islands. Each of these had minor divisions, which also differed in details, although both had the same general character. The two larger divisions differed mainly in the forms of stone implements, pottery, and other artifacts. For instance, 90 per cent of the stone implements of the Greater Antilles have the form of celts pointed at one end and without grooves for handles, while the large majority of implements from the Lesser Antilles are axes with blunt heads. Some of the latter have encircling grooves for the attachment of handles, while others are notched on the edges for the same · purpose. This difference in the culture of the aborigines in the northern and southern islands was noticed by Columbus and is repeatedly spoken of by the early chroniclers, his immediate successors. The inhabitants of the Lesser Antilles were early designated by the name of Caribs, while those of the larger islands were called Arawaks. The main difference in the characters of the two peoples was recognized and described by early writers.

The Caribs were not the original inhabitants of the islands where Columbus found them. They were preceded by an agricultural people whom they had conquered in pre-Columbian times. There is evidence showing that originally all the islands from Cuba to Trinidad had a highly developed population which had been absorbed by Caribs in the southern islands but still persisted in the Greater Antilles. The former home of the earliest inhabitants of the West Indies is unknown, but certain facts point to the conclusion that, while the remote ancestors of the aborigines of the Lesser Antilles came from South America, those of the Greater Antilles were from Central America. This difference of ethnic origin no doubt led to differences in culture, each modified in its development by its environment.

At a meeting of the Society, held November 17, 1914, in the Public Library, Rev. Dr. JOHN LEE MADDOX, Chaplain in the United States Army, read a paper on *The Spirit theory in early medicine*, based in part upon a larger paper submitted as a thesis at Yale University. After stating the general primitive theory, still more or less prevalent among the uneducated, that disease and death are abnormal, the work of malevolent spirits or of witchcraft, he undertook to show that many of our modern medical practices and remedies are the direct descendants of old-time methods and drugs intended to cure the patient by driving out the evil disease spirit through fear or disgust. According to this theory, bitter medicines originated in the revolting doses administered by the primitive medicine men in order to disgust the disease demon with his human habitation; massage originated in the beatings and poundings through which the evil spirit was frightened out of the patient's body; and bleeding and cupping, as also trephining, were originally intended to facilitate its exit. Through long centuries of experience, even with an incorrect theory, it was found that certain drugs and remedies had a beneficial effect upon disease conditions indicated by certain symptoms, and that gentle massage and limited blood letting also might be helpful. Thus the correct practice developed long before the correct theory. As examples of recognized standard remedies derived from Indian doctors, he instanced ipecac and quinine and traced their history from their first introduction to European medical notice until their final acceptance. The paper was discussed by Dr. FEWKES, Dr. MOORE, Dr. E. L. MORGAN, Mr. MOONEY, and others. Dr. FEWKES drew illustrations from the Hopi Indians, Mr. MOONEY from the Cherokee, and Dr. MOORE from the St. Lawrence Island Eskimo.

DANIEL FOLKMAR, *Secretary.*

JOURNAL

OF THE

WASHINGTON ACADEMY OF SCIENCES

Vol. V   MARCH 4, 1915   No. 5

PHYSICS.—*Length standards and measurements.*[1] Louis A. Fischer, Bureau of Standards.

Cognizant of the fact that my election to the presidency of the Philosophical Society a year ago, obligated me to give an address of some sort one year later, I confidently waited for the inspiration that I felt would suggest a fitting subject for the occasion. The expected inspiration did not, however, materialize, and when I was finally compelled a few weeks ago to select a subject, I naturally selected the subject which is announced on your program because that is the one with which I am most familiar.

While many attempts have been made to trace the origin of our earlier standards of length, and volumes have been written upon the subject, I think it may be said that very little is known about the subject, which for that very reason lends itself to speculation. The Book of Genesis mentions the cubit as being in use before the Flood; and in the early history of Egypt we find mention of two different cubits which appear to have been in use. The question as to the values of these standards at one time engaged the attention of no less a personage than Sir Isaac Newton, who in a dissertation on cubits gave it as his opinion that the longer of the Egyptian cubits was equal to 20.7 English inches and that the sacred cubit of the Jews was equal to 24.7 inches.

[1] Presidential address before the Philosophical Society of Washington on January 16, 1915.

Later writers attempt to prove by the measurement made of squared slabs of stone used in the buildings of Babylon that the cubit of 20.7 inches was used in their construction, but a little reflection will serve to show the improbability of our being able to derive the length of any standard to a tenth of an inch from such crude data.

Even when we come to our own yard, which is the earliest standard of length now in use, we are in doubt. King Eadgar is recorded to have decreed with the consent of his Wites or council that "the gird or yard kept at Winchester shall be the standard" but all that can really be said as to the origin of the yard is that it was probably brought over to England by the Saxons.

When we consider the crude means which existed for the construction and preservation of standards and the lack of facilities for constructing accurate copies of them, there is little wonder that their original values should be in doubt. There can be no question but that the unavoidable diversity which must have existed in the standards for the measurement of exchangeable commodities in the early organization of civilized society was a serious embarrassment to commerce. The necessity for standards of reference for purposes of barter was no doubt very soon felt by primitive man; and later on when the commercial idea became developed, the need of such standards was greatly increased. As social and political institutions became more fully developed, the values of the units of these primitive systems not only changed but also the relations of the units, until, at the present time, there is no reason to believe that there survives in any existing system of weights and measures a single value of any unit identical with one in use two thousand years ago. As a matter of fact, it is impossible to trace back with any degree of certainty any of the standards, which are now in use, for even a few hundred years.

In England the first attempts at scientific accuracy in matters of measurement date from the beginning of the seventeenth century when John Greaves, one of the earliest scientific metrologists, called attention to the difference between the Roman and the English foot. He was followed by Edward Bernard, who, in 1685, wrote a treatise on ancient weights and measures; towards the end of the century the measurement of the length of a degree by Picard and Cassini awakened the attention of the French to the importance of rigorously exact standards of length. In considering the development of length standards, we may safely confine our attention to the English yard, the French toise and the meter, since during the last two hundred years they are almost the only standards that have been of any interest to scientific men.

The present English measures of length, as I said before, are supposed to have come down from the Saxons, but the oldest existing standards are the exchequer yards of Henry VII (1490) and Elizabeth (1588). Both are brass end measures, very coarsely made and rudely divided into inches and sixteenths of a yard. Bailey, speaking of one of them in 1836, said that "a common kitchen poker filed at the ends in the rudest manner by the most bungling workman would make as good a standard. It has been broken asunder, and the two pieces have been dove-tailed together, but so badly that the joint is nearly as loose as that of a pair of tongs. The date of this fracture I could not ascertain, it having occurred beyond the memory or knowledge of any of the officers at the Exchequer. And yet, within the last ten years, to the disgrace of this country, copies of this measure have been circulated all over Europe and America with a parchment document accompanying them (charged with a stamp that cost £3, 10s, exclusive of official fees) certifying that they are true copies of the English *Standard*."

In the year 1742, certain members of the Royal Society of London and the Royal Academy of Sciences of Paris proposed that, in order to facilitate a comparison of the scientific operations carried on in the two countries, accurate standards of the measures and weights of both should be prepared and preserved in the archives of each of these societies. This proposition having been approved, two substantial brass rods were made at the instance of the Royal Society, and upon them three English feet were laid off with the greatest care. These two rods,

together with a set of Troy weights, were then sent over to the
Paris Academy, which body, in a like manner, had the measures
of a French half toise laid off upon the rods, and keeping one as
previously agreed upon, returned the other, with a standard
weight of two marcs to the Royal Society. This, I believe, is
the first recorded instance where the standards of two·inde-
pendent nations were compared with one another.

In the year 1758 the House of Commons appointed a committee to inquire into the original standards of weights and
measures of England; under instructions from that committee,
two brass rods were prepared by the celebrated instrument
maker, John Bird, respecting which the committee reports as
follows:

And having these rods, together with that of the Royal Society laid
in the same place, at the Exchequer, all night with the standards of
length kept there, to prevent the variation which the difference in temperature might make upon them, they were all the next morning compared by means of beam compasses and found to agree as near as it
was possible.

The committee recommended that one of these standards
should be made the legal standard of England, but this was not
done. Instead, on December 1 of the same year, Parliament
created another committee on weights and measures, which, in
April, 1759, repeated the recommendation that the standard
made by Bird in 1758 should be legalized, and further recommended that a copy of it should be made and deposited in some
public office, to be used only on special occasions. The copy
was made in 1760, but no legislation followed for sixty-four years.
When in 1824, Parliament at length took final action, Bird's
standard of 1760 was adopted instead of that of 1758. This
bar had been generally accepted as the standard for many years
by English metrologists and copies of it had been widely circulated. One of these, an 82-inch scale made by the celebrated   .
instrument maker, Troughton, of London, was obtained by
Ferdinand Hassler of whom I shall have more to say later, and
the distance between the 27th and 63d inches of that bar, which

was supposed to be equal to Bird's yard, served as the standard for the United States until 1856.

On October 16, 1834 the Imperial standard (Bird's standard of 1760) was destroyed by the burning of the House of Parliament, and very soon thereafter steps were taken to recover its length; but it was not until 1855 that the new Imperial standards were completed and accepted by Parliament.

Turning now to the French standards of length, there is evidence that the earliest of these, the Toise of Paris, goes back to the time of Charlemagne (742–814).   It is stated that:

in 1668 the ancient toise was reformed by shortening it five lines (about one-half inch), but whether this reformation was an arbitrary change, or merely a change to remedy the effects of long use, is not known. The old bar was made of iron with the two ends turned up at right angles so as to form a matrix, and the testing of end measures was effected by fitting them between the bent ends.   Being placed on the outside of some public building, it was exposed to wear from constant use, to rust, and even to intentional injury by malicious persons.

The earliest use of the toise for scientific purposes was by Picard and Cassini in their measurement of a degree of the meridian passing through Paris.   This toise was made in 1668 and would, no doubt, have become the scientific standard of France if it had not disappeared.   The second toise used for scientific purposes was one used in the measurement of the Peruvian Arc. This bar, which is known as the Toise du Perou and made in 1735, was made the legal standard of France by an order of Louis XV, dated May 16, 1766, and is still preserved at the Observatoire at Paris.

As is well known, the meter was intended to be equal to the ten millionth part of the quadrant of the terrestrial meridian; but that the measurements of the arc upon which it was based were referred to the toise is a fact of less common knowledge. The measurement of the meridian was entrusted to Mechain and Delambre by the French Academy of Sciences, who carried it on during seven years from 1791 to 1798.   The unit of length used by them was the Toise du Perou, and from the arc of 9°40′45″ actually measured, they inferred the length of an arc of the meridian extending from the equator to the pole to be 5,130,740 toises, from which it followed that the meter was slightly greater than the one-half toise or 0.513074 toise.

The actual construction of the new standards of length was immediately begun. At first four brass end standard meters were made, each very nearly equal to the computed length of the meter. Then the bar which was found after several comparisons to be nearest to the required length, was selected as the provisional standard. Finally two platinum meters and twelve iron meters were constructed and compared with the provisional meter and with one another by means of a comparing apparatus which was capable of showing differences of 0.001 mm. Also, the rates of expansion of all the meters were carefully determined between 0° and 32°C. The comparisons and adjustments of the several meters were continued until no difference amounting to more than 0.001 mm. could be found at the temperature of melting ice. They were all consequently declared to be exact, and one of the platinum meters, subsequently known as the meter des Archives, from its place of deposit, was reserved as the new prototype measure of length.

The other platinum meter was deposited at the observatory at Paris, while the iron meters were distributed amongst the countries which had coöperated with France in this work.

One of these iron bars was brought to the United States by Ferdinand R. Hassler, who afterwards organized the U. S. Coast Survey, or as it is now known, the Coast and Geodetic Survey.

I am not familiar with what Hassler's purpose was in coming to the United States, but it hardly seems possible that he should have brought with him the standard of length upon which was based all the early work done by the Survey, unless he had in mind the organization of that service, and yet the fact that he presented this standard to the American Philosophical Society of Philadelphia shortly after his arrival contradicts this view. When Hassler was placed in charge of the Coast Survey, he secured the bar from the Philosophical Society and it remained in the possession of the Coast Survey until the organization of the

Bureau of Standards in 1901.   The bar is made of iron, with a cross-section of 9 by 29 mm. and its length is defined by the end surfaces, which are remarkably plane when one considers the age in which the bars were made.   The bar bears the stamp of the committee, which had charge of its construction, namely, a small ellipse, whereof three quadrants are shaded and the fourth one clear, except for the number 10,000,000, which indicates the number of meters in the length of a quadrant of the earth.   It also bears certain prick points which distinguish it from the other meters made at the same time.   In Mr. Hassler's report on the construction of these meters, it is stated, on the authority of Mr. Tralle, a member of the committee, from whom the bar was obtained, that all the meters agreed with the true meter within one-millionth part of the toise which is about one-half the accuracy claimed by the committee.

This bar, which is known as the Committee Meter, served without interruption as the standard to which all scientific work done in the United States was referred from about 1807 to 1893, a period of about 86 years, when it was superseded by the present platinum-iridium line standard in the custody of the Bureau of Standards.   The new platinum-iridium meter not only superseded the Committee Meter, but it also superseded the British yard, inasmuch as in 1893 the yard was defined in terms of the meter, according to the ratio: one yard equals 3600/3937 meter.

In the early development of standards of length, the geodesist has played an important part and the reason for this is at once apparent.   His subject is the study of the size and form of the Earth and, in order to make any progress, work has to be done in different parts of his field.   If arcs are measured in Europe, Asia, or America, the length of the standards in which they are expressed must be known before any deductions can be drawn from them.   In Prussia it is Bessel in 1823, who had a copy of the Toise of Perou constructed by Fortin of Paris, in order that he might express the results of his determinations of the length of his seconds pendulum at Koenigsberg in terms of what was then the generally accepted standard for geodetic work.   The Toise of Bessel was later to take an important part in the history

of geodesy for the reason that it became the point of departure
of a large part of the triangulation made in Europe in the nineteenth century.   Again it was the International Geodetic
Association composed of delegates from the leading countries
of Europe, which, meeting at Berlin in 1867, decided among other
things that the interests of science in general and geodesy in
particular demanded a uniform decimal system of weights and
measures throughout Europe, and recommended the metric
system without essential change.

The action of the Geodetic Association was echoed by the
St. Petersburg Academy of Sciences in 1869, which in a communication to the Paris Academy of Sciences suggested that common
steps be taken towards the establishment of an international
metric system.   Soon after the matter was brought to the attention of Napoleon III, who approved the idea of an international
convention, and the French government extended invitations to
the various governments to send delegates to Paris to discuss
the construction of a new prototype meter as well as a number
of identical standards for distribution to interested nations.

In response to an invitation of the French government, the
following countries sent representatives to a conference which
met in Paris on August 8, 1870:

AUSTRIA, ECUADOR, FRANCE, GREAT BRITAIN, GREECE,
ITALY, NORWAY, PERU, PORTUGAL, RUSSIA, SPAIN, SWITZER-
LAND, TURKEY, UNITED STATES, COLUMBIA.

At this conference, which was of short duration, on account of
the war then raging between France and Germany, the United
States was represented by Joseph Henry and J. E. Hilgard, two
former members of our Society.

A second conference was held two years later, at which 30
countries were represented, the United States again being
among this number.   At this conference it was decided that
new kilograms as well as new meters should be constructed to
conform with the original standards, and a permanent committee was appointed to carry out this decision.   The preparation of the new standards had advanced so far by 1875 that the
permanent committee appointed by the conference of 1872

requested the French government to call a diplomatic conference at Paris to consider whether the means and appliances for the final verification of the new standards should be provided, with a view to permanence, or whether the work should be regarded as a temporary operation.

In compliance with this request a conference was held in the spring of 1875, at which 19 countries were represented, the United States as usual being of this number, and on May 20, 17 of the 19 countries represented signed a convention which provided for the establishment and maintenance of a permanent International Bureau of Weights and Measures to be situated near Paris and to be under the control of an international committee elected by the conference, the committee to consist of 14 members, all belonging to different countries.

In addition to the primary work of verifying the new metric standards the bureau was charged with certain duties, the following being the most important:

(1) The custody and preservation, when completed, of the international prototypes and auxiliary instruments.

(2) The future periodic comparison of the several national standards with the international prototype.

(3) The comparison of metric standards with standards of other countries.

It was agreed that the expenses of the bureau should be defrayed by contributions of the contracting governments, the amount for each country depending upon the population and upon the extent to which the metric system is in use in any particular country. In accordance with the terms of the convention the French government set aside a plat of ground just outside of Paris, and upon this ground, which was declared to be neutral territory, the International Bureau of Weights and Measures was established.

The construction of the meters was entrusted to a special committee, and early in 1887 the committee completed its work and the new meters were turned over to the international bureau for comparison with the standards of the Archives and with one another.

It had been decided as early as 1873 that the new standards should be made of an alloy of 90 per cent platinum and 10 per cent iridium, and that they should be line standards. Altogether 31 meters and 40 kilograms were constructed. By 1889 the entire work was completed and in September of that year a general conference was held at Paris, and by it the work of the international committee was approved.

The meter and kilogram which agreed most closely with the meter and kilogram of the Archives were declared to be the international meter and the international kilogram. These two standards, with certain other meters and kilograms, were deposited in a vault under one of the buildings of the international bureau, where they are only accessible when three independent officials with different keys are present. The other standards were distributed by lot to the various governments contributing to the support of the international bureau. Those falling to the United States were meters Nos. 21 and 27, and the latter of these two standards, which was accepted as the National Prototype, superseded our earlier standards.

Practically all that has been said heretofore has had reference to standards rather than to measurements made with them. In deciding upon what measurements to select for discussion it appeared to me that none were more interesting than the measurement of base lines. Perhaps my interest in them is due to the fact that I was a witness to very radical changes in the method of making them. When I entered the Coast and Geodetic Survey over 30 years ago my first task was to assist in a very minor capacity in determining the lengths of two base measuring bars of a new design which will be found described in appendix No. 7 of the Report of the Survey for 1882.

These bars were supposed to be compensated for temperature, the metals being two steel bars connected to the opposite ends of a zinc bar in such a manner that the expansion of the two different metals would compensate one another. They were end standards and the method of using them in the field was the well known one of supporting the bars on tripods and placing them end to end. The standard with which they were compared consisted of five separate end meters, each one of which had been carefully compared with the committee meter, the 5 meters being placed end to end on a suitable support and kept in contact by the tension of springs. This apparatus was used to measure the Yolo base in California, the probable error of which was computed to be 1 part in 1,750,000.

The next bars used for this work were what are known as 5-meter contact rods and consisted of a single bar of steel enclosed in closely fitting wooden cases afterwards covered with padded canvas. The temperatures of these bars were determined by means of thermometers in contact with the bars some distance from their ends which were read through windows in the wooden case and canvas covering. The method of using these bars in the field was the regular method of mounting them on tripods and placing them end to end.   The accuracy of the measurements of this style of bar in the hands of the party in charge of Mr. O. H. Tittmann in 1891, was about 1 part in 1,700,000.[2]

At the same time that this base was measured with bars 13 and 14, apparatus of an entirely new design by Dr. R. S. Woodward was tried out on the same base. This apparatus, which was described by Professor Woodward before this Society some years ago, consists of a 5-meter bar which, in use, is carried in a steel trough and covered with crushed ice, the trough in turn being supported upon two trucks which travel on a portable track.   Posts are placed in the ground 5 meters apart and upon them micrometer-microscopes are mounted. The operation of measuring consists in bringing the bar under the first two microscopes and then setting the cross wires of the microscope on the lines of the bar. Then without disturbing the reading of the forward microscope the bar is displaced longitudinally until the line on the rear end of the bar is brought under the forward microscope while at the same time an observer at the forward end of the bar points on the line at that end, this process being repeated until the base is completed. A kilometer measured in this way is estimated by Dr. Woodward to have an accuracy of about 1 part in 3,000,000, but the method is extremely expen-

[2] Appendix No. 8, U. S. Coast and Geodetic Survey Report for 189

sive. The other method designed by Professor Woodward consists in measuring the base with 100-meter steel tapes, equipped with special stretching devices and standardized on the kilometer measured in terms of the 5-meter iced bar. Very rapid progress could be made in measuring with these tapes and the preparation of the ground was reduced to a minimum.

The tapes used were ordinary steel tapes and measurements had to be made at night to avoid the direct radiation from the sun; but the results were nevertheless so satisfactory that the method at once attracted attention, the greatest objection to the method was the necessity of carrying the iced bar in the field for the purpose of laying out a hundred meter standard with which the length of the tapes could be frequently checked. While even then the tape method possessed certain obvious advantages the base bar method still had its advocates. After the measurement of the Holton, Md., and St. Albans, W. Va., bases two duplex base bars designed by Wm. Eimbeck were constructed by the Coast and Geodetic Survey and a base line was measured with them near Salt Lake City, Utah, in 1897, with a probable error of 1 part in 800,000.[3] A duplex bar consisted of two concentric brass tubes in the inner of which were mounted a steel and a brass measuring bar. Holes were provided in both the outer and inner tubes for the insertion of thermometers, and the apparatus was so constructed that the inner tube could be rotated 180° and thus equalize the temperature of the brass and steel components if one side of the apparatus should be more exposed to the direct radiation of the sun. Mr. Eimbeck's idea was that if the bars were standardized under a sufficiently wide range of temperature the length of either the brass or steel component could be determined as a function of the difference in the lengths of the bars, and consequently the apparatus itself could serve as a thermometer. Subsequently in measuring a base line the difference in the length of the base as given by the two components would furnish data from which the length of the base could be computed. As a precautionary measure the temperature was observed when standardizing

[3] Appendix 12, Coast and Geodetic Survey Report for 1897.

and using the bars.   It is probable that this form of apparatus would have been extensively used and have superseded all other base bars but for the introduction of tapes.   In 1900 and 1901 a party of the Survey measured nine base lines along the 98th meridian, using these bars and fifty- and one hundred-meter steel tapes.   The tape measures agreed so closely with the bar results that the officials felt justified in discarding bars altogether for base measuring, and in substituting tapes.   Mr. A. L. Baldwin who had charge of this campaign of base measurements described his season's operations in an address before this Society.   An elaborate report on the work is contained in the 1901 report of the Survey.[4]

But the problem of an entirely satisfactory base measuring apparatus was not solved until the discovery of the nickel-steel alloy called "invar" with very small temperature coefficients.   Tapes made of this alloy used during the day and subject to the usual temperature variations, when exposed to the sun's rays, gave better results than the steel tapes used at night, and at a lower cost.   All primary bases of the Coast and Geodetic Survey are now measured with invar tapes, and in each of the other countries conducting geodetic surveys the base apparatus, which is nearly always in the form of tapes or wires, is made of invar.   A paper was read before this Society by Mr. O. B. French in which he gave the results of various tests of invar tapes made at the Bureau of Standards and in the field during actual measurements.

What, may we inquire, were the industries doing for standards while they were in the hands of the geodesists, and before the establishment of the National Standardizing Laboratories? It would be impossible for one to cover the whole field in the time at my disposal nor do I think the development in the different countries was sufficiently different, to require this.

The need of accurate and reproducible standards was nowhere felt sooner in the industries than in the United States,

[4] Other publications of the Survey which give the results of recent measurements of bases are Appendix 5, Report for 1907; Appendix 4, Report for 1910 and Special Publication No. 19.

since this country was the first to specialize in the manufacture of machinery the parts of which are interchangeable. As examples, I need only mention the early manufacturer of watches and sewing machines whose success was absolutely dependent upon the maintenance of one standard throughout their product. That the manufacturer could not go out in the open market and purchase the gauges that were needed is shown by a statement of Prof. W. A. Rogers in 1878, who said:

> I have a large collection of micrometers by different makers, both at home and abroad; I have standards by Froment and Brunner of Paris, and Merz of Munich; I have transfers from every well known precision screw in this country, including such makers as Buff and Berger of Boston; Clark of Cambridge; Brown and Sharpe of Providence; Rutherford of New York; Clement of London; Bianchi, Froment, and Perreaux of Paris. The investigation of these transfers is not yet quite completed, but I feel safe in saying that no two of them agree at a given temperature, and the errors of subdivisions are, in many cases, very large, and in all cases easily measurable. Of the micrometers made abroad, the best I have seen are by Powell and Leland. They are superbly ruled, and the errors of the subdivisions are much less than usual, but in the two plates measured, the unit was found to be nearly $1\frac{1}{2}$ per cent too long.

While anyone comparing the same class of apparatus at the present time would still find differences, they would be of an entirely different order.

Even as late as 1880 the very important relation of the yard to the meter as given by different authorities varied from 39.3697 to 39.3708 or 0.0011 of an inch. This variation was reduced to a little over two ten-thousandths of an inch at this time by Mr. O. H. Tittman,[5] by the apparently simple expedient of referring all the observations to the British Imperial yard and the committee meter at the temperatures at which these bars are standard.

The United States has been fortunate in having two firms who applied themselves to the task of supplying accurate tools and gauges at the time when American industries began to demand them. I refer to the firms of Brown and Sharpe of Providence, R. I., and Pratt and Whitney of Hartford, Conn.,

---

[5] Appendix No. 16, Coast and Geodetic Survey for 1890.

whose work was so precise that they not only made it possible for American manufacturers to lead in many lines, but they also contributed in no small way to the spreading of uniform manufacturers' standards throughout the world. So accurate is their work that it is very often difficult even with our present facilities to determine with certainty the differences in their product. At the present time steel guages may be obtained that are guaranteed by their maker to be correct to within the 1/100,000 part of an inch, and several sets measured at the Bureau of Standards were certainly correct to within twice this error. Roughly speaking the accuracy in their comparison of length standards is about ten times as great as it was forty years ago. At that period, neither the yard nor the meter could be compared with greater accuracy than one part in 400,000, while at the present time it is no difficult feat to compare them to one part in 5,000,000. The establishment of great national standardizing laboratories with their corps of trained metrologists and special apparatus is largely responsible for this. At the present time practically every country has a laboratory whose facilities are available to the manufacturer, while 40 years ago he could only secure reliable standards with great difficulty and was compelled to devise his own means for duplicating them.

I have said nothing whatever about the determination of the distances between the planets nor of the units used by astronomers in reckoning distances of the stars. Neither have I said anything about the measurement of very small distances or objects by interference methods or by means of the ultraviolet microscope. They form, so to speak, other chapters of the subject which I shall leave to some future ex-president of our Society. I have confined my own discussion to measurements that have been within my own experience. I do not claim to have covered even this range with any completeness; but I have merely attempted to give such facts as would interest you, and in doing this it is possible that I have given more prominence to what has been done in the United States and by members of our Society than is justified by the title of this paper.

GEOLOGY.—*Some features of the ore deposits of Gilpin County, Colorado.*[1]   EDSON S. BASTIN and J. M. HILL, U. S. Geological Survey. .

Gilpin County and the adjacent portions of Boulder and Clear Creek counties constitute one of the oldest mining districts in Colorado. Central City, the principal mining camp of the region, was the site of the first discovery of lode gold in Colorado, made by John Gregory in the spring of 1859. The period of greatest prosperity in this region was the seventies and eighties, but it has remained an important producer of gold and silver down to the present time, and will doubtless continue so for many years to come. The region lies in the Front Range of the Rocky Mountains, 30 to 40 miles west of Denver. The principal mining centers are Central City, Idaho Springs, Nederland, Alice, and Dumont.

The geologic groundmass of the region consists of pre-Cambrian rocks, both sedimentary and igneous in origin, and in part dynamo-metamorphosed. The pre-Cambrian sediments are mostly argillaceous and the igneous rocks granitic. Into this groundmass Tertiary igneous rocks have been intruded as stocks and dikes. Monzonite is the predominant rock type among these intrusives, but many other rocks have been derived by magmatic differentiation from the monzonite magmas, titaniferous iron ores and porphyry dikes representing the extreme products. The Tertiary intrusives which are the "porphyries" of the miners are (with few exceptions) older than the ores.

The ore deposits may be classified according to the metals which give them their predominant value as follows:

(1) *Gold-silver ores.* This class is the most widespread and most productive and the only one that will be described in detail in this paper.

(2) *Uranium ores.* These are confined to a small area on Quartz Hill near Central City, and are believed to be a phase of the gold-silver ores.

(3) *Tungsten ores.* These were not studied in detail by the

[1] Published with the permission of the Director of the U. S. Geological Survey.

authors. The tungsten district of Boulder County is the principal producing district in the United States.

(4) *Copper ores.* Ores poor in silver and worked primarily for copper occur in one mine, the Evergreen, near Apex. The copper sulphides here are primary constituents of monzonite dikes.

(5) *Titaniferous iron ores.* These are products of magmatic differentiation within the monzonite stock at Caribou. They have no present or prospective commercial value.

Veins are the predominant structural type among the ore deposits. These commonly follow fracture zones rather than single fractures. The longest is the Mammoth vein near Central City which has been traced continuously for 6000 feet. The greatest depth to which a vein has been followed has been 2250 feet. The vein mineralization has been accomplished in part by fissure-filling and in part by replacement, the latter process being in general predominant. In addition to the veins there are in the region a few stockworks, the best known being the so-called "Patch" near Central City, a pipe-shaped mass of brecciated rock formed at a place where a number of strong vein fractures approach unusually close together. The mineralization of the "Patch" is continuous with that of the veins which enter it and is of the same mineral character. Chamber stopes large enough to accommodate a three-story house have been excavated in the "Patch."

Gold-silver ores. These occur mainly as veins with a few stockworks. The main values are in gold and silver; the subsidiary values in copper, lead, or zinc. They may be classed, on the basis of mineral composition, into the pyritic type, galena-sphalerite type, composite type, and the telluride type. The predominant minerals of the pyritic ores are pyrite and quartz; chalcopyrite and tennantite are usually present. They are essentially gold ores. Their usual composition is as follows: Au 1 to 3 ounces; Ag 4 to 8 ounces; Cu commonly less than $1\frac{1}{2}$ per cent, but in some 15 to 16 per cent. Within a small area near Russell Gulch a number of the pyritic veins carry enargite in place of tennantite, and some of the veins in this region also carry fluorite.

The galena-sphalerite type is less widespread than the pyritic. The predominant minerals are galena, sphalerite and a carbonate (usually calcite or siderite); pyrite, chalcopyrite, and quartz are present in lesser amounts. In the region northeast of Idaho Springs a number of the veins of this type carry rhodochrosite. The metal content is more variable than in the pyritic ores, the usual content being as follows: Au 0.1 to 5.5 ounces; Ag 2 to 25 ounces; Cu commonly less than $1\frac{1}{2}$ per cent, rarely exceeds 10 per cent; Pb 0 to 55 per cent; Zn 0 to 25 per cent. The varieties poor in gold have, in many cases, undergone downward enrichment in silver and constitute the typical silver ores of the region. In contrast to these, certain veins, such as the Klondike in the Topeka mine, are very rich in gold. The Klondike locally carried free primary gold in large plates; an 88-pound piece from this mine yielded upon smelting $5,500.

The composite ores are the result of dual mineralization, first with ore of the pyritic type and then, after brecciation, with ore of the galena-sphalerite type. The reverse relation of pyritic ore filling brecciated galena-sphalerite ore was not observed. Certain veins are pyritic at one end, composite in the middle, and of the galena-sphalerite type at the other end. Composite veins are in general most abundant between areas characterized by pyritic ores and areas in which galena-sphalerite ores predominate.

It is believed that the ores of this region are genetically related to the Tertiary igneous rocks. The copper and iron ores, being products of magmatic differentiation, are obviously so related. In the case of the veins, the agent of ore deposition is believed to have been ascending thermal solutions of an alkaline or neutral character. That the composition of these solutions varied in different parts of the region even at the same period is shown by the presence of enargite in a localized group of the pyritic veins, and the presence of rhodochrosite in a localized group of the galena-sphalerite veins. The composition of the solutions also changed progressively during the mineralizing period, the pyritic ores being deposited in the early part of this period and the galena-sphalerite ores at a later time. From the extent of erosion since the veins were formed it is estimated that they were deposited at depths of from 7000 to 11,000 feet. The temperature of formation can not be accurately determined. A minimum may be placed at 100°C., for this temperature is reached under the "normal" increment of temperature at a depth of about 9000 feet. A maximum may be placed at 575°, for all of the quartz associated with the veins is of the low temperature variety. It is believed that the temperature of formation was probably between 150 and 300°C. The minerals of the veins are those characteristic of moderate depth and pressure.

Downward enrichment. This process has produced important modifications in many of the gold-silver ore deposits. There has been enrichment in one or all of the metals, gold, silver, and copper; enrichment in lead and zinc is insignificant. The water level, as in most mountainous regions, is irregular. In most veins it originally stood 50 to 150 feet below the surface.

Gold enrichment appears to be confined to the oxidized zone and has been accomplished largely by mechanical concentration during weathering. Presumably there was also solution of gold in the oxidized zone, but it is believed that the dissolved gold was promptly reprecipitated within the oxidized zone or immediately below it through the action of primary sulphides or of ferrous sulphate. Careful sampling in a number of the mines failed to show any relation between gold content and depth after the oxidized zone was passed. Gold enrichment in the oxidized zone is most conspicuous in certain so-called silver veins. Where unaltered these carry only about 0.1 of an ounce of gold, but in the oxidized zone this has in some mines been increased to 1.5 or even 3 ounces.

In contrast with gold there has been impoverishment in silver rather than enrichment, in the oxidized zone. The primary silver minerals are silver alloyed with gold, silver-gold tellurides, and possibly argentite. The secondary silver minerals are cerargyrite, pearceite, polybasite, and proustite. The scarcity of silver in the oxidized zone is readily understandable, for it is well known that silver is more readily dissolved than gold and is reprecipitated by fewer of the common sulphides. The silver carried down below the oxidized zone is probably for the most part in balance with the sulphate radicle SO_4. It is redeposited mainly in the form of silver-arsenic sulphides, as replacements of the primary ore minerals or as fillings of small fissures in the primary ore. The chemistry of the process is not well understood, but observations in this region fix certain limiting conditions. It is noteworthy that in the secondary minerals as in the primary minerals arsenic greatly predominates over antimony. Silver enrichment is practically confined to the veins of the galena-sphalerite type and is absent from those of the pyritic type. The most important cause of this restriction is believed to be the presence of carbonates in the galena-sphalerite veins. These carbonates neutralize the descending oxidizing waters and, in the case of siderite, ferrous sulphate, an active silver precipitant, is generated by reaction with sulphuric acid.

Nishihara[2] has compared the neutralizing effect of various minerals on sulphuric acid and also their efficiency in reducing ferric sulphate to ferrous sulphate. Pyrite, quartz, and chalcopyrite, minerals characteristic of the pyritic type of ores, are ineffective in both respects. Galena, sphalerite, and, of course, the carbonates are effective neutralizers and fairly active in reducing ferric to ferrous sulphate. Moreover, galena and sphalerite in contact with solutions carrying sulphuric acid or ferric sulphate generate hydrogen sulphide. The composition of the galena-sphalerite ores favors, therefore: (a) rapid neutralization; (b) reduction of ferric to ferrous sulphate; (c) generation of ferrous sulphate from siderite; (d) generation of hydrogen sulphide. All these actions are believed to favor the precipitation of silver. The pyritic ores, on the other hand, have a mineral composition which favors persistence of acidity and persistence of the iron in the ferric state. Dissolved silver descending through such ore-bodies is likely to remain in solution, to enter the general groundwater circulation, and to be lost so far as the ore deposits in question are concerned.

[2] Nishihara, G. S., The rate of reduction of acidity of descending waters by certain ore and gangue minerals and its bearing upon secondary sulphide enrichment. Econ. Geol., 9: 743–757. 1914.

BOTANY.—*A new genus, Fortunella, comprising four species of kumquat òranges.* WALTER T. SWINGLE, Bureau of Plant Industry.

The kumquat oranges are of very small size, usually less than an inch in diameter. The two species commonly cultivated differ from other oranges in having a relatively thick, fleshy, sweet and 'edible peel and in having only 4 to 7 segments, containing a small amount of acid pulp. Besides the round and oval-fruited species common in culture, there is a third species recently introduced into culture from China, and a fourth occurring wild on the Island of Hongkong.

HISTORY OF THE KUMQUAT ORANGES

The kumquat oranges, though described by early Chinese writers on agriculture, remained practically unknown to Europeans until recent times. The kumquat is mentioned in many early Chinese works and described in some detail by Han Yen Chi in his treatise on the oranges, written in 1178. Later works of both Chinese and Japanese authors treat of it fully, often with fairly good illustrations.

The first vague notice of the kumquat oranges in European literature was published by Ferrarius in 1646 in his Hesperides and was based on reports made to him by the Portuguese Jesuit, Alvaro Semedo, who lived 22 years in China. His successors, Steerbeck, Volckamer, Risso and Poiteau, and other authors of monumental illustrated works on the citrous fruits, add nothing to our knowledge of the kumquat.

Rumphius in 1741 described and figured the round kumquat in his Flora Amboinense. This was the first good account of any kumquat orange to appear in European literature. In 1780 Thunberg assigned the name *Citrus japonica* to the round kumquat, and in 1784 described it more fully in his Flora Japonica, still later (in 1800) publishing a fairly good figure of it in his Icones Plantarum Japonicarum. Loureiro, in 1790, in his Flora Cochinchinensis named the oval kumquat *Citrus margarita*, and also described the round kumquat under the name *Citrus madurensis*.

In spite of Rumphius' and Thunberg's excellent description and illustrations, the kumquat was not known in Europe until 1846, when Robert Fortune, who was collecting in China for the Royal Horticultural Society of London, brought back to England the first kumquat plants. The kumquat did not become generally known on the continent of Europe until much later.

Full descriptions of the round and oval kumquats were published by H. H. Hume,[1] but not until 1912 was a good account of these plants published in Europe, when Dr. L. Trabut[2] described them and distinguished them from the so-called "chinois" or "chinotto" (*C. Aurantium* L., var.), with which they had been confused by Volckamer and many subsequent European writers. In 1914 Dr. Trabut[3] published in Algeria a fuller illustrated account of these plants.

Perhaps because of their relatively late advent into Europe the kumquat oranges have been but little studied by botanists. Apparently no one has questioned the judgment of Thunberg in referring them to the genus Citrus.

THE KUMQUATS NOT PROPERLY REFERRED TO THE GENUS CITRUS

The question of the true relationship of the kumquats to other citrous fruits was forced upon the attention of the writer, in the course of a survey of the plants related to Citrus, by a study of a little known plant of Hongkong, called by botanists *Atalantia Hindsii* (Champ.) Oliv. Good herbarium specimens of this plant, collected by the Wilkes North Pacific Exploring Expedition in 1842 and preserved in the National Herbarium at Washington, D. C., showed the unmistakable facies of a kumquat orange. The thick, rigid leaves, pale and abundantly glandular-dotted below, the angular twigs, small flowers, more or less angular

---

[1] Hume, H. H. The Kumquats. Bull. 65, Fla. Exp. Sta., pp. 550-566, 3 figs. 1903; also, Citrus Fruits and their Culture, 3d ed., p. 18, pp. 53-58, pp. 129-131, *figs. 4, 5, 10, 28.* 1909.

[2] Trabut, L. Chinois et kumquat. Rev. Hort. **84**: 564-567, *figs. 193-195.* 1912.

[3] Trabut, L. Le kumquat. Bull. Agric. de l'Algerie et de la Tunisie II. **20**: 2-11, *4 figs.* 1914.

in the bud, and the small prominently glandular-dotted fruits all resembled most strikingly the round kumquat now commonly cultivated in this country.

Later on other specimens of this plant were studied in the herbaria at Kew Gardens and the British Museum, London, and the Muséum d'Histoire Naturelle, Paris; and through the courtesy of the Superintendent of the Botanical and Forestry Department of Hongkong viable seeds of this species were sent to the writer in 1912. A study of the germination, as well as of the foliar, flower, and fruit characters, showed that in reality this plant is a very primitive kumquat. Thereupon the various forms of the common kumquat in culture in Florida, California, and Algeria were studied, as well as the material in the principal herbaria of Europe and America. As a result of this study the writer is convinced that the kumquats should be placed in a new genus midway between Atalantia and Citrus.

The kumquats are the most primitive living true citrous fruits. The Hongkong kumquat, the only species known in the wild state, is the most primitive of the kumquats and consequently the most primitive of the true citrous fruits. That is to say, it is of all known existing species the most nearly like the ancestral form from which the kumquats and the species of Citrus originated.

On account of their many and important differences from Atalantia and from Citrus it is proposed to create a new genus, Fortunella,[4] to include the kumquats.

---

[4] **Fortunella**, Swingle, gen. nov. *Citro* affinis, foliis unifoliolatis, staminum numero petalorum quadruplo. A *Citro* differt floribus solitariis vel in paniculis paucifloribus dispositis, numero loculorum ovarii numero petalorum aequali vel paulo majore, ovulis collateralibus in loculo geminis, stigmate cavernoso ob glandulas oleiferas profundas, foliis venis non prominentibus subtus pallidioribus punctis glandulosis viridibus numerosissimis instructis, alabastro in sectione plus minusve polygono, fructu mesocarpio crassiore, carnoso et eduli. Rami juniores novelli virentes triangulares, vetustiores teretes. Cotyledones in germinatione ut in *Citro* hypogeae, folia prima ovata subsessilia opposita. Frutices vel arbores humiles.—Species typica, **Fortunella margarita** (*Citrus margarita* Lour.). Colitur Cantone Sinarum.

FORTUNELLA Swingle.   Shrubs or small trees; young branches angular, the older ones rounded; spines borne singly at one side of the bud in the axil of the leaf, or wanting.   Leaves unifoliolate, rather thick, blunt-pointed or even retuse, acute or rounded at the base; veins evident above, scarcely showing beneath; lower surface pale green, densely glandular-dotted; petioles narrowly winged or merely margined, sometimes not articulated with the blade.   Flowers borne singly or in few-flowered clusters in the axils of the leaves, hermaphrodite, 5-merous (rarely 4-, 6-, or 7-merous).   Flower buds small, 8–10 mm. long, more or less angular in cross section.   Petals 5 (rarely 4 or 6), white, acute, 8–12 mm. long.   Stamens 18 or 20, polyadelphous, cohering irregularly in bundles; filaments broad but tapering at the tip.   Pistil seated on a well-marked disc; ovary subglobose, 3–7-(usually 3–6-)celled, with two collateral ovules in each cell; ovary merging gradually or abruptly into the short style, this usually shorter than the ovary, sometimes shorter than the stigma.   Stigma capitate, symmetrical, cavernous within because of the large deep-seated oil-glands (fig. 1).   Fruits small, 18–35 mm. long, 18–25 mm. in diameter, oval or globose; peel rather thick, fleshy and aromatic, sweet-flavored, containing numerous large immersed oil-glands.   Segments 3–6, rarely 7 (figs. 2–5); pulp vesicles small, fusiform or subglobose, stalked, containing an acid juice.   Seeds ovate in outline, smooth; embryo pistache green.   Germination with hypogeous cotyledons; first foliage leaves broadly ovate, subsessile, opposite as in Citrus.

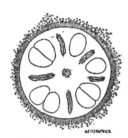

Fig. 1. *F. japonica.* Cross-section of stigma, showing large oil glands between stylar canals, three of them double, two single. Scale 25.

Type species, **Fortunella margarita** (*Citrus margarita* Lour.), cultivated at Canton, China.

The genus Fortunella resembles Citrus in the general appearance of the stems, twigs, spines, leaves, flowers, and fruits and in having the polyadelphous stamens normally four times as numerous as the petals. It differs from Citrus (1) in having an isomerous or hypomerous ovary, normally 3–5-celled (rarely 6 or 7-), not polymerous (8–15- or more celled), (2) in having two collateral ovules in each cell (not 4–12), (3) in having a cavernous stigma containing a few large, deeply immersed, lysigenous oil glands (not asymmetrical and solid or nearly so), (4) in having the under surface of the leaves pale green, nearly veinless and with very numerous, small, deep green glandular dots, (5) in having a sweet and edible, more or less pulpy skin, and (6) in having small more or less angular flower buds.

Fortunella approaches Atalantia and differs strikingly from Citrus in having only two collateral ovules near the top of each cell, whereas Citrus has 4–12 ovules to a cell. Fortunella differs from Atalantia in having twice as many stamens (four times as many, instead of twice as many, as the petals), and in its general agreement with Citrus in twig, leaf, spine, flower, and fruit characters.

The capitate stigmas of all the species of Fortunella contain large oil glands imbedded in their substance, which renders them cavernous.[5] (See fig. 1.)   The stigma of Citrus contains a few scattering oil glands, sometimes one in every space between the radially arranged and expanded stylar canals; but these glands are very near the surface and relatively so small that the stigma lacks entirely the cavernous structure characteristic of Fortunella.[6]   The leaves show very many more oil glands on the underside than in any species of Citrus, often ten times as many.

In superficial fruit characters Fortunella agrees with the Australian desert kumquat (*Eremocitrus glauca*) in many respects. The seeds are very different, however, and the stem, twig, leaf, and flower characters are so strikingly different that it is not possible to regard these genera as closely related.

There are four species of Fortunella known at present. The two commonly cultivated species, the round and oval kumquats of China and Japan, together with the Meiwa kumquat, comprise the subgenus **Eufortunella,** distinguished by several important characters from the Hongkong wild kumquat for which a new subgenus, **Protocitrus,** is described farther on in this paper.

THE SUBGENUS EUFORTUNELLA

The species of Eufortunella may be distinguished by means of the following key:

Fruits globose, 20–25 mm. in diameter, 4 or 5-celled; seeds small, bluntly rounded at tip; leaves pale and veinless below, blunt-pointed . . . . .2. *F. japonica.*

[5] This was noticed as early as 1784 by Thunberg (Fl. Jap. 293), who said, "Stigma . . . . intus multiloculari," in describing the round kumquat; since then no one seems to have observed this fact.

[6] Penzig, O. A. J.   Studi Botanici sugli Agrumi e sulle Piante Affini, pp. 53–75; atlas, *pl. 6.* (Ann. di Agr. no. 116). 1887.

Fruits oval or oblong, 5–7-celled; seeds more or less pointed at tip;
· leaves narrowed toward the tip.
    Fruits oblong, 25–33 mm. long, 20–25 mm. in diameter, usually
      5 or 6-celled; petiole narrowly margined, not winged; pulp
      vesicles fusiform. . . . . .1. *F. margarita.*
    Fruits oval or subglobose, 28–35 mm. long, 22–30 mm. in diameter,
      6 or 7-celled; leaves very thick; petiole plainly but narrowly
      winged at tip; vesicles subglobose or oval. . . . .3. *F. crassifolia.*

THE OVAL KUMQUAT

The oval kumquat has been referred by most botanists to *Citrus
japonica* Thunb., which is based on the round kumquat. These two
kumquats are certainly very closely related, but as they show constant differences of some taxonomic importance in nearly all parts of
the plant, it seems best for the present to consider them as constituting
two distinct species.

1. **Fortunella margarita** (Lour.) Swingle.
    Citrus margarita Lour. Fl. Cochin. **2:** 467.   1790.
    Citrus aurantium olivaeformis Risso, ex Lo˙sel.-Desl. & Michel, Nouv.
      Duham. **7:** 95.   1816.
    Citrus aurantium var. *japonica* Hook. f. Curt. Bot. Mag. III. **30:**
      pl. 6128.   1874.
    Citrus japonica var. fructu elliptico Sieb. & Zucc. Fl. Jap. **1:** 35.
      pl. 15, fig. 3.   1835.
    Citrus Aurantium subspec. *japonica* var. *globifera* subvar. *margarita*
      Engl. in Engl. & Prantl, Pflanzenfam. 3⁴: 199.   1896.
    TYPE LOCALITY: Canton, China (in culture).

The type specimen of *Citrus margarita* seems to have been lost, but
Loureiro's description is very good and can apply only to an oval
kumquat very similar to the one commonly cultivated today in all the
warmer parts of the world.

A lectotype (*Swingle;* C. P. B. No. 7955; February 18, 1915), consisting of a branch of an oval kumquat tree growing in a greenhouse
of the Department of Agriculture at Washington, has been deposited
in the National Herbarium at Washington.

The oval kumquat differs from the round chiefly in the following
respects: (1) The leaves are larger, more acute at the base, less pallid
and more veiny below; (2) the ovary has usually 4 or 5 cells, very
rarely 3 or 6; (3) the fruit is oval, not globose; (4) the style is persistent,
not caducous; (5) the seeds are larger and especially longer, with a
rougher testa. (Fig. 2.) It differs also in being distinctly more

vigorous and attaining a greater height (10–12 ft.); in the somewhat brighter orange color of its fruits; and especially in the harsher, more biting flavor of the peel, which evidently contains an etherial oil more nearly resembling that of the common orange than does that of the round kumquat.

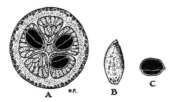 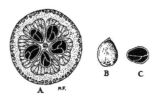

Fig. 2. *F. margarita.* *A*, cross-section of 5-celled fruit; *B*, seed; *C*, seed in cross-section. All natural size.

Fig. 3. *F. japonica.* *A*, cross-section of 5-celled fruit; *B*, seed; *C*, seed in cross-section, showing poly-embryony. All natural size.

THE ROUND KUMQUAT

2. **Fortunella japonica** (Thunb.) Swingle.

八 ? *Chin Kan,* vulgo Fime Tatsbanna. Malus Limonia, fructu pumilo aureo, medullâ dulci. Kaempf. Amoen. Exot., fasc. 5, 801. 1712.

Limonellus madurensis Rumph. Hort. Amboin. **2**: 110. *pl. 31.* 1741.

Citrus japonica Thunb. Nov. Act. Upsal. **3**: 199. 1780.[7]—Fl. Jap. 292. 1784.—Icon. Pl. Jap. **2**: [*pl. 5*]. 1800.

Citrus madurensis Lour. Fl. Cochin. **2**: 467. 1790.

Citrus inermis Roxb. Fl. Ind. **3**: 393. 1832.

Citrus microcarpa Bunge, Mém. Acad. Imp. Sci. St. Petersb. **2**: 84. 1833.

Citrus japonica var. fructu globoso Sieb. & Zucc. Fl. Jap. **1**: 35. *pl. 15, fig. 2.* 1835.

Citrus Aurantium subspec. *japonica* var. *globifera* Engl. in Engl. & Prantl, Pflanzenfam. **3**[4]: 199. 1896.

TYPE LOCALITY: Japan (in culture).—Native in China.

[7] The original publication of this species by citation is on p. 199 as follows:
"Kin Kan, vulgo Fime Tats
    banna, p. 801.   *Citrus Iaponica.*"
Under the heading Characters of New Species it is given as follows, on p. 208:
'Citrus japonica: petiolis alatis, foliis
                                                   acutis; caule fruticoso."

The species is published by the citation on page 199, inasmuch as Kaempfer identifies the plant not only by giving the Chinese characters never applied to any other plant but also the Japanese common name and a short latin phrase sufficient to distinguish it from any other Citrus.

The differences between the round and oval kumquats have already been enumerated under the latter species. (See figs. 2 and 3.)

No type specimen of this species exists, but the specimen figured by Thunberg probably is to be found in the Upsala Museum and may after critical examination prove suitable to be considered a lectotype.

The plants grown in Japan, United States, Europe and North Africa are almost all grafted and consequently show great uniformity.

THE MEIWA, A NEW KUMQUAT, POSSIBLY OF CHINESE ORIGIN

About 1896 or 1897 a new kumquat appeared in Japan, apparently imported from China. It seems to have been listed at first as the Chinese large-fruited kumquat, but soon came to be known as the spotted Meiwa kumquat,[8] and soon simply as the Meiwa kumquat.[9]

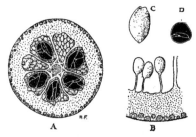

Fig. 4. *F. crassifolia*. *A*, cross-section of 7-celled fruit; *B*, oval pulp vesicles, growing into cell from inner wall of ovary; *C*, seed; *D*, seed in cross-section. *A*, *C*, and *D*, natural size; *B*, scale 1½.

This variety is very prolific, even small shrubs bearing an abundance of fruit. The leaves are decidedly different from those of any other kumquat, being much thicker and folded on the midrib so as to be V-shaped in cross-section. The fruits are slightly oval, often nearly globose, decidedly larger than those of the round kumquat, and distinctly broader at the equator than those of the oval kumquat. They show in cross-section 5, 6 or 7 segments, with one or two seeds in each segment. (Fig. 4.) Upon close study these differences seem to necessitate the recognition of the Meiwa kumquat as a new species.[10]

[8] Hidaka, Kwaji Yen, in Nippon yen gei zatto shi (Bull. de la Soc. d'Horticolture du Japon) **23**: 44. May, 1911.

[9] Some nurserymen give also a variety Nei wa; others consider these synonymous, preferring Meiwa.

[10] **Fortunella crassifolia** Swingle, sp. nov. A speciebus ceteris *Fortunellae* differt foliis crassioribus, canaliculatis, in sectione **V**-formibus, cellulis paliformibus in 4–6 stratis dispositis, fructibus majoribus ovoideis, 5–6–7-locularibus, vesiculis ovoideis vel ellipsoideis nec fusiformibus.—Habitat in China?, cult. in Japonia et America.

3. **Fortunella crassifolia** Swingle, sp. nov.

A dwarf tree or a shrub, often thornless, sometimes with short stout spines 3–10 mm. long; twigs slender, 2.5–5 mm. in diameter, angled when young, dark green, often tufted at the ends of the branches. Leaves lanceolate or ovate-lanceolate, 4–9 (usually 6–8) cm. long, 1.5–4 (usually 2–3.5) cm. broad, tapering toward both ends, often rather sharply, rarely rounded and emarginate at the tip, the base cuneate (especially when not articulated with the tip of the petiole), sometimes more or less broadly rounded; margin entire below the middle and sometimes nearly to the tip, but usually obscurely crenate in the upper third or half; leaves very thick and rigid, folded along the midrib so as to be more or less U- or V-shaped in cross section, on the upper surface glossy dark green, or more or less yellowish green, with veins scarcely visible, paler on the under surface, dotted with very numerous dark green oil-glands and obscurely veined; petioles 7–10 mm. long, at base subcylindric, 1–2 mm. in diameter, the tip narrowly winged, 2.5–4 mm. wide, often not articulated with the blade, the winged petiole then merging imperceptibly into the cuneate base of the leaf. Flowers occurring singly or in pairs in the axil of the leaf, buds at first 5-lobed at the tip, later more or less 5-angled in cross section. Fruits broadly oval or ovate in outline, 25–35 by 25–28 mm., usually 5–7-celled with one or two seeds in a cell, some of the cells usually without perfect seeds. Seeds oval, 9–12 by 5–7 by 4–6 mm., blunt-pointed at both ends; testa larger than the embryo and more or less wrinkled at the projecting ends; embryos often several, green.

Type in the U. S. National Herbarium, no. 694952, consisting of a fruiting branch taken from a cultivated plant in the greenhouse of the U. S. Department of Agriculture, Washington, D. C., *Swingle* (C. P. B. No. 7496–C), February 17, 1915. Merotype,—flowering branch, *M. Kellerman*, February 23, 1915. Additional specimens from nurseries at Port Arthur and Alvin, Texas, are in the U. S. National Herbarium.

This species, although differing in many important characters from the two commonly cultivated species of kumquats, may nevertheless on more thorough study prove to be of hybrid origin or else a mutation. The precocious and abundant fruiting and the presence of many good seeds in the fruits would seem, however, to indicate that it can scarcely be a hybrid between two very distinct species. Besides, it is not easy to see what species could have been hybridized to produce such a form.

In many ways the Meiwa kumquat shows a marked intensification of the characteristics of the true kumquats. Such intensification may result from hybridization or from mutation but may also be the result of long continued, slow, evolutionary change. In any case, the present form doubtless merits a distinctive name, such as is given commonly to hybrids between well marked species and to stable forms of mutative origin.

The very thick and rigid leaves of the Meiwa kumquat show 4 or 5 or even more layers of palisade tissue on the upper side of the leaf. The other two species show only 2 or 3 layers of palisade.

THE SUBGENUS PROTOCITRUS

The Hongkong kumquat, *Fortunella Hindsii*, differs from the round kumquat (*F. japonica*), the oval kumquat (*F. margarita*), and the Meiwa kumquat (*F. crassifolia*) in a number of morphological characters, some of them of decided taxonomic significance in this group. It may be regarded as constituting a new subgenus:

PROTOCITRUS Swingle.[11] Differs from Eufortunella (1) in having the ovary hypomerous (3 or 4-celled, not 5-celled); (2) in the ovary wall

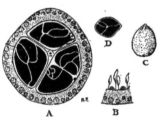

of the mature fruits having on the inside between the stalks of the pulp vesicles a number of minute, wart-like, pale yellow, cellular masses (fig. 5); (3) in having the dissepiments of the fruit dry, and the peel thin and not very fleshy; (4) in having shorter, broader, more brachytic flowers; (5) in having leaves with the veins more prominent on both faces, and less pallid below.

Fig. 5. *F. Hindsii. A*, cross-section of 3-celled fruit, one cell having 2 seeds, another showing a few pulp vesicles; *B*, fusiform Vesicles and verruciform tissue growing into cell from inner wall of ovary; *C*, seed; *D*, seed in cross-section, showing polyembryony. *A*, *B*, scale 2; *C*, *D*, natural size.

The two most important characters distinguishing the subgenus Protocitrus from Eufortunella are the few-celled ovary and the dimorphic *emergencen* from the ovary wall of the fruit, viz.: ordinary pulp vesicles and verruciform tufts of loosely aggregated more or less colored cells. (Fig. 5, B.)

---

[11] Protocitrus Swingle, subgen. nov. A *Eufortunella* differt ovariis hypomeri-bus (3- vel 4- nec 5-locularibus) parietibus dorsalibus locularum fructus maturi verrucosis, verrucis e cellulis luteolis compositis, dissepimentis membranaceis non succosis, exocarpio tenuiori minus succoso, floribus brevioribus latioribus, foliis subtus viridioribus, venis conspicuioribus.

The Hongkong kumquat, which, as already indicated, is the sole species of the subgenus Protocitrus, may be described as follows:

Fortunella Hindsii (Champ.) Swingle.

Sclerostylis Hindsii Champ. Hook. Journ. Bot. III. **3**: 327. 1851.
Atalantia Hindsii Oliver ex Benth. Fl. Hongkong. 51. 1861.—
    Journ. Linn. Soc. **5**, Suppl. 2: 26. 1861.

A spiny shrub or small tree; twigs slender, angled when young; leaves oval-elliptical, tapering sharply at both ends, dark green above and faintly venose, paler and venose below; petioles winged, often merging into the lamina of the leaf without a separative joint. Flowers short, broad, not opening very widely; pistil very short; style shorter than the ovary; stigma large, cavernous; ovary 3 or 4-celled; ovules 2 in a cell. Fruits small, 1.5–2 cm. in diameter, subglobose, bright orange red when ripe, the color of a tangerine orange; pulp vesicles very few, small, fusiform; seeds thick, oval or ovate in outline, plump, 9–11 by 7–8 by 5–6 mm., pistache green in section.

TYPE: Hongkong, *R. B. Hinds*, without number, 1841; a much branched twig with spines, leaves, fruit pedicels, and one young fruit.[12] (Mounted on the same sheet are two twigs collected by Wright.) Herb. Kew.

The Hongkong wild kumquat grows commonly on the dry hills about Hongkong and on the mainland of China opposite.

Much other material from Hongkong and some from Kaulung, on the mainland opposite Hongkong, has been examined by the writer in the collections at Kew, British Museum, Muséum d'Histoire Naturelle, Gray Herbarium, and U. S. National Herbarium. Living plants grown in the greenhouses of the Department of Agriculture from seeds from Hongkong have permitted a comparison of this plant at all stages of growth with the other species of Fortunella.

UTILIZATION OF THE KUMQUATS IN BREEDING NEW TYPES
OF CITROUS FRUITS

In connection with the attempt to breed hardy citrous fruits the attention of the writer was directed some years ago to the kumquat oranges, which are particularly remarkable for their very small size

---

[12] A label in Bentham's (?) writing, reading "*Atalantia monophylla* DC. Hong Kong, Hinds, 1841," is pasted across the base of the twig, which shows it to be without doubt the specimen cited by Bentham (Lond. Journ. Bot. **1**: 480–481. 1842). Some of the petioles of this twig exhibit the curious imperfections in the articulation with the blade characteristic of this species; so it is possible to identify this specimen beyond question.

and for having a relatively thick, sweet, and edible peel. These diminutive fruits, borne on correspondingly dwarfed trees or shrubs, have been found to possess in very high degree winter dormancy, which is so essential to hardiness in citrous fruits grown in the variable climate of Florida and the Gulf States. Recently the kumquat oranges have also been found to be remarkably resistant to citrus canker, the most dreaded of all the diseases affecting citrous trees in the United States. Indeed, many investigators have not succeeded in finding any canker infection on kumquat oranges, and believe them to be immune. Furthermore, hybrids between the two commonly cultivated species of kumquat, the oval and the round-fruited, on the one hand, and the common lime on the other, have proven not only to be very resistant to cold, but to possess a considerable degree of resistance to citrous canker.

ABSTRACTS

Authors of scientific papers are requested to see that abstracts, preferably prepared and signed by themselves, are forwarded promptly to the editors. Each of the scientific bureaus in Washington has a representative authorized to forward such material to this journal and abstracts of official publications should be transmitted through the representative of the bureau in which they originate. The abstracts should conform in length and general style to those appearing in this issue.

METEOROLOGY.—*Frost protection.* W. J. HUMPHREYS. Monthly Weather Review, **42**: 562–569. 1914.

This paper deals entirely with the scientific or theoretical side of orchard heating and other methods of frost protection. It is explained that when frost is most likely to occur, that is, during still clear nights, temperature inversions (increase of temperature with increase of elevation) commonly obtain almost everywhere except on hills and mountains at some elevation above the intervening valleys. This temperature inversion keeps any air that may be artificially warmed near the surface where it may be effective in preventing frost. But for this inversion that acts like a ceiling in restricting vertical convection, the warmed air would rise quite above the tree tops and thus do but little good.

Computations, based on the rate of loss of heat by radiation during clear nights, show that the amount of petroleum necessary to protect a large orchard from frost is, roughly, one liter per tree per hour. Air drainage (so important to consider in locating an orchard), ground covering, screens, sprays, smudges, dry heating and irrigation are all considered. W. J. H.

CHEMISTRY.—*The reaction of cows' milk modified for infant feeding.* WILLIAM MANSFIELD CLARK. Journal of Medical Research, **31**: 431. 1915.

By the use of the hydrogen electrode the hydrogen ion concentrations of human and cows' milk have been compared with those of various formulae of cows' milk modified for infant feeding. The addition of alkalies to modified milk for the purpose of neutralizing the so-called "high acidity of cows' milk" is shown to be a practice not only based upon wrong principles, but a practice which in some instances produces a reaction far too low for even favorable pancreatic digestion. The addition of alkalies to modified milk for the purpose of preventing firm clots of casein in the stomach is shown to be a procedure which may not only be unnecessary to accomplish this purpose, but one which may involve inhibition of gastric proteolysis and lipolysis. Finally, the addition of alkalies to modified milk is criticized because of its tendency to displace from the intestine a normal fermentative bacterial flora and to favor bacterial proteolysis or "putrefaction."

W. M. C.

PHYSICAL CHEMISTRY.—*The ternary system: diopside-forsterite-silica.* N. L. BOWEN. Am. Jour. Sci. (4), **38**: 207–264. 1914.

The results obtained in the investigation of the three binary systems involved are first presented. The system diopside-silica shows the simple eutectic relation, as does also the system diopside-forsterite. The system forsterite-silica shows one intermediate compound, $MgSiO_3$ (clino-enstatite), unstable at its melting-point.

In the ternary system it is found that clino-enstatite and diopside form a complete series of solid solutions (monoclinic pyroxenes) and therefore have a common field. As a further consequence of this unbroken series of solid solutions there is no ternary eutectic, the lowest point of formation of liquid in the system being the binary eutectic diopside-silica.

A brief theoretical discussion of solid solution in ternary systems is given. The course of crystallization in typical mixtures of the present ternary system is described, and the value of certain lines termed three-phase-boundaries is pointed out, especially their usefulness in determining the composition of mix-crystals separating at any temperature. In considering crystallization it is shown that crystallization may proceed according to two different methods: first, that in which the liquid is, at any temperature, in equilibrium with all the crystals and all parts of the crystals occurring in it, and second, that in which the liquid is in equilibrium at any temperature only with the crystals separating at that temperature. In a general way, crystallization of the second type is favored by quick cooling.

The importance of distinguishing between the two types of crystallization is great in the present system. It is shown that the difference between the conclusions arrived at in the present work and those arrived at in an earlier investigation of the pyroxene series carried out at this Laboratory is due largely to the fact that in the earlier work crystallization of the second type occurred in many of the mixtures, whereas, if equilibrium is to be studied, crystallization of the first type must be obtained.

In the optical part of the paper the optical properties of the various crystalline phases are given. The properties of the series of monoclinic pyroxenes extending from diopside to enstatite vary continuously with composition. The artificial pyroxenes are compared with the enstatite-augites of Wahl.

In considering the bearing of the results on petrologic problems attention is called to the resorption of the olivine forsterite in the artificial mixtures and its probable relation to resorption of olivines in natural rocks. The consequences of the possible settling of crystals in a fluid magma (crystallization-differentiation) are discussed in the light of the facts known concerning the artificial mixtures.   N. L. B.

MINERALOGY.—*Hewettite, metahewettite, and pascoite; hydrous calcium vanadates.* W. F. HILLEBRAND, H. E. MERWIN, and FRED. E. WRIGHT. Proc. Am. Phil. Soc., **53**: 31–54. 1914.

Two apparently different calcium vanadates are described, which resemble each other very closely and have the same composition ($CaO \cdot 3V_2O_5 \cdot 9H_2O$) when holding their maximum water-content at room temperatures. One of them, hewettite, occurs at Minasragra, Peru, and has been noticed on a single specimen from Paradox Valley, Colorado. The other, metahewettite, occurs at numerous localities in western Colorado and eastern Utah. Both minerals are sparingly soluble in water.

A third calcium vanadate, pascoite ($2CaO \cdot 3V_2O_5 \cdot 11?H_2O$,) is also described. This occurs with hewettite at Minasragra. It is very soluble in water.

The first and second minerals are regarded as dehydrated acid hexavanadates ($CaH_2V_6O_{17} \cdot 8H_2O$), the third as a normal hexavanadate ($Ca_2V_6O_{17} \cdot 11?H_2O$).

The reasons for specific separation of hewettite and metahewettite are set forth in detail. The two minerals are so sensitive to changes in atmospheric humidity that their water-content varies within wide limits at different times of the year. The removal of all or nearly all the water does not result in breaking down of the crystal structure, and until this has occurred the water is wholly or in great part taken up again when opportunity is offered.

The importance is emphasized of bringing all minerals that behave in this way to a definite maximum water-content before analyzing them and of following carefully the course of dehydration under prescribed conditions. Detailed directions are given for such tests and for avoiding several sources of error.

Attention is also called to two fairly constant associates of metahewettite. One of these (also a constituent of carnotite ores) is a gray hydrous silicate of aluminum, trivalent vanadium, and potassium. The other is elemental selenium, the existence of which as a mineral species seems now for the first time established.   W. F. H.

PETROLOGY.—*An occurrence of pyroxenite and hornblendite in Bahia, Brazil.* HENRY S. WASHINGTON. Am. Jour. Sci. (4), **38:** 79–90. 1914.

The igneous mass occurs near Maracas, in the State of Bahia, intruded into gneisses. The central part is a hornblendite and the outer a pyroxenite, both being exceptionally fresh. Complete analyses of the two are given and their relations to other occurrences are discussed. Both rocks are notable for the large amount of manganese which they contain, which is correlated with the abundance of manganese ores in this part of the State of Bahia. There is also a notable amount of copper.
                                                          H. S. W.

PETROLOGY.—*The mode of formation of certain gneisses in the Highlands of New Jersey.* CLARENCE N. FENNER. J. Geology, **22:** 594–612; 694–702. 1914.

The paper deals with certain geological phenomena which have been observed in an area of ancient crystalline rocks in northern New Jersey, and discusses the manner in which the structures in question have originated. The manner of action of the processes is considered, not only from the geological side, but also from physical and chemical standpoints. A description is first given of the structural relations of the gneisses as observed in the field, and evidence is presented leading to the belief that at this locality the foliation of the gneisses can not well be attributed to the squeezing-out of a partly differentiated magma or to the shearing and recrystallization of a solidified rock, but that its origin must be looked for in a process involving the injection of a thinly fluid granitic magma between the layers of an original rock of a laminated character. Evidence is found which indicates that the process of injection was carried out in a most quiet and gradual manner, and possessed many of the characteristics of a substitution of the original material by the magmatic solution rather than the features of a violent intrusion. The observed relations are very similar to those which certain French geologists have described under the name of *lit-par-lit* injection, and the mode of operation is believed to have been essentially the same.

Certain features which were observed in the gneisses imply properties of the magma which at first sight do not appear mutually consistent. Thus the degree of viscosity implied by the presence of thinly tabular sheets of inclusions within the granite, standing nearly upright and unsupported except by the magma on either side, does not harmonize with the facility with which magmatic material has been transfused into the original rock. In trying to reconcile these features inquiry has been directed toward a consideration of certain of the physical and chemical properties of magmatic solutions. The question of the critical temperatures of volatile substances is discussed in its bearing upon their condition within the magma. Further, the question of the possibility of a viscous magma penetrating the pores of the wall-rock is considered and the problem of a possible differentiation of a magma when injected between the layers of a rock in a multitude of adjacent streams is taken up. Certain inferences are drawn regarding the operation of such processes and the conclusion is reached that under such conditions of injection as prevailed at this locality, the advance of the main body of magma would be preceded by that of a more dilute portion, which would be able to impregnate the wall-rock with facility and initiate processes of transformation and solution which the more concentrated body following would carry farther toward completion. C. N. F.

GEOLOGY.—*The Shinumo Quadrangle, Grand Canyon District, Arizona.* L. F. NOBLE. U. S. Geological Survey Bulletin No. 549. Pp. 100. 1914.

The Shinumo quadrangle lies in the western part of Kaibab division of Grand Canyon, Arizona. Geological formations that outcrop are exposed in cross-section in walls of the mile deep canyon. They are, in age: Archean, Algonkian, Cambrian, Devonian, and Carboniferous. The Archean and Algonkian, and the Algonkian and Cambrian are separated by profound angular unconformities of erosion. The Cambrian and Carboniferous are separated by an unconformity of erosion without unconformity of dip. Devonian strata' are present only here and there; they were deposited in shallow depressions in the eroded surface between the Cambrian and Carboniferous.

The Archean includes the Vishnu schist, made up of gneisses, schists, quartzites, and plutonic intrusive rocks. In the region about the mouth of Shinumo Creek it is a metamorphic complex of quartz, mica, and hornblende schists which are invaded by a mass of quartz diorite and injected by veins of pegmatite and aplite. Farther down the river, gneisses are the prevailing rocks. The schists are believed to be of sedimentary origin, the gneisses, igneous.

About 5000 feet of strata of the Unkar group, Algonkian, Grand Canyon series, are present. They lie in a wedge-shaped mass that is inset in the Vishnu schist by block-faulting along the line of the West Kaibab fault, and are intruded by a sill of diabase 1000 feet thick. Five formations are differentiated: Hotauta conglomerate, overlain by Bass limestone, Hakatai shale, Shinumo quartzite, and Dox sand-stone.

The Cambrian is divided into three formations: Tapeats sandstone, overlain by Bright Angel shale and Muav limestone. The Carboniferous comprises Redwall limestone, Supai formation, Coconino sandstone, and Kaibab limestone. These beds have a gentle southwesterly dip of 100 to 200 feet to the mile. Plateau surfaces on both sides of the canyon are developed on same hard formation, the Kaibab limestone. Course of canyon is at right angles to dip of strata. Therefore the land north of canyon slopes toward the brink, and the land south slopes away; therefore the attitude of the canyon is like that of a trench dug along a hillside. Drainage of plateaus on both sides of the canyon runs southwesterly with the initial slope of the land; on south side of canyon the heads of many plateau valleys are truncated by the southern wall of the canyon.

The factors chiefly responsible in determining topographic form in the canyon country are: the horizontal attitude of the beds; horizontal continuity and vertical variation (alternation of hard and soft); faults traversing them; great height of land above the sea; and aridity of the climate. There is, however, another factor whose importance has not been realized: this is the influence of minor joints and fractures not associated with notable displacement. The courses of most of the smaller side-gorges have been guided by these fractures and most of the buttes and temples have been blocked out by them.

The Esplanade, a wide terrace which runs through the Kanab division of the canyon, is not, as has been thought, a local base-level due to a pause in the uplift of the region, but is a structural bench developed, like the Tonto Platform of the Kaibab division, on one of the hard sets of beds in the Paleozoic.

Examples of pre-Cambrian faults of which the West Kaibab fault is the most notable, additional to those already known along which movement has recurred in post-Paleozoic time, are described and the wide prevalance of this phenomenon in the Grand Canyon region is shown.   L. F. N.

PROCEEDINGS OF THE ACADEMY AND AFFILIATED SOCIETIES

THE WASHINGTON ACADEMY OF SCIENCES

The 94th meeting of the Washington Academy of Sciences was held in the lecture room of the Cosmos Club, the evening of December 3, 1914, with President DAVID WHITE in the chair, and about 40 persons present.

Mr. HENRY S. GRAVES, Chief of the U. S. Forest Service, gave an interesting and instructive talk on *The place of forestry among natural sciences*. (This JOURNAL, **5**: 41. 1915.)

The 95th meeting of the Washington Academy of Sciences, a joint meeting with the Botanical Society of Washington, was held in the lecture room of the Cosmos Club, the evening of January 5, 1915. The hall was crowded, and many were turned away.

Prof. J. C. BOSE of India gave an illustrated lecture on *The response of plants*. The lecturer dealt chiefly with his own extensive investigations which have shown a remarkable parallelism between the response of animals and the response of plants to a wide variety of stimuli. The apparatus used and methods of work were explained, the conclusions enumerated, and in one or two cases an actual plant response was shown to the audience.

The 96th meeting of the Washington Academy of Sciences, the 16th annual meeting, was held in the lecture room of the Cosmos Club, the evening of January 14, 1915, with President DAVID WHITE in the chair and about 100 persons present. The following were elected officers for the ensuing year: *President*, R. S. WOODWARD; *Corresponding Secretary*, GEORGE K. BURGESS; *Recording Secretary*, W. J. HUMPHREYS; *Treasurer*, E. W. PARKER; *Vice-Presidents*, representing the: Anthropological Society, F. W. HODGE; Archaeological Society, MITCHELL CARROLL; Biological Society, PAUL BARTSCH; Botanical Society, W. E. SAFFORD; Chemical Society, CARL L. ALSBERG; Electrical Engineers Society, E. B. ROSA; Engineers Society, WILLIAM BOWIE; Entomological Society, W. D. HUNTER; Foresters Society, G. B. SUDWORTH; Geographical Society, O. H. TITTMANN; Geological Society, ARTHUR KEITH; Historical Society, J. D. MORGAN; Medical Society, FRANK LEECH; Philosophical Society, W. S. EICHELBERGER; *Non-Resident Vice-Presidents*, C. C. NUTTING and E. C. FRANKLIN; *Managers, Class of 1918*, L STEJNEGER and W. H. HOLMES.

After the list of new officers was read the newly elected president, Mr. R. S. WOODWARD took the chair, and the retiring president, Mr. DAVID WHITE gave his address on *Some relations in origin between coal and petroleum.* No review of this excellent paper need be given here as it will soon appear in the JOURNAL.

After this address the Recording Secretary read the minutes of the previous annual meeting and of the various other meetings, all of which was approved. The report of the Corresponding Secretary showed the total membership of the Academy to be 414, a net gain of 46 for the year. It also reminded the Academy that while it had gained largely in numbers it had also suffered severely in the loss by death during the past year, of the following members: Resident, HENRY GANNETT, THEODORE GILL, BERNARD R. GREEN, A. F. A. KING, and F. W. TRUE; non-resident, W. L. DUDLEY, FREDERICK FORCHHEIMER, JOHN MUIR, D. E. SALMON, and NEWTON H. WINCHELL.

The Treasurer's report showed: Total receipts $4,937.69, disbursements $3,340.38, cash on hand $1,597.31, investments $12,590. The report of the Auditing Committee confirming that of the Treasurer, was also received.

The Board of Editors gave an interesting report in which they showed by a number of diagrams the healthy and parallel growth of the Academy and its JOURNAL.

The 97th meeting of the Washington Academy of Sciences, a joint meeting with the Biological Society of Washington, was held the evening of January 19, 1915, in the Auditorium of the National Museum. Vice-President PAUL BARTSCH, President of the Biological Society was in the chair and an audience of about 100 present.

Dr. JOHAN HJORT, director of the fisheries of Norway, gave a talk on *Migrations and fluctuations of the marine animals of western Europe.* The distances and prevailing directions of migration of fish were determined by setting free large numbers that had been properly tagged and noting the times and places of their subsequent capture. This also gave an idea of the ratio, not far from 1 to 10, of the catch of any given year to the total number of fish available.

It was also explained that fish scales have rings indicative of annual growth from which one can safely infer not only the age of any given specimen but also, by the distance between the rings, the amount of growth during any particular year of its life. By these means it was learned, among other things, that fish, whatever their individual ages, grow much faster during certain years than during others. Also that there are great inequalities in the relative numbers of fish of different ages, in some cases the number of one age exceeding the number a year or even two years younger.

In addition to its scientific interest this investigation has already greatly increased and rendered more profitable the enormous fishing industry of Norway and, presumably, that also of adjacent countries.

W. J. HUMPHREYS, *Recording Secretary.*

THE GEOLOGICAL SOCIETY OF WASHINGTON

The 290th meeting was held in the lecture room of the Cosmos Club, on January 27, 1915.

R. S. BASSLER: *Unconformities in limestone.* At a previous meeting remarks had been made to the effect that the Silurian limestones of a certain area passed without break into the Devonian. This suggested to the speaker the idea of citing examples where this was apparently so, but where in reality an unconformity of great extent was present.. A fragment of limestone, only a few inches thick, from Louisville, Kentucky, crowded with Middle Devonian fossils on one side and Middle Silurian fossils on the other, was exhibited to show that such unconformities exist in what is now the same layer. Hand specimens of Ordovician limestone preserving the unconformity between the lower Chazy and Black River formations and taken from the same bed were also exhibited. In fresh fractures the unconformity can hardly be detected, but upon weathered surfaces it is shown as a distinct wavy line.

Discussion: G. F. LOUGHLIN remarked that Bassler's examples were duplicated in certain occurrences in the Tintic District. T. WAYLAND VAUGHAN spoke of the contact of Cretaceous and Eocene limestones along the Frio River in Texas. The two formations were so similar that it was only by fossils that the hiatus could be detected, but after the necessity for it had been discovered a thin band of pebbles was found at the contact.

E. S. BASTIN and J. M. HILL: *Ore deposits of Gilpin County, Colorado.* (Published in full on pp. 160–164 of this issue of the JOURNAL.)

Discussion: F. L. RANSOME inquired regarding the genetic connection between the different classes of ore-bodies, and if there were any indication of the galena giving out with depth. BASTIN replied that the genetic connection was not entirely clear in all cases, but the uranium ores are probably a local phase of the gold-silver ores. The tungsten ores seem to be so localized as to indicate that an unusual phase of magmatic differentiation had been accompanied by an unusual phase of ore-deposition. With regard to the second query—the deposition of galena-sphalerite ores followed a second period of fracturing and occupied the spaces thus opened, and also partly replaced primary ores. The natural consequence is that at ends of veins and bottoms of veins the earlier minerals predominate. It is not certain, however, that some galena-sphalerite veins may not persist. F. L. HESS said that his experience in a portion of the district indicated that tungsten ores, where found, did not completely take the place of other ores. BASTIN agreed. J. B. UMPLEBY inquired regarding the sequence in time and space of the pyritic veins and the galena-sphalerite veins. BASTIN replied that this brought up an interesting but complex problem. He referred to J.

E. Spurr's conclusion that pyritic veins occurred nearer the igneous source and the galena-sphalerite type farther away. The ores of the Erzgebirge show somewhat similar relations. In the Colorado occurrence which he had described there were indications of a halt between the periods of deposition of the two types. It was quite a problem to account for this pulsation of deposition. G. F. LOUGHLIN spoke of analogous occurrences in the Tintic District.

STEPHEN R. CAPPS, JR. *An estimate of the age of the last great glaciation in Alaska.* (This JOURNAL, **5**: 108–115. 1915.)

Discussion: DAVID WHITE spoke of similar root-development observed in connection with coal beds. He wondered if the top of the till showed evidence of a milder climate (such as oxidation), also if there had been a hiatus before the deposition of peat began. He also raised the question of possible shrinkage in the bottom layers of peat. If the peat had been constantly frozen at all periods probably not much shrinkage had taken place. CAPPS replied that the actual contact of peat and till was not well exposed at any place, but in the till itself there was no evidence of oxidation. As to the frozen condition—probably decay had been checked by this. A. H. BROOKS expressed the opinion that the accumulation of frozen material over the till in this place is comparable to that in other parts of the Yukon Basin and that the frozen state had persisted since the glacial period. D. W. WHITE spoke on counting the growth-rings of the trees. He thought that in that climate this should give remarkable precision, as there was little chance of a second ring forming in a year. W. C. ALDEN thought that there was little likelihood of evidences of oxidation showing on top of the till in that region, considering the small amount shown at top of Wisconsin till in milder latitudes. T. WAYLAND VAUGHAN spoke of an interesting calculation he had made in connection with the theory that the submergence of the platforms on which coral reefs have grown has been due to the melting of the glacial ice-cap. He had calculated the time necessary for the Great Barrier Reef to grow to its present thickness, and had made it 11,000 years, showing close agreement with CAPP's calculations.

E. DE K. LEFFINGWELL: *Ground ice wedges. The dominant form of ground ice on the north shore of Alaska.* The permanently frozen ground contracts in the cold Arctic winter and cracks are formed which divide the surface of the ground into polygonal blocks. In the spring these frost cracks become filled with surface water which immediately freezes. In the expansion of the frozen ground with rise of temperature in summer the vein of ice, being more rigid than the country formation, forces readjustment to take place in the latter. The result is to bulge up the enclosed block either bodily, or else locally along the sides of the ice. During the next winter's cold wave a new crack forms at the same locus, so that a continually growing wedge of ground ice is formed. Thus the tundra becomes underlain by a network of ice wedges, which enclose bodies of the original formation. The ice wedges are constantly associated with the frost crack locus.

The above theory was independently formed during the summer of 1914, after nine summers in the field. In reviewing the literature it was found that von Bunge in 1884 had proposed a similar theory for the ground ice in Siberia. Frost cracks which divide the tundra into polygonal blocks are mentioned by several other Siberian investigators. Wedge-shaped and cylindrical earth inclusions are described and shown in photographs and drawings of the same region. Parallel ridges enclosing frost cracks and surrounding pods are also mentioned.

Polygonal surface markings underlain by ice are described in Spitzbergen, photographs of which might well serve for northern Alaska. At Eschscholtz Bay in Alaska, pot-like earth-inclusions in the ice are mentioned, as well as vertical dikes of ice and upturned muck beds. Excellent photographs taken recently upon the Noatak River, Alaska, show wedges of ice 8 to 10 feet wide, separated by from 50 to 100 feet of silt or muck.

Discussion: H. M. EAKIN said that in places in Alaska there are actual strata of buried ice of considerable horizontal extent, although the phenomena described by LEFFINGWELL often gave a false impression as to the prevalence of such strata. He thought the burial of snow-accumulations under dunes would produce such buried lenses of ice. A. H. BROOKS thought that there might be different methods by which buried wedges and strata of ice might be formed in different regions in Alaska under different climatic conditions. F. L. HESS spoke of a 30-foot mine shaft which had been sunk on one of these ice-wedges, and described similar wedges, now empty of ice but filled with peat.

C. N. FENNER, Secretary.

THE BOTANICAL SOCIETY OF WASHINGTON

The 100th regular meeting of the Botanical Society of Washington was held in the Crystal Dining Room of the New Ebbitt Hotel, at 6 p.m., December 1, 1914. One hundred and four members and eight guests were present. A dinner was served at which were featured several dishes made from plants which have been introduced to this country by the U. S. Department of Agriculture. Drs. W. RALPH JONES, J. S. COOLEY, H. V. HARLAN and Messrs. G. F. GRAVATT, G. H. GODFREY, L. M. HUTCHINS, PAUL POPENOE and R. G. PIERCE were unanimously elected to membership. The remainder of the evening was given to a special program dealing with the early history and growth of the Society with the following papers:

Mr. M. B. WAITE, *The Botanical Seminar and the early development of plant pathology in Washington.* The Botanical Seminar was founded in 1893. The purpose of the members was to make the meetings as informal as possible. The monthly meetings were held at the rooms of the various members. There were no officers other than the speaker of the evening who usually was the person entertaining the Seminar. There was no constitution or by-laws. Refreshments were served and very frank discussion and criticisms was encouraged. In 1901 the number of candidates for membership became so great that this method of holding meetings became impossible and the Botanical Seminar was merged with the Washington Botanical Club to form the present Botanical Society of Washington. The speaker sketched briefly the development of the work in plant pathology in Washington from the early beginning, when the pathological work was a very small branch of the botanist's duties, up to the present large body of investigators.

Mr. DAVID FAIRCHILD, *Letters from the boys in Washington.* This consisted in the reading of actual letters from various early workers in plant pathology and physiology and brought home to those present the actual condition of things at that time more vividly than could have been done in any other way.

Dr. EDWARD L. GREENE, *The Washington Botanical Club.* The Washington Botanical Club was founded in 1898 with a very informal organization quite similar to that of the Botanical Seminar. The Botanical Club included more especially the workers in systematic botany. Dr. GREENE was the first president. In 1901 it was merged with the Botanical Seminar to form the Botanical Society of Washington.

Mr. F. V. COVILLE, *Systematic botany.* Mr. COVILLE gave briefly some of the more important features of systematic botany in Washington from the early days up to the present time, emphasizing the use of types of species, which was a direct contribution of the United States Department of Agriculture.

Mr. WALTER T. SWINGLE, *Early history of physiological and plant breeding work in the Department of Agriculture.* This briefly sketched the beginning of the now extensive work in plant pathology and plant breeding in the U. S. Department of Agriculture.

On Tuesday, January 5, 1915, at 8.30 p.m., the Botanical Society of Washington met in joint session with the Washington Academy of Sciences in the Assembly Hall of the Cosmos Club. Prof. J. C. BOSE gave an illustrated lecture on *The response of plants.*

The 101st regular meeting cf the Botanical Society of Washington was held January 9, 1915, at 1.30 p.m., in the West Wing of the new Department of Agriculture building. Thirty-four members were present. Messrs. F. TRACY HUBBARD, HOWARD S. COE, LUTHER P. BYARS and Dr. L. O. KUNKEL were unanimously elected to membership. The resignation of Mr. H. C. GORE as Treasurer of the Society was accepted and Mr. C. E. LEIGHTY was elected to that office. No scientific program was presented.

PERLEY SPAULDING, *Corresponding Secretary.*

JOURNAL

OF THE

WASHINGTON ACADEMY OF SCIENCES

Vol. V   MARCH 19, 1915   No. 6

GEOLOGY.—*Some relations in origin between coal and petroleum.*[1] DAVID WHITE, U. S. Geological Survey.[2]

INTRODUCTION

It is my purpose this evening to present for your consideration some features of the problem of the origin of petroleum and natural gas. The plan followed is to view the question of the origin of petroleum from the standpoint of the origin of coal; to note how some of the fundamental conditions attending the formation of coal and its differentiation in kinds may similarly apply to oil; to call attention to some points both of difference and of agreement as to the paleontologic sources of these two great mineral fuels; and to inquire whether certain of their important characters, that are secondary in origin, are not conditioned by common causes.

At the outset it will be assumed that petroleum, as it occurs in a natural state in oil pools in most parts of the world, is the product of the geodynamic alteration of certain types of organic detritus buried in the strata of the outer shell of the earth; that, in other words, it was produced in accordance with the so-called organic theory. It will, however, not be denied that petroleum may be, and in fact has, in some cases, possibly been formed in accordance with the inorganic theory, which, in broad terms, is that petroleum is made chemically from substances of mineral

---

[1] Presidential address delivered before the Washington Academy of Sciences on January 14, 1915.

[2] Published by permission of the Director of the U. S. Geological Survey.

origin, as, for example, by the contact of percolating waters with deep-seated metallic carbides. The observations presently to be noted bear unfavorably on the theory of the inorganic origin of petroleum. The arguments both for and against all variants of the inorganic theory have been fully summarized by many geologists, both American and foreign,[3] and will not receive further attention in this paper, the aim of which is to throw additional light, from the geological standpoint, on the origin of petroleum.

THE INGREDIENT MATERIALS OF COALS AND OIL ROCKS

It is now almost universally agreed that coal of different kinds had its beginning as relatively pure deposits of more or less decomposed organic débris derived mainly from vascular plants. Coals of the common or humic types had their beginning as peats, mainly freshwater peats, those of the great coal fields having been, for the most part, laid down in great swamps or estuarine marshes.[4] The type of the coal—namely, whether it be xyloid, "amorphous," cannel, etc.—depends on the kinds of ingredient organic matter and on the conditions controlling the deposition of this matter. The common types are, to a great extent, composed of the remains of woody plants, portions of which are readily visible to the unaided eye. The more distinctly xyloid coals are largely made up of somewhat altered, but more or less readily recognizable wood, which may constitute more than 80 per cent[5] of the mass. Wherever the conditions of decomposition have been favorable for a more advanced disintegration of the débris through the action of micro-organisms, of which the most important are the bacteria, megascopic wood in the peat or coal is not so abundant; and where the

---

[3] See: Peckham, S. F., Tenth Census Report, 10: 59. 1884; Orton, Edward, Geol. Surv. Kentucky, Report on the occurrence of petroleum, natural gas and asphalt rock in western Kentucky, p. 31. 1891; Haworth, Erasmus, Kansas Univ. Geol. Surv., 9: 187. 1908; Engler, C., and Höfer, Hans v., Das Erdöl, 2: 59. 1909; Clarke, F. W., U. S. Geol. Surv., Bull. 491: 693. 1911; Höfer, Hans, Das Erdöl und seine Verwandten, p. 214, 1912; Redwood, Boverton, Petroleum, 3rd ed., 1: 268. 1913.

[4] White, D., Bur. of Mines, Bull. 38: 62. 1913.

[5] Thiessen, R., Loc. cit., p. 221. 1913.

microbian action has progressed further the coal-forming substance consists more fully of the products of the biochemical decomposition of the vegetal matter, in which the surviving, often comminuted, structural fragments, consisting of the tissues and plant products most resistant to the agencies of subaqueous decay, are embedded. Coals originating in mature or much decomposed peats and containing little coarse detritus are sometimes called "amorphous," although they are never without vestiges of plant structures.

In many cases the decay of great amounts of resin-bearing gymnospermous wood has, through the disintegration of the woody tissue, set free and effected a concentration of large quantities of resinous matter which was resistant to the decomposing agents in the peat swamps or bogs. Also, under certain conditions of deposition, especially where the water was too deep for the growth of subaerial types of vegetation, and stagnant or nearly so, the organic mass may have been largely or almost wholly made up of the spore and pollen exines and grains of resin, mingled in varying proportions with aquatic plant and animal life of low orders, some of which is plankton. The latter may include the remains of innumerable algæ, with protozoans, small crustacea, insect eggs and larvæ, small gastropods, etc., and even fish. More or less spore, pollen, and resin ingredients enter into the xyloid and other coals of the ordinary types; but whenever they become conspicuous in the composition of the coal, they impart a so-called "fatty" quality to it; and when they form the greater part of it, being generally mingled with increased amounts of plankton material, as is natural in an open water habitat, they form cannels.

Between coals of the ordinary, or humic, types and the cannels there is complete intergradation. Locally, according to the circumstances of deposition, the Paleozoic cannel coals contain peculiar forms of organic remains that have, by most paleobotanists, been regarded as algæ of very low groups.[6] If the so-called algæ and other plankton remains predominate, composing the greater part of the organic deposit, the latter is called

[6] Renault, B., Microorganismes des combustibles fossiles, p. 151. 1893.

a *boghead* or an *oil rock;* although if the rock is sufficiently low in mineral sediments, it is in reality a type of cannel. On the other hand, if mineral sediments are mingled in quantities too high to admit the classification of the rock as a coal, it is known as an *oil shale,* or a *bituminous* shale. Lesser amounts of such organic matter ordinarily gain recognition only as rendering the shale "carbonaceous." Deposits of decaying spore and pollen material, with both vegetal and animal débris, laid down as organic oozes, slimes or muds, were designated by Potonié as "sapropel."[7]

Coals, including cannels, and oil shales from many regions and geologic formations have been examined in detail under the high-power microscope, and the organic detrital remains which compose and characterize the several types have been splendidly, sometimes even elaborately, demonstrated by paleontologists[8] both in Europe and America, though the botanical or zoological classification of the fossil remains composing the deposits may, in many cases, be subject to question. However, for our present purpose, it is important only to note some of the qualities or characteristics which certain among the different kinds of organic débris impart to the deposits which contain them.

The woody matter which forms the large part, at least, of the ingredient substance of ordinary peats and their alteration products, xyloid coals, laminated coals, etc., is largely composed of cellulose, lignose, xylose, etc., comprising carbohydrates relatively high in oxygen. These ordinary coals, including those commonly (though really inappropriately) called "bituminous," are therefore, as will be seen, characteristically high in oxygen. They are, accordingly, characteristically rich in so-called humic acid compounds. Hence, they have very properly been designated[9] as humic coals. On the other hand, the decay-resistant elements, such as spore and pollen exines, seed envelopes and

[7] Potonié, H., Die Entstehung der Steinkohle, 5th Ed., p. 3. 1910.

[8] Renault, B., Microorganismes des combustibles fossiles, 1893; Bertrand, C. Eg., Les charbons humiques et les charbons de purins, 1898; Potonié, H., Die Entstehung der Steinkohle, 1910; Stopes, M. C., and Watson, D. M. S., Phil. Trans. Roy. Soc. London, Ser. B., 200:167. 1909; Thiessen, R., Bur. of Mines Bull. 38, 1913; Jeffrey, E. C., Economic Geology, 9: 730. 1914.

[9] Potonié, H., Die Entstehung der Steinkohle, p. 95. 1910.

certain cuticles, are generally provided with resinous, waxy or oily protective substances. These, as well as the resin grains with which they are in most cases mingled, are all characteristically very high in hydrogen and low in oxygen. Thus it happens that the rocks in which they are prominent are from the start, as initial organic muds, more distinctly bituminous in composition. As the fossil remains last named, mingled with other fat-, oil- and albuminoid-producing animal and plant ingredients, predominate more and more, the contrast with the ordinary—the humic—coals, becomes still stronger, the most marked contrast being found in the so-called algal deposits, which characterize many of the typical *"oil shales."* Further, as the high-hydrogen ingredients become prominent or predominate the fuel in general becomes richer in volatile matter and higher in calorific value. Finally, it is to be noted: First, that these deposits compose or characterize the oil rock series, as has been pointed out by Renault, Bertrand, Potonié and others; and second, that in succession the cannels, boghead cannels, cannel bogheads and bogheads appear to yield, on artificial distillation, larger proportions of petroleum. A Reinschia boghead, the so-called kerosene shale of New South Wales, is said to run as high as 87 per cent in volatile hydrocarbons.

Deposits containing in large proportions such organic detritus, characteristically high in hydrogen and low in oxygen, are typical mother rocks of petroleum. As the proportions of waxes, exines and resins become greater in the deposit, the distillates, obtained by the artificial distillation of the fuel, approach in characters more nearly to the natural petroleums; and when they constitute the greater part of the organic detritus, as in the cannels, or when, finally, the material is more distinctly "sapropelic," containing great numbers of, or even composed almost wholly of the so-called algæ, the artificial distillates are, in general, not only much greater in volume, as is to be expected on account of the composition of the original débris, but they form petroleums of higher ranks. It would appear that, other things being equal, the maximum yield of oils of high quality is obtained from the supposed alga coals or bogheads.

Organic remains of the spore or sapropelic type are found in every bituminous shale or so-called oil rock that has yet been examined. It is to the presence of such carbonaceous débris, embracing sapropelic matter, all more or less disintegrated and decomposed, that, in most cases, are due the dark tints of shales, sandstones and limestones. The sufficiency of such matter to produce the petroleum taken from the oil fields has been well demonstrated. In this connection, it will be recalled that, prior to boring for underground oil in Pennsylvania, about 1848, oil shales in several geological formations were distilled to obtain the petroleum supplies of this country. Shales are now being distilled for oil in Scotland and France.

In this discussion, the terms *oil rock* and *oil shale* are applied only to those rocks that yield petroleums when the organic matter deposited in them as sediments is decomposed by destructive distillation. The terms do not apply to sandstones, porous limestones, or other rocks, in which petroleum is merely occluded or held in the interstices of the grains of mineral matter.

To what extent the characters of the distillates obtained by any given method from the different coals, cannels, bituminous shales, and other oil rocks are due to differences in the composition of the original ingredient organic matter of the deposits is not known. For my own part, I am inclined to attribute to this factor certain differences in the characters of natural petroleums, such for example, as high sulphur or high nitrogen content, richness in asphalt or brownness, rather than any great differences in the rank or grade of the oils. More probably, the principal differences in the actual rank of petroleums are, in general, due to physical causes, as will later be indicated.

TWO PROCESSES IN THE ALTERATION OF THE ORGANIC DETRITUS.

The Biochemical Process

In the foregoing summary we have considered only those differences in the types of coal and other sedimentary organic desposits that were determined at the initial stage, that is, at the time of the deposition of the vegetal and animal débris. These differences between the types of detrital hydrocarbon deposits, humic coals, cannel, boghead, etc., are, as has been indicated, dependent upon (1) the kinds of original contributary, organic material, their chemical compounds and the varying proportions of the latter; and (2) the character and extent of the microbian action, whose work depends, both as to extent and as to character, on the kinds of host detritus and the conditions of deposition. The latter embrace all environmental factors, such as temperature, moisture, access of air, concentration of toxic biochemical products, etc., and flushing by water drainage, on which, to some extent, rests the conservation of the varied biochemical decomposition products, especially those that are liquid or that enter into aqueous solution. All this concerns merely the accumulation and more or less complete decomposition of the organic débris in the form of peat, organic muds, calcareous oozes and so forth. As soon as the organic débris is buried and the oxygen so far exhausted that bacterial action is no longer possible, or when toxicity puts an end to all micro-organic action in the deposit, there comes the end to this, the first stage in the formation of coal. This is the *biochemical stage* of coal formation. The exact point at which the biochemical process terminates has not been accurately observed in any single case, but it appears to correspond approximately to the burial of the peat and the complete smothering of the organic matter in the mud, beneath superposed deposits.

A fact which is most important is that, complicated and indispensable as is this biochemical process, it appears to carry the organic deposits little or no farther than the formation of peats and organic muds, buried oozes, etc.

The Dynamo-chemical Process

Leaving now the work of the biochemical process in the formation of coals and other carbonaceous sedimentary deposits, we pass to the consideration of the *alteration* of these deposits to coals and hydrocarbon rocks of higher ranks, as a result of geo-dynamic action. We have now to do with the changes in the physical and chemical characters of the organic matter, accomplished through the dynamo-chemical process or the second stage in coal formation.

This process covers the compression, the gradual dehydration, lithification and induration of carbonaceous rocks, including the coals; the development of cleavage and even schistosity in the deposits; and, simultaneously and progressively, the elimination of the combined oxygen, the hydrogen, the nitrogen, and a part of the carbon of the organic débris.   By this process the peats are gradually transformed to lignites, sub-bituminous coals, bituminous coals, semi-bituminous coals, anthracites, and even to graphites, while the associated organic muds are altered to oil rocks or cannels, to carbonaceous shales, and finally to graphites or graphitic slates.   This alteration and reduction of the carbonaceous deposits is most clearly marked by the progress of the elimination of the "volatile matter."

The changes both in the physical features and in the chemical composition of the deposit, as it is transformed from peat to graphite, constitute in effect a metamorphism of the organic matter.[10]   The extent of the transformation, that is, its progress, varies with the extent of the dynamo-chemical action.

The study of the coals, in many coal fields, and of different ages, shows that the alteration may be produced in two ways. The first is through distillation, by local heat incidental to contact with sills, dikes or flows of molten rock.   Such contact metamorphism, though frequent and conspicuous, is so closely confined to the near vicinity of the igneous intrusives, that its effects, from a regional standpoint, are practically negligible.[11] The other dynamic cause of the alteration of the organic débris is pressure.

The study of the stages in the alteration of the coal in different regions shows, in general, a close relation between the extent to which the rocks have been subjected to thrust pressure metamorphism and the degree to which the mother peats and sapro-

---

[10] The chemical combinations actually existing in coals and petroleums of different ranks and types are largely unknown.   Portions of the coal leached by reagents and extractions or separations from petroleums have been chemically identified, and products resulting from destructive distillation of both the solid and the liquid fuels have been determined; but most of these probably are compounds obtained by breaking up the largely undetermined original chemical combinations.

[11] Bureau of Mines, Bull. **38**: 101.   1913.

pelic deposits have been altered. This relation has long been recognized and is known to be regional in effect, though the extent of the dynamic influences and the differences in the dynamo-chemical results vary from one point to another within the region. Coal appears to be more responsive to pressure than are the environing strata. Its sensitiveness to dynamic action makes it possible, through the changes in the fuel, to recognize this action in regions where other indications are obscure and difficult to detect.[12]

The explanation of the dynamic alteration of coals as the result of thrust was long ago proposed and has been accepted by most geologists, especially in America, though it has gained fewer adherents in Europe, where the coal fields are smaller and the strata of most of the basins containing higher rank coals are folded and faulted. Anomalous variations in the carbonization of the coals in folded and particularly in faulted strata, and the presence of coal high in volatile matter near faults, all of which at first seemed fatally opposed to thrust metamorphism as a hypothesis, have, on the contrary, been shown to constitute essential proof of the validity of the theory. In another place[13] I have shown that abnormally high percentages of volatile matter sometimes found in coals lying in folds, and generally to be observed near thrust-faults in coal fields, are really due to compensation or neutralization of the thrust by buckling of the beds and by the faults themselves. Through the shortening of the crustal arc by folding or by over-thrust of broken beds the stress is partially compensated and the coals are enabled to escape the maximum pressure intensity. In the regions of great coal alteration, the shortening by mere horizontal compression, which gradually takes up the stress and diminishes the pressure delivered at the far side of the arc, must have been very considerable.

It is probable that, except in cases approaching graphitization, the temperatures of coal alteration were never so high as those necessary to accomplish the earliest effects of metamorphism generally recognized by geologists in other rocks; yet the

[12] U. S. Geol. Survey, Bull. 150: 142–145. 1898.
[13] Bureau of Mines, Bull. 38: 114–125. 1913.

friction heat of molecular displacement caused by the stresses of intermittent thrusts of progressive intensity was generated throughout such an enormous thickness of rocks and through so great an area as to produce sensible temperatures under conditions necessitating long periods for their dissipation.

The effectiveness of thrust pressure as the cause of regional coal alteration is well illustrated in most large areas of high rank coal, but in no part of the world is it more clearly demonstrated than in the great Appalachian coal field.   To show in a general way the progress of the regional alteration in this area, I have, in preparing the accompanying map, first platted the "fixed carbon" (pure coal basis) of the coals at the localities from which samples have been analyzed.[14]   Lines were then drawn through the points of equal fixed carbon (or volatile matter).   Such lines, which were termed "isoanthracitic" lines by Strahan[15] and Pollard, and which I have termed "isovols," are drawn to mark each 5 per cent of increase in the fixed carbon in the pure coal.   The degree of accuracy of the representation will not here be discussed.   The "contouring" of the fixed carbons is subject to minor revision.

A glance at the Appalachian coal field in this map shows the position of the lowest rank coals to be in the western portion of the area, while the highest rank coals, the anthracites, are found at the extreme eastern border.   The isovols show both the extent of the alteration of the coals and the regional progressive character of that alteration toward the Atlantic; that is, in the direction from which the great isostatic Appalachian thrusts are known to have come.   Small areas of coal with slightly higher fixed carbon indicate, in most cases, points of locally greater, perhaps of cumulative, stresses, while "islands" of low fixed carbon probably mark areas of corresponding partial immunity.   The more important thrust faults, lying within or

[14] The use of the fixed carbons, though less satisfactory on the whole than the C-O ratios of the dry coals, makes it possible to employ the great volume of proximate analyses illustrating coals in far greater geographical extent and completeness of representation.   In the regions of lower rank coals, it is necessary to use some other method to show satisfactorily the rank of the fuels.

[15] The Coals of South Wales Coal Field, p. 72.

along the border of the coal field, are also shown on the map. The character of the folding of the valley regions and the faulting to the eastward is shown in the folios of the Geologic Atlas of the United States and in the State geological maps.

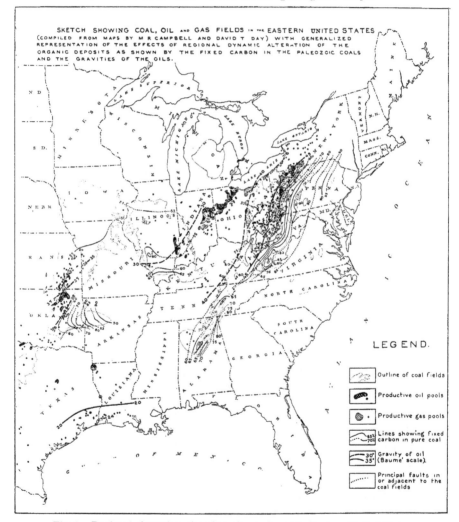

Fig. 1.   Regional alteration of coals and petroleums in Eastern United States.

Without going further, at this time, into details as to the effects of folding and faulting in neutralizing the dynamic stresses, attention is called to (a) the larger volatile content in those parts of the anthracite fields that extend into the region of closer folding; (b) the anomalous variations seen in the Broadtop, the Coosa and Cahaba basins which lie in fault blocks; and (c) the relatively low stage of the alteration of the coals behind the Pocahontas, the Pine Mountain and the Elk Valley overthrusts. Undoubtedly the greatest intensity of initial stress has, in most cases, been exerted where the strata are most folded and broken. Where the stresses have been equal, it has been competency versus compensation. The gradual absorption of the energy of the westward movement by compression in the horizontal series is shown by the westward decrease of minor folding, as well as by the westward increase of volatile matter in the coals. There is no visible evidence that igneous rock metamorphism has caused any regional alteration of the coals in the Appalachian trough.

In the districts where high rank coals occur in the Cretaceous and Tertiary formations of western America, the evidence of the efficiency of thrust pressure, as the dynamic force causing the chemical change of the coals, is hardly less evident than in the Appalachian province, the phenomena being the same as in the Paleozoic areas, though the ranges in rank are often greater. In the western regions, the influence of igneous intrusives, which are relatively numerous, is conspicuously restricted and ineffective in the regional sense.

THE "DEVOLATILIZATION" OF THE ORGANIC DÉBRIS

In the laboratory methods of "approximate" analysis of coals and other carbonaceous deposits, the oxygen, hydrogen, nitrogen and a part of the carbon of the organic débris are distilled by a dry and semi-open air process, the matter, eliminated in the form of gases, being known as "volatile matter." It seems to be assumed that, in the geologic processes also, the substances eliminated are all in gaseous form and, accordingly the results are frequently described as the "devolatilization" of the organic deposits. Nevertheless, when it is remembered that the organic compounds actually present in coals and bituminous shales are largely undetermined; that the conditions of geologic distillation are fundamentally different from those provided in the laboratory, and that the residues obtained at all stages in the laboratory process are widely different from those found in the earth, doubt is cast not only on the assumed similarity in the states and chemical composition of the eliminated matter but also as to whether all the matter is expelled as gases. Furthermore, it is probable that the natural distillates, generated under different geological conditions (from organic matter which itself may vary widely in chemical composition), vary both as to their chemical compounds and as to their properties far more widely than do the artificial distillates obtained from the same organic deposits.

Attention has already been given to the differences between the high-oxygen ingredient matter of the typical humic deposits (coals) and the high-hydrogen ingredient material of the typical cannels and oil rocks. Obviously, the volatile matter expelled from the former contains larger amounts of oxygen in some one or more combinations, while the volatile matter from the latter is rich in hydrogen. The reduction of these organic deposits, which intergrade one with another, will be discussed more fully in a later report. The two most important facts to be noted in passing are, first, that coals and oil rocks have yielded "volatile matter" products in different proportions and probably in very different compositions and structures also; and, second, that in both cases the processes of "devolatilization" result in the reduction of the solid residues through chemical changes that accomplish, in effect, their carbonization.

REGIONAL ALTERATION OF ORGANIC DÉBRIS AND CORRESPONDING
REGIONAL DIFFERENCES IN PETROLEUMS

Having briefly reviewed some of the effects of regional dynamic influences, principally thrust pressure, in the progressive alteration of the carbonaceous residues, represented by coals, oil rocks, carbonaceous shales, etc., we will next inquire whether

202 WHITE: RELATIONS BETWEEN COAL AND PETROLEUM

the liquid distillates, the petroleums, found in different regions reveal any differences corresponding to the stages in the regional alteration of the carbonaceous residues.

In entering on the observations necessary to the comparison of petroleums from regions of varying degrees of alteration of the organic detrital deposits, many difficulties are encountered: There is no adequate volume of chemical analyses of petroleums from different oil fields and geologic formations. On the other hand, we find fractionation, lacking as to uniformity of method, and often made from deteriorated or unreliable samples, for commercial information. In comparatively few cases is the proportion of any single hydrocarbon determined. The only data obtained by approximately standardized methods and covering samples of geographic and geologic range, sufficient for comprehensive inter-regional comparisons, consist of specific gravity determinations. These, though they are the best criteria at hand, are also far from satisfactory, for, while in general the oils of lightest gravity are of the highest rank, containing the largest amounts of light (saturated) hydrocarbons, with largest proportions of hydrogen, and of lightest density, the gravity records can not take the place of chemical determinations of the hydrocarbon compounds in the study of the genetic features and the chemical classification of the petroleums. Furthermore, the gravity records contain unknown errors, due to the conditions of the samples as well as to the sources of the latter. Many of them represent shallow sand oils, from which the lighter elements have escaped up the dip or to the surface; which have stood in tanks or in wells intermittently pumped; which are affected by meteoric waters; or which were taken from mere seeps, shafts or springs. On the whole, however, the gravities of representative samples approximately show the rank of the petroleums and may, therefore, be utilized in a rough comparison of the oils from different regions. In view of the present lack of standardized analytic or fractionative criteria in sufficient abundance from both the stratigraphic and geographic standpoints for detailed studies, the conclusions which I have to offer are to be regarded as a report of progress.

Conforming to the prevailing usage in this country, I have, in the following discussion, used the Baumé system, in which the increase in the number of degrees is inverse to the increase in gravity.

In most petroliferous regions of the world the oil pools lie in or near (often beneath) formations carrying coals. Accordingly, it is generally possible to learn the stage of the regional metamorphism, approximately at least, by the extent of the alteration of the coals where, as in most cases, analyses of the carbonaceous shales in the oil-bearing strata are lacking. The geographic relations of petroleum pools to the coal fields will be at once seen if David T. Day's oil map of the United States, recently published by the U. S. Geological Survey, be compared with M. R. Campbell's coal map, published in Mineral Resources for 1910. (See also Coal Resources of the World, Ottawa, 1914.)

OCCURRENCES OF HIGHER RANK OILS IN REGIONS OF GREATER ALTERATION OF CARBONACEOUS RESIDUES

Is there any relation between the rank of the oils of any region and the degree of the alteration of the carbonaceous matter of the organic débris in the oil-bearing or in the overlying formations? Do the petroleums show regional differences of rank corresponding to or comparable with the differences in the rank of the coals in the various provinces? Unsatisfactory as the criteria employed in the comparisons may be, the answer to these questions is not only affirmative but it is conclusively so. A review of the data reported from the various oil fields of the world leaves no room for doubt on this question.

If we examine the oils of the United States, we find that in those formations and regions in which the carbonaceous detrital deposits (coals) are but little altered by dynamic influence, the oils are heavy and of low rank; that is, they are of high gravity. On the other hand, in regions of more advanced alteration of the residual organic débris, the oils are in general of correspondingly higher ranks (lower gravities), the highest degree of alteration of the residues being, in general, noted in the regions of highest rank oil pools.

In the Coastal Plain regions of Texas and Louisiana, where the coals of the Tertiary formations have not passed the stage of brown lignites, the oils of the associated beds are low in rank, with gravities falling, in most cases, between 17° and 24°, though tests of samples from certain localities are reported to show a gravity as low as 33° Baumé. The Tertiary oils in California are, on the whole, similar in gravity range. Some notable fluctuations in the oils of this State are apparently to be accounted for as due to deteriorated samples, to losses through porous covering strata, to local dynamic action, etc. A number of samples of oils of exceptionally low gravity from this State, as well as from the Olympic region of Washington, may owe their peculiarities to filtration or to greater local alteration of the rocks in folded districts. These exceptions affect but slightly the general average of the pools or fields. The Cretaceous rocks in northern California, in which the alteration of the carbonaceous deposits is more advanced, appear to contain oils of distinctly higher rank, corresponding to the oils in sub-bituminous areas or in regions of low rank bituminous coals. In the Coalinga field, the middle Tertiary oils, many of which may have probably suffered losses, average between 18° and 20° Baumé, but a gravity of 34° is reported for the oil in the Cretaceous underlying the anticline at Oil City at the northern border of this field. Similarly, the oils in the Texas Cretaceous, which carries sub-bituminous coals, range from 32° to 39° in gravity; the still higher grade oils, ranging from 39° to 43° in gravity, in the Caddo field of Louisiana, are found in sands near the base of the Upper Cretaceous.[16]

In Wyoming the evidence is somewhat conflicting, apparently on account of the nature of the samples tested, many of these having been taken from springs or from wells of so light production or of so shallow a depth as to be subject to the effects of either evaporation or contamination. It appears, however, that the oils from rocks of the lignitic stage of alteration in this State average about 22° to 24° in gravity, while the oils from

---

[16] Caddo Lake is probably over the westward trending Appalachian coal measures and may possibly have derived its oils from the latter.

Cretaceous beds, associated with or underlying sub-bituminous coals, show gravities averaging about 35° or 36°. In the Evanston region, where the oils range from 38° to 43°, the coals of the overlying formation are reported to be of high sub-bituminous rank.

In Utah and Colorado, the oils of the Green River formation, in which the carbonaceous deposits have not passed the lignitic stage, are of low rank, having gravities of 26° or less; but the oils found in the Rangeley field, in Cretaceous strata beneath rocks containing medium rank bituminous coal in the same basin, show a gravity of 43° which corresponds to the stage of the alteration of the coals. In the Florence oil field in Colorado, oils averaging 30° or 31° are found in shales underlying coals of very low bituminous rank. Oil of 39° gravity in the Boulder coal field is said to occur in the Pierre shale at depths of more than 2000 feet below the base of the Laramie of the region, in which the coals, of high sub-bituminous rank at Marshall, appear to be progressing in alteration westward toward the oil field.

The broad area of almost undisturbed upper Paleozoic strata in the Mississippi Valley and middle States offers an unrivalled field for the study of petroleum with reference to the regional alteration of the carbonaceous deposits. In eastern Kansas the oils, which occur in Pennsylvanian strata carrying coals of very low bituminous rank, range, for the most part, from 32° to 34° in gravity, though in passing southward to the Oklahoma line and onward through the Osage Nation and beyond the Glenn pool, the oils show an increase in average gravity;[17] those in the Osage region ranging, in general, from 33° to 36°. Farther southeastward the gravities rise to 39° or 40° at the edge of the developed field.

The Madill oil, found in the basal sands of the Cretaceous, undoubtedly owes its low gravity, 47°, to its source in the immediately underlying Pennsylvanian strata, which are tilted and compressed in the Arbuckle uplift.

In the coal fields of Illinois and Indiana, where the coals are of low bituminous rank, but somewhat better than those of

[17] See R. H. Wood, U. S. Geol. Survey, Bull. **513**: 36. 1913.

eastern Kansas, the oils in the Pennsylvanian rocks appear to range from 29° to 39° Baumé, averaging about 31° to 34° in gravity. In this field there appears to be slight evidence of betterment of the rank of the oil in passing southward, as is to be expected in view of the southward improvement in the rank of the coals, though the data examined are not really sufficient.

It is interesting to note that the oils of the "Trenton" in eastern Indiana and northwestern Ohio, as well as those in the Silurian and Devonian of eastern Michigan and western Canada, though of gravities to be expected in regions where the nearest coals in younger formations are of bituminous rank, are not of so high rank as the oils in Carboniferous rocks in the regions. of greater alteration nearer the eastern border of the Appalachian oil fields. This circumstance I believe to be due to the diminution of the intensity of the post-Paleozoic thrusts in this region, while the rocks of Trenton age and other pre-Carboniferous formations have not been subjected to dynamic stresses so vigorous as those endured by the Carboniferous rocks in West Virginia and western Pennsylvania. It is, however, to be noted that the "Trenton" oils are of higher gravity than the Carboniferous oils in the bituminous coal regions of Indiana and Illinois and it is almost certain that they are of higher rank than would be found in overlying Pennsylvanian rocks were the latter present in the "Trenton" region. It is also seen that the oils of the "Clinton" sand districts of Ohio are but slightly better in gravity than those of the Carboniferous nearest on the east.

In the great Appalachian oil field, the petroleums found in the Carboniferous sands range, in general, from gravities of 38° to 44° on the western, to gravities of 46° to 48° Baumé on the eastern margin of the productive field. The best oils, showing gravities of 49° and 50° or even 52° are found along or near the eastern margin of the field, in northern West Virginia, western Pennsylvania and western New York.[18]

[18] The gravities of the oils in this region vary somewhat from point to point and from sand to sand, the rank of an oil in a Devonian sand being locally inferior to that in the overlying Carboniferous, though, in general, it appears that, even in this region, the sands in the older or underlying formations contain oils of highest rank.

It is thus seen not only that the oils found in the regions of higher alteration of the carbonaceous deposits are in general higher in rank than are those in regions of lesser alteration, but also that in a single region the rank of the oil increases, *pari passu*, in the same direction as does the alteration of the carbonaceous deposits. This is clear when reference is made to the progressive alteration of the coals in passing eastward through this region, as is indicated on the map. Doubtless some of the local fluctuations are due to local variations in the intensities of the dynamic stresses. Others may be due to unknown circumstances connected with the sampling, to variations due to filtration, or to differences in the composition of the organic débris in the mother rock.

A further examination of the map for the purpose of comparing the trend of the eastern border of the productive oil region with the trend of the isovols (isoanthracitic lines) which have already been described, shows a degree of parallelism which is all the more surprising when it is known that the "contouring" of the fixed carbons of the Coals was done long before the inspection of the oil maps suggested a close comparison. It is seen that, in general, the eastern border of the oil field falls near the 60 per cent fixed carbon line, though small pools appear to have been found near the 65 per cent line. Gas pools fringe the oil field in a zone of higher alteration, but no pool of commercial size appears to have been found anywhere in the Appalachian trough so far east as the 70 per cent line. In fact, it appears probable that a revision of the isovol lines, based on more complete data, may show no pools of oil in rocks of higher carbonization than 65 per cent fixed carbon. It will also be noted that the eastward trend of the isovols in the southern Virginia region, on account of fault compensation of the stresses, finds a response in an eastward oil pool trend, which will probably be more clearly shown when the eastern Kentucky region is more fully explored by the drill. Moreover it appears that not only does the eastern border of the oil field swing eastward in Kentucky, but the oils, even those in pre-Carboniferous strata, lying in the strike of the high gravity oil pools to the northeast are of lower gravity corresponding to the lesser alteration of the coals of the region in eastern Kentucky.

If now, turning to Oklahoma, attention be given to the southeastern border of the mid-continent oil field, it will again be seen that the commercial pools, so far as discovery has gone, appear not to reach the 65 per cent fixed carbon isovol, though the marginal developments parallel this line.

In view of the eastward continuation of the oil-bearing formations, including the oil sands both in the Appalachian region and in Oklahoma and Arkansas, and taking into account their porosity as ascertained from drillings, and the distinctly favorable structures, elevations, etc., of the beds—in short, in view of the absence of any other visible geological reasons why commercial oil pools do not occur in regions of higher carbonization of the residual organic débris—two questions arise. The first is whether oils, in commercial pools, are anywhere found in or beneath formations in which the regional alteration of the coals is marked by fixed carbon percentages of more than 65 or 70. The second question is why the oil stops near this line. As to the first, I can only say that the relations to be observed in other North American oil fields conform to those found in the Appalachian province. Further, that so far as I have had the opportunity to gather the information concerning the oil fields and the coals in other continents, no productive pools are present in such areas of greater alteration.[19] In fact, though the examination of the data is not yet fully completed, it has been carried far enough to make practically certain the conclusion that commercial oil pools have never been found in regions of further reduction of the carbonaceous detrital deposits, and to establish with nearly equal assurance the conclusion that productive oil pools do not exist in those regions.

Assuming, however, that variable intensities of thrust, due perhaps to local structures, have permitted the escape of small isolated areas from the more advanced alteration in regions of higher rank carbonization, it may be more conservative, pro-

[19] Possible exceptions are to be sought in the Katalla field in Alaska and in the provinces of Shansi and Shensi in China.

visionally, to place the ultimate limit at the 70 per cent fixed carbon line in the coals, though it is not probable that many large pools will be found near this limit. As related to the oil field limit, as here defined, mention may be made of the evidence of the transformation and reduction of the lump resins in the Tertiary and Mesozoic coals when these coals reach a stage of about 68 per cent or 70 per cent of fixed carbon, as I have described in another paper.[20] It will also be recalled that in the regions of more advanced alteration, as in the semi-bituminous coal fields (75 per cent or more of fixed carbon), the cannels appear to have lost their characteristic fatty characters and to have become deadened so as to give essentially the same analyses as the associated humic coals. Field examinations indicate that deposits, once cannels, are as numerous in the semi-bituminous and anthracite coal fields as in the average "bituminous" coal field.

According to the conclusions here given as to oil field limits we appear to have at hand a basis on which to exclude large areas of sedimentary strata from the provinces in which we may, with any hope of success, undertake the costly search for oil by the drill. No oil is reasonably to be hoped for in the Paleozoic formations throughout the greater part, at least, of the area of the Arkansas coal field nor for some distance beyond the margin of this field on the sides toward which the fixed carbon is increasing in direction. Similarly, the very low limits placed on the distribution of oil pools by the regional alteration of the hydrocarbon deposits show the hopelessness of any search for oil in commercial quantities in the Carboniferous or older formations of central and southern New England and of the Appalachian region to the east of the 65 or 70 per cent fixed carbon lines in the carbonaceous deposits. This does not preclude the discovery of pools in the overlying Triassic deposits wherever they are not too far altered, nor in the Coastal Plain deposits to the eastward and southward. However, it is probable that any commercial deposits of oil that may be found in

[20] Resins in Paleozoic plants and in coals of high rank, U. S. Geol. Survey, Prof. Paper 85: 65–96. 1913.

the Atlantic Coastal Plain formations will be of comparatively low rank, and that those of the Tertiary will not be better than 25° or 27° Baumé. On the other hand, in the Paleozoic areas of the southern Allegheny region, oil pools of commercial value may, if other geologic factors are favorable, be expected wherever the fixed carbon of the coals does not exceed 60 per cent in the pure coal, with a less promising possibility of finding pools as far east as the 65 per cent isovol.

The relations between the rank of the oils and commercial oil field limits on the one hand, to the progressive alteration of the organic detrital deposits on the other, appear to be as significant in the Cretaceous and Tertiary formations of western America and Mexico as in the eastern Paleozoic areas.

CONCLUSIONS

The comparison of the gravities of the oils in different formations and regions, with especial reference to the stages of the regional alteration of the mother rocks and other carbonaceous deposits found in the same formations or in formations overlying the oil pools in the various regions, though it is somewhat unsatisfactory on account of the lack of better information as to the chemical characters of the petroleums, leads to the following conclusions:

(1) Petroleum is a product generated in the course of the geodynamic alteration of deposits of organic débris of certain types buried in the sedimentary strata.

(2) The quantity and characters of the oils generated are determined by: (a) the composition of the organic deposit at the beginning of its dynamo-chemical alteration; (b) by the stage in the progress of the dynamo-chemical alteration of the organic substances; (c) by the elimination, under certain conditions, of the heavier and more viscous hydrocarbons through filtration incident to migration. How far each of the above mentioned factors is responsible for the characters of the petroleums remains to be determined by observation and investigation, both in the field and in the laboratory. It is probable

that the composition of the mother organic deposit largely regulates the types of oils. It may account for the nitrogen, sulphur content, color, etc., just as the nature of the ingredient débris controls the types of the coals. On the other hand, we may conclude that, further in parallelism with the residual coal débris, the rank of the oils within each type is mainly governed by the stage in the progressive alteration (really the natural distillation) of the organic deposits.

(3) In general, it is seen that the lowest rank oils of each type are found in the regions and formations in which the carbonaceous deposits are least altered; that the oils in formations showing greater alteration of the organic débris, as in subbituminous coals, are of higher rank, the oils being still more clearly of high rank in the regions and formations of bituminous coals; and that in regions of still further alteration the oils are still better, the highest rank oils being, on the whole, found in regions where the carbonaceous deposits in the same or in overlying formations have been brought to corresponding higher ranks.

(4) The effect of progressive regional dynamic alteration is marked by a concentration of hydrogen in the distillates and a concentration of carbon in the residual débris (coal, carbonaceous shale, etc).

(5) Abnormally light oils, occurring sporadically in pools of lower rank are, in most cases at least, probably due to filtration, though it is not improbable that, in some cases, these oils are migrates from underlying formations of more advanced alteration.

(6) In general, at a given point the oils found in successive underlying formations or in stratigraphically lower sands in the same formation are progressively higher in rank. In other words the principle that the increase in the gravity of the oil is inverse to the stratigraphic depth of the well, proposed by Engler, finds its parallel in the downward increase in the carbonization of coals, according to the law of Hilt.[21] Occurrences of lighter

---

[21] Oils found so near the outcrop or at such shallow depths as to have permitted the evaporation of the lighter hydrocarbons or the intrusion of oxygen in meteoric water should be regarded with suspicion.

oils in sands overlying others, in the same geologic formation, carrying heavier oils, may, in many cases at least, be due to differences in the mother organic deposits.   However, the effects of filtration are not to be overlooked.

(7) In regions where the progressive devolatilization of the organic deposits in any formation has passed a certain point, marked in most provinces by 65 to 70 per cent of fixed carbon (pure coal basis) in the associated or overlying coals, commercial oil pools are not present in that formation nor in any other formations normally underlying it, though commercial gas pools may occur in a border zone of higher carbonization.   The approximate carbonization limits of the rocks containing or overlying oil pools may be found to vary somewhat in different provinces according to the characters of the original organic débris, the circumstances attending its deposition and the geologic structure.

(8) Wherever the regional alteration of the carbonaceous residues passes the point marked by 65 per cent or perhaps 70 per cent of fixed carbon in the (pure) coals, the light distillates appear, in general, to be gases at rock temperatures.   Occluded oils may, in some cases, have escaped volatilization.

The observations and conclusions here offered suggest a wide range of problems, both scientific and economic, that merit thorough investigation with greater refinement of criteria as well as of methods.   A greater volume of detailed analytical data concerning petroleums is needed for comparisons from the geographic and stratigraphic standpoints.   Detailed paleontological investigations should be made of the detrital organic deposits laid down under different conditions in marine and fresh waters, and the decomposition products generated in the biochemical process, as well as in the dynamo-chemical process, should be chemically studied in detail.

Some of the features of the regional alteration of coals and petroleums that are here lightly touched upon will be more fully discussed in a more extended paper now in preparation for publication by the U. S. Geological Survey.

ZOOLOGY.—*The bathymetrical and thermal distribution of the unstalked crinoids, or comatulids, occurring on the coasts of China and Japan.* AUSTIN H. CLARK, National Museum.[1]

The fauna of the coasts of China and Japan includes 92 recognized species and subspecies of comatulids, of which 2 are probably best considered as local aberrant forms, so that the actual number may be placed at 90.

Of these 90, 61 belong to the Indo-Pacific fauna, characterizing the Southern Japanese division of that fauna, which ranges from Hong Kong and Formosa to the Korean Straits and thence eastward to Tokyo Bay; 22 are Malayan, wide ranging types, each with a distribution different from that of the others; 4 are Antarctic, reaching Japan from the northeastward by way of Alaska and the Aleutian Islands; and 3 (plus varieties of one of them—5 in all) are Arctic. One of these last, *Heliometra glacialis maxima* (with *Heliometra glacialis biarticulata* and *Heliometra glacialis brachymera*) is very closely related to *Heliometra glacialis glacialis*, which occurs in the Arctic Ocean from west of Greenland to the Kara Sea, and southward to Nova Scotia and northern Norway, but the other two are of quite

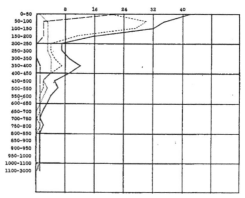

Fig. 1. The frequency at different depths of the comatulids of the coasts of China and Japan. ------ The Species of the Indo-Pacific Fauna; ——— The Species of the Malayan Fauna; .... The Species of the Arctic and Antarctic Faunas; ——— The Total for all Species.

different origin; *Psathyrometra erythrizon* was originally Antarctic, like *Psathyrometra fragilis*, to which it is closely related, and entered the Seas of Okhotsk and Japan from the northeastward; *Thaumatometra tenuis* is most closely related to species in the

[1] Published by the permission of the Secretary of the Smithsonian Institution.

Bathymetric and thermal ranges of the comatulids occurring along the coasts of China and Japan

		Depth in fathoms	Temperature
M	*Comatella stelligera*	0–36	(24+)
	Comatella decora	95–106	13.28
M	*Capillaster macrobrachius*	0	(24+)
	Capillaster mariæ	0–59	16.72
M	*Capillaster multiradiata*	0–160	(24+)
M	*Comatula solaris*	0–14	(24+)
ﾒ	*Comatulides decameros*	170	?
M	*Comaster gracilis*	0–30	(24+)
M	*Comaster fruticosus*	19–58	24.28
	Comaster serrata	30–106	13.28
	Comantheria intermedia	83	?
	Comantheria grandicalyx	0	(24+)
	Comantheria imbricata	36–50	?
	Comanthus (Bennettia) solaster	0–108	13.28–18.00
	Comanthus (Bennettia) pinguis	21–125	14.33–15.89
	Comanthus (Bennettia) japonica	0–140	11.28–16.72
M	*Comanthus (Vania) parvicirra*	0–44	(24+)
M	*Zygometra comata*	0–49	(24+)
	Eudiocrinus variegatus	60	?
	Catoptometra rubroflava	14–100	16.72
	Catoptometra hartlaubi	63–152	13.33
M	*Amphimetra schlegelii*	0	(24+)
M	*Amphimetra variipinna*	0	(24+)
M	*Amphimetra sinensis*	0	(24+)
M	*Amphimetra lævipinna*	0	(24+)
M	*Himerometra magnipinna*	0–21	(24+)
M	*Craspedometra acuticirra*	0	(24+)
M	*Dichrometra flagellata*	0–14	(24+)
	Dichrometra dofleini	83	(24+)
	Dichrometra döderleini	0–84	23.78
	Mariametra subcarinata	22–59	16.72
	Mariametra delicatissima	84	23.78
	Liparometra grandis	40	?
M	*Lamprometra protectus*	0–12	(24+)
M	*Cenometra bella*	0–20	(24+)
	Cyllometra albopurpurea	12–139	11.61–23.78
	Decametra tigrina	8–34	(24+)
	Prometra owstoni	55	?
	Oligometra japonica	5–8	?
M	*Oligometra serripinna*	0–50	(24+)
	Tropiometra macrodiscus	0–50	?
M	*Tropiometra encrinus*	0	(24+)
	Neometra multicolor	11–333	13.28–15.89
	Gephyrometra versicolor	53	16.50
	Gephyrometra propinqua	95	13.28

	Depth in fathoms	*Temperature*
Pectinometra flavopurpurea......	63–200	8.67–17.22
Calometra callista.............	107–139	11.61
Calometra separata............	55–150	13.28–15.89
Asterometra macropoda.........	103	15.89
Asterometra anthus............	103	15.89
Asterometra lepida............	35	?
Cosmiometra aster.............	369–405	4.44– 5.44
Cosmiometra conifera..........	?	?
Stenometra dorsata............	52–170	11.28–15.89
Daidalometra hana............	107–139	11.61
Parametra alboflava...........	103	15.89
Parametra orion..............	71–170	10.78–15.89
Thalassometra latipinna.......	345	5.05
Thalassometra pubescens.......	440	5.44
Pachylometra septentrionalis....	?	?
Glyptometra lata.............	361	5.95
Chlorometra garrettiana........	95	13.28
Strotometra hepburniana.......	100–135	11.28
Pœcilometra scalaris..........	361	5.95
Euantedon sinensis............	?	(24+)
Compsometra serrata..........	8–35	?
Iridometra adrestine..........	13–107	11.61
Iridometra psyche............	30–107	11.61
Iridometra briseis............	59	16.72
Thysanometra tenelloides.......	70–197	8.67–13.50
Arc. *Psathyrometra erythrizon*......	390–406	0.39
Ant. *Psathyrometra fragilis*........	300–533	1.61– 2.17
Perometra diomedeæ..........	39–139	11.61–20.39
Erythrometra ruber...........	55–150	11.11–15.89
Arc. *Heliometra glacialis maxima*....	32–428	−1.22– +1.72
Arc. *Heliometra glacialis biarticulata*.	?	?
Arc. *Heliometra glacialis brachymera*.	[172]	[1.05]
Ant. *Florometra mariæ*.............	70–337	4.83–13.50
Ant. *Florometra rathbuni*..........	533–587	2.17–383
Cyclometra clio.............	107	?
Nanometra bowersi...........	139–191	9.67–13.33
Arc. *Thaumatometra tenuis*.........	80–620	0.39–1.72
Thaumatometra isis...........	361	5.95
Thaumatometra comaster.......	300–533	1.61– 2.17
Thaumatometra cypris.........	775	3.11
Thaumatometra parva.........	120–265	?
Ant. *Bathymetra abyssicola*.........	2900	1.83
Thaumatocrinus borealis.......	361	5.95
Pentametrocrinus tuberculatus. ..169–333		8.89
M *Pentametrocrinus diomedeæ*......103–186		13.33–15.89
Pentametrocrinus japonicus.....139–662		3.17–13.33
M *Pentametrocrinus varians*......361–1050		3.17– 5.95

The frequency at different depths of the comatulids occurring on the coasts of China and Japan

Fathoms	All species	Indo-Pacific species	Malayan species	Arctic and Antarctic species.
0–50........	42	20	21	1
50–100.......	35	30	2	3
100–150.......	32	27	2	3
150–200.......	16	11	2	3
200–250.......	7	4	0	3
250–300.......	7	4	0	3
300–350.......	9	5	0	4
350–400.......	12	7	1	4
400–450.......	9	4	1	4
450–500.......	5	2	1	2
500–550.......	6	2	1	3
550–600.......	4	1	1	2
600–650.......	3	1	1	1
650–700.......	2	1	1	0
700–750.......	1	0	1	0
750–800.......	2	1	1	0
800–850.......	1	0	1	0
850–900.......	1	0	1	0
900–950.......	1	0	1	0
950–1000......	1	0	1	0
1000–1100......	1	0	1	0
1100–3000......	1	0	0	1

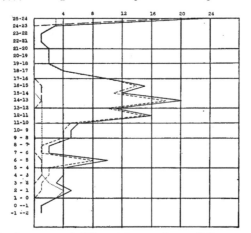

Fig. 2.   The frequency at different temperatures of the comatulids of the coasts of China and Japan. - - - - - -   The Species of the Indo-Pacific Fauna; ———— —— The Species of the Malayan Fauna; ....   The Species of the Arctic and Antarctic Faunas; ————— The Total for all Species.

The frequency at different temperatures of the comatulids occurring on the coasts of China and Japan

Degrees Centigrade	All species	Indo-Pacific species	Malayan species	Arctic and Antarctic species
25–24	23	3	20	0
24–23	3	3	0	0
23–22	1	1	0	0
22–21	1	1	0	0
21–20	2	2	0	0
20–19	2	2	0	0
19–18	2	2	0	0
18–17	4	4	0	0
17–16	10	10	0	0
16–15	15	14	1	0
15–14	12	11	1	0
14–13	20	18	1	1
13–12	11	10	0	1
12–11	16	15	0	1
11–10	6	5	0	1
10– 9	5	4	0	1
9– 8	5	4	0	1
8– 7	2	1	0	1
7– 6	2	1	0	1
6– 5	10	8	1	1
5– 4	4	2	1	1
4– 3	4	2	1	1
3– 2	3	1	0	2
2– 1	5	1	0	4
1– 0	3	0	0	3
0– −1	1	0	0	1
−1– −2	1	0	0	1

Southern Japanese division of the Indo-Pacific fauna, and probably reached the Sea of Japan through the Korean Straits.

In the foregoing lists are included all the comatulids known from Chinese and Japanese waters, with their bathymetric and thermal ranges. The fauna to which each belongs is indicated as follows: *M.*, Malayan; *Arc.*, Arctic; *Aṇt.*, Antarctic; those not especially marked belong to the Southern Japanese division of the Indo-Pacific fauna.

In the diagram (fig. 1) on which are shown the bathymetric ranges of the species of the different faunal units which collectively constitute the comatulid population of the Chinese and

Japanese coasts it is interesting to note that the species of each of these units show the same line that the corresponding species of the same units show in other parts of the world. The mingling of the faunas here, as elsewhere, has resulted in a distinctive collection of individuals which, however, is easily resolved into the original component units, and these component units are found to retain all the distinctive features of the parent faunal groups from which they were originally derived. In their relation to temperature the three faunal groups are very different. The Malayan species, which are mostly confined to the littoral, almost all occur in water with a temperature above 23°, but they are also represented between 12°, and 16°, and 2° and 7°. The Indo-Pacific species have their maximum between 10° and 18°, and especially between 13° and 14°; they are also numerous between 5° and 6°. The Arctic and Antarctic types, which do not occur in water warmer than 15°, are most numerous between 0° and 2°.

We get, therefore, the following optimum temperatures for these three components of the Japanese and Chinese fauna:

Malayan................	**23+°**	12°–16°	2°–7°
Indo-Pacific..........	23+°	**13°–14°**	5°–6°
Arctic and Antarctic...			0°–2°

The point 2° to 7° (including 5° to 6°) is characterized especially by the genera of Oligophreata with highly developed side- and covering-plates along the ambulacra of the pinnules and arms (included in the families Thalassometridæ and Charitometridæ) which, occurring from 0 to 1600 fathoms, are most noticeable between 350 and 400 fathoms; most of these belong to the Indo-Pacific fauna, but a few are Malayan.

Although on the Japanese coast it is possible to take species of the Indo-Pacific and the Antarctic, and of the Indo-Pacific and Malayan, faunal units in one and the same dredge haul, it is evident that this overlapping, which in some places is quite extensive, does not mean that these faunal units here have lost or are losing their identity.

ANTHROPOLOGY.—*Institutional marriage.* J. R. SWANTON, Bureau of Ethnology.

Much of ethnological investigation consists in a study of various manifestations of the conscious and the habitual, and the determination of the relative influence exerted by them on a certain people, a certain feature of their life, or a certain epoch of their history. We have here to deal, however, not with individual consciousness and individual habit, but with collective consciousness and collective habit. A study of the manifestations of these two forces as exhibited in almost every department of primitive life, whether material, esthetic, social, or religious, would be both interesting and instructive. Here it is proposed merely to consider the part they play in the single, albeit important, institution of marriage.

At all periods of the world's history and in all parts of the world known to us man has exhibited a preference for marrying among certain races, classes, or groups, and an aversion against marriage in certain others. Broadly speaking there are two different forms which the aversion takes—aversion towards marriage between persons closely related by blood or supposed to be so, and aversion toward marriage between those of very diverse races, tribes, social status, beliefs, and mentality generally. The origin of the latter is in some measure comprehensible, but the origin of the former not so clear and it has been the subject of considerable discussion. Yet the fact is well known and may, for our present purpose, be assumed. Under both of these aversions it must be remembered that we include, not so much the aversion of certain persons to marry, as the aversion to have them marry on the part of the entire community, the social aversion so to speak.

Aversion to marriage beyond certain limits operated in primitive society to prevent many marriages from taking place outside of the tribe, and at best such marriages were confined within a relatively restricted area. As national units grew larger and means of communication easier this area constantly expanded; it was never larger than it is today, but is still in evidence as applied to certain races, peoples and religious sects.

Where the aversion to close marriages obtains we should expect the exogamous group to consist of the blood relations of each individual, the number of such individuals within the tabooed class being determined either by the intensity of the opposition to intermarriage of blood kin or the ability of the people to trace relationship. Such a condition is found in modern white society, though it is not pressed to the extreme limit. Among the primitive races of North America, to which I shall particularly devote my attention, it is present among the Eskimo of the Arctic shores and islands, among the northern Indians in contact with them, among most of the Athapascan, Salishan, and Shoshonean peoples from the Mackenzie and Yukon rivers on the north to the borders of Mexico, and among most of the tribes of California. Here we may say that exogamy is consciously, and to a certain degree intelligently applied to individuals related by blood. Exceptions may occur in cases of adoption, and no doubt there are other exceptions, but they do not modify the truth of this statement to any appreciable extent.

When we turn to the other portions of North America north of Mexico, however, to the tribes of the North Pacific coast, to the Pueblo Indians of New Mexico and Arizona, to the occupants of the eastern and southeastern woodlands, some of the peoples of the Plains, and one or two in California, we find a very different social condition. There the exogamous group, instead of being determined almost uniformly by blood, is found to be a conventional body which includes persons related by blood and persons not related by blood and excludes persons related by blood and persons not related by blood. Numerous theories have been suggested to account for this apparently anomalous state of affairs, some of which explain it as an institution or condition more primitive than that of the exogamous group founded on blood and would derive the latter from it. One who has carried on investigations among tribes of this class with an unbiased mind, however, can hardly fail to come to the conclusion that the recognition of consanguinity is an original element, and that where an entire class of persons is called by the same term as the true father, mother, uncle, aunt, brother, sister, son, daughter, nephew, niece, etc., it is rather that the general application is an extension of the particular than the particular a specialization of the general. Such being the case we have to inquire whence came the largest groups over which these terms were extended. Although their origin may have been various there is reason to believe that in the majority of cases these clans or gentes, as we now call them, have originated in geographical groups or bands. At any rate the class of tribes first considered is divided into just such geographical groups, and on the north Pacific coast we find the tribes with clans preserving geographical names for their minor divisions which are in other respects analogous to the clans found elsewhere. On the other hand, in the first class of tribes we find some in which marriage rarely takes place within the band; not because such marriage is prohibited, but because each band being comparatively small, considerably more than half may be recognized as blood relations by most of its members. This condition of affairs is believed to have passed over into a tribal system with clans or gentes through the tendency to marry outside of the band, based on nothing more pronounced than blood relationship, which made clan endogamy successively avoided, looked down upon, tolerated, and finally prohibited. Be that as it may, the terms of relationship originally based on consanguinity came to be associated with social groups or clans which had only incidental connection with blood relationship, and, so identified, its original significance became obscured or lost; it became a conventionalized institution in which was preserved to only a slight degree the consciousness of its origin. This was the same evolution as that gone through by the people in their material culture, arts, and ceremonial life. We will now turn to a consideration of some of the different directions in which it was developed.

In the first place tribes of this class may be divided between those reckoning descent through the father and those reckoning it through the mother. When the group into which marriage is prohibited becomes stereotyped into an artificial body it is evident that the particular body to which each child is to belong has to be determined in some definite manner. Conceivably he might have rights of membership in two clans at the same time, or he might belong to either in accordance with his own choice, and we do indeed find just this condition among some of the Salish tribes of British Columbia, notably the Lillooet. It is, however, evident that such an arrangement would present certain practical difficulties. In the first place, it would be unstable and likely to disintegrate or to change into something else. Secondly, it would be difficult to preserve a balance between the different groups, and we know that such groups were usually jealous of losses. For this and probably other reasons it came about that in almost all tribes with clans the clanship of the child was determined at birth either into the clan of the father or that of the mother. In the former case a man considered his father's clansmen to all intents and purposes as his family, and in the alternative case he so regarded his mother's clansmen. This meant that marriage could not be contracted by him in the one case into the clan of his father and in the other case into that of his mother. Among some tribes this appears to have been the sole marriage prohibition, but in far more there was also strong opposition to marriage into the clan of the other parent. The opposition was probably stronger in very early times than later; but it is usually present in some form or other, varying all the way from mild disapproval to absolute prohibition. It is one of those indications that avoidance of close marriage was, at root, the main object of the regulations. Now, granted these two regulations in full force, a married man would have peculiar relations to at least three clans, those of his father, his mother and his wife, and in fact we find that in certain tribes three classes of men and women of as many different clans are fathers, uncles, brothers-in-law, aunts, mothers, and sisters-in-law to each married man.

Of course this is on the assumption that there were more than two clans or exogamous groups in the tribe. We have a number of cases, however, in which there were in fact but two such groups, although then we usually call them "phratries" or "moities" instead of "clans." In tribes of this description it is evident that we have only one possible choice in marriage. Each man or woman must mate in the other half of the tribe, and theoretically all of the men and women of one-half are fathers or mothers, and uncles or aunts, brothers and sisters, and nieces and nephews or children, while those on the other side are after marriage brothers-in-law, sisters-in-law, and the complementary relations in the fathers' and children's generations. Practically, these terms were sometimes more limited because in large tribes the two exogamous groups were subdivided and a man's attitude toward individuals of the minor groups to which his blood or marriage relations belonged was distinguished in some degree from the rest. This was, however, only an occasional modification.

In tribes with three clans one clan would contain fathers, aunts, brothers and sisters, another mothers, uncles, and perhaps cousins, and a third brothers- and sisters-in-law. In other words, as was the case with two-clan tribes, the whole nation would bear some relation to each individual. Another thing to be noticed is that with absolute exogamy enforced, as respected the clans of both father and mother, there would be a regular sequence of clans in each strain of blood. For if the tribe consists of three clans, Wolf, Bear, and Panther and we assume that marriage takes place between a Wolf man and a Panther woman, descent being male the children will all be Wolves. Now, as they cannot marry into either the clan of the father or into that of the mother, they must marry into the Bear. The children of the boys will belong to the Wolf, of course, and when they marry must marry into the Panther. The children of the girls will be Bear, but they also must marry into the Panther. If we follow the male line we shall, indeed, never have any other clan than the Wolf, but the clan of the mother will alternate in every generation from Panther to Bear and back again to Panther. If we follow the female line we shall have a regular change in each generation from Wolf to Bear, and then to Panther and back again to Wolf. If descent is female the result will be just the converse of this but in its practical results will differ none at all.

Tribes with two exogamous divisions are fairly numerous. Among such may be mentioned the Iroquois, the Choctaw and Chickasaw, the Haida, and the Tlingit, and there are traces in other parts of North America. Tribes with three exogamous divisions are rare, but perhaps further investigation would show that the three Delaware totems were of this character.

In still other tribes we have several clans, but it must be remembered that not all of these clans intermarried freely, certain clans being linked together into phratries, and beyond this each tribe with several clans often consisted of several towns in which not all of the exogamous groups were represented. Thus in the case of the Creek Indians it happened that there were probably few towns which contained more than six or eight exogamous groups and of these some were so insignificant or so slimly represented that there were in most cases not more than four or five exogamous divisions of real importance, and it was between these that nine-tenths of the marriages took place. Such being the case it is evident that in any line of descent there would be a frequent repetition of certain exogamous groups, although the far greater number of clan names would tend to obscure the fact.

Now, although we can not know positively it is possible that, if we could plot the succession of exogamous groups, we should have a somewhat regular alternation. If we assume four exogamous divisions represented by the clans Wolf, Panther, Bear, and Deer, descent being in the female line, we would have the husbands of Wolf women drawn successively from the Panther, Bear, and Deer clans, while in the male line we might have the regular sequence Wolf, Panther, Bear and Deer. It is probable that something approximating this may have existed among the tribes with many clans such as the Chippewa and other central Algonquian peoples, the Creeks, the Pueblos, Navaho and Tsimshian; but for lack of careful investigation, we cannot say so with absolute certainty. Still we do know that such a sequence was bound to occur with tribes of three exogamous groups and something near it would happen with four, for it must be for the women's husbands successively Bear or Deer, in the first generation and a choice of two only out of the four every time afterward. In the case of the men the succession would be to some extent determined along certain lines, though of course there is no necessity that the line should return regularly to the beginning. Nevertheless, absolute regularity would be attained if the repugnance to close marriages should extend one generation back of that of the parents—on the male side in case descent is matrilineal and on the female side in case it is patrilineal. Supposing that this actually took place and that the parents of self are Wolf and Panther, and the father's father or mother's father (as the case may be) is Bear, there would be, under the conditions laid down, but one clan into which self could marry, viz., Deer. Assuming male descent we should then find that the wives of a succession of Wolf men were Deer, Bear, and Panther in order, this order being repeated over and over indefinitely. In the case of a woman we should have Wolf, Deer, Bear, Panther, back to Wolf again. With matrilineal descent we would have the converse.

Limitation of marriage in these cases would be due to the extension of the repugnance toward marriage in related groups, an exceptional distance from the parties concerned, and the inevitable result would be that a man or woman must marry into some particular clan, not because that clan was arbitrarily picked out but because all others happened to contain persons supposed to be too closely connected. Some of the complications we observe in Australian society may be due to this cause, but many must be attributed to the segmentation of two or four original major divisions or the affiliation of groups of four or eight into two major divisions or moieties. In any case the direct result is to limit the choice of a prospective bridegroom or bride to a small fraction of an already small tribe. In this way there has grown up an artificial determination of marriage which has become so much a part of the habitual life of the tribe as to appear not merely right but necessary.

As if the limitations brought about in this way were not sufficient we have in many tribes in addition separation into castes. Besides dividing into or combining together several coördinate groups social complexes resulted in many places in which some were considered superior and some inferior—some, in other words, with peculiar privileges which others did not have. Thus, on the north Pacific coast of America we have several small clans known by the opprobrious term "food steamers," and among the Natchez there was a superior caste and a crowd of commons beneath. The patricians and plebeians of ancient Rome present a classic example. Except among the Natchez, where conditions were peculiar, the almost uniform accompaniment of a caste system was endogamy of the higher castes, resulting in enforced endogamy of the lower castes. And naturally where there were several grades as many degrees of marriage preference tended to develop, until it came about that the range of selection was reduced from this cause alone within very narrow limits. A contributing cause particularly active in societies divided into castes is the desire to hold together, and perpetuate the property as well as the privileges of a certain limited group. Thus, on the north Pacific coast, although group exogamy is strictly enforced, its effects are nullified by the selective inbreeding of two or three clans of the same caste, whereby practically the same bulk of property is kept within the group and so transmitted.

There were of course various other artificial or institutional limitations placed upon marriage, prominent among which may be mentioned those set by religious creed and sect. While these prohibitions and specifications have resulted from conscious determinations at various times, they have become imbedded in the institutional life of the tribe and produce almost instinctive reactions.

The geographical limits set to intermarriage were and still are to a considerable extent unavoidable; and the racial and tribal limits are both unavoidable and, for the present at least, necessary; but the artificial identification of relationship with groups having no natural connection with it, and the further limitation by caste lines reinforced by economic and religious considerations have made marriage an artificial institution in many countries of the civilized as well as the uncivilized world, and are bound to react injuriously upon their inhabitants. Under such conditions natural sympathy is overridden and the sexes are brought into unions on materialistic or institutional grounds which result in an unstable combination. Secondly, legitimate procreation being impossible as the result of mutual regard it takes place merely to satisfy the purely sensual appetites and is bound to reacth armfully on the parents and to the detriment of the future generations. Finally, law having proscribed as "immoral" natural unions founded on sympathy and having prescribed as moral those founded on convention, the perception of what constitutes true morality is difficult if not impossible of apprehension, with the result that truly normal unions may take place not recognized by society as moral, prostitutions occur sanctified by law and by religion, while in the face of this grotesque failure of society to recognize true values some will throw over all belief in and practise of morality and will form and break off unions to suit their every caprice, thus practically throwing the whole marriage institution overboard. Yet in such cases the first sinner is society itself, in prescribing unions from irrelevant considerations of clan, caste, sect, propinquity, property, and position.

PROCEEDINGS OF THE ACADEMY AND AFFILIATED SOCIETIES

THE CHEMICAL SOCIETY

The 244th meeting was held at the Cosmos Club on Thursday, January 21, 1915. The following resolution, presented by the committee, F. W. CLARKE, W. F. HILLEBRAND, and F. P. DEWEY, was adopted:

"ALBERT CHARLES PEALE, geologist and paleobotanist, and since 1898 in charge of the paleobotanical collections of the U. S. National Museum, died in Philadelphia on Saturday, December 5th, in the 65th year of his age. Dr. Peale was one of the original members of the Washington Chemical Society, and was for several years its secretary; for although he was not specifically a chemist, his interest in chemistry was very strong. His one noteworthy contribution to chemistry was Bulletin No. 32 of the United States Geological Survey, published in 1886, entitled "Lists and Analyses of the Mineral Springs of the United States;" a valuable compilation of all the data then accessible to the author, and very useful to chemists. He was also a pioneer in studying the thermal waters of the Yellowstone National Park. For more than forty years Dr. Peale was connected with the scientific service of the United States, and his friends in Washington are very numerous. The Washington Section of the American Chemical Society hereby expresses its appreciation of Dr. Peale as a man and a scholar, and its sincere regret at his loss."

Waiver of jurisdiction, as a local section of the American Chemical Society, was unanimously made in order to provide for the formation of a Virginia section of the Society.

The following papers were read:

C. O. JOHNS, of the Bureau of Chemistry: *Syntheses of methyl- and methylamino-purines.* A resumé of the work, conducted at the Sheffield Laboratory by Johnson in conjunction with Johns and others on the synthesis of pyrimidines and purines, was presented. In more detail an account was given of the synthesis of the alkyl purines by the author after many unsuccessful attempts had been made.

W. S. HUBBARD and W. L. MITCHEL, of the Bureau of Chemistry, (presented by Mr. HUBBARD): *The hydrolysis of sugar solutions under pressure.* The title might better be the hydrolysis of sugar solutions at elevated temperatures, but to the manufacturer the present title better conveys the idea of the process used. That bacteria, enzymes, acids, salts, elevated temperatures, and pressures under certain conditions bring about hydrolysis is quite well known. In this work high temperatures were obtained by steam under pressure and the hydrolysis occurred without caramelization. It is necessary to choose the sugar and water with considerable care. A temperature of 124°C., corresponding to a pressure of 1.375 kg. above atmospheric, was found to give the best results under the conditions of the experiment. (Author's abstract.)

Discussion. PHELPS pointed out the possibility that the change in the rate of hydrolysis might be due to the change in H ion concentration. HUDSON spoke of CO_2 under pressure as an agent for the inversion of sugar and the fact that it is generally regarded as a strictly mechanical effect. JOHNSTON pointed out that the effect of pressure alone on reacting solid or liquid systems is greatly overestimated, the temperature and concentration being the important factors. According to PHELPS, in these experiments, pressure increase alone had no effect on the rate of hydrolysis. HUDSON spoke of the work of SPRING as showing the effect of pressure on heterogeneous systems containing no gas phases. JOHNSTON said that SPRING's evidence was very poor and that the strictly pressure effects were very small in cases of true equilibria.

H. C. GORE, of the Bureau of Chemistry: *The concentration of apple juice by freezing.* By freezing, centrifuging to remove the ice and filtering through infusorial earth, apple cider was concentrated to 50 per cent total solids at a cost of 20 cents per gallon of concentrated juice. This juice can be kept without adding preservative. Other fruit juices have been concentrated in the same way.

Discussion: HUDSON inquired whether the juice was filtered before or after concentration. Speaker stated that the filtration could be carried on as easily after as before and was generally done in that way. BERG inquired as to the use of centrifugal filters. Speaker stated that these were found lacking because no suitable clarifier had been found while infusorial earth was entirely satisfactory.

The 245th meeting was held at the Cosmos Club on Thursday, February 11, 1915. Dr. JOHNSTON on behalf of the committee on communications briefly announced a new policy in regard to the programs for the meetings. The aim being to make the programs of wider scope in their interest, the main material is to be furnished on invitation from the committee. In addition it is proposed to have short informal communications, each limited to five minutes. As far as possible it is desired that these informal communications have some bearing on the general topic under discussion.

Carrying out the above policy the following papers were presented: F. E. WRIGHT, of the Geophysical Laboratory: *The petrographic microscope in analysis.* Attention was directed to the fundamental difference between a petrographic microscope and an ordinary microscope. The latter is essentially a magnifier and serves to render visible minute objects and details which are then recognized by their shape, size, and color. In the case of bacteria the differences in behavior with respect to certain stains aid in the diagnosis, while in other lines of investigation micro-chemical reactions serve the same purpose. The petrographic microscope, on the other hand, is not only a magnifier but also, and essentially, a measuring instrument of precision for ascertaining the optical properties of minute crystal fragments and grains a few hundredths, or even thousandths, of a millimeter in diameter. After a description of the petrographic microscope, considerable stress was placed on the fact that chemists had used, only to a very slight degree, the quantitative aspects of crystals as a means of identification. The various optical properties of crystals that offer possibilities in this direction (refractive index, birefringence, optic axial angle, extinction angle, etc.), and their quantitative determination were briefly described. The potential value of refractive index determinations for identification of either pure substances as such or in crystalline mixtures seems to be little realized among chemists. The method is applicable to quantities (a few hundredths of a milligram) much smaller than can ordinarily be subjected to chemical analysis and the time required is hardly appreciable in comparison. Such measurements of the optical properties of minute crystal grains have been used with great profit at the Geophysical Laboratory in the identification of phases in crystal mixtures and in the study of crystal growth. Of the possible lines of application of petrographic microscope methods in the field of chemical research some of the more important are: The identification and testing of drugs, of poisons, of dyes, of chemical reagents in crystal form, of chemical precipitates, baking powders, sugars and candies, spices, cements, abrasives; in short, of any solid material whether in powder form or in larger masses, crystalline or amorphous. For homogeneity and purity tests the preparation is immersed in a liquid of the refractive index of the main crystal substance which then practically disappears and any foreign material (adulteration or impurity) can be detected at a glance. Methods are also available for estimating the relative amounts of the different substances present in an aggregate. The presentation was accompanied by interesting lantern projections showing the appearance and behavior of minute crystals under the microscope.

Discussion: Many members of the Society took part in the discussion, arising in connection with inquiries as to the application of the methods in certain fields. Such methods have been in use in the study of soils; and the multiplicity of places, in the work of the chemist, where they might be applicable, was soon apparent. Special emphasis was put upon their use in drug identification and in the study and synthesis of organic substances. It was brought out that the practical applicability and importance of the methods will be greatly enhanced when investigators have determined the optical properties of the large number of substances that must be considered in their use in the different branches of chemistry and chemical technology.

L. H. ADAMS, of the Geophysical Laboratory: *Application of the interferometer to the quantitative analysis of solutions.* The principles of working and use of the Zeiss portable interferometer for liquids were described. The instrument has been found useful in the analysis of aqueous solutions and is applicable to a large number of liquid binary systems. The sensitiveness in terms of refractive index is about 2 in the seventh decimal place, and therefore salt solutions, for example, may be analysed with an accuracy of 0.0002 per cent. The possibility of error resulting from the wandering of the achromatic fringe was discussed together with methods for the avoidance of this difficulty. Several possible fields of use for the instrument were mentioned.

Discussion: It was brought out in the discussion that the temperature effects, in the comparison of liquids of different concentrations at different times as in the determination of the fixed points of a series of solutions, were not important, since the temperature coefficients of refractive index of the solutions of about the same concentration were nearly identical. The applicability of the instrument to the analysis of alcohol-water mixtures was mentioned, in answer to an inquiry, as being somewhat limited by the solubility of the cement used in making the glass cell container and the difficulties in making up and maintaining known solutions.

An informal communication was presented by E. G. WHERRY of the National Museum on *The detection of certain elements by their absorption spectra.* The spectra of the light reflected from minerals and gems of certain kinds have been found of considerable importance in the identification of these materials. Some 13 or 14 of the elements in their compounds are capable of identification in this way. Most of these belong to what are generally regarded as the rarer elements. The methods developed, in which only the visible spectrum was used, were described. The possible application to the detection of certain elements in other materials was mentioned.

Discussion: The use of the invisible part of the spectrum so as to give the method a greater range of applicability was suggested.

E. C. McKELVY, *Secretary.*

THE BOTANICAL SOCIETY OF WASHINGTON

The 102d regular meeting of the Botanical Society of Washington was held in the Assembly Hall of the Cosmos Club at 8 p.m., Tuesday, February 2, 1915. Fifty-two members and six guests were present. Messrs. P. A. YODER, STEPHEN ANTHONY, and JAMES M. SHULL were elected to membership. The following scientific program was presented:

S. C. STUNTZ: *Bamboo possibilities in America.* After a brief introductory statement outlining the past history of bamboo introduction into the United States, and sketching the present condition of bamboo planting in this country, attention was directed to the possible future uses for bamboo. Furniture, basketry, especially for parcel post shipments, Venetian blinds, and barrel hoops were suggested as probable industries in which bamboo would find use, while the development for ornamental planting, and as a possible stock for paper was especially emphasized. Lantern slides of bamboo plantations and uses abroad and in the United States were shown, together with a considerable exhibit of manufactured bamboo articles.

O. F. Cook: *Botany of cacao and patashte.* The patashte tree is a relative of the cacao, known to botanists under the name *Theobroma bicolor* Humboldt and Bonpland. It has dimorphic branches like cacao, the lateral branches being formed in whorls at the ends of the upright shoots, but only 3 laterals in a whorl, instead of 5 or 6, as in cacao. Many other differences in leaves, inflorescences and flowers were shown. The inflorescences of patashte are confined to new growth at the ends of the lateral branches, while cacao is caulocarpous, with all of the flowers produced from the old wood on the trunk and larger limbs of the tree. The various features were explained with lantern-slide illustrations, and the paper was followed by a brief discussion of the question whether trees with such numerous and definite differences should be classified in the same genus.

W. E. Safford: *Rediscovery of Lignum nephriticum.* Lignum nephriticum is a remarkable Mexican wood which was celebrated throughout Europe in the 16th, 17th, and the early part of the 18th centuries, not only for its reputed medicinal properties, but on account of the wonderful fluorescence of its infusion in spring water. Scarcely a fragment of this wood is now to be found in drug collections, and its very name has disappeared from encyclopedias. It is celebrated as the substance with which the Hon. Robert Boyle made his first investigations in the phenomenon of fluorescence. After giving a history of the literature on the subject Mr. Safford called attention to the confusion surrounding the origin of the wood, and the causes which prevented its botanical identification. For the first time specimens of the wood accompanied by herbarium material of the plant from which it was obtained have been the subject of critical study. The heartwood produced the characteristic fluorescence described by Robert Boyle, and the botanical material corresponded with Hernandez' original description of the plant yielding lignum nephriticum. This proves to be **Eysenhardtia polystachya** (Ortega) Safford (*Viborquia polystachya* Ortega, *Eysenhardtia amorphoides* H. B. K.). The lecture was illustrated by lantern slides, specimens of the wood and botanical material, photographic enlargments of sections of the wood made by Dr. Albert Mann, plant morphologist; and also by exhibition of the fluorescence of the extract of the wood in the rays of an arc light by Dr. Lyman J. Briggs, physicist, Bureau of Plant Industry, with remarks as to the value of lignum nephriticum as an indicator in titrimetric determinations. (Author's abstract.)

Perley Spaulding, *Corresponding Secretary.*

JOURNAL

OF THE

WASHINGTON ACADEMY OF SCIENCES

Vol. V   APRIL 4, 1915   No. 7

PHYSICS.—*Characteristics of radiation pyrometers.*[1] George K. Burgess and Paul D. Foote, Bureau of Standards.

Although this investigation, which is largely made up of instrumental details, does not readily lend itself to a brief summary, yet the following conclusions of a general nature may be mentioned.

The Stefan-Boltzmann law $E = (T^4 - T^4_0)$ is not, in general, except by accident, obeyed in its exactness by any of the pyrometers examined. The similar equation $E = a. T^4. T^{b-4}$, in which b is slightly different from 4 (usually neglecting the T_0 term) is, however, obeyed with sufficient exactness by all total radiation pyrometers.

The main factors influencing the value of the exponent b are the geometry and mechanical construction of the instrument; the value of b for 20 thermoelectric pyrometers ranged from about 3.5 to 4.5. The same instrument of the Féry type may have a different exponent according to its use with or without the sectorated diaphragm for increasing the temperature range. In general, a radiation pyrometer behaves not as a "black" or total receiver of energy, but as a "gray" receiver for the ordinary range of temperatures. For the Féry pyrometer with a gold mirror, for example, the effect of selective reflection of the gold mirror does not become practically appreciable until above 2500°C. but may cause an error of 500°C. at the temperature of

[1] To appear as a Scientific Paper of the Bureau of Standards.

the sun. The auxiliary apparatus, galvanometer or potentiometer, and recording devices, can be constructed so that their errors will be practically negligible. For the work of the highest accuracy the potentiometric method of measurement is to be preferred with thermoelectric radiation pyrometers.

The principal errors to which the several types of radiation pyrometers are subject are shown to lie in the design and mechanical construction of these instruments, and certain of these inherent errors, such as lag or slowness in reaching an equilibrium reading, require for satisfactory results, that the pyrometer be calibrated and used under similar conditions of time of ex-posure, distance from and aperture of source. Wide variations in the lag effect exist among apparently similar instruments, ranging from a few seconds to an hour or more. These and other errors of appreciable magnitude, such as stray reflection, convection currents, intervening atmosphere, size of source, tarnishing of receiving mirror, etc., should be considered in accurate work. It is shown that errors greater than 100°C. may readily be caused by dirt on, or oxidation of, mirror. The magnitude of errors due to varying the focusing distance, may amount to several hundred degrees if suitable precautions are not taken.

A convenient method for the rapid comparison of different types of pyrometer, and for determining the effects of size of aperture and focusing distance was devised, consisting of a wide nickel (oxide) strip heated electrically, a series of circular, water-cooled diaphragms, and an optical bench.

The methods in use at the Bureau of Standards for the calibration of radiation pyrometers by means of especially designed experimental "black bodies" are described in detail and methods of extrapolation outlined, as well as methods of use of radiation pyrometers, including methods of obtaining approximately correct temperatures for the case in which a source of insufficient size is sighted upon. The application of the radiation pyrometer to the determination of the total emissivity of non-black substances and to the measurement of temperatures is also discussed in detail.

PHYSICS.—*A study of some recent methods for the determination of total sulphur in rubber.*[1] J. B. TUTTLE and A. ISAACS, Bureau of Standards.

This investigation was undertaken to learn whether or not the methods recently published for the determination of sulphur in rubber were any improvement over the Waters and Tuttle method, the one now in use at the Bureau of Standards. The methods investigated were those of Spence and Young; of Deussen, of Alexander, of the Joint Rubber Insulation Committee, of Kaye and Sharp; of Frank and Marckwald, and of Waters and Tuttle. These were subdivided, according to the method of attack, into three classes: direct solution, direct fusion, and solution and fusion methods. A large number of determinations was made on a number of samples, two of the latter being of known composition which were specially prepared by one of the authors.

The methods which have been compared may be divided into two classes, viz. those for the determination of the total sulphur and those for the determination of sulphur other than that present in the insoluble sulphates. It was found that the methods of the second class could not be relied upon to give accurate results.

The direct solution methods, those of Spence and Young, and of Deussen, involve the use of concentrated nitric acid. This was first suggested by Henriques but is objectionable because it gives rise to low results.

The direct fusion methods, those of Alexander, of the Joint Rubber Insulation Committee, and of Kaye and Sharp, are reliable only when the free sulphur content is low, and are therefore not applicable to routine analysis.

The solution and fusion method of Frank and Marckwald was found to be unreliable when the free sulphur was high. The Waters and Tuttle method was found to give satisfactory results and is recommended for general use.

A new suggestion is offered, namely, to determine separately

[1] Detailed paper to appear in the Bulletin of the Bureau of Standards.

the free sulphur and the sulphur remaining after the extraction, reporting the sum of the two quantities as the total sulphur. This procedure eliminates the troublesome effect of the free sulphur upon the determination of the total sulphur.

BOTANY.—*Glaucothea, a new genus of palms from Lower California.* O. F. COOK, Bureau of Plant Industry.

The type of the new genus is **Glaucothea armata** (S. Wats.),[1] commonly known in cultivation as the "blue palm," on account of its extremely glaucous foliage. The peculiar color is due to the presence of an unusually thick coating of wax, and may be considered as an adaptive specialization to desert conditions. Glaucothea is known in a wild state only from the interior of the northern part of Lower California, about sixty miles below the international boundary. It is the nearest neighbor of *Washingtonia filifera*, the only native palm of California, found in the canyons along the eastern base of the San Jacinto Mountains, in the Salton Basin.

The new genus is separated from Erythea, whose type is *Erythea edulis* (Wendl.) S. Wats., a native of Guadelupe Island, off the coast of Lower California. The difference in habitat appears significant when Erythea and Glaucothea are observed in cultivation. Erythea, being a maritime palm, is entirely at home in the cool climate of the Coast Belt of California, flowering and fruiting with great regularity after the proper age has been reached. Glaucothea makes rather slow growth in the Coast Belt, seldom produces flowers, and does not fruit, probably for lack of sufficient heat. Though planted in large numbers in California, the supply of seed is still limited and precarious, being obtained only from the wild palms in the canyons of Lower California. But there is no apparent reason why seed should not be produced eventually by the palms that have been planted in recent years in the drier and warmer interior districts of southern California and Arizona, as at Riverside and Phoenix.

[1] *Brahea* (?) *armata* S. Wats. Proc. Am. Acad. **11**: 146. 1876.
    Erythea armata S. Wats. Bot. Calif. **2**: 212. 1880.

Glaucothea appears to be well adapted to these arid regions, and as hardy as *Washingtonia filifera*, which produces fruit in abundance in the Salt River valley of Arizona, as well as in southern California, though not near the coast.

Glaucothea shares with Washingtonia the habit of not producing flowers when young, or until the trunk has attained a height of 15 or 20 feet, while *Erythea edulis* commonly flowers at 5 or 6 feet. Another point of agreement between Washingtonia and Glaucothea is the production of very long slender inflorescences, extending far beyond the leaves. These are in striking contrast with the inflorescences of *Erythea edulis*, which hardly exceed the petioles of the leaves. The massive trunk and heavily armed petioles of Glaucothea afford further analogies with Washingtonia and obvious contrasts to Erythea.

Though more closely allied in its botanical characters to Erythea, the new genus may be distinguished at once, in any stage of development, by the color of the foliage. The floral structures are similar to those of Erythea, but definite specializations are shown. As in many desert plants, the flowers are reduced in size and of thicker texture, and the buds are protected by relatively larger and more fleshy sepals. The petals are attached close to the rim of the staminal cup and are not opened widely at the time of flowering, which no doubt reduces the danger of drying the stigma and thus preventing pollination. These and other differences are summarized in the following diagnosis:

Glaucothea Cook, gen. nov.

Distinguished from Erythea by the very robust trunk, strongly armed petiole, thin, papery ligule, decurved midrib, narrow median segments and glaucous, wax-covered leaf-surfaces; inflorescences slender, elongate, greatly exceeding the leaves, the lower primary branches subtended by spathes, the others without spathes; sepals thick and fleshy; petals broadly triangular, rounded at the apex, attached close to the broadly sinuate rim of the staminal cup.

The type species, as already stated, is *Glaucothea armata* (S. Wats.), from the northern part of Lower California. The generic name was suggested by the relationship with Erythea, though not derived in the same manner. Glaucothea means "Gray Goddess," and may be considered as allusion to Minerva, whose familiar Greek name was "Athene Gray-eye." The olive tree, with its glaucous foliage, was sacred to Athene, and this palm has a similar claim to distinction among the members of its order. The foliage is of a very peculiar, pearly grayish-green, sometimes with a slight tinge of purple. Well-grown individuals are extremely beautiful, and strikingly different from any other fan-palms that have been introduced into the United States.

Following are more extended descriptions of Glaucothea and Erythea, with the contrasting characters stated in greater detail.

GENERIC DESCRIPTION OF GLAUCOTHEA

Trunk large and very robust, tapering gradually from a thick, somewhat bulbous base.

Leaves very numerous, nearly circular in general form, composed of many numerous deeply divided segments; leaf-sheaths recurved only near the end; petioles armed along the margins with numerous strong, hooked spines; ligule thin, without cushions of tomentum; midrib distinctly developed, decurved somewhat as in Inodes, and with several of the median leaf-segments reduced in size; leaf surfaces rendered glaucous by a thick coating of wax.

Inflorescences slender, erect, greatly exceeding the leaves, the axis enclosed in numerous, slender, naked spathes, 3 to 5 of these borne on the elongated base of the inflorescence, below the branches; primary branches of two classes, the lower 4 or 5 large and subtended by spathes, the others small, numerous and without spathes, together forming a terminal panicle like one of the large primary branches; flowering branchlets simple, very long and slender, with the flowers solitary or in clusters of 2 or 3.

Flowers minute, dull purplish, only slightly opened; sepals thick and fleshy to the end, scarious only on the margins; petals broadly triangular, with a rather blunt apex, strongly thickened within, the stamens accommodated by deep excavations; staminal cup with entire, broadly sinuate margins between the abruptly broadened bases of the filaments, bearing the petals near the rim of the cup; pistils set compactly together. Fruit rather small, with a thin pericarp.

SPECIFIC DESCRIPTION

The following details may be added to Watson's brief description of the species, which gave no information regarding the inflorescence or flowers.

Glaucothea armata (S. Wats.) Cook.

Trunk in robust specimens attaining a circumference of about 11 feet, or a diameter of over 3 feet, the height said to attain 40 feet and upward in the wild state, but most of the cultivated individuals still under 20 feet.

Leaves very numerous, forming a large crown, the basal sheath becoming everted only near the end, but much farther up than in Erythea, the petioles thus appearing shorter; surface of petioles beset with small deep purplish-brown scales, these more numerous in the lower part, but much less abundant than in Erythea; margins of petioles indurated, ivory white, armed with strong, curved white teeth, these extremely variable in form and distribution; ligule thin and papery, not densely tomentose-spongy as in Erythea; rachis evident, distinctly decurved; several of the median segments distinctly narrowed, and also some of the basal segments, but much fewer than in *Erythea edulis*.

Spathes green and glaucous when young, without pubescence or scurf except on narrow lines along the margins; lowest spathe about 2 feet long and 3 inches broad, split on both sides at apex, the others split on only one side.

Flowers dull purplish in color instead of creamy white as in *Erythea edulis*, smaller in size and much less conspicuous at the time of flowering, not opened widely; buds also of different shape, more rounded at apex and relatively wider at base because of the large fleshy sepals; flower-clusters subtended by minute bracts less conspicuous than those of Erythea.

The descriptions of the inflorescences and flowers are based on material taken from a living palm in the collection of Mr. C. B. Hale at Santa Barbara, California, July 7, 1913. The specimens are in the U. S. National Herbarium, under numbers 694866 and 694867.

CONTRASTING CHARACTERS OF ERYTHEA[2]

Trunk rather slender, in comparison with Glaucothea, columnar, scarcely thickened at the base.

Leaves fewer and broader than in Glaucothea; leaf-sheaths recurved well below the end, the recurved portion distinguished by the fibers along the margins, functioning with the petiole and increasing its apparent length; margins of petiole denticulate near the base, often

[2] For the original description of Erythea, see Watson, S., Botany of California, **2**: 211. 1880.

smooth above; ligule with large, spongy cushions of tomentum; mid-rib rudimentary, scarcely decurved, only a few of the median segments narrowed; leaf-surfaces vivid green, not concealed by a covering of wax.

Inflorescences robust, spreading, shorter than the leaves, the main axis enclosed in short, robust, shaggy, scale-covered spathes; primary branches 9 to 11, each subtended by a spathe, and with 1 or 2 additional spathes at the base; flowering branchlets simple, rather long and robust, the flowers in clusters of 3 to 6.

Flowers larger, more conspicuous and more widely opened than in Glaucothea; sepals fleshy at base, the upper half thin and scarious, with a reddish costa; petals triangular, with a rather thin, tapering and sharp-pointed apex, spreading wide apart at the time of flowering; staminal cup with deep sharp incisions between the broadly sloping bases of the filaments, each alternate filament subtended by a strong vertical carina on the inner face of the staminal tube.

Fruits large, the seed surrounded by a thick, firm pericarp, fleshy and edible when mature.

COMPARISON OF INFLORESCENCES

Perhaps the most striking differences between the two genera are those that determine the forms of the inflorescences. With respect to these characters Erythea might be compared with Inodes, while Glaucothea is more like Washingtonia, both with respect to the greater length of the inflorescences as a whole and the more elongate form of the individual spathes. In Erythea the flowers are borne on rather stiff, spreading branches and appear in large billowy masses inside the crown of leaves, while in Glaucothea they are carried out beyond the leaves and suspended on long drooping, tassel-like panicles. The inflorescence of Erythea is relatively unspecialized, with the numerous primary branches each subtended by a spathe, while the inflorescence of Glaucothea is specialized in two ways. Instead of having a short base with only one or two empty spathes below the branches, as in Erythea, there is a long, slender, stalk-like base with 4 or 5 tubular spathes. Following these are 4 or· 5 other ensiform or spathulate spathes, subtending a like number of large primary branches. The remaining primary branches, to the number of 15 or more, are left without spathes; but they are much smaller than the others and all together form a large drooping panicle, like one of the larger branches that are provided with spathes. The total number of spathes is about the same as in Erythea, but the spathes do not stand in the same relation with the branches. At the base of the inflorescence there are several spathes without branches, and at the end of the inflorescence many branches without spathes. The number of primary branches is greater in Glaucothea, not being limited by the number of spathes.

OTHER RELATED PALMS

The relationships of Erythea and Glaucothea lie on the one side with the fan-palms of the Pacific islands and on the other side with those of Mexico and Central America. In its very large fruits and thick exocarp, Erythea represents the extreme of the American series, and the nearest approach to the Pacific island fan-palms. The foliage is somewhat similar, and the very abundant scaly tomentum of the petioles and spathes is another common feature; but the sepals of the American genera are not thick and woody nor completely coalesced to form a deep cup, as in the Pacific island genus.[3]

The genus Brahea may be considered as the nearest Mexican relative of Glaucothea. It shares with Glaucothea the slender exserted inflorescence, with several empty spathes below the branches. But the species of Brahea are smaller and more slender palms, with small narrowly oval fruits, and the albumen grooved on one side like that of the date palm.

[3] It has long been known that the name Pritchardia is incorrectly applied to the Pacific Island palms, but no satisfactory substitute seems to have been proposed. To supply this deficiency the new name **Styloma** is suggested, in allusion to the large indurated styles. The type species is **Styloma pacifica** (*Pritchardia pacifica* Seem. & Wendl.), from the Fiji Islands. Fifteen other species are known, as recognized in Beccari's revision of the genus (Webbia, **4**: 220–240. 1913), nine of these being from the Hawaiian Islands, and six from other parts of Polynesia; all were described originally under Pritchardia. The Hawaiian species of Styloma are as follows: **S. hillebrandii, S. gaudichaudii, S. martii, S. arecina, S. rockiana, S. lanigera, S. eriostachys, S. eriophora and S. minor.** The remaining species are: **S. thurstonii**, from Fiji; **S. vuylstekeana** and **S. pericularum**, from Pomotu; **S. remota**, from Bird Island; **S. maideniana** doubtfully reported from Melanesia; and **S. insignis**, of unknown origin. Beccari also unites with Pritchardia the Cuban genus Colpothrinax, but this should be retained as distinct from Styloma.

ABSTRACTS

Authors of scientific papers are requested to see that abstracts, preferably prepared and signed by themselves, are forwarded promptly to the editors. Each of the scientific bureaus in Washington has a representative authorized to forward such material to this journal and abstracts of official publications should be transmitted through the representative of the bureau in which they originate. The abstracts should conform in length and general style to those appearing in this issue.

METEOROLOGY.—*Types of storms of the United States and their average movements.* EDWARD H. BOWIE, and R. HANSON WEIGHTMAN. Washington, 1914, 37 pages; 114 charts (U. S. Weather Bureau, Monthly Weather Review, Supplement No. I).

The authors have classed the storms (lows) of the United States according to their point of apparent origin. In this classification they have wisely followed the geographic divisions adopted by an earlier investigator of the subject.

The period covered includes the twenty-one years 1892–1912, and the total number of lows considered was 2597.. The authors have departed from the traditional way of portraying storm paths. Instead of indicating by a single continuous line the average path of a group of storms they have taken as the geographic unit of movement the successive five-degree squares across the country, from the Pacific to the Atlantic, and have computed for each five-degree square the mean direction and 24-hour travel, based on the total number of lows of the group under consideration that temporarily occupied the square during the entire period. The results have been expressed by a series of arrows, one for each square. Each arrow shows, first, the number of lows that have temporarily occupied the square, and upon which the computations have been based; second, the mean direction and 24-hour travel of the lows, the length of the arrows being proportional to the average number of miles covered by the lows. Notwithstanding the very large number of lows used, not a few squares are represented by less than five lows, but such deficiency is incident to a work of this character, especially in those regions where lows pertaining to a certain group seldom penetrate.

The advantage of this system lies in the fact that it shows at a glance the scattering which takes place in the distribution of the several groups of lows in latitude. Thus, the North Pacific group, which is essentially a storm moving in high latitudes, has on the average for January, beginning with latitude 55°, along the 95th meridian and proceeding southward by five-degree steps, seven, six, seven, and four lows, respectively. The corresponding numbers for July are three, one, four, and one. The senior author concludes the paper with a number of precepts collected by him during his service as a forecaster.

W. J. H.

METEOROLOGY.—*The thunderstorm and its phenomena.* W. J. HUMPHREYS. Monthly Weather Review, **42**: 348–380. 1914; Journal of the Franklin Institute, **178**: 517–560, 751–776. 1914.

The Simpson theory, that the great amount of electrical separation in a thunderstorm is due to mechanical rupture of raindrops, the best supported and most consistent theory of this phenomenon, is explained in detail. From this theory it follows, as was already evident from other considerations, that thunder and lightning are neither storm-originating nor storm-controlling factors, but themselves the result of those violent winds that obtain beneath and within large cumulo-nimbus clouds.

Hence those conditions essential to the production of cumulus clouds, that is, abundant humidity and that temperature distribution which induces strong vertical convection, are also essential to, and likewise sufficient for, the genesis of the thunderstorm. This in turn explains why, over land areas, these storms are more frequent in the afternoon than at night, more frequent in summer than in winter, and more frequent in equatorial regions than in higher latitudes.

According to the distribution of barometric pressure and surface temperatures, thunderstorms are divided into five distinct classes, and each class illustrated by a group of three meteorological charts. One of each group gives the typical conditions in question. The other two show respectively the 12 hour antecedent and the 12 hour subsequent conditions.

The abrupt and marked changes in temperature, pressure and wind velocity that accompany the onset of a thunderstorm are all discussed in detail, as are also the downrush of cold air and the uprush of warm, the genesis of hail, the formation of "thunder heads," roll scud, and other details of the storm.

The various forms of lightning, streak, rocket, ball, sheet, beaded, return and dark, are described, in part by the aid of photographs obtained by rotating cameras, and are in a measure explained. The question as to whether the lightning discharge is direct or alternating is discussed and reasons offered for believing it to be usually if not always direct.

In addition to the above such subjects as the spectrum of lightning, duration of discharge, length of streak, chemical effects and danger; cause of thunder, distance heard, rumbling, etc., are all briefly discussed.   W. J. H.

BOTANY.—*A text-book of grasses*. A. S. HITCHCOCK. The Macmillan Co. Pp. 1–276. September, 1914.

The work consists of two parts, the first being devoted to economic agrostology, the second to systematic agrostology. Part I includes an elementary account of such subjects as pastures, meadows, lawns, reclaiming sand-dunes, and the grass-crop areas. Part II is devoted to morphology and taxonomy, with a chapter on ecology and another on nomenclature.

The morphology of the vegetative and floral organs is discussed in considerable detail. The classification adopted is essentially that of Hackel in Engler and Prantl's Pflanzenfamilien. Although this arrangement, especially of the tribes, is in some respects unsatisfactory and artificial, it is, according to the author, the best system yet proposed. There is a key to the 13 tribes and, under each tribe, keys to the genera found in the United States. Paragraphs are devoted to those genera that include economic species, and the more important of these are described and illustrated. Special paragraphs are devoted to such subjects as the origin and classification of the wheats, the cultivated varieties of sorghum, and the weedy species of Bromus.

Appended to Part I is a list of government publications referring to forage crops and special uses of grasses; and to Part II a list of books and articles relating to taxonomic agrostology.

A. S. H.

REFERENCES

Under this heading it is proposed to include, by author, title, and citation, references to all scientific papers published in or emanating from Washington. It is requested that authors coöperate with the editors by submitting titles promptly, following the style used below. These references are not intended to replace the more extended abstracts published elsewhere in this JOURNAL.

METEOROLOGY

ABBE, CLEVELAND, JR. *Washington and Paris winters.* Monthly 'Weather Review, **42**: 626–628. 1914. (An interesting comparison of the winter temperatures of these two cities.—W. J. H.)

ABBOT, C. G. *Extracts from the annual report of the Smithsonian Astrophysical Observatory.* Monthly Weather Review, **42**: 621–623. 1914. (Discusses the recent work at Washington and in California of the Smithsonian Astrophysical Observatory.—W. J. H.)

BATEMAN, H. *Influence of meteorological conditions on the propagation of sound.* Monthly Weather Review, **42**: 258–265. 1914. (A convenient summary of what is known on this subject, with many references.—W. J. H.)

BEALS, E. A. *Frost forecasts and protection in Oregon, Washington and Idaho.* Monthly Weather Review, **42**: 587. 1914.

BESSON, L. *The halos of November 1 and 2, 1913.* Monthly Weather Review, **42**: 431–436. 1914. (Translated by C. F. TALMAN. Describes and explains an unusually complex halo that was seen in many portions of the central and eastern United States. For criticism see Monthly Weather Review, **42**: 619. 1914.—W. J. H.)

BESSON, L. *The different forms of halos and their observation.* Monthly Weather Review, **42**: 436–446. 1914. (Translated by CLEVELAND ABBE, JR., from Bulletin de la Société astronomique de France, mars, avril et mai 1911. A description of many forms of halos that have been reported.—W. J. H.)

BEZOLD, W. VON. *Theoretical meteorology: more particularly the thermodynamics of the atmosphere.* Monthly Weather Review, **42**: 453–455. 1914. (Communicated to the International Meteorological Congress at Chicago, Aug., 1893.)

BLAIR, W. R. *The diurnal system of convection.* Bulletin Mount Weather Observatory, **6**: 221–243, 1914.

BLAIR, W. R. *Free air data at Mount Weather from July 3, 1913, to May 7, 1914, on "International Days."* Bulletin Mount Weather Observatory, **6**: 244–252. 1914.

BLAIR, W. R., and GREGG, W. R. *Free air data in southern California, July and August, 1913.* Monthly Weather Review, **42**: 410–426. 1914. (A discussion of the meteorological portion of an investigation undertaken jointly by the Astrophysical Observatory of the Smithsonian Institution and the Mount Weather Observatory of the Weather Bureau. The data consist of observations taken by free balloons sent up from Avelon, and of captive balloons and mountain observations obtained on and near Mount Whitney. —W. J. H.)

Bowie, E. H , and Weightman, R. H. *Types of storms of the United States and their average movements.* Monthly Weather Review Supplement No. 1, 1914. (Divides American storms into ten types according to region of origin, and gives on full page charts, the distribution and average 24-hour movement of each type for each month.—W. J. H.)

Briggs, R. R. *Frost protection in Arizona.* Monthly Weather Review, **42**: 589–590. 1914.

Brooks, C. F. *The distribution of snowfall in cyclones of the eastern United States.* Monthly Weather Review, **42**: 318–330, with 11 full page charts. 1914.

Carpenter, F. A. *Flood studies at Los Angeles.* Monthly Weather Review, **42**: 385–389. 1914.

Carpenter, F. A. *Utilization of frost warnings in the citrus region near Los Angeles, Cal.* Monthly Weather Review, **42**: 569–571. 1914. (Discusses practical work in connection with the protection of citrus groves from frost.— W. J. H.)

Carpenter, F. A. and Garthwaite, J. W. *Memorandum on air drainage in the vicinity of the Corona district, Cal.* Monthly Weather Review, **42**: 572– 573. 1914.

Cline, J. L. *Frost protection by irrigation in southern Texas.* Monthly Weather Review, **42**: 591–592. 1914.

Coberly, E. D. *The hourly frequency of precipitation at New Orleans, La.* Monthly Weather Review, **42**: 537–538. 1914.

Coblentz, W. W. *The exudation of ice from the stems of plants.* Monthly Weather Review, **42**: 490–499. 1914. (An interesting account with abundant illustrations, of the formation of ice fringes on the stems of plants rich in sap tubes, analogous to the formation of the familiar columns of "ground-ice."—W. J. H.)

Ekholm, Nils. *Influence of the deviating force of the earth's rotation of the movement of the air.* Monthly Weather Review, **42**: 330–339. 1914. (Communicated to the International Meteorological Congress at Chicago, August, 1893. Discusses a well known phenomenon with simple mathematics.— W. J. H.)

Erskine-Murray, J. *The function of the atmosphere in [wireless] transmission.* Monthly Weather Review, **42**: 534–537. 1914. (Reprinted by request from Year Book of Wireless Telegraphy and Telephony, 1914. Regards the atmosphere as divisible into a lower nonconducting layer and an upper conducting layer.—W. J. H.)

Fujiwhara, S. *The horizontal rainbow.* Monthly Weather Review, **42**: 426– 430. 1914. (Revised and reprinted from Jour. Metr. Soc. Japan, March, 1914. A mathematical discussion of an unusual optical phenomenon.— W. J. H.)

Garthwaite, J. W. *Letter on frost and frost protection.* Monthly Weather Review, **42**: 571–572. 1914. (Comments on frost protection by a practical citrus grower.—W. J. H.)

HALL, M. *Photometric measures of the zodiacal light.* Monthly Weather Review, **42**: 311–317. 1914.

HALL, M. *Notes on observing the zodiacal light.* Monthly Weather Review, **42**: 521. 1914.

HANN, J. *Daily march of the meteorological elements in the Panama Canal Zone.* Monthly Weather Review, **42**: 526–534. 1914. (Translated from Sitzungsb. d. Kaiserl. Akad. d. Wissens. in Wien, Math.-naturw. Kl., Jan. 1914.)

HANN, J. *Remarks on the nature of cyclones and anticyclones.* Monthly Weather Review, **42**: 612–615. 1914. (Communicated to the International Meteorological Congress at Chicago, 1893. Discusses objections to the convectional theory of storms.—W. J. H.)

HARRINGTON, M. W. *Systematic exploration of the upper air with estimates of costs.* Monthly Weather Review, **42**: 619–621. 1914. (Read before the International Conference on Aerial Navigation, Chicago, August, 1893. Interesting in the light of subsequent events.—W. J. H.)

HASTINGS, C. S. *On halos.* Monthly Weather Review, **42**: 617–619. 1914. (Extract from his book "Light," supplemented by recent remarks.—W. J. H.)

HENRY, A. J. *Artificial deepening of the Arkansas at Wichita, Kans.* Monthly Weather Review, **42**: 391–393. 1914. (Bed of river has been lowered five or six feet during the past ten years.—W. J. H.)

HERBERTSON, A. J. *The thermal regions of the globe.* Monthly Weather Review, **42**: 286–289. 1914. (Reprinted from the Geographical Journal, London, Nov., 1912.)

HERRMANN, C. F. VON. *Protection against frost in Georgia.* Monthly Weather Review, **42**: 585–586. 1914.

HUMPHREYS, W. J. *The planets and the weather.* Monthly Weather Review, **42**: 346–347. 1914. (Computes the possible temperature changes caused by the planets and the moon, amounting at times to 0.01°F. to 0.02°F.— W. J. H.)

HUMPHREYS, W. J. *The thunderstorm and its phenomena.* Monthly Weather Review, **42**: 348–380. 1914. Journal of the Franklin Institute, **178**: 517–560, 751–776. 1914. (Discusses the origin of thunderstorm electricity, the kinds and nature of lightning, the mechanics of the thunderstorm and conditions favorable to its development.—W. J. H.)

HUMPHREYS, W. J. *Frost protection.* Monthly Weather Review, **42**: 562–569. 1914. (A discussion of the scientific principles that underly artificial protection against frost.—W. J. H.)

KILLAM, S. D. *Graphical integration of functions of a complex variable with applications.* Monthly Weather Review, **42**: 277–283. 1914. (An entirely mathematical paper.—W. J. H.)

KIMBALL, H. H. *Relation between solar radiation intensities and the temperature of the air in the Northern Hemisphere in 1912-1913.* Bulletin Mount Weather Observatory, **6**: 205–220. 1914. (Discusses the decrease in the intensity of direct solar radiation that followed the eruption of Katmai in June, 1912.—W. J. H.)

KIMBALL, H. H. *Solar radiation intensities at Mount Weather, Va., during April, May and June, 1914.* Monthly Weather Review, **42**: 310–311. 1914.

KIMBALL, H. H. *The total radiation received on a horizontal surface from the sun and sky at Mount Weather, Va.* Monthly Weather Review, **42**: 474–487. 1914. (Total radiation is divided into two parts, direct solar and diffuse sky radiation, and values by decades through the year given for all hours of the day.—W. J. H.)

KIMBALL, H. H. *Solar radiation intensities at Mount Weather, Va., during July, August and September, 1914.* Monthly Weather Review, **42**: 520. 1914.

KIRK, J. M. *Halos and precipitation at Wauseon, Ohio.* Monthly Weather Review, **42**: 616. 1914.

LYMAN, T. *The absorption of the atmosphere for ultra-violet light.* Monthly Weather Review, **42**: 487–489. 1914. (A summary, with references, of all that is known on this subject.—W. J. H.)

MARVIN, C. F. *Are lightning flashes unidirectional or oscillating electric discharges?* Monthly Weather Review, **42**: 499–501. 1914. (Questions the adequacy of recent observations by De Blois to answer this question.— W. J. H.)

MARVIN, C. F. *Air drainage explained.* Monthly Weather Review, **42**: 583–585. 1914. (Explains the phenomenon in a different manner from that of the text-books.—W. J. H.)

MITCHELL, A. J. *Frost and frost protection in Florida.* Monthly Weather Review, **42**: 588–589. 1914.

MÖLLER, MAX. *Mechanics of atmospheric air within cyclones and anticyclones.* Monthly Weather Review, **42**: 265–270. 1914. (A paper communicated to the International Meteorological Congress at Chicago, August, 1893, and therefore, while still good, open to considerable revision and extension. —W. J. H.)

NAKAMURA, K. *Observations of horizontal rainbows.* Monthly Weather Review, **42**: 430–431. 1914. (Reprinted from Jour. Metrl. Soc. Japan, June, 1914.)

OKADA, T. *Notes on the formation of glazed frost.* Monthly Weather Review, **42**: 284–286. 1914. (Reprinted from Jour. Metrl. Soc. Japan, May, 1914. Contains a mathematical discussion of the cooling of rain drops.—W. J. H.)

PALMER, A. H. *Halos and their relation to weather.* Monthly Weather Review, **42**: 446–451. 1914.

REED, C. D. *Drought at New York City.* Monthly Weather Review, **42**: 629–631. 1914. (Tabulates data concerning the principal droughts at New York City during the years 1871–1914.—W. J. H.)

REED, W. G. *Meteorology at the Lick Observatory.* Monthly Weather Review, **42**: 339–345. 1914. (Discusses a continuous record of the meteorological elements of approximately 34 years' length.—W. J. H.)

ROVER, W. H. *A mechanism for illustrating certain systems of lines of force and stream lines.* Bulletin Mount Weather Observatory, **6**: 195–204. 1914.

SANDSTRÖM, J. W. *Influence of terrestrial rotation on the condition of the atmosphere and ocean.* Monthly Weather Review, **42**: 523–526. 1914.

SMITH, G. W. *Forecast distribution.* Monthly Weather Review, **42**: 541–545. 1914.

SMITH, J. WARREN. *Frost warnings and orchard heating in Ohio.* Monthly Weather Review, **42**: 573–583. 1914. (Discusses the practical application of orchard heating in Ohio.—W. J. H.)

SPRAGUE, M. *Frost and frost protection in Texas.* Monthly Weather Review, **42**: 590. 1914.

THIESSEN, A. H. *Protection from frost in Utah.* Monthly Weather Review, **42**: 586–587. 1914.

VOORHEES, J. F. *Notes on frost protection in the vicinity of Knoxville, Tenn.* Monthly Weather Review, **42**: 587. 1914.

WARD, R. DE C. *Land and sea breezes.* Monthly Weather Review, **42**: 274–277. 1914. (Communicated to the International Meteorological Congress at Chicago, August, 1893. A summary of what was then known about these winds, to which not much has since been added.—W. J. H.)

WINSLOW, C. E. A., and BROWNE, W. W. *The microbic content of indoor and outdoor air.* Monthly Weather Review, **42**: 452–453. 1914.

ENTOMOLOGY

BACK, E. A., and PEMBERTON, C. E. *Life history of the melon fly.* Journal of Agricultural Research, **3**: 269–274. December 15, 1914.

CAUDELL, A. N. *Orthoptera of the Yale-Dominican expedition of 1913.* Proceedings of the U. S. National Museum, **47**: 491–495. October 24, 1914. (Lists all of the material collected and describes 2 new species.—J. C. C.)

COAD, B. R. *Feedings habits of the boll weevil on plants other than cotton.* Journal of Agricultural Research, **2**: 235–245. June 15, 1914. (Gives results of experiments of feeding on *Sphaeralcea lindheimeri*, *Callirrhoe involucrata*, *C. pedata*, and *Hibiscus syriacus;* also results of experiments showing that it is possible for the boll weevil to breed in the buds of Hibiscus.—J. C. C.)

DAVIDSON, W. M. *Walnut Aphides in California.* Bulletin of the U. S. Department of Agriculture, No. 100. Pp. 1–48, plates 1–4, figs. 1–18. August 31, 1914. (A professional paper containing descriptions of the species, together with the natural enemies and artificial means of control.—J. C. C.)

DAVIS, J. J. *The oat aphis.* Bulletin of the U. S. Department of Agriculture, No. 112. Pp. 1–16, figs. 1–9. August 21, 1914. (Gives a description, together with description of species likely to be mistaken for the oat aphis; give its life history and discusses depradations and remedial measures.—J. C. C.)

DYAR, H. G. *The larvae of some Lepidoptera from Mexico.* Insector Inscitiae Menstruus, **2**: 113–117. August, 1914. (Describes the larvae of 9 species.—J. C. C.)

DYAR, H. G. *Utetheisa in Porto Rico.* Insector Inscitiae Menstruus, **2**: 129–131. September, 1914. (Describes 2 new varieties.—J. C. C.)

DYAR, H. G. *Descriptions of new species and genera of Lepidoptera from Mexico.* Proceedings of the U. S. National Museum, **47**: 365–409. October 24, 1914. (In this paper the author describes the new genera Nudur in the Lithosiidae; Neomanobia, Calocea, Cacofota, Gorgora, in the Noctuidae; Zaparasa in the Cochlidiidae; Cosmothyris in the Thyrididae; Tippecoa, Cromarcha, Balidarcha, Anemosella, Myolisa, Zaboba, Shacontia, Deuterolia, Euparolia, Mildrixia, Pseudodivona, Cactobrosis, Moodnopsis in the Pyralidae; together with 141 new species and one new subspecies.—J. C. C.)

PROCEEDINGS OF THE ACADEMY AND AFFILIATED SOCIETIES

THE PHILOSOPHICAL SOCIETY OF WASHINGTON

The 752d meeting was held on February 13, 1915, at the Cosmos Club, President Eichelberger in the chair; 48 persons present. MR. F. B. LITTELL presented a paper on *The Washington-Paris longitude by radio signals*. Transit instruments used were of recent type. The observatory standard Riefler clocks were used and ran so well as to justify interpolation over intervals of several days, thus permitting utilization of all the radio work. The lags of clock signals in passing through relays, which in some cases amounted to one-half second, were measured frequently and resulting corrections were applied. The radio signals from the over-sea station were usually extremely faint and oftentimes unobservable. The errors and personal equations due to the radio work were of the same order of magnitude as those due to the astronomical work. From the work of 39 nights, when radio observations in both directions were secured, the double transmission time, free from the errors of clock corrections, was found to be $0^s.0437 \pm 0^s.0039$. The preferred resulting value for longitude is $5^h\ 17^m\ 36^s.66 \pm 0^s.003$. This agrees well with the adjusted value for 4 cable determinations, viz., $5^h\ 17^m\ 36^s.69 \cdot$ The paper was discussed by Messrs. PAUL, BOWIE, ABBOT, and PAULING.

Mr. A. J. LOTKA then spoke on *Efficiency as a factor in organic evolution*. Using the rate of increase per head, r, of a given species of organisms as an index of its adaptation to existing conditions, the functional relationship between r and the efficiency of the organism was investigated by analytical methods, making use of the objective standard of values developed by the speaker previously. This efficiency depends on the errors of observation, operation, and mentation of the type-individual, and on the errors of valuation of the representative individual. An expression was obtained for the partial differential coefficient of r with regard to a suitable parameter capable of serving as an index of the imprecision of the organism in a given activity. A separate expression was obtained for the partial differential coefficient of r with regard to errors of valuation. The paper was discussed by Mr. ABBOT with reference to applications to economic questions, and by Mr. BURGESS.

The 753d meeting was held on February 27, 1915, at the Cosmos Club, President EICHELBERGER in the chair; 54 persons present.

Mr. C. G. ABBOT presented a paper entitled, *Experiments in measuring solar radiation from balloons.* The author stated that close agreement had been obtained in spectro-bolometric determinations of the solar constant of radiation at four stations; the mean result of about 700 independent determinations is 1.93 calories per sq. cm. per minute. Although these results depend on estimates of the transmission of the atmosphere, the diversity of the circumstances of the observations is such that the agreement of results strongly indicates their accuracy. It is, however, maintained by some that the work is wholly unsound, and that the real solar constant value is 3.5 calories per sq. cm. per minute or more. Accordingly, a recording pyrheliometer has been devised for use with sounding balloons. It is modified from the silver-disk pyrheliometer now in general use. A blackened disk, lying horizontally, is alternately exposed to the sun and shaded by a conical reflecting shutter at four-minute intervals. A thermometer whose reading is photographically recorded measures the rise and fall of the temperature of the disk. A barometric element records pressure of the atmosphere. Five ascents were made from Avalon, California, in 1913, and three ascents from Omaha in 1914, by coöperation with the United States Weather Bureau. All instruments were recovered. The most successful flight, at noon on July 11, 1914, reached an altitude well above 20,000 meters. Three excellent records of solar radiation were secured near maximum elevation, where the barometric pressure is less than $\frac{1}{20}$ of that at sea-level. These results are in good agreement, and (reduced to mean solar distance) yield a mean value of 1.85 calories per sq. cm. per minute. It is thought that about 2 per cent should be added for the effect of the remaining air, making the value 1.89 for this day. Its probable error is about 3 per cent. The paper was discussed by Mr. WHITE as to the effect of the downward current of air in balloon work; by Mr. WOODWARD, who questioned the usual method of estimation of the quantity of the atmosphere above any level; and by Mr. LAMBERT with reference to the grounds upon which certain investigators base a value of the solar constant at a value near 4 calories.

Mr. R. S. WOODWARD then presented a paper on *The compressibility of the earth's mass,* in which he considered the problem of the radial compressibility of the earth's mass due to change in internal or to surface stress. Assuming this mass to be spherical and that its density is a function only of distance from the center, the variation in length of the radius due to condensation (or dilatation) was shown to be equal to the volume-integral of the condensation divided by the area of the sphere. Application was made of the law of condensation defined by Laplace's hypothesis connecting density and stress in any mass. Using round numbers, this hypothesis leads to the conclusion that if the pressure of the atmosphere were doubled, the radius of the earth would be diminished by two meters. The importance of this conclusion in geology especially was emphasized.

J. A. FLEMING, *Secretary.*

THE GEOLOGICAL SOCIETY OF WASHINGTON

The 291st meeting was held in the lecture room of the Cosmos Club on February 10, 1915.

INFORMAL COMMUNICATIONS

· S. R. CAPPS: *An unusual exposure of a great thrust-fault.* A remarkable exposure of a great thrust-fault in the canyon of Nizina River, Alaska, near the mouth of West Fork, was described. A photograph was exhibited, showing a great cliff, about 5,000 feet high, in which the fault is developed in almost diagrammatic perfection. The rocks involved are the Nicolai greenstone (probably Carboniferous), and the Triassic Chitistone limestone and McCarthy shales. A displacement of about one-half mile has taken place; the Chitistone limestone has been reduplicated to almost twice its normal thickness. The crumpling of the overridden beds and the drag of the overriding beds were well brought out.

D. F. HEWETT: *Calculation of the thickness of strata represented in a series of outcrops of varying dip.* A formula was presented for calculating the thickness of folded beds between two horizons of widely diverse inclination. The formula was based upon the assumption of parallel folding, and the degree of accuracy of the various factors involved in the calculation was stated.

Discussion: M. I. GOLDMANN inquired more particularly as to the basis on which the calculations had been made, and this was explained by Hewett. C. E. LESHER mentioned a graphical method which had been proposed for the solution of the problem.

REGULAR PROGRAM

F. C. SCHRADER: *Some features of the ore deposits in the Santa Rita and Patagonia Mountains, Arizona.* The deposits are exposed in about a thousand mines and prospects scattered throughout the mountains. They occur in two sharply contrasted groups that differ considerably in age and represent two distinct periods of mineralization. The earlier and more valuable group occurs in association with the Paleozoic sedimentary rocks and the Mesozoic granular intrusives, and is referred to the late Mesozoic epoch of metallization.

The later group belongs to the great group of metalliferous deposits formed near the surface in the Tertiary volcanic rocks throughout the West by ascending thermal solutions, and in genetic connection with the associated rocks. It is referred to the Miocene and to the late Tertiary epoch of metallization. Its deposits occur chiefly as copper-, silver-, lead-, and gold-bearing fissure veins, in which the filling is mainly quartz, fluorite, and calcite.

The older deposits contain the metals or minerals of gold, silver, copper, lead, zinc, tungsten, and molybdenum. They were apparently deposited at considerable depths, chiefly by ascending thermal solutions that circulated as a close after-effect of the intrusion of Mesozoic magmas. They comprise three main classes: contact-metamorphic, fissure-vein, and replacement deposits.

The oldest are the contact-metamorphic deposits. Their formation was accompanied by mineralization and the development of the usual garnet zone containing a dozen or more contact-metamorphic minerals. The ferruginous or metallic constituents of these minerals, as andradite, gedrite, and others, were derived chiefly from the magmatic or ensuing solutions of the intrusive rock and not from the host limestone. The deposits are mainly copper-bearing; the chief primary ore minerals are chalcopyrite and cupriferous pyrite. From these two minerals, copper carbonates, oxide, and secondary sulphides, constituting the present workable ore bodies, were formed by oxidation and secondary enrichment.

The fissure veins are numerous and widely distributed. They are about 6 feet in average width. Some are a mile long, and have a known vertical range of nearly a thousand feet. The filling is chiefly quartz, fluorite, and barite. The ore minerals are chiefly argentite, cerargyrite, bromyrite, native silver, gold, pyromorphite, pyrargyrite, various lead, copper, and zinc minerals, molbydenite, wolframite, and scheelite.

The replacement deposits are associated with the contact-metamorphic deposits and some of the vein deposits described above. They occur chiefly in limestone in association with the intrusive rocks. Their principal metallic constituents are lead and silver. To this class apparently belong in large part the deposits at the Mowry mine and at the Total Wreck mine. The Mowry deposits occur on a steeply northward-dipping fault-contact between quartz monzonite on the south and Paleozoic limestone on the north, with altered gabbro underlying the limestone and forming the hanging wall in the deep part of the mine. They are opened to the depth of 500 feet, and for 600 feet longitudinally along the fault, and they extend laterally 100 feet or more back from the fault into the limestone. They consist mainly of lenses or chimney-shaped, nearly vertical bodies, standing or lying parallel with the fault plane, and are composed chiefly of argentiferous ore minerals, cerusite, coarse galena, anglesite, and bindheimite, all contained in a manganiferous and ferruginous gangue consisting principally of psilomelane and massive pyrolusite and hematite. The ore is mostly oxidized to the depth of 300 feet. The deposits are thought to be genetically connected with the gabbro, which seems best able to have supplied the iron and manganese constituents found in the gangue. They were probably deposited in the sulphide form as metasomatic replacements; from the sulphide minerals the present ore minerals and gangue were derived by processes of oxidation. They seem to be similar in character and origin to the Leadville, Colorado, deposits recently described by Philip Argall. (A fuller account is to appear in the forthcoming *U. S. Geol. Survey Bulletin 582*).

Discussion: N. L. BOWEN referred to the analysis of the gabbro as exhibited on the blackboard, and pointed out its remarkable composition, referring to the 7.25 per cent of alkalies and the 1.29 per cent of

MgO. He inquired as to the mineral composition, remarking that
with such a large amount of alkalies, alkaline pyroxenes should be expected. SCHRADER had no description of the mineral composition at
hand. G. F. LOUGHLIN spoke of the difference between the specimen
of quartz monzonite exhibited and the Leadville porphyry. The Arizona
specimen appeared more like the quartz monzonites of Utah. He also
called attention to the chemical affinities between the analyses of
gabbro and quartz monzonite shown, and thought it quite probable
that the ores might have been derived from the gabbro.

F. E. MATTHES. *Studies on glacial cirques in the Sierra Nevada.*
The better preserved cirques of the central High Sierra, especially those
hewn in fairly massive igneous rocks, are found to consist of two distinct and contrasting parts, a lower bowl with smooth, concave slopes,
in many instances holding a tarn, and an upper cliff rising from the
periphery of the bowl, with rough, hackly face, and nearly vertical
profile. The relative proportions of bowl and cliff are by no means
the same in all cirques; but the bowl is in every case the dominant feature, constituting the main part of the cirque, while the cliff is distinctly
accessory in character, although occasionally assuming considerable
height.

The riven, hackly face of the cliff clearly bespeaks frost action.
The verticality of its profile and the tendency to overhang, moreover,
point to basal sapping; that is, they show that the locus of most intense
frost action is situated at the base of the wall. The conspicuous smooth-
ness of contour and the striated and polished surface of the concave
bowl-slopes, on the other hand, attest corrasion, principally abrasion—
by moving ice. This abraded appearance sets in immediately below
the base of the cliff, showing that at that line frost action ceases abruptly
and that there is no transition zone in which the two processes blend
their effects. The base of the cliff accordingly constitutes a well-defined and conspicuous boundary line, which is interpreted as indicating
the depth to which the bergschrund of the ancient glacier opened and
to which frost action was permitted to penetrate. (Willard Johnson
and Gilbert have referred to it as the "sap line.") If this interpretation is correct, it necessarily follows that the entire cirque bowl—the
major part of the cirque—is elaborated through the corrasive action of
the ice masses contained in it. Mass corrasion, accordingly, would
appear to be the dominant cirque sculpturing process, while bergschrund
sapping, as T. C. Chamberlin and R. D. Salisbury have suggested,
is merely a peripherally working, auxiliary process. The two processes,
while associated, do not necessarily work at the same rate. In many
instances cliff sapping appears to have outstripped mass corrasion, because it was aided by the development of joints in the upper parts of
the rock mass through weathering at the preglacial surface of erosion.
In such cases the cliff stands back from the bowl rim and is separated
from it by a narrow shelf. Abrasion by snow shod with rocks fallen
from the cliff smooths the shelf and transforms the bowl rim into a
rounding curve.

That the ice masses accumulating in a cirque are competent to generate through corrasion alone a bowl characterized by smooth, concave slopes, and hollowed out so as to hold a lake basin, can be demonstrated by analysis of the mechanics involved. Similarly it can be shown that the ice masses flowing out of the cirque are competent by their corrasive action alone to produce a U-shaped trough. Frost sapping, it is true, does take place along the margins of the outflowing glacier, but it does not contribute to the elaboration of the U-trough any more than it contributes to the elaboration of the cirque bowl. It is effective only to the shallow depth to which the marginal crevasses open, and gives rise to special marginal features above the edges of the U-trough; namely, to a shelf or shoulder, and a cliff or scarp. In fact, the marginal shoulder and scarp of the outflow canyon are but the continuations of the shelf and cliff of the cirque, while the U-trough, properly speaking, is the continuation of the cirque bowl. It is not contended that these sculptural features are characteristic of cirques and outflow canyons in all parts of the world. They can acquire prominence only in cirques and canyons carved from prevailing massive rocks, such as those of the Sierra Nevada, for such rocks do not lend themselves well to plucking, and in them mass corrasion must perforce consist mainly of abrasion, which is productive of smoothly curving surfaces, contrasting strongly with the hackly faces of frost-riven cliffs. In densely jointed rocks, on the other hand, mass corrasion may consist of both plucking and abrasion, and the surfaces produced by it are likely to be more or less hackly and therefore not greatly different in appearance from those resulting from frost sapping. In cirques laid in thin-bedded, finely jointed sedimentary rocks, accordingly, one should not expect to find any pronounced contrast in appearance between the bowl slopes and the cliff.

Again, the features of some Sierra cirques are particularly clean-cut because the uniformity of the rock structure makes for uniformity and continuity of the individual sculptural units, and as a consequence the boundary between those units—between bowl and cliff—is sharply defined and regular. Local variations in structure and in resisting qualities, on the other hand, commonly occur in the rocks of most mountain regions. As a consequence, irregularities in cirque sculpture are the rule. Rocks of locally varying structure and resistance, further, are likely to develop ragged surfaces, giving rise to several successive, and more or less discontinuous bergschrunds, and in them clean-cut, simple cirque forms can not be realized. No doubt it is the prevailing irregularity of the cirque forms, due to interfering structures, that has prevented observers in most mountain regions from clearly apprehending the relative importance of the two processes involved in cirque erosion—mass corrasion, and bergschrund sapping. Another circumstance, finally, that appears to have favored the production of a pronounced sap line in the cirques of the High Sierra is indicated by a study of the level reached in the cirques and canyon by the ice of each of the two pleistocene glacial epochs that have occurred in the Sierra

Nevada. The earlier glaciation was much more extensive than the later one, and the ice levels of the two consequently lie several thousand feet apart in altitude on the middle flanks of the range. As the levels are traced upward, however, they are found to converge until in the immediate vicinity of the Sierra crest they cannot be distinguished from each other. Evidently, then, the ice of the two epochs reached practically the same height in the crestal cirques, and the later glaciers started from substantially the same sap line as did the earlier ones. Furthermore the moraines indicate that the glacierets of recent historic time, many of which were less than one mile long, also started from the sap line left by the Pleistocene glaciers. It is to be inferred, therefore, that at all stages of glaciation the ice filled the crestal cirques to approximately the same depth, and that consequently every glacial episode has reaccentuated the sap line, and has resumed the modeling of the cirques essentially along the lines established by its predecessors.

Discussion: S. R. CAPPS said that it was not entirely evident to him why the sap-line should have had the same level at different 'glacial epochs. MATTHES replied that he had come to his conclusion on this matter not by analytical reasoning but by following to their convergences the trend of the ice-lines or markings on the rocks made at different epochs. CAPPS favored the idea that the position of the sap-line was due to the height to which snow could accumulate before flow-movement began. MATTHES thought this explanation might well be consistent with his idea.

W. C. ALDEN said that his experience in glacial studies had been chiefly in regions of sedimentary rocks, and spoke of the phenomena in Glacier National Park. In the development of the fine cirques in thin-bedded sedimentaries there shown he believed plucking had been a very great factor. He had not observed MATTHES' sap-line in these cirques. There was good evidence of plucking-effects but not much of abrasion-effects.

R. H. CHAPMAN said that in his opinion the great variety of profiles in cross-sections of cirques in the Glacier Park regions could be ascribed to differences in dip of sedimentary beds.

C. N. FENNER, *Secretary.*

THE BOTANICAL SOCIETY OF WASHINGTON

The 103d regular meeting of the Society was held in the Crystal Dining Room of the New Ebbitt Hotel, at 6.45 p.m., Tuesday, March 2, 1915. Eighty-two members and seventy-eight guests were present, this being the regular annual open meeting for the President's address.

The retiring President, DR. C. L. SHEAR, delivered an address on *"Mycology in relation to Phytopathology."*

MR. A. S. HITCHCOCK addressed the Society concerning the proposed publication of a local flora, covering the flowering plants and vascular cryptogams of Washington and vicinity, which is being prepared by Washington botanists under the leadership of MR. FREDERICK

V. COVILLE and himself. The flora, as planned, is to include an introduction, a key to the families, keys to the genera of each family, keys to the species of each genus, and statements concerning the habitat, abundance, and local distribution of each species, with suitable references to outside range. Formal descriptions will be omitted, but statements may be given concerning useful or poisonous qualities, economic value, peculiarities of structure, or other points likely to be of interest to the users of a local flora. The area to be covered by the Flora is approximately a circle of 15 miles radius with the capitol as a center, this territory being practically that covered by Ward's Flora of Washington, though it is not intended to exclude from consideration localities that lie a short distance outside of the 15 mile circle. The formal list is to include all indigenous and introduced plants and those that have escaped from cultivation. In addition there will be brief references to the common species of cultivated plants. All the species listed in Ward's Flora or its supplements are to be accounted for, even though they can not now be verified by specimens.

It is proposed to publish in the spring of 1916, if practicable, a preliminary edition of the Flora which shall include the flowering plants and ferns. This will allow one intervening collecting season for collating data and confirming previous records. It is hoped that later editions may be published which shall include the cryptogams.

In 1906 a list of the vascular plants of the District of Columbia and vicinity was compiled by MR. P. L. RICKER, and copies were struck off by mimeograph. This list was based upon Ward's Flora and its supplements. MR. RICKER has prepared and placed on file a card index of additions to the above-mentioned list. At the National Herbarium the District Flora, consisting of all specimens from the area mentioned, has been segregated and can be readily consulted. There is also accessible a detailed outline of the plan of the·Flora and a sample illustrating the form to be followed in preparation of manuscripts. Many botanists have been consulted in relation to the project and 29 have signified their willingness to contribute manuscript of particular families or genera.

It is regarded as very desirable also that work should be started this season upon the cryptogams, and it is hoped that as many botanists as possible will coöperate in collecting material or in preparing manuscript for the cryptogams to be included in future editions. All persons interested in the general project of a District Flora are invited to consult with MR. FREDERICK V. COVILLE at the Department of Agriculture or with the speaker at the National Herbarium.

The Society also passed resolutions of regret upon the death of DR. CHARLES E. BESSEY.

PERLEY SPAULDING, *Corresponding Secretary.*

THE SOCIETY OF AMERICAN FORESTERS

MEETINGS

Nine open and six executive meetings of the Society of American Foresters were held during 1914. The following list gives a program of the meetings: first open, then executive:

Open Meetings. January 8: HERMAN H. CHĂPMAN, *Methods of studying yields per acre on the basis of age for all-aged stands.* February 5: D. T. MASON, *The management of lodgepole pine.* March 5: FRANKLIN W. REED, *The proper basis for land classification.* April 2: BRISTOW ADAMS, J. H. FOSTER, and F. F. MOON, *New developments in the eastern woodlot problem.* May 7: EARLE H. CLAPP, *The National Forests of Alaska.* October 22: G. A. PEARSON, *Forest planting in Arizona and New Mexico.* November 19: C. J. BLANCHARD, *Reclamation and Forestry.* December 17: KARL W. WOODWARD, *Administration of the National Forests in the Southern Appalachians.*

Executive Meetings. January 22: Annual executive meeting. May 16: Executive meeting to consider report of executive committee. June 17: To adopt resolutions on the death of OVERTON W. PRICE, active member. July 29: To adopt resolutions on the death of LOUIS MARGOLIN, active member. November 7: To adopt resolutions on the death of HENRY GANNETT, associate member. November 20: To consider question of meeting places.

The fifteen meetings of the year represent the largest number held so far in a twelve-month.

The average attendance at open meetings was 50, also the largest average attained, due in part to the open meeting at Cornell in May, attended by 256. The lowest attendance was 8; the average leaving out these two extremes was 27. At the executive committee meetings the average attendance was 16, with the largest at Cornell in May with 31 members present.

Membership. During the year the Society lost, by death, three members, two active and one associate—OVERTON W. PRICE and LOUIS MARGOLIN, and HENRY GANNETT.

A general reorganization of membership in accordance with the revised constitution is in progress, but has not been completed at this date.

During the year 18 active and 8 associate members were added. The present membership is 299, divided as follows: *Active* 240, *Associate* 58, *Honorary* 1, Total 299.

Annual Election. In the annual election closed January 8, 1915, the following candidates were elected: *President,* W. B. GREELEY; *Vice President,* RAPHAEL ZON; *Secretary,* KARL W. WOODWARD; *Treasurer,* LOUIS S. MURPHY; *Executive Committee:* R. S. HOSMER, FILIBERT ROTH, H. O. STABLER, F. A. SILCOX, R. Y. STUART.

KARL W. WOODWARD, *Secretary.*

THE BIOLOGICAL SOCIETY OF WASHINGTON

The 525th regular meeting was held in the Assembly Hall of the Cosmos Club, Saturday, April 4, 1914, with Vice-President Hay in the chair and 35 persons present. The following program was presented:

Notes on the hatching of a local terrapin, Kinosternon pennsylvanicus, WILLIAM PALMER.

An account of a visit to some of the smaller museums, O. P. HAY.

The fishes of the Lahontan Basin, Nevada, J. O. SNYDER.

The 526th regular meeting was held in the Assembly Hall of the Cosmos Club, Saturday, April 18, 1914, with Vice-President Rose in the chair and 40 persons present. The following program was presented:

Notes on Bermuda birds, TITUS ULKE.

Reactions of corals to food and to non-nutrient particles, and the nature of the food of corals, T. WAYLAND VAUGHAN.

The plankton resources of some Massachusetts ponds, A. A. DOOLITTLE.

The 527th regular meeting was held in the Assembly Hall of the Cosmos Club, Saturday, May 2, 1914, with Vice-President Hay in the chair and 46 persons present. The following program was presented:

A journal of the Wilkes Exploring Expedition, W. P. HAY.

The home and country of Linnaeus, S. M. GRONBERGER.

Exhibition of lantern slides of Washington wild flowers, L. D. HALLECK.

W. L. MCATEE, *Acting Recording Secretary.*

The 528th meeting was held in the Assembly Hall of the Cosmos Club, Saturday, October 17, 1914, with President BARTSCH in the chair and 36 persons present. The president announced the death of Theodore N. Gill, a founder and a former president of the Society, and asked the secretary to read the following resolutions which had been adopted by the council:

Whereas, it has pleased Divine Providence to remove our friend, fellow member, and former president, Dr. Theodore N. Gill from the scene of his earthly labors,

Wherefore, be it resolved: That his profound erudition, devotion to research, long continued industry, and voluminous publications on various branches of science justly entitled Dr. Gill to especial distinc-tion as a zoologist, while his kindly nature and generous devotion of his time and thought to the assistance of younger and less experienced students will ever remain a cherished memory among us;

Also, resolved: That to his surviving relatives we tender our sincere sympathy, and the secretary of the Society is requested to communicate to them this expression of our regret for the loss sustained by them and by the scientific world.

WM. H. DALL,
L. O. HOWARD, } *Committee.*
L. STEJNEGER,

The program was then taken up.   Under the heading Brief Notes, Book Reviews, etc., L. O. HOWARD referred to the report that arsenical spraying in connection with the destruction of gipsy moths in New England had destroyed many birds, and stated that investigations had failed entirely to show that any birds were killed.   Dr. Peters had suggested to him that the absence of birds in the region of spraying operations was probably due to the fact that the absence of insect food had led them to leave the district.   PAUL BARTSCH reported that English sparrows were seen feeding freely on the army worm in the Smithsonian grounds during the recent invasion of that insect.

The regular program consisted of three communications:

A mouse which lived in tree-tops, VERNON BAILEY.   The speaker gave an account of the history and habits of *Phenacomys longicauda,* a little known arboreal mouse which inhabits the deep Douglas spruce forests of the Cascade region of the northwest.   Personal experiences in hunting the nests of the species and climbing to them were related, and a perfect specimen obtained last summer at Eugene, Oregon, was exhibited.   The communication was discussed by W. H. OSGOOD.

Botanical collecting in the Northwest, A. S. HITCHCOCK.   The speaker gave a general account of his summer's collecting trip to the northwestern part of the United States and British Columbia.   His itinerary included Nebraska, the Black Hills, Glacier Park, Banff, Mt. Baker, Mt. Ranier, and Mt. Hood, in all of which ·places interesting species of grasses were obtained.

The present state of fox-farming, NED DEARBORN.   Last spring the speaker was sent by the Biological Survey to investigate the methods and progress of this industry in Prince Edward Island and elsewhere. He gave a history of fox-farming and its development to the present time, together with personal observations among the fox ranches. The financial inflation of the business and the methods of some of the promoters of fox companies were not commended, but it is his opinion that the industry can be developed into commercial importance.   The communication was discussed by T. S. PALMER and by J. WALTER JONES, of Charlottetown, Prince Edward Island.

The 529th meeting was held in the Assembly Hall of the Cosmos Club, Saturday, October 31, 1914, with President BARTSCH in the chair.   One hundred and ten persons were present.   Five persons were elected to active membership.

The secretary read a letter from Herbert A. Gill acknowledging receipt of resolutions of the Society relating to the death of his brother, Dr. Theodore N. Gill.

Two communications were presented, the first being *Pelage varia-ations of American moles*, by HARTLEY H. T. JACKSON. The speaker classed the variations as generic, geographic, seasonal, senile, and individual, and showed under each class the tendencies of the different genera to show differences in pelage. Under geographic variation he noted that, unlike the eastern moles which are lightest toward the south, *Neurotrichus* is darkest toward the south, and that *Parascalops* darkens southward along the coast, while in the mountains it darkens toward the north. The seasonal variations are especially marked by differences in the location on the body of the animal where the moult begins. *Scalopus* has great seasonal changes and the moult starts on the central line of the body. In *Scapanus* the moult begins at the head and is completed at the posterior. In *Condylura* the moult starts on the flank; in *Neurotrichus* in the head. The remarks were illus-trated by specimens which showed the variations under discussion, as well as interesting mutations. In discussing the paper D. E. LANTZ spoke briefly of a possible market for mole fur in the United States.

The second communication was by R. L. GARNER, who related some of his experiences during twenty-five years' study of the great apes of western Africa. He told how he first came to engage in his experi-ments in investigating the speech of monkeys and how he finally under-took researches in the wilds of the French Congo. His experiences and observations during many years residence at L'Ibesoille and other places, during which he had many opportunities of studying gorillas and chimpanzees at close range, were related. He showed many lantern slides depicting natives and their houses, as well as physical features of the country and the tropical vegetation. Pictures of the large gorilla kept at Breslau for seven years and of "Susie," the chim-panzee trained by Mr. Garner, were also shown. At the conclusion of his remarks he answered many questions from the interested audience.

The 530th regular meeting was held in the Assembly Hall of the Cosmos Club, Saturday, November 14, 1914, with President BARTSCH in the chair and 37 persons present. Three persons were elected to active membership.

Under the heading Brief Notes, etc., M. W. LYON stated that he had recently seen a specimen of the American coot which had been killed on the top of a mountain and inquired whether the occurrence of the species in such localities was common. General T. A. WILCOX remarked that he had seen a similar case. L. O. HOWARD exhibited a canine of the saber-toothed tiger which he recently picked up in the asphalt desposits near Los Angeles, California. A. D. HOPKINS told of cypress wood from the same locality which showed borings of insect larvae. W. H. OSGOOD told of a well preserved tree which he had seen in the same deposit.

The first communication of the regular program was by WILLIAM PALMER, on *Certain Miocene fossils*. The fossils under consideration were obtained in the Miocene cliffs below Chesapeake Beach, Maryland.

Owing to the very scanty material from which Cope and others had described the types in the Museum of the Philadelphia Academy of Natural Sciences it was extremely difficult to identify the material collected by the speaker. He had collected the skulls of three species of porpoises but no vertebrae of the same individuals. As Cope's type specimens of these animals from the Miocene consisted only of a few vertebrae the speaker was not able to determine which name to apply to these skulls. Mr. Palmer exhibited teeth like those which had once been the basis for the false statement that the Hippopotamus was among the early animals of America. Leidy had described similar teeth as those of a porpoise, but the speaker thought they belonged to another animal because of their peculiar structure. The communication was illustrated by many specimens, among which was the skull of a small Zeuglodon. Many of these Miocene fossils are similar to Pliocene types from the cliffs near Antwerp, Belgium, and a comparison of the American and European material is extremely desirable. The communication was discussed by M. W. LYON.

The second communication was by PAUL B. POPENOE who presented an account of *Arabic zoology*. After a short sketch of the rise of Arabic zoology he gave some curious extracts from the writings of Kamal al Din Muhammad ibu Musa al Damiri, whose encyclopedic work, Hayat al Hayawan or the Lives of Animals, finished in 1371, has since been the standard authority among the Moslems. The amusing extracts related to the elephant, the cat, the gorilla, and other species.

The third communication, by WELLS W. COOKE, was an account of the *National Bird Census* taken last July by the Biological Survey in coöperation with the ornithologists of the United States. The objects of the census and methods employed were given, together with results based on the reports that had been obtained. An account of the speaker's personal enumeration of the birds near Viresco, Virginia, and results were exhibited by figures on the blackboard. Several persons took part in the discussion which followed.

The 531st meeting was held in the Assembly Hall of the Cosmos Club, Saturday, November 28, 1915, with President BARTSCH in the chair and 31 persons present. One person was elected to active membership.

Under the heading Brief Notes, etc., C. W. STILES gave a short account of certain results of his efforts at sanitation in relation to intestinal parasites. Messrs. HOWLAND and LYON, took part in the discussion. WM. PALMER exhibited some interesting fossils from the Miocene deposits of the Chesapeake collected by him during the present week.

The regular program consisted of three communications:

A porcupine skull showing an extra pair of upper incisors: M. W. LYON, JR. The specimen under consideration was the skull of a half grown porcupine collected in Borneo by Dr. Abbott which, so far as can be learned, is unique in character in having two upper incisors instead of one on each side. The speaker considered it a milk incisor that has persisted. He showed lantern slides of the specimen. Messrs. GIDLEY and HOWLAND participated in the discussion, both agreeing with the theory advanced by the speaker.

Notes on some fishes collected by Dr. Mearns in the Colorado River: J. O. SNYDER. The species found in the Colorado basin are distinct from species found elsewhere. The faunas of the river basins of the West show the same feature. From the evidence shown by genera obtained in the different river basins, the speaker concluded that communication must have been at a very remote period. He exhibited specimens collected by Dr. Mearns.

Notes on some birds observed on the Florida Keys in April, 1914: PAUL BARTSCH. The speaker gave an account of observations on birds made during an eight-day cruise among the Florida Keys in April, 1914, and showed by means of lantern slides most of the species in their natural surroundings. Most of the time was spent at Bird Key. Pictures of frigate birds and various species of terns were also used in illustration.

The 35th annual meeting and 532d regular meeting was held in the Assembly Hall of the Cosmos Club, Saturday, December 12, 1914, with President Bartsch in the chair and 18 members present.

The minutes of the 34th annual meeting were read and approved, and the annual reports of the officers and committees were presented.

The election of officers for the year 1915 took place, resulting as follows: *President*, PAUL BARTSCH; *Vice-Presidents*, A. D. HOPKINS, W. P. HAY, J. N. ROSE, MARY J. RATHBUN; *Recording Secretary*, M. W. LYON, JR.; *Corresponding Secretary*, W. L. McATEE; *Treasuer*, W. W. COOKE; *Members of Council*, HUGH M. SMITH, VERNON BAILEY, WM. PALMER, N. HOLLISTER, J. W. GIDLEY.

President PAUL BARTSCH was selected to represent the Society as Vice-President in the Washington Academy of Sciences.

The President appointed as the Committee on Publication: N. HOLLISTER, W. L. McATEE, and W. W. COOKE.

D. E. LANTZ, *Recording Secretary*.

ANTHROPOLOGICAL SOCIETY OF WASHINGTON

At the 478th meeting of the Society held December 1, 1914, in the Public Library, Dr. GEORGE S. DUNCAN, of Johns Hopkins University, delivered an address on *The Sumerian people and their inscriptions*. About 140 persons were present. The land between the lower Tigris and Euphrates in very ancient times was inhabited by a non-Semitic people called Sumerians. Their oldest inscriptions antedate 3000 B.C., but the beginning of Sumerian civilization are far older than any inscriptions. The Enlil temple in Nippur dates back probably to 6000 B.C. Semites from Arabia conquered the Sumerians and by 2100 B.C.

ruled over the whole land from Babylon as the capital. Of the Sumerian cities only Lagash and Nippur have been thoroughly excavated. These have yielded most important finds. The Sumerians had a pointed, narrow nose with a straight ridge and narrow nostrils. The cheek bones were high, the mouth small, the lips narrow and finely rounded. The lower jaw was very short, the pointed chin not extending far forward. The eyes were almond shaped. The forehead was rather low, and extended far back from the root of the nose. The face was flat, and the head short. The head and face were shaved. The people were apparently short in stature and thick-set. There is a general agreement that the Sumerians were neither Semites nor Indo-Europeans. A majority of scholars would class them among the Mongolians. Sumerian is an agglutinative language. The only garment worn by the Sumerians was a rough woolen skirt fastened around the waist by a girdle. Agriculture was a common occupation. Great crops of cereals, such as wheat, barley, millet, and vetches, were grown. The chief fruit tree was the date palm. Many persons were employed as fishers, hunters, weavers, fullers, dyers, brickmakers, potters, smiths, carpenters, boat-builders, goldsmiths, jewelers, sculptors, and carvers in wood and ivory. The learned professions included priests, teachers, librarians, scribes, publishers, notaries, physicians, astronomers, and musicians. The country was divided up into a large number of city states ruled by kings. The oldest Sumerian art is very crude. The highest artistic development was reached about the age of Gudea, circa 2600 B.C. The Sumerians were very religious. The three chief divinities were Anu, god of the sky, Enlil, god of the earth, and Enki, god of the water. The Sumerian religion was a kind of nature worship. The temples consisted of a complex of buildings, the most prominent part of which was the temple tower, a solid strucutre in the shape either of a square or of a parallelogram rising in platforms, one above the other. The temples seem to have had departments for religion, business, administration, law, education, and a library. The priests were the learned men of the time. There were orders of priests and priestesses. The inscriptions of the Sumerians mainly consist of historical records, laws, contracts, epics, and various kinds of religious texts. The oldest records of a paradise, a fall, and a flood are found in Sumerian tablets.

DANIEL FOLKMAR, *Secretary.*

JOURNAL

OF THE

WASHINGTON ACADEMY OF SCIENCES

Vol. V   APRIL 19, 1915   No. 8

PHYSICS.—*Some notes on the theory of the Rayleigh-Zeiss interferometer*. By LEASON H. ADAMS, Geophysical Laboratory. Communicated by ARTHUR L. DAY.

In the course of some work on the freezing point of dilute aqueous solutions in which a Zeiss interferometer was employed as a means of determining the concentration of the equilibrium solutions,[1] some trouble was experienced at first in obtaining thoroughly concordant readings; this was found to be due to an alteration of the achromatic reference fringe produced by differences in optical dispersion. In order to guard against error from this source it proved necessary to investigate the relationships in order to derive formulae from which the exact amount of shift of the achromatic fringe could be predicted. The appropriate formulae for this type of instrument have apparently not been worked out heretofore;[2] consequently it has seemed worth while to call attention to these relationships and to put the formulae on record so as to save trouble to future users of this most useful type of instrument.

1. *The optical path-differences resulting from the tilting of a plane-parallel glass plate*. In the form of interferometer under consideration the difference in optical path-length of the two interfering beams of light is compensated by tilting one of two

[1] L. H. Adams, J. Am. Chem. Soc., 37, 481 (1915). A paper dealing with the use of this form of interferometer in the analysis of solutions is in course of publication in the J. Am. Chem. Soc.

[2] Except, possibly, in part by Siertsema in 1890 in a Groningen dissertation, a copy of which I have been unable to secure.

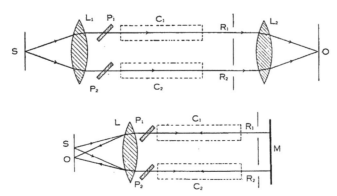

Fig. 1. Diagram of optical arrangement of interferometer; the two interfering beams are separated and reunited in (a) by two lenses, in (b) by a single lens.

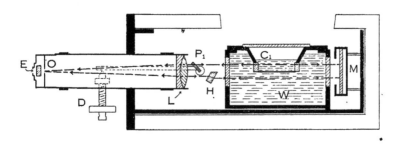

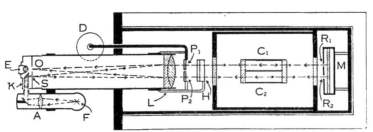

Fig. 2. Drawing in plan (below) and elevation (above) of the Zeiss Water Interferometer.

interposed glass plates (P_1, P_2, fig. 1); the amount of this tilting is then a measure of the path-difference between the two sides and hence of the difference in refractive index of the contents of the pair of cells C_1, C_2. The compensator plate is fastened at an angle of about 45° to a movable arm parallel to the direction of the light and is tilted by means of a micrometer screw which bears against the arm and moves in a fixed direction perpendicular to the arm when in its zero-position (see fig. 2). The optical path-difference resulting from the tilting of the plate through a certain angle θ may be calculated as follows:

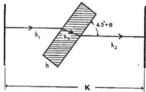

Fig. 3. Diagram to illustrate path of light beam through compensator plate.

Consider a certain path, of length K, traversed by a beam of light, and introduce into this path a plane-parallel glass plate (fig. 3). Let 45° + θ be the angle of incidence, h the thickness of the plate, n its refractive index and n_o that of the surrounding medium (air). It may easily be shown that the air-path of the beam

$$k_1 + k_3 = K - \frac{h}{\sqrt{2}}\left[\cos\theta + \sin\theta + \frac{n_o\,(1 - \sin 2\theta)}{\sqrt{2n^2 - n_o^2(1 - \sin 2\,\theta)}}\right]$$

and that the glass-path

$$k_2 = \frac{\sqrt{2}\,n\,h}{\sqrt{2\,n^2 - n_o^2\,(1 - \sin 2\,\theta)}}$$

Now the optical path-length P is by definition equal to $\Sigma\,k\,n$. Accordingly,

$$P = n_o\,K - \frac{h}{\sqrt{2}}\left[\sqrt{2\,n_2 - n_o^2\,(1 - \sin 2\,\theta)} - n_o\,(\cos\theta + \sin\theta)\right]$$

Ordinarily $n_o - 1$ is very small compared to $n - 1$; consequently we may put $n_o = 1$. Then if we write $H = 2n^2 - 1$, we have

$$(1) \qquad P = K - \frac{h}{\sqrt{2}}\left[\sqrt{H + \sin 2\,\theta} - (\cos\theta + \sin\theta)\right]$$

In the initial position (angle of incidence = 45°) $\theta = 0°$, and therefore

(2) $$P_0 = K - \frac{h}{\sqrt{2}}\left(\sqrt{H} - 1\right)$$

Hence, the optical path difference p resulting from the tilting of the plate through an angle θ is .

(3) $$p = P_0 - P = \frac{h}{\sqrt{2}}\left[\sqrt{H} - 1 - \sqrt{H + \sin 2\theta} + \cos\theta + \sin\theta\right]$$

This formula may be applied in a number of ways. For a compensator plate of given thickness and refractive index one can calculate the sensitiveness of the instrument by differentiating with respect to θ; moreover its range for given values of θ may be readily computed.

It is interesting to note the relation between sensitiveness and refractive index of the plate. For $\theta = 0°$

(3a) $$\frac{dp}{d\theta} = \frac{h}{\sqrt{2}}\left(1 - \frac{1}{\sqrt{H}}\right)$$

The values of $dp/d\theta$ for plates of unit thickness are shown below.

refractive index n	sensitiveness $dp/d\theta$
1.5	0.34
2.0	0.44
2.5	0.51
3.0	0.54

Inspection of this table shows the comparatively small influence of refractive index on the sensitiveness of the compensator plate.

In a modified form it may also be used to obtain a small correction to the reading (on the drum D of the micrometer screw) such that the "corrected reading" will be strictly proportional to the refractive index difference (ν) of the solutions or mixtures under investigation. Thus if R is the travel in mm. of the screw and a the length in mm. of the arm—that is the constant perpendicular distance between the center of rotation and the line of motion of the screw—then $\theta = \tan^{-1}\frac{R}{a}$. Hence eliminating θ from equation (3) we have

$$(4) \qquad p = \frac{h}{\sqrt{2}} \left(\sqrt{H} - 1 - \sqrt{H + \frac{2Ra}{R^2 + a^2}} + \frac{R + a}{\sqrt{R^2 + a^2}} \right)$$

which reduces with sufficient approximation to the power series

$$(5) \qquad p = \frac{h}{\sqrt{2}} \left[R \frac{1 - \frac{1}{\sqrt{H}}}{a} - R^2 \frac{1 - \frac{1}{H^{1.5}}}{2a^2} + R^3 \frac{\frac{1}{\sqrt{H}} - \frac{1}{2}}{a^3} \right]$$

Now let R'^{-1} be a quantity such that

$$\frac{R'}{a} = \frac{\sqrt{2}\, p}{h \left(1 - \frac{1}{\sqrt{H}} \right)}$$

then

$$(6) \qquad R' = R - R^2 \frac{1 - \frac{1}{H^{1.5}}}{2a \left(1 - \frac{1}{\sqrt{H}} \right)} + R^3 \frac{\frac{1}{\sqrt{H}} - \frac{1}{2}}{a^2 \left(1 - \frac{1}{\sqrt{H}} \right)}$$

As an example, in our instrument (the Zeiss Water-Interferometer) $a = 110$ mm. and $n_D = 1.514$; moreover, if r represents the number of divisions on the drum corresponding to a given value of R, $r = 200 R$ (also $r' = 200 R'$); for these values formula (6) reduces to the expression

$$(6a) \qquad r' = r - 41.07 \left(\frac{r}{1000} \right)^2 + 0.12 \left(\frac{r}{1000} \right)^3$$

in which the last term is almost entirely negligible. Values of R' (and hence also of r') calculated in this way are proportional to the decrease in optical path resulting from the tilting of the compensator plate, and therefore strictly proportional to the quantity ν, the refractive index difference of the solutions.

Another use to which formula (3) may be put is the calculation of the variation with refractive index n of the path difference p corresponding to a given angle θ. Thus by differentiation,

$$(7) \qquad \frac{dp}{dn} = \sqrt{2}\, h\, n \left(\frac{1}{\sqrt{H}} - \frac{1}{\sqrt{H + \sin 2\,\theta}} \right)$$

whence by combination with (3), we have

$$(8) \qquad \frac{dp}{p} = 2\, n\, dn\; \frac{\dfrac{1}{\sqrt{H}} - \dfrac{1}{\sqrt{H + \sin 2\,\theta}}}{\sqrt{H} - 1 - \sqrt{H + \sin 2\,\theta} + \sin \theta + \cos \theta}$$

For small values of θ (the usual case) we may write $\sin \theta = \theta$ and $\cos \theta = 1$. The above expression then reduces with sufficient approximation to the following:

$$(9) \qquad \frac{\Delta p}{p} = \frac{2\, n\, \Delta n}{H\,(\sqrt{H} - 1\,)}$$

For ordinary crown glass $n = 1.52$ and the above formula reduces to

$$(9a) \qquad \frac{\Delta p}{p} = 0.94\, \Delta n$$

Now for the change of path p, caused by the insertion of successive plane-parallel plates perpendicular to the direction of the light, $p_1 = h(n - 1)$ and therefore $dp_1/p = dn(n- 1)$. But $dn/(n - 1)$ is the ordinary "relative dispersion." Hence if we write (9) in the form

$$(10A) \qquad \frac{\Delta p}{p} = q\, \frac{\Delta n}{n - 1}$$

where

$$(10B) \qquad q = \frac{2\, n\,(n - 1)}{H\,(\sqrt{H} - 1)}$$

q is then the factor by which we must multiply the relative dispersion of the glass plate in order to obtain the proportional change of path ($\Delta p/p$) resulting from a given increase (Δn) of the refractive index of the plate. The value of q for ordinary crown glass (n = 1.52) is 0.48. We shall have occasion to use formula (10) when we come to the subject of the alteration of the achromatic fringe in white light.

As a check on the above relations some observations with monochromatic light (obtained by means of a Monochromatic Illuminator) of several wave lengths were made on the relation between the number of divisions on the drum and the number of fringes crossing the field. For wave lengths 0.5876 and 0.5461 He and Hg tubes respectively were used, and an arc lamp for wave-lengths 0.6396 and 0.4861, the slits of the Illuminator in the latter case being very narrow, in order to obtain sufficiently homogeneous light. The character of the results is shown by Table I for wave-length 0.5876 −.

TABLE I

N	r	r'	r'/N	δr OBS.-CALC.
5	112	111.5	22.25	−1.0
10	227	225	22.50	+0.5
20	459	450.5	22.52	+1.5
30	695	675	22.50	+1.7
40	934	898	22.45	+0.1
60	1429	1345	22.42	−1.7
80	1950	1795	22.44	−0.6
100	2499	2244.5	22.445	−0.2
120	3080	2693.5	22.445	−0.3

Average = 0.8

The first and second columns give respectively the number of fringes N and the corresponding observed number of scale divisions r. The third column gives the values of r' calculated by equation (6 a) and the fourth, the quotient r'/N which inspection shows to be practically constant, as it should be. The least square mean value of this quotient is 22.447; the differences between this mean and the individual observations, when computed back in terms of r, are given in the last column, which shows that this discrepancy is no larger than the error of reading (1 division, which is less than 1/20 of a band).

The values of r'/N for the other wave-lengths, determined similarly are shown in the second column of the table 2.

TABLE II

λ	r'/N	r'	N_x	$N_x\lambda$ $(= p_x)$	$\dfrac{\Delta p}{p_x}$	Δn	Δn (DIRECT DETN.)
0.6396	24.456	(2634)	107.70	68.88	0.0068	0.0072	0.0074
0.5876	22.447	(2634)	117.34	68.94	0.0058	0.0062	0.0056
0.5461	20.812	(2634)	126.56	69.11	0.0035	0.0037	0.0036
0.4861	18.462	(2634)	142.67	69.36	(0.0)	(0.0)	(0.0)

These values of r'/N were used to caluclate the values of N_x in the fourth column, N_x being the wave-lengths for various numbers of fringes corresponding to $r = 3000$ (and hence to $r' = 2634$). The next column contains the values of $N_x\lambda$, which is equal to p_x, the path difference (for 3000 divisions) for the given wave-length, while the sixth and seventh columns contain respectively the proportional variation of p_x (that is, $\Delta p/p_x$), and the change (n) of refractive index of the compensator plate calculated from $\Delta p/p_x$ by means of formula (9 a). The values of Δn calculated in this way agree satisfactorily with the direct measurements (shown in the last column) of the refractive index of the plate for the various wave-lengths.

2. *The shift of the achromatic fringe in white light.* This shifting of the achromatic fringe relative to the original central reference fringe is common to all compensation interferometers when used with white light. We may best understand what happens by supposing that the concentration of a solution in C (figs. 1 and 2) is increased slowly and continuously from zero onwards and that at the same time the original achromatic band is kept central by appropriate movement of the compensator. We would then in most cases observe, that the original achromatic band gradually becomes colored at the edges, while the adjacent bands to right and left become respectively more and less strongly colored; with further increase of concentration the central band becomes identical in appearance with the band on the left, and at length the latter is achromatic while

the central band is now particolored like the right hand band was originally. The comparison band has thus *apparently* shifted one band to the left; with further increase of concentration the same sequence of events occurs, and the apparently correct comparison band is shifted one additional band to the left for a certain concentration difference, this difference being (on our instrument) about 0.07 per cent (300 divisions) for KCl while for KNO_3 this concentration interval is considerably less. Now, since in making readings on a series of solutions of a substance we must obviously always make the final setting upon the same band, we shall err if the setting is made each time upon the most nearly achromatic band; and there will be one discontinuity for each such "concentration interval." The explanation of this shift of the achromatic band is found in the relative optical dispersion of solution and water, on the one hand, and of glass (of the compensator plates P_1, P_2) and air, on the other hand; for it is to be noted that in the type of instrument under consideration the lengthening of the optical path due to replacement of water by solution is compensated by the shortening of the *same* path by decreasing the effective thickness of an interposed glass plate. We shall now proceed to develop a formula by the aid of which errors arising from this source can be readily obviated.

This equation may be derived by making use of the principle that in general the position of the achromatic fringe is determined not by the condition (as in the case of the central fringe in monochromatic light) that the geometrical path difference shall be equal to the optical path difference, but by the condition that at the center of the achromatic fringe the change of phase with respect to wave-length shall be a minimum.[3] Accordingly if the combined effect of a decrease p in optical path-length due to the movement of the compensator and of an increase in path-length due to the replacement of a thickness l of water by solution is to displace the central bright band to a point O', this displacement N_λ, in terms of fringes for the wave-length λ, is given by

[3] See R. W. Wood, Physical Optics, 2nd Ed., 1911, p. 140.

$$N_\lambda = \frac{D}{\lambda}$$

D being the geometrical (and also the optical) path difference at O'. The achromatic fringe will similarly be displaced N'_λ fringes (again of wave-length λ) to a point (say Q), where

$$N'_\lambda = \frac{D'}{\lambda}$$

Now if the refractive indices of solution, water, and glass are represented by n_1, n_2 and n respectively and if we put $\nu = n_1 - n_2$ (with appropriate subscripts attached to ν and n to denote the wave-lengths to which they refer), then

$$D = \nu\, l - p$$

Consequently since ν, n, and hence p are all functions of λ we may write

$$D = f(\lambda)$$

We next determine D' in terms of $f(\lambda)$. Now the phase difference ϕ at Q is

$$\phi = 2\pi(D' - D)/\lambda;$$

Applying the necessary condition, $d\phi/d\lambda = 0$, we find

$$D' = f(\lambda) - \lambda f'(\lambda)$$

where $f'(\lambda) = df(\lambda)/d\lambda$. Accordingly

$$N_\lambda - N_\lambda = \frac{D'}{\lambda} - \frac{D}{\lambda} = -f'(\lambda)$$

To evaluate $f'(\lambda)$ we write for the variation of refractive index with wave length, according to the simple dispersion formula

$$n = A + \frac{B}{\lambda^2}$$

also

$$n_1 = A_1 + \frac{B_1}{\lambda^2}$$

and

$$n_2 = A_2 + \frac{B_2}{\lambda^2}$$

Therefore

$$N'_\lambda - N_\lambda = -f'(\lambda) = \frac{2}{\lambda^3}(B_1 - B_2)\,l - \frac{dp}{d\lambda}$$

Eliminating dp by formula (10) we obtain finally

(11) $$N'_\lambda - N_\lambda = \frac{2}{\lambda^3}\left[(B_1 - B_2)\,l - qp\frac{B}{n-1}\right]$$

This expression gives the position of the achromatic fringe relative to the central fringe for any wave-length λ. Now if by the combined effect of the change in concentration of the solution and of movement of the compensator the position of the fringes for wave-length λ remains unchanged—that is, if, as in actual practice, the solution has shifted these fringes N_t fringes to the left and the compensator an equal number to the right—then $N_\lambda = 0$; moreover

$$N_t = \frac{\nu\,l}{\lambda} \quad \text{and obviously must also } = \frac{p}{\lambda}$$

Combining these relations with (11) we have

(12) $$\frac{N'_\lambda}{N_t} = \frac{2}{\lambda^2}\left(\frac{B_1 - B_2}{\nu} - q\,\frac{B}{n-1}\right)$$

It will be convenient to take for λ that wave-length which corresponds to maximum luminosity in the spectrum of the light source (a tungsten lamp); this was found to be $\lambda = 0.58$. Now since $n_F - n_C = B\,[1/(.486)^2 - 1/(.656)^2] = 1.91\,B$, it follows that

$$\frac{B}{n_D - 1} = \frac{\beta''}{1.91}$$

where β'' is the ordinary relative dispersion of the glass plate, and similarly if we define the dispersive power[4] (β')

[4] It is to be noted that β' is not the same as the difference in relative dispersion of the solution and water; i.e.,

$$\frac{n_{1F} - n_{1C}}{n_{1D} - 1} - \frac{n_{2F} - n_{2C}}{n_{2D} - 1}$$

is not equal to $(\nu_F - \nu_C)/\nu_D$. Values of β' and β'' can be found, or calculated from data, in tables of constants.

of the solution with respect to water by the relation

$$\beta' = \frac{\nu_F - \nu_C}{\nu_D}$$

then $(B_1 - B_2)/\nu = \beta'/1.91$.   Finally therefore

(13) $$\frac{N'_\lambda}{N_t} = \frac{2(\beta' - q\beta'')}{(.58)^2 \times 1.91} = \frac{\beta' - q\beta''}{0.320}$$

This expression gives the numbers of fringes N'_λ through which the comparison band apparently shifts, in relation to the total number of fringes N_t corresponding to the position of the compensator; in actual practice it is more convenient to put $N_t = r/r_f$ where r_f denotes the number of divisions on the drum corresponding to one fringe in white light.   Making this substitution, and putting $N'_\lambda = 1$, we find the corresponding reading r_1 to be

(13 a) $$r_1 = 0.320\, r_f/(\beta' - q\beta'')$$

in other words, for each interval of $0.320\, r_f/(\beta' - q\beta'')$ divisions the achromatic fringe will have shifted one fringe to the left of the original bright band.   Consequently for any solution or mixture for which β' is known, the amount of shift can be accurately calculated in advance;[5] the shift can therefore be allowed for, and any error from this source obviated.

In conclusion it may be remarked that in two of the three forms of Zeiss instrument—viz., in the portable gas interferometer and the water interferometer—the light passes twice through the compensator plate and hence the right hand member of equations 1 to 7 inclusive must be multiplied by 2 when applied to these instruments.   Only slight modification of the formulae is required to enable them to be applied to any form of compensation interferometer.

---

[5] Examples of the application of this formula may be found in the paper already referred to, now in course of publication.

PHYSICAL CHEMISTRY.—*A vacuum furnace for the measurement of small dissociation pressures.* R. B. Sosman and J. C. Hostetter, Geophysical Laboratory.

The study of those silicate systems which contain iron requires the measurement of a wide range of oxygen pressures. The first problem in this connection is the study of the dissociation pressures of the oxides of iron themselves. For this purpose the apparatus described below has been developed.

Vacuum furnaces in considerable variety have already been described, but none of these was exactly suited to the work in hand. Furnaces like those of Arsem, Ruff, and numerous others, in which the heating element is of graphite or carbon, are of course out of the question when iron and oxygen are to be studied. Tungsten and molybdenum furnaces, like that of Birnbräuer, cannot be used with oxygen. Slade's platinum tube furnace is designed for a horizontal heating tube, which is not suitable for the quenching of silicate melts by dropping them into mercury. Another disadvantage of Slade's furnace is the softness of platinum at high temperatures, permitting the heating tube to be easily deformed.

Our furnace and accessory apparatus are shown in somewhat diagrammatical section in figure 1. The design could no doubt be improved, as some parts are the product of evolution rather than of original design, but the description covers the apparatus as it is actually being used for the measurement of small dissociation pressures. In principle, the furnace is similar to that of Slade.[1] It consists essentially of two parts: (1) the furnace tube, which serves both as the furnace wall inclosing the "inside vacuum" and as the heating element; (2) the water-cooled jacket, which surrounds the furnace tube and incloses the "outside vacuum."

An alternating current at low voltage is sent through the furnace tube, which is made of an alloy of 80 parts platinum and

---

[1] R. E. Slade, An electric furnace for experiments in vacuo at temperatures up to 1500°. Pr. Roy. Soc. London. **87** A: 519–524. 1912.

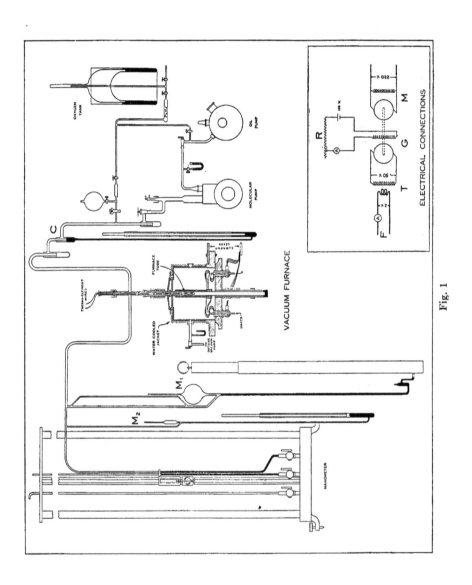

Fig. 1

20 rhodium.[2]   The tube is 15 mm. inside diameter and 200 mm. long, with walls 1 mm. thick.   The current is carried in by water cooled terminals; the upper terminal is fixed to the furnace jacket, while the lower terminal moves with the expansion and contraction of the furnace tube.   The cooling water is led into the lower terminal by lead pipes, and the current is carried by a sheaf of flexible copper strips.   The lower leads are insulated from the furnace jacket by the stone base of the jacket, and are prevented from accidentally touching the walls by mica sheets around the inside of the jacket.

The platinum-rhodium alloy has the great advantage over pure platinum of great mechanical strength and stiffness.   Platinum-iridium alloys are even stronger mechanically, but the volatility of the iridium forbids its use where thermoelements are to be used.   The stiffness of platinrhodium is shown by our experience with the nitrogen thermometer, which had a 200 cc. bulb made of the alloy containing 20 per cent rhodium.   At 1100°, one atmosphere outside with about 200 mm. pressure inside produced no observable change in the volume of the bulb after cooling, although a difference of 0.05 cc. or 1 part in 4000 could have been easily detected.   The strength of the platinrhodium tube was put to the test when during some measurements at 1300° a glass connection was broken, allowing air at atmospheric pressure to rush into the inside of the furnace tube while the outside was still evacuated; we could detect no bulging of the furnace tube resulting from the accident.

The lower end of the platinrhodium tube is extended by a steel tube, capped with a screw cap and sealed with kollolith.[3]   The upper end is likewise extended by a steel tube into which a glass tube is sealed, by the method of Kraus.   This is an extremely useful type of joint, now being used in the manufacture of X-ray tubes, and should come into much wider use in vacuum apparatus.

[2] The tube was made by Dr. Heraeus of Hanau, to whom we have several times had occasion to express our indebtedness for his interest in the forwarding of high temperature investigations.

[3] A Canada balsam substitute of constant melting point and low vapor pressure, made by Voigt & Hochgesang.

Branches from the glass tube connect with the Gaede molecular vacuum pump on the one hand and with the pressure gages on the other. These connections are made with wide bends to take up stresses due to movements of the furnace and gages with changing temperature. All the glass tube connections are large, to facilitate rapid pumping to low pressures. The molecular pump delivers into a Gaede oil box pump, with which it is connected by a wide glass tube. The glass connection from the furnace to the molecular pump is provided with a removable conical ground cap (as shown in fig. 1), so that the pump can be washed without interference with the rest of the apparatus. A stopcock is also attached here, so that the pump can be used for other work. A $CaCl_2$ drying tube connected between the molecular and box pumps allows the pumps to be filled with dry air before stopping. The interior of the furnace and gages is kept dry by a tube of P_2O_5 in the bottom of the steel extension of the furnace tube.

The charges are contained in a small platinum crucible suspended by two platinum wires sealed into a glass cap, which is attached to a ground glass conical joint at the top of the tube above the furnace. The two wires of the platinum-platinrhodium thermoelement are also sealed through this glass cap, and the four wires are insulated from one another by transparent fused silica or Marquardt porcelain capillaries. The two suspension-wires may also be used as the leads for the determination of melting points, et cetera, by the quenching method.

There are three pressure gages: (1) a McLeod vacuum gage of 500 cc. capacity from Leybold (shown at M_1), (2) a similar gage of 50 cc. capacity made in this laboratory (M_2), (3) a mercury manometer read by means of parallel knife edges and a vernier, and reading to 0.01 mm. The latter is the manometer used in previous work on the nitrogen thermometer.[4] It has an excellent scale, calibrated throughout its length to 0.01 mm. by the Normal-Aichungs-Kommission in Charlottenburg. We removed the fixed level point used with the gas thermometer,

[4] Am. J. Sci. (4) 26: 415. 1908. Carnegie Inst. Washington, Publ. No. 157, p. 19.

connected this arm across to the vacuum apparatus by a wide glass tube, and evacuated and sealed the open arm, thus making a closed U-tube manometer of the apparatus. The three gages, compared against one another at various pressures within their ranges, agreed within the error of their readings. We have in this combination of gages a range of pressure measurement from 0.000 001 mm. mercury up to about 2.5 atmospheres.

The furnace jacket is an inverted iron pot, closed at the bottom by a disk of Alberene stone through which pass (1) the two conductors in parallel which carry the current to the lower end of the platinrhodium tube, together with the tubes for the cooling water, and (2) the steel extension of the platinrhodium tube. The latter is surrounded by a water-jacketed steel tube and cap. A little mercury is placed in the bottom of the steel tube to insure good thermal connection with the furnace tube, so that the lower end of the latter will always be kept cold. The joint between the stone base and the flange of the jacket is made tight by means of a plastic cement made by Mr. J. Jost of the instrument shop of this Laboratory.

The jacket is evacuated independently of the inside vacuum by means of a May-Nelson pump. There is no connection between the inside high vacuum and the outside "ordinary" vacuum. No insulation or refractory material is used excepting a magnesia tube surrounding the platinrhodium tube. The outside vacuum removes any danger of collapsing the hot furnace tube at high temperatures, and also provides an efficient heat insulation. The furnace jacket is cooled by a coil of lead pipe on the outside carrying cold water. An observation window permits optical temperature measurements to be made from without as a check on the thermoelectric measurements within the tube.

The magnesia tube does not greatly affect the loss of heat from the furnace tube at the lower temperatures, where the loss by radiation is not great, but does have a noticeable effect on the efficiency at higher temperatures. For instance, 386 amperes raised the temperature to 790° without the tube, and to 809° with the tube in place. 510 amperes, however, which produced only 1100° without the tube, gave 1308° when the tube was in place.

The uniformity of temperature was not tested by direct measurement, as a complicated arrangement of apparatus would have been necessary to permit of moving the thermo-element up and down in the completely sealed furnace. An equally sensitive test was made, however, by taking a series of measurements of the oxygen pressures produced by 0.5 gram charges of Merck's ferric oxide, heated under similar conditions but at various levels in the furnace. In our preliminary measurements of dissociation pressures the thermo-element junction was always placed 3 to 5 mm. above the top of the charge of oxide, so that the change in weight of the charge could be determined without uncertainty due to oxide adhering to the wires. It is obvious that near the top of the furnace the thermo-element, under these conditions, will be colder than the bottom of the charge, whereas near the bottom of the furnace the reverse will be true. Hence if the temperature of the thermo-element is set to the ṣame value in both positions, the temperature of the charge, and therefore the pressure obtained, will be greater near the top than near the bottom of the furnace. If two or more pressures obtained near the middle of the furnace agree within the range of reproducibility of these pressures, proof is afforded that there is a space of uniform temperature equal to the distance between the highest position of the thermo-element and the lowest position of the bottom of the charge. Measurements can therefore be made on charges set in this part of the furnace with the assurance that the temperature of the charge is uniform and is represented accurately by the temperature of the thermo-element. This condition is further assured by packing deep charges into the crucible with a polished steel plunger which shapes the surface with a central well, so that the thermo-element can be placed actually within the charge without coming into contact with it.

The result of the uniformity tests is shown in Table I. The distance from the top of the furnace tube to the top of the crucible in millimeters is given in the third column, and the

pressure in millimeters of mercury in the fourth column. The
degree of reproducibility of the pressures is shown by the second,
third, fourth, and fifth measurements. The pressures at depths
of 85, 92, and 95 mm. are practically constant. Since the depth
of the crucible is 18 mm. there seems therefore to be a range
of about 25–30 mm. in which the temperature is uniform within
one degree, judging from the variation of pressure, which is of
the order of magnitude of 0.01 mm. per degree under the conditions of the tests. For subsequent measurements the crucible
was always placed in the middle of this zone, and the thermo-
element brought near the center of gravity of the charge as
explained above. The charges varied in depth from 5 to 10
mm.

TABLE I

Pressures obtained from Merck's Fe_2O_3 at 1100° at various levels in furnace

NO.	WEIGHT OXIDE	DISTANCE FROM TOP	PRESSURE
	mg.	*mm.*	*mm.*
1345.................	493.3	65	0.610
1347.................	502.9	75	0.330
1349.................	504.0	75	0.305
1351.................	502.9	75	0.320
1355.................	503.8	75	0.315
1358.................	501.8	85	0.215
1362.................	501.6	92	0.210
1360.................	507.1	95	0.195
1361.................	499.6	107	0.120

Glass stopcocks are the most troublesome part of a vacuum
apparatus. We have found Gundelach's large right-angle stopcocks (Schiff's form) satisfactory for the present work. A
stiff rubber-paraffine-vaseline stopcock grease must be used,
however, to prevent the atmospheric pressure on the large surface from causing the cock to stick fast. The grease should
be renewed occasionally, also, as it becomes gummy after use
for a long time in a vacuum.

As Professor Morley has well said, a stopcock is usually nothing
more than a located leak. It is necessary, then, to shut off the
located leaks in the connections to pumps and oxygen supply
by a mercury cutoff, shown at C in figure 1. Its construction

is evident from .the drawing. This cutoff, like the gages, is operated by a plunger instead of a movable reservoir. The glass traps on either side prevent mercury from being shot into the furnace or the.pumps by any accidental rush of gas.

With the mercury cutoff closed and the joint of the crucible suspension sealed with kollolith the apparatus is absolutely free from leaks. It has stood 27 days without showing a pressure greater than 0.0052 mm. of mercury. This pressure seems to have been produced by the slow evolution of gas from the large surface of glass exposed. This matter will be discussed more in detail in a later paper on the iron oxides.

The plunger-lift for the large McLeod gage, M_1, consists of a steel plunger in a smooth wrought-iron pipe, as the necessary dimensions are too large to permit of the use of glass. The dimensions need to be carefully proportioned, since the displacement of mercury by the plunger must be equal to the volume of the gage plus the volume of mercury in the annular space between plunger and cylinder when the gage is at its highest reading. The greater the clearance between plunger and cylinder, therefore, the greater must be the diameter of both. Ours consists of a plunger 50.5 mm. in diameter and 100 cm. long in a cylinder 53 mm. inside diameter and 102 cm. long. The steel plunger is just floating in the mercury when the gage is nearly filled, so that the mercury columns can be set accurately · by a slight pressure on the plunger. The use of a plunger-lift of this kind does away with the raising and lowering of an awkward mercury reservoir, with its accompanying rubber tubing, leaks, and sulfur contamination of the mercury.

Oxygen is admitted by way of one or both of the calibrated bulbs at the right of the apparatus. We have made no provision for exact measurement of the amount of oxygen to be admitted, as it can be just as exactly measured by its pressure after admission to the apparatus. It is possible to get any desired amount of oxygen by expanding slowly from either the small or large bulb. These bulbs also serve, together with the space between the mercury cutoff and the pump stopcock, for the withdrawal of known amounts of oxygen from the apparatus.

The oxygen is stored over mercury in the glass gas-holder at the right.

To hold the temperature at 1450°, the furnace requires 580 amperes at about 1.8 volts. Its power consumption is therefore no greater than that of an ordinary wire-wound furnace, when the loss of heat in regulating-rheostats in connection with the latter is taken into account.

The current is supplied to the furnace from the secondary of a small 25 : 1 transformer. The primary of the transformer is supplied by a motor generator of 60 cycles and a voltage range from 0 to about 300 volts. The generator voltage is regulated by means of its field current, which is supplied by a 110 volt storage battery and passes through rheostats alongside the potentiometer. By regulation of the field current the furnace current can be regulated without any waste of electrical energy, and if the voltage applied to the motor of the motor-generator is reasonably constant, the temperature can be held constant without difficulty to one degree at 1500°. This degree of constancy is very often necessary for accurate measurements of the dissociation pressures of iron oxides, as these pressures change quite rapidly with changes of temperature.

BOTANY.—*Spring flowers in the fall.* J. B. NORTON, Bureau of Plant Industry.

To the ordinary observer of living things in their natural surroundings the various evidences of evolution have appealed in a more or less remote way as something that happened in the distant past. The modern experimental methods of hybridization and of study of mutating strains do not appeal with the necessary force to make us realize that evolution is potent now, as it was in the Carboniferous age. While these researches are interesting as showing means of preserving new characters once they originate, the average layman wants to see the actual appearance of a new character. The origin of some characters and their progressive development by gradual accumulation to a point at which the new element is of value to the organism has always been more or less of a stumbling block to many students.

At the present season the varying blooming time of related species always has a direct interest from its evolutionary meaning. As an example, take our native and cultivated maples and magnolias. Some species bloom early in the spring before the leaves appear, while others wait until the foliage is developed and then bloom well on into summer. From our observations on other groups of plants or on the individuals in one species, this change does not seem hard to account for. In another case, however, the blooming period offers more serious difficulty. The common witch-hazel in this region blooms late in the fall, and yet shows by its behavior that it is a typical spring flowering tree, its fruit developing normally the next season. It seems as though this change must have happened all at once by a big mutation because the winter months would so seriously affect the young flowers and developing fruit that the evolution by slow change would not be able to take place.

Fig. 1. Flower buds of *Cornus Mas*, March, 1912, showing fruits of the previous fall. In the lower branch the bud scales have been removed. (× 1½)

Many other spring flowers have been known to bloom in the fall; but most of these cases are caused by a moist period following the summer drought, this alternation of drought and moisture serving the same purpose as that of cold and warmth. It is an interesting thing that this fall or winter blooming is associated with many of our weeds and ornamental plants introduced from the Old World.   Among them are some that are unusually interesting in that they perhaps throw some light on the problem of the origin of fall blooming in witch-hazel.   On the Agricultural Grounds in Washington there is a specimen of *Cornus Mas* with a peculiar blooming habit.   Every fall this tree blooms more or less abundantly and in many cases sets good fruit.   An interesting feature is that not all the buds in an umbel covered by the same set of bud scales will necessarily develop into fall flowers.   Many umbels hold some of the buds until spring, so that we have fall fruit and spring flowers existing in the same umbel (fig. 1).   Apparently the tree is in a satisfactory transition condition between spring and fall blooming from which the development of a fall blooming form could be easily accomplished by gradual changes in future generations.   This perhaps sheds some light on the development of the fall flowering of witch-hazel without the necessity of a sudden mutation or without the necessity of moving its blooming period gradually through the winter months.

BOTANY.—*Tribroma, a new genus of tropical trees related to Theobroma.*   O. F. Cook, Bureau of Plant Industry.

In connection with a study of the branching habits of *Theobroma cacao*, attention has been given to a related tree known in Guatemala as patashte, which affords a still more striking example of the phenomenon of dimorphism of branches.[1]   The patashte tree has been placed with the cacao hitherto as another species of Theobroma, under the name *Theobroma bicolor*, but after a somewhat detailed comparison of the two trees in eastern Guatemala in 1907 it did not appear reasonable to assign them to the same genus.   This opinion was strengthened during another visit to Guatemala in the spring of 1914, and it is now proposed to treat the patashte tree as the type of a new genus. The distinctive characters are stated in the following description:

[1] Cook, O. F., Dimorphic Branches of Tropical Plants: Cotton, Coffee, Cacao, the Central American Rubber Tree, and the Banana.   U. S. Department of Agriculture, Bureau of Plant Industry, Bulletin 198.   Pp. 39.   1911.

Tribroma Cook, gen. nov.

Slender, erect trees, with strong upright shoots, each ending in a whorled cluster of 3 lateral branches; leaves of upright shoots with long petioles and broadly ovate-cordate blades, palmately veined, naked above, clothed underneath with a very fine dense appressed stellate pubescence, like the surfaces of the branches and petioles; leaves of lateral branches broadly ovate-oblong, subsessile, the petioles very short, representing only the confluent pulvini; inflorescences with pseudodichotomous branching, with bracts at the articulations, forming a broad, loose panicle or dichasium, produced near the ends of the lateral branches, above the axillary buds of the young leaves, entirely confined to the new growth; flowers small, inconspicuous, dark-colored, dull reddish purple, the petals minute and the sepals only partly opened; sepals broadly triangular, inflexed; petals much shorter than the sepals, the basal hood with a single median rib, the limb rudimentary, represented by a minute oval, reflexed, nearly sessile appendage; staminodes robust, clavate, clothed above with short pubescence, naked below; ovary 5-angled, finely pubescent like the pedicels, sepals, petals and staminodes, but none of the pubescence glandular; fruits ellipsoid, with a very hard woody shell, the surface broken by deep irregular lacunae.

Type, **Tribroma bicolor** (*Theobroma bicolor* Humb. & Bonpl., Pl. Equinox. **1**: 94, *pls. 30a, 30b.*).

The generic name Tribroma alludes to the fact that the lateral branches are always produced in whorls of three. In Bernouilli's monograph of Theobroma the name Rhytidocarpus was used for the section that included *T. bicolor;* but to advance this name to generic rank seems inadvisable, in view of the previous applications of closely similar names, such as Rhytidocarpaea and Rhyticarpus, in other groups of plants.

The patashte tree is probably of South American origin, though the original habitat has not been determined. In Central America it is widely but rather sparingly cultivated by the Indians. The seeds are used for the same purpose as those of the cacao tree, though generally considered inferior in quality. The comparison of cacao and patashte was made at a locality called Cacao or Secacao, on the Trece Aguas Estate of Don Ricardo Fickert-Forst, in the Senahú District of the Department of Alta Verapaz, eastern Guatemala. Specimens collected at Cacao in May, 1914, are in the U. S. National Herbarium, the sheets bearing numbers 862202-5.

The contrasting characters of the genus Theobroma, as represented by its type species, *T. cacao*, may be stated as follows:

Low, shade-tolerant trees of tropical undergrowth, the lateral branches formed in terminal clusters of 5, rarely 4 or 6; leaves elliptic-obovate, narrowed toward the base, pinnately veined, naked on both surfaces, the petioles and young shoots hirsute with stiff erect bristles; leaves of lateral branches of the same form as those of the upright shoots, the petioles somewhat shorter, but the pulvini distinct at each end; inflorescences reduced to minute fleshy twigs, only the terminal joints distinct and these shorter than the pedicels of the flowers, produced from adventitious buds on old wood of the main trunk or the larger branches, long after the leaves; flowers larger than in Tribroma, the sepals and petals both conspicuous, light colored, widely expanded; sepals narrow, tapering and reflexed; petals longer than the sepals, strongly curved or folded in the bud, the basal hood with two strong parallel ribs, the limb longer than the hood and with a slender base folded down around the end of the hood; staminodes slender, naked and tapering above, laterally compressed below, with bands of long hairs on the lateral faces; ovary rounded, covered with glandular pubescence like the sepals and the pedicel; fruits obovate or fusiform, with a thick fleshy rind, longitudinally ridged and furrowed, the surface smooth or tuberculate.

A more detailed account of the differences between the two trees, with special reference to their habits of branching and their floral biology, illustrated by photographs, is being offered for publication in the Contributions from the United States National Herbarium.

PROCEEDINGS OF THE ACADEMY AND AFFILIATED SOCIETIES

THE BIOLOGICAL SOCIETY OF WASHINGTON

The 533d meeting of the Society was held at the Cosmos Club, Saturday, January 9, 1915, with President BARTSCH in the chair. About 40 members were present. WALDO SCHMITT of the U. S. National Museum was elected to active membership.

Under the heading Brief Notes and Exhibition of Specimens L. O. HOWARD made remarks on the meetings held at Philadelphia during convocation week. Dr. PILSBRY discussed certain aspects of the Hawaiian land shell problem, stating that early collecting was done in the valleys, but that recent work showed the chief home of species to be on the ridges. The distribution of forms occurred in groups and there were many instances of Mendelian inheritance between different forms carried out on a large natural scale.

The first paper on the regular program was by WM. PALMER: *An unknown fossil.* Mr. PALMER exhibited the specimen from the Calvert Cliffs of Chesapeake Bay and hoped members would express views as to its nature. His own view was that it might represent the lower jaw of an unknown turtle. From same locality other fossils were shown that had previously proved very difficult to identify. Mr. PALMER's communication was discussed by Professor HAY.

The second paper was by Professor HAY: *An albino terrapin.* The unique specimen was exhibited; it was hatched near Beaufort, N. C.; an attempt was made to raise it, but it lived only a few months. Professor HAY took occasion to show excellent lantern slides of certain interesting crustaceans especially of *Limnoria lignorum*, a wood boring Isopod, and of *Xylotria*, a wood boring mollusk. The communication was discussed by Messrs. BARTSCH, WILCOX, PALMER, SMITH, and HOPKINS, and by Miss RATHBUN.

The last communication was by M. W. LYON JR.: *Notes on the physiology of bats.* The speaker stated that little was known of the exact physiology of bats, but discussed the subject from the broad standpoint of their physiology of locomotion, of food, of adaptation, and of special senses. The need of careful experiments on use of, and modern histological work on structure of noseleaves was pointed out. The paper was discussed by Messrs. HOWARD, BISHOP, HUNTER, WM. PALMER and STILES; Mr. BISHOP giving an account of a bat roost near San Antonio, Texas, erected with the idea that bats would consume large numbers of malarial mosquitoes; Mr. HUNTER stating that an examination of stomach contents of bats showed that the food of *Nytinomus mexicanus* consisted of 95 per cent moths, the rest being carabid beetles, hymenopterous insects, and a few crane flies—the only Diptera found, no mosquitoes being observed.

On Tuesday, January 19, 1915, at 8.30 p.m., the Society held a joint meeting with the Washington Academy of Sciences in the Auditorium of the National Museum. Dr. JOHAN HJORT, Director of Fisheries of Norway, delivered an illustrated lecture on *Migrations and fluctuations of the marine animals of western Europe.* About 200 persons were present.

The 534th meeting of the Society was held at the Cosmos Club, Saturday, January 23, 1915, with President BARTSCH in the chair and 75 persons present. Mr. R. A. WARD was elected to active membership.

Under heading Brief Notes etc., Dr. JOHAN HJORT, Director of Fisheries of Norway, called attention to the large numbers of herring caught in Norwegian waters during the last few years, most of them belonging to what he termed the "1904 Class." Dr. HJORT attributed the great success of the "1904 Class" to the known lateness of season when it had been spawned and when the plankton was abundant. Early in spring the sea is practically barren of plankton and fish hatching at that time have little food.

The regular program consisted of an illustrated paper by Mrs. AGNES CHASE on *Developing instincts of a young squirrel.* Mrs. CHASE had made careful observations and notes on the bringing up of a young gray squirrel during the spring and summer of 1914. The animal was very young when received, needing to be fed on milk with a medicine dropper. Mrs. CHASE described its growth and its acquisition of squirrel-like habits and instincts. It was not brought up as a pet, but was given every freedom to develop its natural traits. At maturity it met with wild members of its own species, at first returned home, but finally remained away.

The rest of the evening was given over to an exhibition of lantern slides on biological subjects. W. W. COOKE showed views of bird life; H. M. SMITH, of the Japanese silk industry; WM. PALMER, of seals and birds of Pribilof Islands; PAUL BARTSCH, of local birds.

The 535th meeting of the Society was held at the Cosmos Club, Saturday, February 6, 1915, with Vice-President HOPKINS in the chair and 35 persons present.

Under heading Book Notices and Brief Notes Dr. RANSOM called attention to a new biological journal under the editorship of Professor Ward, of the University of Illinois, to be devoted to animal parasites. Mr. COOKE read a letter from Dr. B. W. Evermann, now of San Francisco, a former president of the Society.

The first paper of the regular program was by T. WAYLAND VAUGHAN: *Remarks on the rate of growth of stony corals.* Dr. VAUGHAN reviewed the work done by previous investigators and gave results of his own carefully conducted experiments at Tortugas. The paper was fully illustrated by lantern slides showing apparatus and methods employed in planting corals and results of one and of several years' growth of various corals.

The second paper was by J. N. Rose: *Botanical explorations in South America.* Dr. Rose spoke concerning a botanical exploration on the western coast of South America, which he made during the summer and fall of 1914. He stated that when he took up the study of the Cactaceae for the Carnegie Institution of Washington, it was with the understanding that it should embrace not only herbarium and greenhouse studies, but extensive field work in all the great cactus deserts of the two Americas. His going to the west coast was therefore simply part of a large scheme for botanical exploration. He further stated that plans had been made for similar field work in the deserts of the east side of South America during the coming summer. He gave detailed accounts of his work in the deserts of Peru, Bolivia, and Chile, and the peculiar Cacti which he found, described particularly the climatic conditions in those countries, and told of the remarkable crescent-shaped sand dunes of southern Peru. On this trip Dr. Rose collected more than a thousand numbers, obtaining not only herbarium and formalin specimens, but also living material. His collection of living plants, which was very large, has been sent to the New York Botanical Garden. Dr. Rose's communication was illustrated by maps of the regions traversed, by apparatus used in collecting specimens, and by preserved specimens. The paper was discussed by Messrs. Hitchcock, Vaughan, Goldman and Townsend.

The 536th meeting of the Society was held at the Cosmos Club, Saturday, February 20, 1915, at 8 p.m., with President Bartsch in the chair and 65 persons present.

Dr. Charles Monroe Mansfield, of the Bureau of Animal Industry, was elected to active membership.

Under the heading of Brief Notes, Gen. T. A. Wilcox made observations and inquiries concerning the color of the eyes of certain turtles. His remarks were discussed by W. P. Hay. Dr. L. O. Howard described the successful campaign carried on against mosquitoes in New Jersey.

Under the heading Exhibition of Specimens, Wm. Palmer exhibited the tip of the tongue of a sulphurbottom whale and considered the probable utility of its peculiar shape. Messrs. Bartsch, Hay, and Lyon took part in the discussion.

The regular program consisted of an illustrated lecture by H. C Oberholser entitled: *A naturalist in Nevada.* Mr. Oberholser gave an account of a biological survey of parts of Nevada made by himself and others some years ago, and described the geologic, geographic, and climatic characters of the route traversed by his party. He mentioned in particular the plants, mammals, birds, and reptiles observed and collected by the expedition, and pointed out how they were influenced in kind and numbers by the unusual geographic and climatic conditions found in Nevada. He showed many excellent views of the country and of the animals and plants encountered.

Mr. Oberholser's paper was discussed by Messrs. Hay, Bartsch, Bailey, Lyon, Goldman, Wetmore, and Wm. Palmer.

M. W. Lyon, Jr., *Recording Secretary.*

JOURNAL

OF THE

WASHINGTON ACADEMY OF SCIENCES

Vol. V   MAY 4, 1915   No. 9

PHYSICAL CHEMISTRY.—*The reduction of iron oxides by platinum, with a note on the magnetic susceptibility of iron-bearing platinum.* R. B. Sosman and J. C. Hostetter, Geophysical Laboratory.

In the course of an investigation on the dissociation pressures and melting temperatures of the oxides of iron, we have repeatedly observed that the platinum crucibles used gained in weight and became stiff, evidently through the absorption of iron from the charges.

Proof of the reduction of magnetite. The following experiment demonstrates the absorption of iron from magnetite by platinum under a very low oxygen pressure. About 1 gram of natural crystalline magnetite from Mineville, N. Y., was heated to 500° in a new platinum crucible (Heraeus "extra rein," dimensions 18 mm high, 8–10 mm diameter) in a platinrhodium tube vacuum furnace,[1] and then cooled. A small amount of gas was given off and was not reabsorbed. This gas produced a pressure of 0.045 mm in a volume of 1300 cc, and was probably nearly all gas "adsorbed" by the magnetite. This gas was pumped out, and the charge then heated to various temperatures between 600° and 1200°. The temperatures were measured by a platinum-platinrhodium thermo-element and potentiometer, and the pressures were read on a 500 cc McLeod gage. A condensed record

---

[1] This Journal, **5**: 277–285. 1915.

of the first series of heatings is given in Table I. The furnace
was then cooled, and the residual gas pumped out. The charge
was again heated as recorded in the second part of Table I.
The results are shown graphically in figure 1.

TABLE I

FIRST SERIES

TEMPERATURE t	TIME HELD AT t	INITIAL PRESSURE	FINAL PRESSURE	REMARKS
degrees	minutes	mm.	mm.	
First Series				
22.5		0.00016		
600	18	0.0112	0.0148	Rising at decreasing rate
1000	20	0.0510	0.0562	Rising steadily
1200	23	0.0665	0.0776	Rising steadily
23		.	0.0744	
Second Series				
21.0		0.00012		
600	26	0.0111	0.0164	Rising steadily
1000	16	0.0171	0.0216	Rising steadily
1200	18	0.0236	0.0344	Rising steadily
1000	18	0.0350	0.0360	Nearly constant
600	19	0.0350	0.0352	Constant
1200	12	0.0396	0.0447	Rising steadily
600	11	0.0429	0.0426	Constant
21			0.0398	

It is evident from the figures of Table I that a reaction is going
on at 1000° and higher which is supplying gas at a fairly steady
rate, and that this rate is greater, the higher the temperature.
The changes in weight of charge and crucible, given in Table II,
indicate that this reaction consists in the liberation of oxygen
and the solution of metallic iron in the platinum. When heated
in air after cleaning, the crucible showed on the inside the characteristic reddish black color which appears on heating platinum
contaminated with iron.

It is also evident that a small amount of gas absorption takes
place as the temperature is lowered, since the pressure decreases
more than can be accounted for by the cooling of the furnace

tube, but that there is no approach to a complete reabsorption of the oxygen. This decrease of pressure on cooling probably represents the re-oxidation of a small amount of dissociated mag-

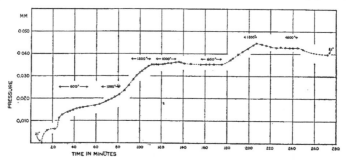

Fig. 1. Evolution of oxygen from magnetite heated in platinum (see Table I).

netite; the dissociation product is as yet unknown. No metallic iron was found in the charge either by solution in hydrochloric acid, which yields bubbles of hydrogen if metallic iron is present, or by the more sensitive copper sulphate test under the microscope.

TABLE II

	INITIAL WEIGHT	FINAL WEIGHT	CHANGE IN WEIGHT
	mg.	*mg.*	*mg.*
Charge and crucible............	4265.8	4264.7	− 1.1 (loss)
Crucible alone.................	3261.4	3263.2	+ 1.8 (gain)
Charge alone.................	1004.4	1001.5	− 2.9 (loss)

The gain in weight of the crucible, shown in Table II, has been caused partly by the absorption of metallic iron from the oxide, and partly by the absorption of rhodium and also platinum[2]

[2] The analysis of the crucibles shows that the combined weight of rhodium and iron is less than the total gain in weight. No appreciable amounts of other metals seem likely to be present, nor were any found by the analysis. Heating a part of crucible No. 1 in hydrogen for an hour at about 600° produced no measurable loss of weight, showing that no oxide of platinum or iron is present. Some platinum must therefore have been carried from the furnace tube to the crucible, either on account of a temperature gradient between furnace and crucible, or by some disintegrating effect due to the current, or by both causes combined.

from the furnace. The amount of iron absorbed, as calculated from the amount of oxygen evolved and remaining in the apparatus after cooling to room temperature, making no allowance for any permanent thermal dissociation of the magnetite, is found to be 0.9 mg. This is one-half of the total gain in weight.

Magnetite is also reduced by platinum at high temperatures in the open air. 6.608 grams of Merck's reagent Fe_2O_3 was heated to a maximum of 1612° in an open platinum crucible (No. 509) in a 25 mm vertical-tube platinum wire furnace. The charge melted down at about 1582°, yielding black crystalline "magnetite" on cooling. The crucible, which originally weighed 9517.3 mg, increased in weight to 9521.2 mg, a gain of 3.9 mg. Certain points on the bottom of the crucible attracted a light magnetic needle.

Reduction of ferric oxide. Products containing more ferric oxide than magnetite, as well as magnetite itself, seem to be reduced by platinum under a low pressure of oxygen. This action is evident even in products which are practically pure Fe_2O_3. One crucible (No. 2) used in our work on the system Fe_2O_3-Fe_3O_4, after 18 series of measurements, had increased in weight from 2851.8 mg to 2863.0 mg, a gain of 11.2 mg or 0.39 per cent. About one-fourth of this gain is found to be due to iron absorbed. At the close of the measurements this crucible showed the usual iron coloration, produced by cleaning and heating for a few minutes in a flame. Various points on the crucible also attracted a light magnetic needle.

Under 10.2 mm oxygen pressure at 1200°, under which conditions the magnetite is nearly completely oxidized to Fe_2O_3, this crucible gained 1.6 mg. Another similar crucible containing Fe_2O_3 gained 1.0 mg under 18.3 mm oxygen pressure at 1200°. A part, at least, of these gains must be due to absorbed iron. In order to establish definitely the presence of iron in the crucibles, and to determine its amount, we have made both chemical analyses and magnetic tests on the crucibles in question.

Methods of analysis. For the analysis of one portion of crucible No. 2 the platinum metals were separated from the iron by precipitating the former with hydrogen in sulphuric acid solution.[3] For the other portion of crucible No. 2, and for crucible No. 1, the method of Mylius and Mazzucchelli,[4] by which all metals present could be determined, was employed. In addition to iron, this method showed the presence of rhodium in both crucibles, and this latter metal was also determined. The order of agreement between the two methods for iron is shown in Table III, in which the results of the analyses are given. To test the determination of iron by the method of Mylius and Mazzucchelli, a solution containing 977 mg platinum and 5.00 mg iron was subjected to analysis; 4.83 mg iron was recovered.

TABLE III

METHOD OF ANALYSIS	CRUCIBLE NO.	RHODIUM		IRON	
		Per cent	Amount in crucible	Per cent	Amount in crucible
			mg.		mg.
Mylius and Mazzucchelli.......	1	0.077	2.40	0.158	4.90
Mylius and Mazzucchelli.......	2	0.127	3.62	0.098	2.80
Hydrogen precipitation.........	2			0.085	

Magnetic properties of iron-bearing platinum. The apparatus for the magnetic tests was suggested by Dr. C. W. Burrows, of the Bureau of Standards, to whom we are greatly indebted for advice and information in connection with these tests. The procedure consists essentially in weighing the pull exerted on the specimen by a strong electromagnet. In paramagnetic and diamagnetic bodies the force is practically independent of the shape of the specimen.

Since we wished to obtain only comparative figures, we did not attempt to determine the field strength or field gradient. With our apparatus, as set up, 870.2 mg of ferrous ammonium sulphate gave a pull of 1.74 mg, equivalent to 2.00 mg per gram. The pull can be determined to about 0.02 mg by the method of swings.

---

[3] For the details of this method and for many helpful suggestions, we are indebted to Dr. E. T. Allen of this Laboratory.

[4] Zs. anorg. Chem., 89: 1–38. 1914.

The mean of two sets taken with reversal of the current eliminates a small correction due to the steel parts of the balance.

One-half of crucible No. 2 had already been dissolved for analysis. The other half was tested magnetically and gave a pull of 0.20 mg. This was so much smaller than the effect which we expected on the basis of preliminary results obtained by Burrows and Burgess at the Bureau of Standards, that we experi-

TABLE IV

TREATMENT	TOTAL WEIGHT	WEIGHT OF IRON IN CRUCIBLE	MAGNETIC PULL	REMARKS
	mg.	mg.	mg.	
Crucible tested alone.....	3125.2	0	0.0	
Iron deposited electrolyti- cally.	3153.2	27.4	543.0	Deposit weighs 28.0 mg. but contains some hy- drogen, carbon, and moisture.
Heated at 1200° and 0.001 mm. for 8 min.........	3152.6	27.4	35.5	Film of iron still on sur- face.
Heated at 1200° and 0.0005 mm. for 30 min.......	3152.5	27.4	23.8	Film of iron still on surface.
Boiled in HCl, ignited 1 min. in Bunsen flame, oxide dissolved off in HCl....................	3151.4	26.3	25.2	Film removed.
Ignited in blast lamp, ox- ide dissolved off in HCl	3149.2	24.1	9.6	
Heated at 1400° and 0.002 mm. for 8 min........	3149.3	24.1	1.56	
Heated at 1400° and 0.0007 mm. for 11 min........	3149.7⁵	24.1	1.49	

mented further on the magnetic effects produced by known percentages of iron added to pure platinum. For this purpose a new 10 x 18 mm platinum crucible (Heraus "extra rein") was first tested and found to give no measurable magnetic pull. Iron was deposited in the crucible electrolytically from oxalate solution, and it was then heated in the vacuum furnace, first at 1200°, later at 1400°, in order to dissolve the iron in the platinum. The results are recorded in Table IV.

Nearly twice as much iron was deposited in the same way in a similar crucible, which was similarly treated and tested. In this case the iron was deposited chiefly on the inside of the crucible near the bottom, whereas the iron of Table IV was distributed uniformly over inside and outside. The results of the second test are given in Table V.

TABLE V

TREATMENT	TOTAL WEIGHT	WEIGHT OF IRON IN CRUCIBLE	MAGNETIC PULL	REMARKS
	mg.	mg.	mg.	
Crucible tested alone..........	3235.6	0	0.0	
Iron deposited electrolytically	3285.9	44.8	1110.	Deposit weighs 50.3 mg. but contains hydrogen, carbon, and moisture.
Heated at 1400° and 0.001 mm. for 5 min....................	3280.4	44.8	80.	Unabsorbed iron near bottom.
Heated at 1400° and 0.001 mm. for 5 min....................	3280.3	44.7	60.	Thin unabsorbed film remains.
Cleaned in HCl, dried.........	3278.8	43.2	54.	Film removed.
Heated at 1400° and 0.001 mm. for 10 min..................	3279.2	43.2	2.56	
Heated at 1400° and 0.0005 mm. for 10 min..................	3279.5⁵	43.2	1.57	Crucible stuck to furnace tube.
Heated at 1400° and 0.0007 mm. for 10 min..................	3279.6⁵	43.2	1.46	Crucible stuck to furnace tube.

Figure 2 shows that the magnetic effect is very nearly proportional to the weight of the deposit of iron, before heating has driven it into the platinum. (The first point of the curve represents a preliminary plating of crucible No. 3).

The immediate drop in the magnetic effect as soon as the iron diffuses into the platinum is very evident from Tables IV and V,

⁵ The crucible stuck to the furnace tube; the gain in weight is probably due to rhodium absorbed.

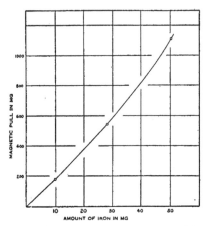

Fig. 2. Relation of magnetic pull to weight of unabsorbed iron.

and from figure 3, which represents graphically the data of Table V. The surprising part of the result is that practically the same ultimate magnetic pull is attained, although one crucible contains nearly twice as much iron as the other. Furthermore, the iron of Table V is concentrated in à smaller area of platinum surface than that of Table IV, which might be expected to make its magnetic effect more than proportional to the amount of iron, instead of which it is found to be independent of the amount. The position of the dissolved iron in the magnetic field is without any important effect, since turning the crucible upside down makes only a few hundredths mg difference in the final magnetic pull.

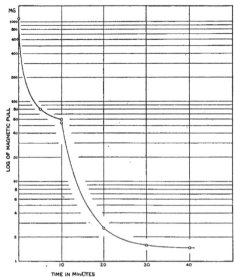

Fig. 3. Relation of magnetic pull to time of heating iron-plated platinum at 1400° (see Table V).

The summarized figures showing the amounts of iron in the various crucibles referred to, and their magnetic effects, are given in Table VI.

It is evident from Table VI that the magnetic pull must depend not only upon the amount of iron present, but also upon other factors, perhaps its concentration, distribution in the platinum, heat treatment, impurities, or other variables. As we were not prepared to make any extensive study of the questions opened by these results, we have been forced to conclude for the present that the magnetic test alone gives only a qualitative indication of the presence of iron, but no quantitative measure of the amount present.

TABLE VI

	TOTAL WEIGHT	WEIGHT OF IRON	PER CENT IRON	MAGNETIC PULL
	mg.	mg.		mg.
Ferrous ammonium sulfate...............	870.2	124.0	14.25	1.74
Crucible No. 509 (page 5)...............	9521.2	3.9	0.04	0.74
		(or less)		
Crucible No. 1, used in vacuo...........	3098.4	4.90	0.158	0.40
" " 2, " " "	2863.0	2.80	0.098	0.39
" " 3 (Table V)...............	3279.6	43.2	1.32	1.46
" " 4, (Table IV)...............	3149.7	24.1	0.76	1.49

The work of Isaac and Tammann[6] indicates the cause of the small magnetic effect produced by a considerable percentage of iron when dissolved in platinum. They have found that the magnetic transformation point, which is about 770° in pure iron, is rapidly lowered by the addition of platinum, until at 50 weight per cent platinum it is near 100°. Near pure platinum it would seem to be below room temperature. It is possible, though not proven by their results, that the magnetization of the alloys between 30 and 0 per cent of iron is due to an "α' form" of solid solution crystals, with an inversion curve which falls rapidly with increasing iron content, just as the inversion curve of the α-form of pure iron and of the iron-rich alloys falls rapidly with increasing content of platinum.

Cause of reducing action of platinum. We have shown that platinum acts on both hematite and magnetite at 1200° under low pressures of oxygen, absorbing iron and giving off oxygen.

[6] Isaac and Tammann. Zs. anorg. Chem., **55**: 63–71. 1907.

It also reacts with magnetite in the same way at 1600° and at the usual atmospheric pressure of oxygen. (Hematite is not · stable in air at 1600°, but goes over into magnetite). On the other hand, it is well known to analysts that platinum crucibles in which Fe_2O_3 is ignited in air for weighing in analytical procedures take up no such amounts of iron as we have described in previous paragraphs. The reason for these differences of behavior is readily found in the phase rule and the relations of iron and platinum in their alloys.

The system contains 3 components: platinum, iron, and oxygen. Iron and platinum form a continuous series of solid solutions. The oxidation of the iron causes it to separate from the platinum as an oxide. If we now have present the three phases: iron-platinum alloy, solid oxide, and gaseous oxygen, and assume a certain concentration of iron in the platinum (say 0.01 per cent), and a certain temperature (say 1200°) then there must be a definite oxygen pressure in equilibrium with this system. If the existing pressure of oxygen is less than this equilibrium pressure, the oxide will dissociate and metallic iron will be absorbed by the platinum. If the pressure of oxygen be greater, on the other hand, iron from the platinum solution will be oxidized, the oxide will separate on the surface of the metal, and the concentration of the iron in the platinum will be reduced.

It is evident from the fact that melted magnetite is reduced by platinum in air that at 1600° the oxygen pressure of the air (about 152 mm) is less than the oxygen pressure in equilibrium with dilute solutions of iron in platinum. Similarly, at 1200°, 18 mm oxygen is less than the equilibrium oxygen pressure, and at this temperature and pressure iron is absorbed by platinum from all oxides between Fe_2O_3 and Fe_3O_4. The 152 mm oxygen, however, is greater than the oxygen pressure of any but the most extremely dilute solution of iron in platinum at 1200°, and at this temperature, which is seldom exceeded in igniting iron oxide precipitates for analysis, there is no appreciable reduction of Fe_2O_3 by platinum in the open air.

These considerations explain the very common occurrence of small amounts of iron in platinum, since platinum will exercise its reducing action on any material containing iron oxides with which it comes in contact, provided the temperature is sufficiently high. At low temperatures, on the other hand, and with abundant access of atmospheric oxygen, no appreciable reduction is to be expected.

BOTANY.—*The Australian Fugosias.*[1]   F. L. LEWTON, National Museum.

While engaged in a critical study of the species of Gossypium the writer has become convinced that the Australian shrubs assigned by von Mueller and by Todaro to that genus and placed by Bentham under the name Fugosia should be given another designation, as in his opinion neither of the genera named is represented on the Australian continent except by cultivated plants.

A study of the relationships of the twelve species of Fugosia, so called, which have been described from Australia is rendered very difficult by the incomplete description of many of the older species and by the meager representation of plants in American herbaria. The writer has, however, received herbarium specimens of three species directly from Australia and in addition has studied carefully all the material belonging to this group to be found in the United States National Herbarium, the herbarium of the Academy of Natural Sciences of Philadelphia, the combined herbaria of the New York Botanical Garden and Columbia University, the Gray Herbarium of Harvard University, the Field Museum of Natural History and the herbarium of the Missouri Botanical Garden. His conclusions as to the relationships, names and synonymy of these twelve Australian plants are here presented.

As already pointed out by Garcke[2] and by Todaro,[3] the name Fugosia was proposed without any justification by Jussieu[4] in

[1] Published by permission of the Secretary of the Smithsonian Institution.
[2] Bonplandia 8: 148. 1860.
[3] Relazione sulla cultura dei cotoni in Italia, pp. 86–87. 1878.
[4] Gen. Pl. 274. 1789.

1789 as a substitute for Cienfuegosia, published three years earlier by Cavanilles,[5] who gave the name in honor of Bernard Cienfuegos, a Spanish botanist of the sixteenth century, to a plant collected by Adanson in Senegal.   In spite of a partial restoration of the older name by Willdenow[6] and by Sprengel,[7] and its complete restoration by Bartling;[8] Persoon,[9] DeCandolle[10] and Endlicher[11] used Jussieu's abridged form of Cavanilles' name and were followed by later systematic writers, especially Bentham, Hooker, and von Mueller.

The Australian shrubs described by von Mueller and by Bentham as species of Fugosia, when compared with the American and African plants assigned to that genus, appear so distinct in habit and gross anatomy as to warrant their being excluded from the genus, the type species of which is, as above stated, a native of Africa.   Furthermore, the Australian species are easily divisible into two groups, already indicated in the Flora Australiensis.   Even a very cursory examination of the plants is sufficient to convince one that these two groups have very little in common.   In the writer's view they represent two distinct genera, here discussed separately.

THE GENUS NOTOXYLINON

The larger group of Australian Fugosias comprises eight species: *F. australis* Benth., *F. flaviflora* von Muell., *F. latifolia* Benth., *F. populifolia* Benth., *F. robinsonii* von Muell., *F. thespesioides* Benth., *F. punctata* Benth., and *F. pedata* Bailey; which have all, at one time or another, excepting the last, been placed in the genera Hibiscus, Cienfuegosia, or Gossypium.   They differ from the African and American species of Fugosia, as the genus is commonly defined, in having the involucre 3-bracted and the black oil glands not restricted to the sepals and capsules but

[5] Monodel. Classis Diss. Decem. 174, *pl. 72, fig. 2.*   1786.
[6] Sp. Pl. **3**: 723.   1800.
[7] Syst. Veg. **3**: 64.   1826.
[8] Ord. Pl. 346.   1830.
[9] Syn. Pl. **2**: 240.   1807.
[10] Prod. Syst. Veg. **1**: 457.   1824.
[11] Gen. Pl. 983.   1840.

found in all parts of the plant except the cotyledons. In all the American and African species assigned to Fugosia the black glands are arranged in rows on the sepals, while these Australian plants agree in having the black glands scattered promiscuously over the surface of the calyx and involucre. From the genus Gossypium they differ, principally, in the total absence of the black oil glands from the cotyledons.

In 1875 Ferdinand von Mueller[12] stated that these species should in his judgment be placed in the genus Gossypium, and three years later Todaro[13] placed them in subdivisions of Gossypium which he named Thespesiastra and Hibiscoidea. The species of the first group were characterized as having small deciduous bracts and a 5-toothed calyx, and those of the Hibiscoidea as having linear, persistent bracts and the calyx 5-parted. The distinctions between deciduous and persistent bracts and between a 5-toothed and a 5-parted calyx can hardly be regarded as of primary importance in this case, since between species which must undoubtedly be classed as true members of Gossypium these same differences actually occur.[14]

It seems to the writer, therefore, that the eight species above mentioned constitute a well-marked group of generic rank for which the name Notoxylinon[15] is appropriate; the new genus to include Todaro's two sections, Thespesiastra and Hibiscoidea. The type of Notoxylinon will be *Gossypium australe* F. von Mueller,[16] which was the first of the included species to be described and is probably the most common in herbaria.

Notoxylinon Lewton, gen. nov.

Shrubs or undershrubs with the habit of Gossypium, glabrous, except on young parts, or tomentose throughout, more or less glandular-dotted. Leaves entire, lobed or pedately parted, with a nectary below near the base of the midvein. Flowers borne on short, extra-axillary branches; peduncle thickened upwards with 3 nectaries at its summit. Involucre of 3 distinct bracteoles, these linear-lanceolate

[12] Fragm. Phyt. Austr. **9**: 127. 1875.
[13] Relazione sulla cultura dei cotoni in Italia, pp. 97–98. 1878.
[14] Compare *Gossypium harknessii*, *G. irenaeum* and *G. hirsutum*.
[15] From νότος, the south wind, and ξύλινον, the cotton plant.
[16] Fragm. Phyt. Austr. **1**: 46. 1858.

or subulate, sometimes reflexed or deciduous. Calyx 5-lobed or 5-parted, conspicuously gland-dotted. Corolla large and showy, yellow or pink, usually with a reddish-purple spot at the base of the petals. Ovary 3- or 4-celled, with 3 or more ovules in each cell. Style undivided, thickened upwards, slightly 3-lobed; stigmas sulcate. Capsule woody, orbicular or ovate. Seeds woolly.

The genus Notoxylinon may be distinguished from Hibiscus by the undivided style and the presence of black glands; from Cienfuegosia by the irregular distribution of the black glands and the 3-bracted involucre; from Gossypium by the absence of the black glands from the cotyledons.

The species of Notoxylinon may be recognized by means of the following key:

Calyx truncate; lobes or teeth small.
    Plant glabrous; bracteoles persistent . . . . 1. *N. populifolium.*
    Plant more or less tomentose; bracteoles deciduous.
        Leaves orbicular-ovate, acute entire; bracteoles subulate. . . . . 2. *N. thespesioides.*
        Leaves rhomboid, 3-lobed; bracteoles setaceous . . . . 3. *N. flaviflorum.*
Calyx 5-parted or deeply lobed; lobes acuminate.
    Plant glabrous or slightly tomentose.
        Leaves 3-lobed . . . . 4. *N. robinsonii.*
        Leaves ovate, entire.
            Petioles less than 1 inch long . . . . . . 5. *N. punctatum.*
            Petioles 1 inch or more long . . . . . . 6. *N. latifolium.*
    Plant soft hairy or tomentose.
        Leaves entire or 3-lobed, densely short tomentose . . . . 7. *N. australe.*
        Leaves pedately 5-parted, coarsely stellate hairy . . . . 8. *N. pedatum.*

1. **Notoxylincn populifolium** (Benth.) Lewton.
    Fugosia populifolia Benth. Fl. Austr. **1:** 221. 1863.
    Gossypium populifolium F. von Muell. Fragm. Phyt. Austr. **9:** 127. 1875.
    Hibiscus populifolius Kuntze, Rev. Gen. Pl. **1:** 69. 1891.
    Cienfuegosia populifolia Hochr. Ann. Conserv. Jard. Bot. Genève **6:** 57. 1902.

2. **Notoxylinon thespesioides** (Benth.) Lewton.
    Hibiscus thespesioides R. Br. in herb.
    Fugosia thespesioides Benth. Fl. Austr. **1:** 220. 1863.
    Gossypium thespesioides F. von Muell. Fragm. Phyt. Austr. **9:** 127. 1875.
    Cienfuegosia thespesioides Hochr. Ann. Conserv. Jard. Bot. Genève **6:** 58. 1902.

3. **Notoxylinon flaviflorum** (F. von Muell.) Lewton
   Fugosia flaviflora F. von Muell. Fragm. Phyt. Austr. **5**: 44. 1865.
   Gossypium flaviflorum F. von Muell. op. cit. **9**: 127. 1875.
   Hibiscus flaviflorus Kuntze, Rev. Gen. Pl. **1**: 69. 1891.
   Cienfuegosia flaviflora Hochr. Ann. Conserv. Jard. Bot. Genève
      6: 56. 1902.
4. **Notoxylinon robinsonii** (F. von Muell.) Lewton.
   Fugosia robinsonii F. von Muell. Fragm. Phyt. Austr. **9**: 126. 1875.
   Gossypium robinsonii F. von Muell. loc. cit.
   Hibiscus robinsonii Kuntze, Rev. Gen. Pl. **1**: 69. 1891.
   Cienfuegosia robinsonii Hochr. Ann. Conserv. Jard. Bot. Genève
      6: 57. 1902.
5. **Notoxylinon punctatum** (Benth.) Lewton.
   Hibiscus punctatus A. Cunn. in herb.
   Fugosia punctata Benth. Fl. Austr. **1**: 220. 1863.
   Gossypium cunninghamii Todaro, Relaz. Cult. Cotoni Italia, 110.
      1877.
   Cienfuegosia benthamii Hochr. Ann. Conserv. Jard. Bot. Genève
      6: 55. 1902.
6. **Notoxylinon latifolium** (Benth.) Lewton.
   Fugosia latifolia Benth. Fl. Austr. **1**: 221. 1863.
   Gossypium costulatum Todaro, Relaz. Cult. Cotoni Italia, 109.
      1877.
   Hibiscus latifolius Kuntze, Rev. Gen. Pl. **1**: 69. 1891.
   Cienfuegosia latifolia Hochr. Ann. Conserv. Jard. Bot. Genève
      6: 57. 1902.
7. **Notoxylinon australe** (F. von Muell.) Lewton.
   Gossypium australe F. von Muell. Fragm. Phyt. Austr. **1**: 46.
      1858.
   Sturtia hibiscoides F. von Muell. op. cit. **3**: 6. 1862.
   Fugosia australis Benth. Fl. Austr. **1**: 220. 1863.
   Cienfuegosia australis K. Schum. in Engl. & Prantl. Nat. Pflanzen-
      fam. **3⁶**: 50. 1890.
   Hibiscus australis Kuntze, Rev. Gen. Pl. **1**: 69. 1891.
8. **Notoxylinon pedatum** (Bailey) Lewton.
   Fugosia pedata Bailey, Queensland Agric. Journ. **25**: 286, *pl. 28,
      fig. 1.* 1910.

THE GENUS ALLOGYNE   .

The two species of succulent seaside shrubs constituting the
smaller group of the Flora Australiensis, *Fugosia hakeaefolia* and
F. cuneiformis, have been placed at different times in at least
three genera, but at no time were they in agreement with the
other species of these genera as regards several of their easily
observed taxonomic characters. In 1863, Dr. Friedrich Alefeld

proposed the genus Allogyne[17] for *Fugosia hakeaefolia*, and although mistaken in stating that the involucre is wanting, he was correct in separating this species form Hibiscus, where it had been placed when first described by Giordano[18] in 1834.   With *F. hakeaefolia* are to be associated three nearly related species, *Hibiscus multifidus* Paxton, *H. lilacinus* Lindley, and *Fugosia cuneiformis* Benth., the four constituting the genus Allogyne.

Allogyne Alefeld.

Succulent, glabrous seaside shrubs, sometimes gland-dotted. Leaves cuneate or spatulate and entire or lobed, or deeply divided into terete or flattened, sometimes deeply toothed segments. Flowers borne on thickened peduncles, showy, not evanescent, persisting several days. Involucre a shallow 5- to 7-toothed cup, situated 3 to 5 mm. below the calyx, the ovary thus appearing stipitate. Calyx deeply 5-parted, its base (within the involucre) covered with nectar-secreting hairs. Sepals lanceolate, not completely valvate, only partially enclosing the bud. Corolla white, blue, or lilac, usually with a crimson-purple eye in the throat. Ovary 4- or 5-celled; style 1; stigma 1, slightly 4- or 5-lobed. Capsule 4- or 5-celled, usually covered with appressed silky hairs. Seeds bristly with spreading hairs, not downy.

The genus Allogyne may be distinguished from Hibiscus by the undivided style, the aestivation of the sepals, and the presence of black glands; from Notoxylinon by its succulent character, epidermal covering, and extra-floral nectary; from Cienfuegosia by the distribution of the black glands and the extra-floral nectary; from Gossypium by the absence of black dots from the cotyledons; and from all the above-named genera by the form of the involucre and the persistent character of the flowers.

The species of Allogyne may be recognized by the following key:

Leaves undivided or occasionally lobed, cuneate
    or spatulate; flowers white.................   1. *A. cuneiformis.*
Leaves bipinnate or deeply parted; flowers blue,
    lilac, or purple. .
        Leaf segments flat; corolla without crimson-
        purple eye............................   2. *A. lilacina.*
        Leaf segments terete; corolla with crimson-
        purple eye.

[17] Oesterr. Bot. Zeitschr. **13**: 12. 1863. (Here the name of the genus is spelled Alyogyne and on the opposite page Alyogone, both evidently printed in error for Allogyne, from ἄλλος, different, and γύνη, stigma.)

[18] Atti del real instituto d'incoraggiamento alle scienze naturali. **5**: 252. 1834.

Involucre conspicuous; corolla lilac-
  purple............................ 3. *A. hakeaefolia.*
Involucre almost wanting; corolla azure-
  blue.............................. 4. *A. multifida.*

1. **Allogyne cuneiformis** (DC.) Lewton.
  Hibiscus capriodorus A. Cunn. MSS. in Herb. Hook.
  Hibiscus cuneiformis DC. Prod. **1**: 454. 1824.
  Lagunaria cuneiformis G. Don. Syst. **1**: 485. 1831.
  Fugosia cuneiformis Benth. Fl. Austr. **1**: 219. 1863.—Curt. Bot.
    Mag. *pl. 5413*. 1863.
  Fugosia cuneifolia F. von Muell. Fragm. Phyt. Austr. **9**: 127.
    1875.
  Cienfuegosia cuneiformis Hochr. Ann. Conserv. Jard. Bot. Genève
    6: 56. 1902.

2. **Allogyne lilacina** (Lindley) Lewton.
  Hibiscus lilacinus Lindley, Edwards' Bot. Reg. *pl. 2009*. 1837.
  Lagunaria lilacina Walpers, Bot. Rep. **1**: 311. 1842.
  Hibiscus coronopifolius Miquel in Lehm. Pl. Preiss. **1**:239. 1845.
  Fugosia hakeaefolia var. *coronopifolia* Benth. Fl. Austr. **1**: 220.
    1863.
  Fugosia lilacina G. Don, ex Loud. Encyc. Pl. Suppl. **2**:1426. 1866.
  Cienfuegosia hakeaefolia var. *lilacina* Hochr. Ann. Conserv. Jard.
    Bot. Genève **6**: 56. 1902.

3. **Allogyne hakeaefolia** (Giordano) Alefeld, Oesterr. Bot. Zeitschr.
    13: 12. 1863.
  Hibiscus hakeaefolius Giordano, Att. Real Inst. Sci. Nat. **5**: 252.
    1834.
  Fugosia hakeaefolia Hooker, Curt. Bot. Mag. *pl. 4261*. 1846.
  Alogyne hakeifolia Alefeld, Oesterr. Bot. Zeitschr. **13**: 12. 1863.
  Cienfuegosia hakeaefolia var. *genuina* Hochr. Ann. Conserv. Jard.
    Bot. Genève **6**: 56. 1902.

4. **Allogyne multifida** (Paxton) Lewton.
  Hibiscus multifidus Paxton, Mag. Bot. **7**: 103. *pl.* 1840.

ZOOLOGY.—*The correlation of phylogenetic specialization and
bathymetrical distribution among the recent crinoids.*[1] AUSTIN
H. CLARK, National Museum.

In the recent crinoids there are thirty-seven pairs of obvious
contrasted characters which are commonly employed in distinguishing the various genera and families, and which are similarly used in their fossil representatives.

The two contrasted characters in each pair always differ in
that one represents a higher grade of phylogenetic specialization

---

[1] Published by permission of the Secretary of the Smithsonian Institution.

of development than the other; and the one representing the greater degree of specialization always differs from the more primitive in the partial or complete suppression of some structural feature, indicating that phylogenetic progress in the crinoids has been along the line of progressive structural degeneration, resulting in a constantly increasing structural simplification.

If in each contrasted pair we place under each of the two contrasted characters the crinoid families in which it is manifested it is evident that, although in nearly every case the families will be differently divided, an examination of the bathymetrical range of all of the entries under the more specialized characters taken together, contrasted with that of all of the entries under the less specialized characters taken together, will enable us to ascertain with a greater or lesser degree of accuracy the relationship between phylogenetic development and depth.

The number of contrasted pairs in each of the divisions of the crinoid body, and the number of separate items or entries in each of the divisions—that is, the number of citations of families under all the subheadings taken together—are as follows:

	Number of headings	Number of separate items
Calyx	10	68
Arms	9	63
Column	7	42
Pinnules	5	35
Disk	5	28
General	1	7
Total	37	243

Being composed of the greatest number of structural units—each a group of similar structural elements—all of which vary more or less independently, the calyx is naturally the most changeable division of the crinoid body.

The arms, through their differentiation into phylogenetically very distinct distal and basal portions, and through the close interdependence of the latter upon conditions in the calyx, form the next most changeable division.

The column, in spite of being fundamentally a simple linear series of similar ossicles, shows very great diversity; and it is chiefly as a result of this diversity in the column and the consequent necessity for a compensating mechanical readjustment that the calyx exhibits such a great amount of variation.

The pinnules and the disk, owing to their intimate connection with the gathering of the minute organisms which serve as food, are able to vary but little from a fixed optimum type.

If we take all of the entries under all of the more primitive characters (1) in all of the thirty-seven contrasting pairs, and similarly all of the entries under all of the more specialized characters (2), and determine their frequency at different depths, we get the following table. Under the heading "General" is included only the number of component ossicles in the skeleton, which decreases greatly more or less in correlation with phylogenetic progress along other lines.

TABLE 1

Frequency at different depths of the more primitive (1) and the more specialized (2) characters, arranged according to the divisons of the body

	Calyx		Column		Disk		Arms		Pinnules		General	
	1	2	1	2	1	2	1	2	1	2	1	2
0–50	12	14	4	8	7	7	11	15	9	6	1	2
50–100	15	20	8	11	8	9	14	21	14	6	1	3
100–150	15	20	8	11	8	9	15	21	14	6	1	3
150–200	13	15	5	8	5	7	12	15	10	5	1	2
200–250	13	15	5	8	5	7	12	15	10	5	1	2
250–300	15	19	11	9	9	8	20	15	15	5	1	3
300–350	15	19	11	9	9	8	20	15	15	5	1	3
350–400	19	20	11	9	9	8	19	16	15	5	1	3
400–450	19	20	11	9	9	8	19	16	15	5	1	3
450–500	19	20	11	9	9	8	19	16	15	5	1	3
500–550	24	25	15	12	9	10	25	18	19	6	1	4
550–600	28	30	20	14	12	10	29	23	23	7	1	5
600–650	28	30	18	14	12	10	29	23	23	7	1	5
650–700	28	30	18	14	12	10	28	22	23	7	1	5
700–750	28	30	18	14	12	10	28	22	23	7	1	5
750–800	23	25	14	11	11	8	22	20	19	6	1	4
800–850	22	25	14	11	11	8	22	19	19	6	1	4
850–900	22	25	14	11	11	8	22	16	19	6	1	4
900–950	22	25	14	13	11	8	22	16	19	6	1	4
950–1000	18	20	11	9	9	8	18	11	15	5	1	3
1000–1100	18	20	11	9	9	8	18	11	15	5	1	3

TABLE 1—Continued

	Calyx		Column		Disk		Arms		Pinnules		General	
	1	2	1	2	1	2	1	2	1	2	1	2
1100–1200	18	20	11	9	9	7	18	11	14	5	1	3
1200–1300	18	20	11	9	9	7	18	11	14	4	1	3
1300–1400	18	20	11	9	9	7	18	10	14	4	1	3
1400–1500	13	20	11	9	7	7	17	10	13	4	0	3
1500–1600	13	20	11	9	7	7	17	10	13	4	0	3
1600–1700	13	20	11	9	7	7	17	10	11	4	0	3
1700–1800	13	20	11	9	7	7	17	10	11	4	0	3
1800–1900	11	19	11	9	7	7	16	10	11	4	0	3
1900–2000	11	19	11	9	7	7	16	10	11	4	0	3
2000–2500	11	19	10	9	7	7	16	10	11	4	0	3
2500–3000	9	19	9	9	7	6	16	10	11	4	0	3

The same, expressed as percentages of the whole number in each category:

TABLE 2

	Calyx		Column		Disk		Arms		Pinnules		General	
	1	2	1	2	1	2	1	2	1	2	1	2
0–50	18	21	9	19	25	25	17	24	26	17	14	29
50–100	22	29	19	26	28	32	22	33	40	17	14	43
100–150	22	29	19	26	28	32	24	33	40	17	14	43
150–200	19	22	12	19	18	25	19	24	28	14	14	29
200–250	19	22	12	19	18	25	19	24	28	14	14	29
250–300	22	28	26	21	32	28	32	24	43	14	14	43
300–350	22	28	26	21	32	28	32	24	43	14	14	43
350–400	28	29	26	21	32	28	30	25	43	14	14	43
400–450	28	29	26	21	32	28	30	25	43	14	14	43
450–500	28	29	26	21	32	28	30	25	43	14	14	43
500–550	35	37	36	28	32	36	39	29	54	17	14	57
550–600	41	44	48	33	43	36	46	36	66	20	14	71
600–650	41	44	43	33	43	36	46	36	66	20	14	71
650–700	41	44	43	33	43	36	44	35	66	20	14	71
700–750	41	44	43	33	43	36	44	35	66	20	14	71
750–800	34	37	33	26	39	28	35	32	54	17	14	57
800–850	32	37	33	26	39	28	35	30	54	17	14	57
850–900	32	37	33	26	39	28	35	25	54	17	14	57
900–950	32	37	33	31	39	28	35	25	54	17	14	57
950–1000	26	29	26	21	32	28	29	17	43	14	14	43
1000–1100	26	29	26	21	32	28	29	17	43	14	14	43
1100–1200	26	29	26	21	32	25	29	17	40	14	14	43
1200–1300	26	29	26	21	32	25	29	17	40	11	14	43
1300–1400	26	29	26	21	32	25	29	16	40	11	14	43
1400–1500	19	29	26	21	25	25	27	16	37	11	0	43
1500–1600	19	29	26	21	25	25	27	16	37	11	0	43
1600–1700	19	29	26	21	25	25	27	16	31	11	0	43
1700–1800	19	29	26	21	25	25	27	16	31	11	0	43

TABLE 2—Continued

	Calyx		Column		Disk		Arms		Pinnules		General	
	1	2	1	2	1	2	1	2	1	2	1	2
1800–1900	16	28	26	21	25	25	25	16	31	11	0	43
1900–2000	16	28	26	21	25	25	25	16	31	11	0	43
2000–2500	16	28	24	21	25	25	25	16	31	11	0	43
2500–3000	13	28	21	21	25	21	25	16	31	11	0	43

Averaging all of the more primitive characters (in the columns numbered 1) and all of the more specialized characters (in the columns numbered 2) we get the following table.

TABLE 3

	Totals of the columns numbered "1"		Totals of the columns numbered "2"	
	with "General"	without "General"	with "General"	without "General"
0–50	18	19	22	21
50–100	24	26	30	28
100–150	25	27	30	28
150–200	18	19	22	21
200–250	18	19	22	21
250–300	28	31	26	23
300–350	28	31	26	23
350–400	29	32	27	23
400–450	29	32	27	23
450–500	29	32	27	23
500–550	35	39	34	29
550–600	43	49	40	34
600–650	42	48	40	34
650–700	42	48	39	34
700–750	42	48	39	34
750–800	35	39	33	28
800–850	35	39	32	28
850–900	35	39	31	27
900–950	35	39	32	28
950–1000	29	31	25	22
1000–1100	29	31	25	22
1100–1200	28	31	25	21
1200–1300	28	31	24	21
1300–1400	28	31	24	20
1400–1500	22	27	24	20
1500–1600	22	27	24	20
1600–1700	22	27	24	19
1700–1800	21	27	24	19
1800–1900	20	25	24	20
1900–2000	20	25	24	20
2000–2500	20	24	24	20
2500–3000	19	23	23	20

The averages given in the preceding table are plotted in figure 1.

In this we see that the more specialized characters outnumber the more primitive down to 250 fathoms, but from that point downward the more primitive characters outnumber the more specialized.

Unfortunately the course of the lines in figure 1 is so irregular as.to render difficult a true appreciation of the interrelationships

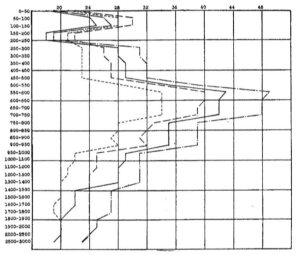

Fig. 1. The bathymetrical distribution of structural characters in the recent crinoids; ———, the more primitive characters, including those under the heading "General;" —.—, the more primitive characters, without those under the heading "General;" — — —, the more specialized characters, including those under the heading "General;" - - - - -, the more specialized characters, without those under the heading "General."

of the two sets of characters. This difficulty may best be overcome by ascertaining the excess of the primitive or of the specialized characters at the various depths. The figures representing this are given in the following table.

Plotting these (fig. 2), we find that above 250 fathoms the specialized characters predominate; if we include the characters under the heading "General" we find a well marked node at 50–

TABLE 4

Difference between the percentages of the characters "1" and "2" at different depths

	with "General"		without "General"	
	excess of "1"	*excess of "2"*	*excess of "1"*	*excess of "2"*
0–50	0	4	0	2
50–100	0	6	0	2
100–150	0	5	0	1
150–200	0	4	0	2
200–250	0	4	0	2
250–300	2	0	8	0
300–350	2	0	8	0
350–400	2	0	9	0
400–450	2	0	9	0
450–500	2	0	9	0
500–550	1	0	10	0
550–600	3	0	15	0
600–650	2	0	14	0
650–700	3	0	14	0
700–750	3	0	14	0
750–800·	2	0	11	0
800–850	3	0	11	0
850–900	4	0	12	0
900–950	3	0	11	0
950–100	4	0	9	0
1000–1100	4	0	9	0
1100–1200	3	0	10	0
1200–1300	4	0	10	0
1300–1400	4	0	11	0
1400–1500	0	2	7	0
1500–1600	0	2	7	0
1600–1700	0	2	8	0
1700–1800	0	3	8	0
1800–1900	0	4	5	0
1900–2000	0	4	5	0
2000–2500	0	4	4	0
2500–3000	0	4	3	0

100 fathoms, lying in a zone of higher temperature than the optimum for these animals.

Disregarding the characters under the heading "General," we see that the primitive characters aré always in excess below 250 fathoms; this excess reaches a maximum at 550–600 fathoms, slowly rising to only one-third as much at 2500–3000 fathoms.

Including the characters under the heading "General," we

note a maximum development of primitive characters between 850 and 1400 fathoms, beyond which point there is a sharp rise so that from 1500 to 3000 fathoms the specialized characters are in excess.

In regard to the characters under the heading "General" we should remember that, while the number of component ossicles in the skeleton is of considerable phylogenetic significance in shallow water, it decreases rapidly in importance with depth, for the conditions in the abysses are typically such that, chiefly on account of the very limited food supply, no crinoid can grow to the phylogenetically normal size, and hence all the species are necessarily dwarfs, unable to develop to the full the skeleton normal to their type. In other words, in the deeps we find a semi-pathological condition inducing degeneration along the same lines taken by normal phylogenetic advance. It is this semi-pathological degeneration simulating phylogenetic advance which causes the rise in the line representing the figures without those under the heading "General" from 550-600 to 2500-3000 fathoms. This occurs in all the differential characters, but its importance in the skeleton as a whole is here exaggerated for the reason that in this feature we have included only one contrasted pair.

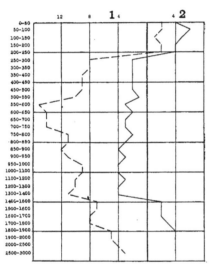

Fig. 2. The excess among the recent crinoids of primitive (1) or specialized (2) characters at different depths, including (————) and without (- - - - - -) those under the heading "General."

Probably in the present study we are most nearly correct if we take above 250 fathoms the line representing the characters including those under the heading "General," and below 250 fathoms the line representing those without.

If we do this, we find the highest degree of specialization in the recent crinoids above 250 fathoms, and especially between 50 and 150 fathoms, which represents a zone above the optimum temperature for the group.

The least degree of specialization is reached between 550 and 750 fathoms, and this is possibly the maximum depth to which a crinoid can ordinarily descend without undergoing semi-pathological degeneration.

Below 750 fathoms the excess of primitive characters becomes slowly less and less pronounced through semi-pathological changes simulating true phylogenetic advance, so that at 2500–3000 fathoms it is only slightly less than the excess of specialized characters at the surface.

If the preceding deductions are justified,

(1) The most marked phylogenetical advance, which is always evidenced by a greater or lesser suppression of some structural feature, occurs not under optimum conditions for the type under consideration, but under the more or less unfavorable conditions of the warm littoral.

(2) Progressively more and more unfavorable conditions induce a correlated phylogenetical conservatism, and finally a phylogenetical stagnation.

(3) Very unfavorable conditions induce a progressively increasing semi-pathological degeneration which, though usually very different in the details of its manifestation, is biologically the equivalent of phylogenetical advance under the optimum conditions.

(4) Many deep sea types, or types living under similarly unfavorable conditions, which exhibit an extraordinary mixture of very primitive and very highly specialized characters, are to be interpreted as primitive types upon which is superposed a pseudo-specialization induced by the pathological effect of their environment.

ANTHROPOLOGY.—*Fragmentary textiles from Ozark caves.*
DAVID I. BUSHNELL, JR., Bureau of Ethnology.

Throughout the Ozarks, from the banks of the Mississippi to the western foothills, and through the northwestern part of Arkansas, caves and smaller rock shelters are to be found in the cliffs bordering the numerous streams as well as in the adjacent valleys. These, with few exceptions, show evidence of long occupancy by Indians. Masses of wood ashes and charcoal, intermingled with fragmentary pottery, some objects of bone and stone, bones of animals, shells, etc., have accumulated near the openings of the caverns, but nothing has been discovered to indicate great antiquity. Many caves within this area have been partially excavated, but unfortunately no complete description of the contents of any one has been published.

It is reasonable to suppose that various pieces of basketry, cloths, and other textiles, all of a perishable nature, have at different times been recovered from masses of ashes in the dry caves, but only two such discoveries can be traced, one in Mc-Donald County, Missouri, the other in Benton County, Arkansas, adjoining it on the south. The specimens are in the United States National Museum and are now described for the first time.

The cave in McDonald County,[1] in which the specimens were found, is described as being "in the valley of Little Sugar Creek," in the southern part of the county not far from the Arkansas line. Little Sugar Creek is about forty miles west of James River, formerly known as the Great North Fork of White, down which valley Schoolcraft passed during the autumn of 1818 and there "saw many of the deserted pole camps of the Osages, none of which appeared, however, to have been recently occupied."[2] This was the hunting ground of the Osage as it had been for many generations, and for this reason the greater part of the material met with in the caves should undoubtedly be considered as being

[1] This was evidently the cave later partially examined by C. Peabody and W. K. Moorehead and briefly described by them in Bulletin I, Dept. of Arch., Phillips Academy, Andover, Mass., 1904.

[2] Schoolcraft, H. R., The Indian in his wigwam. Buffalo, 1848, p. 62.

of Osage origin.   However, one piece from the ashes in the cave
on Little Sugar Creek probably came from the far Southwest, as
there is no evidence of coiled basketry having been known to the
Osage or neighboring tribes.   This is shown in figure 1. (U. S.
N. M. 230,529).   It is a fragment of a coiled basket or shield,
probably the former.   The average diameter of the outer edge
is about 20 cm.   The diameter of each coil is about 1 cm.   The
coils are formed of bunches of grass which, on account of the condition, cannot be identified.   The other element, which serves

Fig. 1b.   One-half nat-
ural size

Fig. 1a.   One-fourth natural size

to bind the coils, is black or a very dark brown, very hard, and
with a glossy surface; it resembles the fiber obtained from the
seed pods of *Martynia louisiana*, known commonly as the unicorn
plant or Devil horn.   This often attains a length of 35 cm. and
was used by the Apache and other tribes in basket work.[3]

The finding of this example of coiled basketry far from its
probable place of origin may be accounted for by the fact that
the tribes of the southern plains carried on an extensive trade
with the Pueblo Indians, while the Osage were their neighbors
to the eastward.   The trade between the various tribes occupy-

[3] Coville, F. V., Plants used in Basketry; in, Aboriginal American Basketry,
by O. T. Mason, in Report of the United States National Museum for 1902, Washington, 1904, p. 207.

ing the vast territory from the Mississippi to the Rio Grande was evidently quite extensive, and long journeys were often undertaken by individuals or large parties. The coming of a trading party from the Pueblos is the event recorded in the winter count of the Kiowa for 1872–1873:

"*Teguăgo Tsän-de Sai*, 'Winter that the Pueblos came.' In this winter, while most of the Kiowa were encamped on the Washita near Rainy Mountain, a party of Pueblo Indians and Mexicans visited them to trade *biscocho*, or Pueblo bread, and eagle feathers for horses and buffalo robes."[4]

The following four specimens were likewise found in the cave "in the valley of Little Sugar Creek."

Fig. 2.   Natural size

Figure 2.   (U. S. N. M. 230,534).   Border of a mat or basket. The upper line of the drawing represents the finished edge.   Each element is about 5 mm. in diameter, but the material is badly decomposed and cannot be identified.

Fig. 3.   One-half natural size

Figure 3.   (U. S. N. M. 230,536).   A loosely twisted cord of Indian hemp, *Apocynum cannabinum*.

Figure 4.   (U. S. N. M. 230,538).   A fragment of a piece of cloth which at the time of its discovery is said to have been about

[4] Mooney, James, Calendar history of the Kiowa Indians, in Seventeenth Ann. Rept. Bureau of Ethnology, Washington, 1898, p. 336.

45 cm. square, but unfortunately it was cut. The horizontal elements, as shown in the drawing, are about 1 cm. apart; the strands passing in the other direction are rather compact. The former are made of Indian hemp, *Apocynum cannabinum*, dyed red and black, the colors being used alternately. The other strands are hard and brittle and the material was probably derived from the outer surface of a nettle, Urticaceae, used at the present time by the Osage. According to Mr. Francis LaFlesche this is undoubtedly of Osage origin. The blue-black dye used in coloring the strands of Indian hemp resembles the dye even now made by them. It is prepared by boiling together, in water, a quantity of maple bark and red ocher, the latter having first been roasted. To this liquid is added a certain quantity of grease, the result being a blue-black dye or paint.

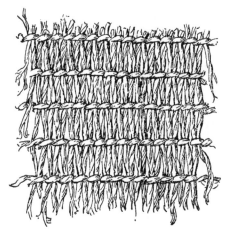

Fig. 4.   Natural size

This specimen at once suggests a piece of cloth recovered from a rock shelter on the bank of Cliff Creek, Morgan County, Tennessee, in 1885. The technique of the two is the same, but the latter measures about 115 cm. by 60 cm. and is made entirely of Indian hemp. This, and other objects were "Found in a grave 3½ feet below the surface in earth strongly charged with niter and perhaps other preservative salts. The more pliable cloths, together with skeins of vegetal fiber, a dog's skull, some bone tools, and portions of human bones and hair, were rolled up in a large split-cane mat."[5] These are among the most interesting specimens in the National Museum collection.

[5] Holmes, W. H., Prehistoric textile art of the Eastern United States, in Thirteenth Annual Report, Bureau of Ethnology, p. 30.

Figure 5. (U. S. N. M. 230,533). Fragment of a loosely woven mat or bag. The technique is similar to that of the preceding example. The material has not yet been identified.

Fig. 5. Natural size

Figure 6. (U. S. N. M. 230,714). This was recovered "From a rock shelter on the farm of Mrs. Hardin. The shelter is below a high bluff, known as Eden Bluff, on the north bank of White River and 1 mile south of the town of Monte Né, Benton County, Arkansas. It was found in a mass of dry ashes, intermingled with fragments of limestone. Above the ashes, to a height of 5 or 6 feet, and extending for a distance of 60 or 70 feet, were numerous pictographs in red paint. Other objects found in the shelter were grains of charred corn, corncobs, a strand of coarse grass with a knot, hickory nuts, charred oak, stone implements, bones, shells, etc."[6]

This piece, of unknown use, is about 35 cm. in length. It is made of the inner bark of the basswood, *Tilia americana*. At each end the strands of fiber have been formed into rather tightly wrapped rolls, which, however, do not contain any other substance. The strands extending between the rolls are loose. The fiber is in a remarkably perfect state of preservation.

The Osage at the present time make use of the barks of the basswood, the slippery elm, and the pawpaw.

The discovery of fragments of basketry in a cave within the

[6] Quoted from the notes by E. H. Jacobs, by whom the material was collected. The rock shelter at Eden Bluff is mentioned in the article by Peabody and Moorehead (op. cit.): "The rock-shelter was used in early times for burials, and five or six skeletons have at different times been exhumed; a feature was the 'wild hay,' dried, found in connection with the burials." Unfortunately the 'wild hay' was not identified, and it may, in reality, have been basswood bark.

former Osage area, at once suggests a well-known statement by Hunter[7] when referring to the art of making pottery vessels: "Another method practiced by them is to coat the inner surface of baskets made of rushes or willows with clay to any required thickness, and when dry, to burn them. . . . In this way they construct large, handsome, and tolerably durable ware, though latterly, with such tribes as have much intercourse with the whites, it is not much used, because of the subsition of cast-iron ware in its stead." This referred primarily to the Osage.

Fig. 6.   One-fourth natural size

Very large pottery vessels have been discovered on different sites in the eastern part of Missouri near the Mississippi, important sites being located near Kimmswick, in Jefferson County, and at the mouth of the Saline, in Ste. Genevieve County. Two distinct forms of ware are met with, one bearing the imprint of textiles on the outer surface, the second being smooth on both the outer and inner surfaces. Of these the former is the older.[8]

Among the fragments of pottery recovered from these ancient sites are many bearing the imprint of textiles similar to certain pieces from the McDonald County cave. Although at no time since the discovery of the Mississippi valley have the Osage occupied villages in the eastern part of their territory, which extended to the Mississippi, nevertheless they undoubtedly did so at an earlier day. Consequently the Osage were probably the makers of the large cloth-marked vessels which represent the earlier of the two periods of occupancy, while the smooth ware may be attributed to some Algonquian tribe of a later time.

[7] Hunter, John D., Manners and customs of several Indian tribes located west of the Mississippi, Philadelphia, 1823, p. 297.

[8] Bushnell, D. I., Jr., Archeological Investigations in Ste. Genevieve County, Missouri. Proc. U. S. Nat. Mus. **46**: 662. 1914.

REFERENCES

Under this heading it is proposed to include, by author, title, and citation, references to all scientific papers published in or emanating from Washington. It is requested that authors coöperate with the editors by submitting titles promptly, following the style used below. These references are not intended to replace the more extended abstracts published elsewhere in this JOURNAL.

MAMMALOGY

ALLEN, G. M. *A new bat from Mexico.* Proceedings of the Biological Society of Washington **27**: 109–112. July 10, 1914. (Describes *Rhynchiscus naso priscus,* subsp. nov.—N. H.)

ALLEN, J. A. *The generic names Speothos and Icticyon.* Proceedings of the Biological Society of Washington **27**: 147. July 10, 1914. (Icticyon is shown to be the proper generic name of the South American bush-dogs.—N. H.)

BAILEY, V. *Eleven new species and subspecies of pocket gophers of the genus Thomomys.* Proceedings of the Biological Society of Washington **27**: 115–118. July 10, 1914. (Brief diagnoses in advance of a monograph nearing completion.—N. H.)

CLARK, A. H. *Two interesting mammals from the island of Tobago, West Indies.* Annals and Magazine of Natural History, Ser. 8, **13**: 68–70. January, 1914. (Notes on specimens of Marmosa and Dasypus.—N. H.)

COPELAND, M. *Pipistrellus in Maine.* Proceedings of the Biological Society of Washington **27**: 227. December 29, 1914. (Records of *Pipistrellus subflavus obscurus* from Maine.—N. H.)

GRINNEL, J. *A new race of* Microtus montanus *from the central Sierra Nevada.* Proceedings of the Biological Society of Washington **27**: 207, 208. October 31, 1914. Describes *Microtus montanus yosemite,* from Yosemite Valley. —N. H.)

HANNA, G. D. *Interesting mammals on the Pribilof Islands.* Proceedings of the Biological Society of Washington **27**: 218. October 31, 1914. (Records of polar bears, walrus and sperm whale.—N. H.)

HELLER, E. *New subspecies of mammals from equatorial Africa.* Smithsonian Miscellaneous Collections **63**[7]: 1–12. June 24, 1914. (Describes 15 new subspecies of carnivores and rodents.—N. H.)

HOLLISTER, N. *Descriptions of four new mammals from tropical America.* Proceedings of the Biological Society of Washington **27**: 141–144. July 10, 1914. (Describes one new form each of Ateles, Procyon, Mustela, and Loncheres.—N. H.)

HOLLISTER, N. *A systematic account of the grasshopper mice.* Proceedings of the U. S. National Museum **47**: 427–489, pl. 15, text figs. 1–3. October 29, 1914. (Monograph of the genus Onychomys, with description of one new subspecies from Mexico.—N. H.)

HOLLISTER, N. *New mammals from Costa Rica and Mexico.* Proceedings of the Biological Society of Washington **27**: 209, 210. October 31, 1914. (A new brocket, *Mazama tema cerasina*, and a new two-toed anteater, *Cyclopes mexicanus*, are described.—N. H.)

HOLLISTER, N. *The systematic name of the Brazilian crab-eating raccoon.* Proceedings of the Biological Society of Washington **27**: 215. October 31, 1914. (*Procyon nigripes* Mivart antedates *P. cancrivorus brasiliensis* Von Ihering.—N. H.)

HOLLISTER, N. *The technical names of the common skunk and mink of the eastern states.* Proceedings of the Biological Society of Washington **27**: 215. October 31, 1914. (The skunk known as *Mephitis putida* becomes *M. nigra* and the mink known as *Mustela vison lutreocephala* becomes *M. v. mink*, both dating from Peale and Beauvois, 1796.—N. H.)

HOLLISTER, N. *On the systematic names of the cheetahs.* Proceedings of the Biological Society of Washington **27**: 216. October 31, 1914.

HOLLISTER, N. *The spotted tiger-cat in Texas.* Proceedings of the Biological Society of Washington **27**: 219. October 31, 1914.

HOLLISTER, N. *Two new South American jaguars.* Proceedings of the U. S. National Museum **48**: 169, 170, pl. 5. December 16, 1914. (Describes *Felis paraguensis*, from Paraguay, and *F. notialis*, from Argentina.—N. H.)

HOWELL, A. H. *Revision of the American harvest mice (genus Reithrodontomys).* North American Fauna No. 36. Pp. 1–97. June 5, 1914. (Complete synopsis of the known forms, seven of which are described as new.—N. H.)

LANTZ, D. E. *Economic value of North American skunks.* U. S. Department of Agriculture Farmers' Bulletin 587. Pp. 1–22. June 4, 1914. (Discusses the value of skunks to agriculture, their value as fur bearers, and the possibilities of raising them for their fur.—N. H.)

LYON, M. W., JR. *Tadarida Rafinesque versus Nyctinomus Geoffroy.* Proceedings of the Biological Society of Washington **27**: 217, 218. October 31, 1914. (Tadarida apparently antedates Nyctinomus.—N. H.)

LYON, M. W., JR. *Lichtenstein's plural distributive generic names Bubalides, Connochaetes and Gazellae.* Proceedings of the Biological Society of Washington **27**: 228, 229. December 29, 1914.

MERRIAM, C. H. *Descriptions of thirty apparently new grizzly and brown bears from North America.* Proceedings of the Biological Society of Washington **27**: 173–196. August 13, 1914. (Preliminary descriptions to be followed in the near future by more complete accounts in monographic form.—N. H.)

MILLER, G. S., JR. *Directions for preparing specimens of mammals.* Fourth edition, revised. Part N of Bulletin No. 39, U. S. National Museum. Pp. 1–24. August, 1914.

MILLER, G. S., JR. *Two new North American bats.* Proceedings of the Biological Society of Washington **27**: 211, 212. October 31, 1914. (Describes *Myotis longicrus interior*, from New Mexico, and *M. l. amotus* from Vera Cruz.—N. H.)

MILLER, G. S. JR. *The generic name of the collared peccaries.* Proceedings of the Biological Society of Washington **27**: 215. October 31, 1914. (Dicotyles Cuvier replaces Pecari Reichenbach.—N. H.)

MILLER, G. S., JR. *The generic name of the common flying-squirrels.* Proceedings of the Biological Society of Washington **27**: 216. October 31, 1914. (Pteromys Cuvier, 1800, replaces Sciuropterus.—N. H.)

MILLER, G. S., JR. *A new bat from Cuba.* Proccedings of the Biological Society of Washington **27**: 225, 226. December 29, 1914. (Separates the Cuban specimens of Chilonatalus as *C. macer.*—N. H.)

MILLER, G. S., JR. *Further note on the generic name of the collared peccaries.* Proceedings of the Biological Society of Washington **27**: 229. December 29, 1914. (Pecari is here considered the correct name, instead of Dicotyles.— N. H.)

SCHEFFER, T. H. *The common mole of the eastern United States.* U. S. Department of Agriculture Farmers' Bulletin 583. Pp. 1–10. May 14, 1914. (An economic paper, with instructions for destroying the animal when this becomes desirable.—N. H.)

STEJNEGER, L. *En ny sten til den skotsk-norske landbro.* Naturen (Bergen) **38**: 50–52. February, 1914. (Recently discovered living mammals furnish additional evidence of a former Scoto-Norwegian land bridge.—N. H.)

STEJNEGER, L. *The systematic name of the Pacific walrus.* Proceedings of the Biological Society of Washington **27**: 145. July 10, 1914. (*Odobenus divergens* replaces *O. obesus,* shown to be a nomen nudum.—N. H.)

ENTOMOLOGY

DYAR, H. G. *Note on Hemihyalea and some species of Amastus.* Insecutor Inscitiae Menstruus, **2**: 146–151. October, 1914. (Gives a key to the species of Hemihyalea, describing one new species; also a key to some of the species of Amastus, describing one new species.—J. C. C.)

DYAR, H. G. *Lepidoptera of the Yale-Dominican expedition of 1913.* Proceedings of the U. S. National Museum, **47**: 423–426. October 24, 1914. (Lists all of the material collected and describes 7 new species and one new sub-species. —J. C. C.)

GATES, B. N. *The temperature of the bee colony.* Bulletin of the U. S. Department of Agriculture, No. 96. Pp. 1–29, figs. 1–8. July 22, 1914. (A professional paper detailing the methods used in the work and results obtained, together with certain phenomena observed in connection with various disturbances of the colony.—J. C. C.)

HEINRICH, C. *A new Californian Coleophora on plum.* Insecutor Inscitiae Menstruus, **2**: 145. October, 1914.

HUNTER, W. D. *The pink bollworm.* Circular of the U. S. Department of Agriculture, Bureau of Entomology. Pp. 1–6, figs. 1–5. August 7, 1914. (An account of an insect injurious to cotton and likely to be introduced into this country.—J. C. C.)

KELLY, E. O. G. *A new sarcophagid parasite of grasshoppers.* Journal of Agricultural Research, **2**: 435–445, plate 40. September 21, 1914. (An account of a new species of Sarcophaga, described in this paper by J. M. Aldrich, together with notes on the other species of the genus known to parasitize grasshoppers.—J. C. C.)

KNAB, F. *Simuliidae de Chile septentrional.* Anales de Zoologia Aplicada. **1**: 17–22, plate 1. April, 1914. (Describes one new species.—J. C. C.)

KNAB, F. *The oriental trigonometopine flies.* Insecutor Inscitiae Menstruus, **2**: 131–133. September, 1914. (Describes Diplochasma, new genus, and one new species.—J. C. C.)

MARLATT, C. L. *The periodical cicada in 1914.* Circular of the Bureau of Entomology, U. S. Department of Agriculture. Pp. 1–3, figs. 1–3. May 27, 1914.

MYERS, P. R. *Results of the Yale-Peruvian expedition of 1911. Addendum to the Hymenoptera Ichneumonoidea.* Proceedings of the U. S. National Museum, **47**: 361–362. October 24, 1914. (Describes one new species.—J. C. C.)

PARKER, W. B. *Quassiin as a contact insecticide.* Bulletin of the U. S. Department of Agriculture, No. 165. Pp. 1–8, fig. 1. December 31, 1914. (An account of experiments indicating this preparation has possibilities as a commercial insecticide of moderate cost.—J. C. C.)

QUAINTANCE, A. L., and BAKER, A. C. *Classification of the Aleyrodidae.—Part II.* U. S. Department of Agriculture, Bureau of Entomology, Technical Series, No. 27, Part II. Pp. 95–109, plates 35–48. September 9, 1914. (Gives a table of the genera and describes Aleuroplatus, Dialeurodoides, Pealius, Bemisia, Aleurocybotus, Aleurotullus, Aleurocanthus, Aleurotrachelus, Aleurothrixus, Aleuroparadoxus, Aleurotithius, Aleurolobus, new genera of the authors, together with one new species and the new genera Dialeurodes and Tetraleurodes, Cockerell.—J. C. C.)

QUAYLE, H. J. *Citrus fruit insects in Mediterranean countries.* Bulletin of the U. S. Department of Agriculture, No. 134. Pp. 1–35, figs. 1–2, plates 1–10. October 7, 1914. (Gives an account of the various insects, including their life history, and of species likely to be mistaken for the injurious ones; discusses natural enemies of the various injurious insects and methods in use for the control of these insects.—J. C. C.)

ROHWER, S. A. *Vespoid and sphecoid Hymenoptera collected in Guatemala by W. P. Cockerell.* Proceedings of the U. S. National Museum, **47**: 513–523. October 24, 1914. (Lists all of the species collected in these groups and describes 11 new species.—J. C. C.)

SCOTT, E. W., and PAINE, J. H. *Lesser bud-moth.* Journal of Agricultural Research, **2**: 161–162. May 25, 1914.

SCOTT, E. W., and PAINE, J. H. *The lesser bud-moth.* Bulletin of the U. S. Department of Agriculture, No. 113. Pp. 1–16, fig. 1, plates 1 and 2. August 22, 1914. (A professional paper giving description, life history, distribution, food plants and recommendations for control.—J. C. C.)

TOWNSEND, C. H. T. *New muscoid flies, mainly Hystriciidae and Pyrrhosiinae from the Andean Montanya.* Insecutor Inscitiae Menstruus, **2**: 123–128 (continued). August, 1914. (Describes the new genera Eusignosoma and Uruhuasia, together with 5 new species.—J. C. C.)

WHITE, G. F. *Destruction of germs of infectious bee diseases by heating.* Bulletin of the U. S. Department of Agriculture, No. 92. Pp. 18. May 15, 1914. (Gives a short account of the four bee diseases now known to be infectious and the minimum temperatures that can be employed for their destruction by means of heat.—J. C. C.)

PROCEEDINGS OF THE ACADEMY AND AFFILIATED SOCIETIES

THE GEOLOGICAL SOCIETY OF WASHINGTON

The 292d meeting was held in the lecture room of the Cosmos Club, on February 24, 1915.

INFORMAL COMMUNICATIONS

M. R. Campbell, *Movement of sand-dunes on the California coast.* The dunes described occur near Monterey. Ordinarily they are not in motion, but are covered with a growth of chaparral, and the impression first produced was that their present stationary condition might denote a change of climate since their formation. Later it was observed that occasional breaches are formed, from which the sand is swept forward in long tongues. After a certain period movement at such a location ceases and the newly formed dunes become covered with chaparral. Thus movement is occurring only here and there at any one time, but after a certain period the material of the whole dune has become shifted.

Discussion: A. C. Spencer inquired as to the cause of the primary breach. Campbell believed this might be due to a severe storm or an extraordinary wind.

REGULAR PROGRAM

C. J. Hares: *Correlation of some of the Cretaceous and Eocene formations of Central Wyoming.* The uniformity of the Cretaceous formations over much of Wyoming indicates that sedimentation was unobstructed and that the present mountain chains contributed little, if any, of those sediments. The Cretaceous sediments were probably derived in great part from farther west. The mountains rose later, though movement was probably initiated in late Cretaceous.

The best comparison of these formations may be obtained by using the Niobrara as a datum plane. The Niobrara is composed of 200 to 1,700 feet of calcareous shale and limestone, bearing the distinctive *Ostrea congesta* fauna, and marks the maximum extension of deep marine water. The Niobrara is succeeded in Natrona County by 2000 to 3000 feet of dark, marine shale, which is equivalent to the Steele shale of Carbon County. The Steele and underlying formations, except for a narrow outcrop of a White River formation, are continuous from Carbon to Natrona County, but the overlying formations have been eroded. The Steele formation in Carbon County is overlain by the Mesaverde, which is composed of 1500 to 3000 feet of sandstone, shale, and coal, generally forming two prominent ridges. The lower ridge-forming sandstone of the Mesaverde corresponds to the Parkman sandstone, and its upper ridge-forming sandstone represents the Teapot sandstone of Natrona County. The Parkman and Teapot, with the intervening shaly sandstone, are from 800 to 1500 feet thick. The Mesaverde roughly corresponds to the Judith River of Montana and marks the maximum withdrawal of the Montana sea. Succeeding the Mesaverde in Carbon County is from 600 to 3000 feet of marine shale (Lewis) and marine sandstone in the base of the Lower Laramie. This marine series above the Mesaverde is equivalent to the 1000 ± feet of marine shale and sandstone in Natrona County between the Teapot sandstone and the Lance. It probably includes within its upper portion beds which are equivalent to the Fox Hills of northeast Wyoming. The Lewis is approximately the time equivalent of the Bearpaw and marks the last great incursion of the Cretaceous sea, which, receding, laid down the Fox Hills sandstone. The upper limit of the marine beds in this area serves as another datum plane. The marine deposits in Carbon County are overlain by 1000 to 6000 feet of continental deposits (Lower Laramie), which are identical in lithologic character, manner of bedding, and topographic expression (moderate ridges) with the 2000 to 3000 feet of Lance beds in Natrona County, which are only 36 miles away. In both there is an entire absence of conglomerate and both have taken part fully in the orogenic movements affecting all the lower formations. The Lance in Natrona and adjacent counties is overlain by 2400 to 4500 feet of Fort Union. The Lance and Fort Union are structurally conformable, as are the Lower Laramie and parts of the Upper Laramie. The peculiar irregularity of structure in the lower Fort Union beds gives them a rough appearance and they form a pronounced ridge in the topography. They are precisely like the basal part of the Upper Laramie in Carbon County. In both Natrona and Carbon Counties these beds contain cherty conglomerate and at Alkali Butte and at Whiskey Peak in Fremont County they contain fragments of Mowry shale, which is a formation in the Colorado group stratigraphically about 10,000 feet below either the Upper Laramie or Fort Union. The first appearance of these fragments of Mowry in any overlying formation is indicative of important orogenic uplifts, and the significance of the evidence cannot be disregarded. This lithologic evidence has been interpreted by Veatch to indicate the existence of an unconformity between the Lower and Upper Laramie, but the remarkable relations of overlap on older beds inhibited by a part of the Upper Laramie may be interpreted as due to an unconformity within the Upper Laramie. At Alkali Butte in Fremont County the Fort Union is only 250 feet above the marine beds, indicating either an unconformity below the Fort Union or an extraordinary thinning of the Lance. The unconformity described by Veatch is not stratigraphically at the place of the assumed unconformity at the top of the Fox Hills.

The fossil evidence is partly in harmony and partly at variance. The Lance contains a *Triceratops* fauna, but the Lower Laramie has been supposed to be entirely barren of dinosaur remains; however, dinosaurs occur in it. Fragments of bones collected near the mouth of Little Medicine Bow and west of Rawlins, about 2000 feet above the top of the Lewis and near the same horizon as some of the *Triceratops* zones in Natrona County, were identified in one case as ceratopsian bones and in the other as dinosaurian. *Triceratops* has been collected from the lower 1000 feet of the Upper Laramie. This is evidence that the Lance is equivalent in age to the lower part of the Upper Laramie, or perhaps that *Triceratops* has a greater stratigraphic range than hitherto assigned, or that faunal zones do not coincide with lithologic boundaries. The invertebrates, *Tulotoma thompsoni* and other fresh or brackish water shells, occur in the Lance and the Lower Laramie. The plants in the Lance as well as in the Upper Laramie are stated to be of Fort Union age, and those in the Lower Laramie of Cretaceous age. The Fort Union flora of the Lance has come chiefly from the upper half of the formation in the Dakotas and Montana, but not from the type Lance in Converse County or the Lance of Natrona County, while that from the Lower Laramie in Carbon County has come in most cases from the very base or from the lower 2000 feet of the formation. This may make some difference in our views regarding the character of the flora, because this series of beds may range up to 6000 feet thick. Most of the leaves that have been collected in Natrona County from the base of the Lance have Cretaceous affinities. Some leaves collected 600 feet above the base of the Lower Laramie have Fort Union affinities. With so much of the Lower Laramie removed by erosion from the syncline east of Walcott, it is easy to see that the Fort Union species which exist elsewhere in the upper part of the Lower Laramie and the Lance may have been missed at that place. The present status of facts does not warrant correlating beds mapped as Lance in Natrona and Converse counties wholly with the Upper Laramie, but, on the contrary, they should for the most part, if not entirely, be correlated with the Lower Laramie.

W. B. HEROY: *The relation of the Upper Cretaceous formations of southern Wyoming and northeastern Colorado.* The upper part of the Upper Cretaceous section in Carbon and Sweetwater counties in southern Wyoming has been described as containing the following formations: Steele shale, 4000 feet; Mesaverde formation, 2000 feet; Lewis shale, 500 feet; Lower Laramie, 1000–6500 feet. The Steele shale is correlated with the upper part of the Mancos shale of Colorado and Utah and with the lower part of the Pierre shale of the Great Plains region. The Mesaverde formation consists generally of two prominent sandstone members separated by a series of softer shaly beds, the lower being approximately equivalent to the Parkman sandstone and the upper to the Teapot sandstone of central Wyoming. The Lewis shale is widely distributed over southern Wyoming and northwestern Colorado. It has been recognized by Hares in his work in central Wyoming as the shale which lies above the Teapot sandstone and below a marine sandstone which is correlated with the Fox Hills of northeastern Wyoming and of the type locality in South Dakota.

The Fox Hills of central Wyoming is represented in the southern Wyoming section near Rawlins by the lower 800 feet of the "Lower Laramie," a series of sandstones which yields a marine Cretaceous fauna. In Carbon County, as mapped by Veatch, this zone is found in the upper part of the Lewis, the base of the Lower Laramie having been drawn at the top of the marine beds. It thus appears that the Fox Hills sandstone of the type locality is represented in southern Wyoming by a marine sandstone which overlies or forms the upper part of the Lewis. If the Mesaverde of Carbon County, Wyoming, is traced eastward into the Laramie Basin, it is found that the lower member (Parkman) forms the conspicuous "Pine Ridge" near Rock River Station, the upper portion of the Mesaverde (Teapot) having been either entirely removed or obscured by overlying beds. The Lewis shale is not recognized in the Laramie Basin, and together with the overlying marine sandstone member of the Laramie (which is correlated with the Fox Hills), appears now not to extend east of the Medicine Bow. In the Laramie quadrangle, as mapped by Darton in the Laramie-Sherman folio, Steele shale is overlain by Mesaverde sandstone, while the corresponding section east of the Laramie Mountains on Horse Creek, shown on the Sherman quadrangle, consists of Pierre shale overlain by "Fox Hills" sandstone. Darton regards the base of the Mesaverde as mapped on the Laramie quadrangle as the approximate stratigraphic equivalent of the base of the "Fox Hills" of the Sherman quadrangle, and this view is confirmed by Lee, who visited and collected from both localities in 1914. The base of the "Fox Hills" as mapped on the Sherman quadrangle would thus be the same as the base of the Mesaverde (Parkman) This horizon is about 4000 feet lower stratigraphically than the Fox Hills of central Wyoming, which overlies the Lewis shale.

The "Fox Hills" of the Sherman quadrangle as exposed on Horse Creek has heretofore been regarded as the stratigraphic equivalent of the "Fox Hills" of the Denver Basin, which has been traced by Darton northward from the original locality near Platteville to the Wyoming line. The "Fox Hills" of the Denver Basin corresponds with the "Fox Hills" of the Colorado Springs region as described by Richardson and others. If the "Fox Hills" of the Denver Basin is the same as that of the Sherman quadrangle, then it appears probable that the term "Fox Hills" as used in the Denver Basin relates to a much lower stratigraphic horizon than that occupied by the Fox Hills of northeastern Wyoming and in the type locality in northern South Dakota. The "Fox Hills" of the Denver Basin is apparently equivalent to the lower Mesaverde (Parkman) of southern Wyoming, while the Fox Hills of the type locality is equivalent to the basal "Lower Laramie" of southern Wyoming, the top of the Lewis as mapped by Veatch.

G. H. ASHLEY: *The physiography of the Rockies in the Cretaceous-Tertiary period.* The speaker first outlined the physiographic history of the region, pointing out that during Upper Cretaceous time and before the Rocky Mountain region had been the scene of slow, persistent, crustal depression, during which from 1 to 3 or more miles of sediments were laid down. The period closed with movement that stopped sedimentation in the Gulf area and over most of the Rocky Mountain area, though sinking and sedimentation continued in the center of the old basin, resulting in the laying down of the Laramie, Lower Laramie, Black Buttes and possibly Lance rocks. Pronounced uplift followed, resulting in mountain building and the subsequent erosion that cut through the supermontane deposits and base-leveled the elevated Piedmont areas. Then came a period of renewed depression and sedimentation, in which were laid down the Fort Union and possibly Lance formations at the north and many local deposits at the south, including the Raton, Denver, Puerco, Ohio Creek, Upper Laramie, Evanston, and other associated deposits, which were derived from the recently uplifted lands and overlie unconformities in the Piedmont regions but not away from the mountains. Renewed uplift and erosion preceded the deposition of the Wasatch of early Eocene age.

The position of the Lance in this physiographic outline was discussed in some detail from both the stratigraphic and paleontologic sides, the conclusion being reached that while many facts suggest correlation with the Laramie, and that while the formation was laid down before the first mountain-uplift, the evidence as a whole strongly points to the post-Laramie age of the beds.

Comparison was then made between the physiographic history of this period in the Rocky Mountain province and that in the Gulf province, the comparison seeming to show that the sea withdrawal in the Gulf region corresponded to the sea withdrawal and the first period of mountain building in the Rockies, and that the return of the sea in the Gulf region and the laying down of the Eocene Midway and Willcox formations in that region corresponded in time with the deposition in the Rocky Mountain region, of the Fort Union, and possibly Lance formations at the north and with the local sediments referred to at the south, and that on that basis those formations must have been of Tertiary age.

Discussion of the papers of Hares, Heroy, and Ashley: W. T. LEE spoke in confirmation of the correlation of the Mesaverde of the Laramie Basin with the socalled Fox Hills of the Sherman quadrangle east of the Laramie Mountains. His opinion was based on stratigraphic succession and on marine fossils collected in both regions. T. W. STANTON said that as regards the correlation of the Mesaverde of Laramie Basin with the Fox Hills sandstone of Horse Creek, Wyoming, as advocated by LEE and HEROY, the views expressed might possibly be correct. The section at Horse Creek is obscured by overlap of the White River group. The highest fossils from Cretaceous beds in the neighborhood are certainly older than Fox Hills. But even if the sandstone mapped as Fox Hills at Horse Creek should prove to be Mesaverde, this would not have any necessary bearing on the correlation of the Fox Hills sandstone of northern Colorado. The area from Fort Collins and Greeley south to Boulder has recently been examined with care, and full collections of fossils have been obtained from the Fox Hills. The Fox Hills fauna of this area corresponds closely with the typical Fox Hills fauna of northern South Dakota, and the identification of the same formation in the two areas is as complete as can be expected over such a great distance. While it is true that the Fox Hills fauna may be considered the littoral facies of the Pierre fauna, and that in a broad sense it began long before Fox Hills time in the Eagle and was repeated in the Claggett, yet each of these recurrences has its distinctive species, so that when the fauna of the whole formation is considered it is not difficult to distinguish Fox Hills from Claggett and Eagle, though they have a good many species in common.

The true Fox Hills fauna of the type area is distinguished from all the earlier faunas of the region by the presence of the ammonite *Sphenodiscus* instead of *Placentoceras*, by a group of *Scaphites* including *S. conradi*, *S. nicolleti*, *S. cheyennensis*, *S. mandanensis*, by a number of gastropod genera and species, and by the absence of *Baculites*, *Inoceramus*, etc. In all these respects the Fox Hills fauna of northern Colorado is identical. HEROY's proposed correlation of the Fox Hills of northern Colorado with the Mesaverde of northern Wyoming cannot be accepted because the detailed paleontologic evidence is opposed to it, and because there are several important lower sandstones within the Pierre shale of northern Colorado which probably represent Mesaverde sedimentation. Time was lacking for an adequate discussion of the papers by HARES and ASHLEY. Concerning the latter, STANTON remarked that many of the opinions expressed could be characterized as "interesting if true."

C. N. FENNER, *Secretary.*

THE BIOLOGICAL SOCIETY OF WASHINGTON

The 537th meeting of the Society was held at the Cosmos Club, Saturday, March 6, 1915, at 8 p.m., with Ex-President STEJNEGER in the chair and 60 persons present.

Under the heading Brief Notes A. S. HITCHCOCK called attention to the plans and methods of work in preparing a new Flora of the District of Columbia, which it is hoped, will be completed within a year. It will contain analytical keys to the genera and species of ferns and flowering plants found within a radius of 15 miles of the city of Washington, but will not include descriptions.

The first paper of the regular program was by J. W. GIDLEY: *Notes on the possible origin of the bears.* After the examination of much fossil and living material the speaker had arrived at the conclusion that the bears, constituting a small homogeneous, widely distributed group, are not closely related to the Carnivores. From a consideration of the tooth structure, the bones of the feet, and the basal cranial foramina, Mr. GIDLEY concluded that the bears were probably derived from the *Claenodon* group of the Creodonts, and that the Carnivores were descended from the Miacidae, a family of Creodonts not distantly related to the *Claenodon* group.

The second communication was by the sculptor, H. K. BUSH-BROWN: *The evolution of the horse.* The speaker was present by special invitation of the President and was introduced to the Society by Ex-President STEJNEGER. He discussed briefly the geological evolution of the horse, and then spoke at some length on the evolution of modern breeds of horses, particularly the Arab, the effects of breeding it with other races, and its development in this country. His paper was well illustrated by lantern slides showing anatomical characteristics of various horses, as well as external appearances.

On Thursday, March 11, 1915, at 8.30 p.m., the Biological Society held a joint meeting with the Washington Academy of Sciences in the Auditorium of the National Museum. Mr. WILFRED H. OSGOOD, of the Field Museum of Natural History, and a member of the special commission for investigating the fur seal question for the Department of Commerce during the summer of 1914, delivered a lecture illustrated by stereopticon and motion pictures of the fur seals and other animals of the Pribilof Islands. All phases of the life of the seals on the islands, methods of killing, skinning, salting, etc., and the introduced herds of reindeer, the Steller's sea-lions, and the native birds were shown in motion pictures. About 350 persons were present.

The 538th meeting of the Society was held at the Cosmos Club, Saturday, March 20, 1915, with President BARTSCH in the chair and 45 persons present.

Under the heading Brief Notes, General WILCOX called attention to a Cedar of Lebanon near Jackson's statue in Lafayette Square.

The first paper of the regular program was by T. S. PALMER, *Notes on the importation of foreign birds.* The speaker discussed the subject with special reference to canaries, parrots, and game birds. He stated that about 500 permits for importation of birds are issued annually by the Department of Agriculture, the number of birds imported in a year amounting to about half a million, as many as 17,000 birds arriving in a single day. The number of species imported is about 1500, though canaries constitute by far the largest number brought in. Methods of breeding birds abroad, caring for them in transit, and selecting and teaching singers and talkers were explained. Dangers of importing contagious diseases, as the "quail disease," and methods of quarantining were pointed out. The effect of the European war on the importation of birds was commented upon. The paper was discussed by Messrs. BARTSCH, STILES and GOLDMAN.

The second paper was by NED DEARBORN, *Notes on the breeding of minks in captivity.* Among the habits of the mink attention was called to their profound diurnal sleep, cries emitted, polygamous nature, and cat-like character of food. The speaker stated that the period of gestation was found to be 42 days; number of young at birth 1 to 8; eyes of young remain closed for one month after birth; young may be weaned at 6 weeks; minks breed when a year old; their fur is suitable for market at a year and a half; experiments showed that different types of diet had no effect on quality of fur. The speaker concluded that breeding of minks for commercial purposes was possible. The paper was discussed by Messrs. WETMORE, A. B. BAKER, and COOKE.

The third paper was by M. W. LYON, JR., *Endamoeba gingivalis and pyorrhea.* The speaker discussed the cause of pyorrhea or Rigg's disease, the *Endamoeba gingivalis*, recently discovered by Dr. ALLEN J. SMITH and others. He called attention to the pathologic lesions produced by the Endamoeba and by the various bacteria associated with it; mentioned the amoebicidal action of emetin hydrochlorid administered systemically or locally; and reviewed some of the early references to the Endamoeba before it was considered the cause of pyorrhea. The paper was illustrated by lantern slides of Gros' original drawing of the organism, and of several photomicrographs and drawings of living and stained Endamoebas, bacilli, and spirochaetes from a case of pyorrhea. The paper was discussed by Messrs. STILES and GOLDMAN.

M. W. LYON, JR., *Recording Secretary.*

THE ANTHROPOLOGICAL SOCIETY OF WASHINGTON

The 479th meeting of the Society was held Tuesday evening, December 15, 1914, in the lecture hall of the Public Library. The speaker of the occasion was the distinguished German scholar, Geheimrat Dr. FELIX VON LUSCHAN, director of the Museum für Völkerkunde in Berlin and for a number of years in charge of the archeologic excavations carried on under the auspices of the German government in Asia Minor. Doctor VON LUSCHAN had been a delegate in attendance at the Australian meeting of the British Association in September, but owing to the outbreak of the war has been compelled to make a somewhat extended stay in this country before endeavoring to return home. He is utilizing this time in a study of race mixture in the American negro, having already visited for this purpose a number of points in the southern states, including Tuskegee, and traced out for future analysis several hundred pedigrees of mixed Afro-American origin. He is accompanied by Mrs. VON LUSCHAN, who is herself a competent authority and an efficient helper in his anthropological investigations.

In his lecture before the Society Doctor VON LUSCHAN chose for his subject, *The excavation of a Hittite capital,* dwelling chiefly upon his work at Boghaz-Keui, the site of the capital of the ancient empire of the Hittites, who, fifteen centuries before the birth of Christ, occupied the central portion of Asia Minor and for hundreds of years held the balance of power between Egypt and Babylonia, until finally over-thrown by Sargon, King of Assyria, in 717 B. C. They were variously known as Hethites, Hittites, Hatti, Khiti, etc., and, from their sculptures, appear to have been a broad-headed people of rather short stature and irregular features, of the physical type represented by the modern Armenians, although their linguistic affinity is not yet established. Their inscriptions are recorded both in hieroglyphic and in cuneiform characters. Their sculptural art is crude but strong, the winged lion, winged sun, and double eagle motifs being of frequent occurrence. Facsimiles in plaster of a number of the more important sculptures taken out under Doctor VON LUSCHAN's supervision are now in our own National Museum by courtesy of Berlin. The lecture was illustrated with a fine series of lantern slides.

At the 480th meeting of the Society, held January 5, 1915, in the Public Library, Dr. JOHN R. SWANTON, of the Bureau of American Ethnology, read a paper on the *Ethnologic factors in international competition.* About 25 persons were present. Dr. Swanton reviewed the different factors tending to bring about union and disunion between human societies. He showed that these had been operative in all parts of the world and stood for two great complementary principles which were probably necessary to the best development of the race as a whole. At the same time it is not necessary or desirable for the principle of disunion to extend to open war. The end of warfare may be confidently predicted from the constant increase in size and decrease in number of political units, from the progressive weaving of the world more closely together by means of transportation facilties and other means of communication, not to mention the gradual international bankruptcy which war entails. Next, the evolution of a standing army was traced and its copartnership noted with an aristocratic ruling class. The integration of smaller states into larger was shown to be brought about in two ways; by the alliance of coordinate units, and by combinations in which some were subordinate and some dominant. States of the latter class have resulted largely from war; and it was shown that two kinds of subordination took place, subordination of peoples as a whole without the entire break up of their internal organization and subordination of classes. It was stated that this latter kind of subordination was largely responsible for slavery and serfdom successively; and it was alleged that it has left its stain upon modern society, in which subjection has been transferred to the economic field and has been accomplished by an extension of the laws of property enabling one class to levy a heavy toll for the use of things which another class needs. There can be no permanent peace until exploitation of one nation or class by another comes to an end and the principle of "home rule" is extended with due relativity down to the smallest political and industrial groups.

Several members discussed the paper.

DANIEL FOLKMAR, *Secretary.*

JOURNAL

OF THE

WASHINGTON ACADEMY OF SCIENCES

Vol. V   MAY 19, 1915   No. 10

PHYSICS.—*An aneroid calorimeter.*[1]   H. C. Dickinson and N. S. Osborne, Bureau of Standards.

The term "aneroid calorimeter" is applied to a type of calorimeter in which equalization of temperature is secured by means of the thermal conductivity of copper instead of by the convection of a stirred liquid. The calorimeter consists of a thick walled cylindrical vessel of copper, in the walls of which is embedded a coil of resistance wire to supply heat electrically, and of a platinum resistance coil for use as a thermometer; it has been found useful over a wide range of temperatures and is applicable to a variety of problems.

For use at low temperatures the calorimeter is mounted in a jacket surrounded by a bath of gasoline the temperature of which can be controlled thermostatically to within a few thousandths of a· degree at any temperature between −55° and +40°C., or it can be changed rapidly in order to keep it the same as that of the calorimeter when heat is being supplied to the latter. Differences·in temperature between the surface of the calorimeter and that of the jacket are measured by means of multiple thermocouples which have ten junctions distributed over the surface of each, thus making it possible to apply accurate corrections for thermal leakage between calorimeter and jacket even when the temperatures of both are changing rapidly.

[1] To appear in the Bulletin of the Bureau of Standards.

The platinum resistance coil (for use as a thermometer) embedded in the calorimeter shows slight irregularities in its behavior, probably due to the difference in expansion between the platinum and the copper which surrounds it. Uncertainties on this account, while in general negligible, can be avoided by measuring the temperature of the outer bath with a standard resistance thermometer, using the thermo-couples to measure the small difference, usually not more than a few thousandths of a degree, between the calorimeter and the jacket. The thermometer could probably be improved by changing the construction.

Results of a series of experiments give the constants of the resistance thermometer and the heat capacity of the calorimeter including a tin lined cell for use in determining the specific heat of ice and water and the latent heat of fusion of ice.

A series of check experiments on the specific heat of water show the order of reproducibility of results, which can be obtained with this calorimeter, to be 1 part in 2000. Measurements made at temperatures between 0° and 40°C. gave results which agree to within the limits of experimental accuracy with the unpublished results of a long series of experiments made in the usual form of stirred water calorimeter. The results are also in satisfactory agreement with the most probable values deducible from the data of the most careful investigations published by other observers.

PHYSICS.—*The specific heat and heat of fusion of ice.*[1]   H. C. DICKINSON and N. S. OSBORNE, Bureau of Standards.

Results of previous determinations of the specific heat of ice by certain observers have indicated a rapid increase in the specific heat on approaching the melting point; whereas A. W. Smith[2] has found the heat capacity of ice to be practically constant up to temperatures very close to zero, provided great care and refinement are used to insure the purity of the ice, and that

[1] To appear in the Bulletin of the Bureau of Standards.
[2] Physical Review 17: 193. 1903.

sensible increases in the apparent heat capacity with ice samples of only ordinary purity are accounted for by the assumption of incipient fusion caused by the lowering of the melting point by the dissolved impurities.

The present investigation has been undertaken with the object of securing further evidence as to the thermal behavior of ice at temperatures near the freezing point, and of obtaining reliable data for the construction of tables of total heat of ice and water in the range of temperature with which refrigerating engineers are concerned.

The measurements were made by means of a calorimeter of aneroid type (i.e., without stirred liquid as calorimetric medium) which is described in detail in the foregoing paper. Briefly described, the tin lined metal cell containing the specimen is enclosed within a shell of copper, the copper acting as the calorimetric medium for transmission and distribution of heat electrically developed in a coil built into the shell. The calorimeter is surrounded by air and enclosed in a metal jacket which is surrounded by a stirred liquid bath, the temperature of which can be controlled within a few thousandths of a degree at any temperature between $-55°$ and $+40°C$. Measured amounts of heat are supplied to the calorimeter electrically by means of the built-in heating coil. The calorimeter temperature is measured by means of a platinum resistance thermometer also built into the shell. Differences in temperature between the calorimeter and jacket surfaces are measured by means of multiple thermocouples distributed on the surfaces. During an experiment thermal leakage is minimized by keeping the temperature of the jacket nearly equal to the changing temperature of the calorimeter.

The samples used were from 400 to 470 grams each. Three samples were of redistilled water of fairly high purity, while a fourth, which was distilled directly into the container, appeared from the experimental results to have a much higher degree of purity.

In the determinations of specific heat it is found that over the range of temperature covered by the experiments, i.e., $-40°$

to $0°.050C.$, the specific heat, S, in $20°$ calories at any temperature θ, of the four ice samples is represented within the limit of experimental error by the equation:

$$S = 0.5057 + 0.001863\ \theta - 79.75\ \frac{l}{\theta^2}$$

in which the constant l is assumed to represent the initial freezing point of the specimen and has the following values:

Sample	l
1	0.00125
2	0.00120
3	0.00095
4	0.00005

From the fact that the term which represents the departure of the specific heat from a linear function of the temperature is found to depend on the purity, being less the purer the ice, it' is concluded that the specific heat of pure ice in $20°$ calories may be closely represented by the equation:

$$S = 0.5057 + 0.001863\ \theta$$

Determinations of the heat of fusion made upon three of the samples used for the specific heat determinations gave the following values:

Sample No.	Heat of Fusion Cal$_{20}$/g
1	79.68
2	79.85
4	79.75
Mean	79.76

The results of a previous investigation at the Bureau of Standards, using very different methods to determine the heat of fusion of ice, give when corrected for the newly found value for specific heat a mean value of 79.74 $20°$ calories per gram. The mean for the two investigations is: 79.75 $20°$ calories per gram. For the use of engineers a table of total heats of ice and water is given expressed in B.t.u. per pounds at temperature from $-20°F$. to $+100°F$.

PHYSICS.—*Covellite*: *A singular case of chromatic reflection.*   H. E. MERWIN, Geophysical Laboratory.

To describe and to account for some striking color changes in covellite when it is immersed in colorless inert liquids of different refractions is the object of this study.

Covellite, crystalline cupric sulphide, in finest powder is very dark blue; brilliant crystal surfaces or polished plates, whether obliquely or vertically illuminated, are lighter, and vary noticeably in color with differences in crystallographic section.   In obliquely incident daylight a plate, parallel to the cleavage, immersed in alcohol (refractive index, $n = 1.36$) appears brilliant purple,[1a] in benzene ($n = 1.50$) it appears reddish purple,[1b] and in methylene iodide ($n = 1.74$) it appears red.[1c]   A plate perpendicular to the cleavage changes only to purple in methylene iodide.

Natural crystals have not yielded flakes thin enough to transmit sufficient light for optical study but some synthetic crystals prepared in this laboratory by E. G. Zies and by Eugene W. Posnjak were found suitable for microscopic study.   These crystals are hexagonal scales or piles of scales reaching 0.5 mm. in diameter, and 0.002 mm. in maximal thickness.   The thicker plates transmit scarcely perceptible amounts of light even when illuminated by direct sunlight, the thinner ones are yellowish green[2] to dark olive.   By both a spectrometer eye-piece and a prism monochromatic illuminator the yellowish green color was found to be caused by less transmission of the red and violet than of the middle of the spectrum.   The fall in relative transmission from green to violet—at least as far as $410\mu\mu$—is not apparently very great; it is greater in the red from about 630 to $700\mu\mu$ mm. The transmission is shown in a general way in figure 1.

Plates probably not exceeding 0.0005 mm. in thickness served

---

[1] The colors were compared with Ridgeway's standards.   Although the standards are less brilliant approximate matches were made.   (a) Between violet-purple and true purple.   (b) Near rhodamine purple.   (c) Between spectrum red and rose red.

[2] E. Weinschenk prepared similar plates and noted the red color reflected after mounting in Canada balsam. Z. Kryst., **17**: 497. 1890.

for determinations of refractive index.[3]   The following observed values are plotted in figure 1:

wave length μμ	refractive index n
635	1.00
610	1.33
589	1.45
570	1.60
520	1.83
505	1.97

Different directions in the plane of the plate give the same value. Between crossed nicols, flat-lying plates appear dark and exhibit no distinct interference figure.   Yet tilted plates are

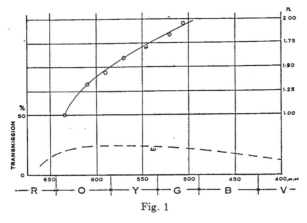

doubly refracting and pleochroic. One ray vibrates in the plane of the plates and is darker for all colors.   For both rays there appear to be regions of much stronger absorption at both ends of the visible spectrum.   These are closer together for the ray vibrating in the plane of the plates.

Fig. 1

[3] Practically opaque plates, measured with the micrometer caliper, were only 0.002 mm. thick. Moderately transparent plates were so thin that the displacement of the bright border of light produced in determining the refractive index was so slight that high magnification and a very perfect fine adjustment screw were required to make the displacement evident. Even then differences of less than ±0.03 in refractive index could not be detected, owing partly to diffraction. In many plates the diffraction bands entirely obscured the phenomena of refraction. The method finally pursued involved the use of a monochromatic illuminator. Only such plates were used as showed a pronounced reversal of the position of the bright border for wave-lengths about 10 μ greater or less than that for which the determination of refractive index was made.

Absorption is so strong that the color of covellite even in the finest powder is due to light reflected directly from the surfaces of grains. Yet differences in absorption of different colors are not sufficient to cause marked differences in the reflection of these colors. Therefore we look to the refractive index and reflective power to explain the color effects already described.

I have estimated that for light from orange to violet which enters the surface at normal incidence about one-fourth is transmitted by a plate 0.5 μ thick. For these colors the absorption index, κ, is of the order of 0.1; for red it may have twice[4] this value. Absorption has, therefore, very little effect upon the reflective power of the mineral in the visible spectrum.   The reflecting power, R, represents the reflected fraction of the normally incident light as given by the equation

$$R = \frac{n^2\kappa^2 + (n - 1)^2}{n^2\kappa^2 + (n + 1)^2}$$

in which n is the refractive index for the wave-length having the absorption index (extinction coefficient) κ. The following equations define κ:

$$I = I_1 e^{\frac{-4\pi n \kappa d}{\lambda}} \; ; \text{ or } I = I_1 e^{\frac{-4\pi \kappa d}{\lambda_1}} \tag{1}$$

The intensity of the light entering the surface is I_1. After traversing the distance d the intensity is I. The wave-length of the incident light in the ether is λ. The other symbols have their usual significance. λ_1, is the assumed wave-length within the absorbing medium. If I and I_1 represent amplitudes of vibration then the exponent of e becomes $\frac{-2\pi n \kappa d}{\lambda}$. These equations define κ according to the usage of most of the recent writers.   Yet in the following physical tables both the name and the definition of this symbol vary.   In *Tables Annuelles Internationales*, page 133, for 1912, names and definition are as above; in *Landolt, Börnstein and Roth*, page 966 (1912) the symbol k, called the absorption index, $= n\kappa$ above; in *Smithsonian Physical Tables*, page 195 (1914) first two equations, k, called the absorption index, $= \kappa$. Also in Wood's *Physical Optics* (1911) in the chapter on the optical properties of metals κ is named and defined as above, but in the chapter on the theory of dispersion $= n\kappa$ above.

For values of $n < 3$ the reflective power increases much faster than n. For white light incident from air at an angle of 60° on plates cut parallel to the cleavage about 20 per cent of the blue

[4] Or several times, for W. W. Coblentz found very high reflecting power in the near infra-red on an inclined section (Carnegie Inst. Wash. Pub. 97).

and violet light is reflected;[5] 15 per cent of the green; 12 of the yellow; 5 of the orange; and none of the red. The resulting color is blue. At angles less than 60° the colors are reflected in about the same proportions as at 60°. At larger angles blue and violet are less dominant.

Light incident at 60° from water has a little more than half as much of its green, blue, and violet reflected as in case of air; and *all of the red and about half of the orange is entirely reflected*, because the angle of incidence is greater than the critical angle. Yellow is reflected scarcely at all because for it, water and covellite have nearly the same refractive index. As the angle of incidence decreases orange and then red cease to be totally reflected, but the relative proportions of the other colors do not change greatly. For more oblique rays total reflection extends a little further into the orange. The total color effect is purple.

Similarly, oblique reflection from covellite in benzene (n = 1.50) contains still more of the colors of the red end of the spectrum and less of the violet end, and in methylene iodide (n = 1.74) orange is the predominating color. In the latter at 60° only about 5 per cent of the blue and violet are reflected as against 20 per cent in air.

The light reflected in air from surfaces perpendicular to the cleavage is blue, but brighter than from those parallel to the cleavage. This stronger reflection indicates higher refraction for at least the red end of the spectrum. Red is totally reflected at large angles of incidence in liquids of higher refraction than 1.64. Therefore the index of refraction ϵ_{Li} is about 1.5. A large amount of blue is also reflected (not totally) in liquids of even higher refraction, indicating that ϵ for blue must be considerably higher than 1.75. Thus throughout the visible spectrum $\epsilon > \omega$. The differences in color of the light reflected parallel and perpendicular to the cleavage are independent of the pleochroism observed in transmitted light.

---

[5] Calculated by the formula for transparent substances, for it has already been shown that absorption in this case effects the reflection of different colors about the same amount. The fraction reflected

$$= \tfrac{1}{2} \left\{ \frac{\sin^2 (i - r)}{\sin^2 (i + r)} + \frac{\tan^2 (i - r)}{\tan^2 (i + r)} \right\}$$

where i and r are the angles of incidence and of refraction, and $\sin i = n \sin r$.

GEOLOGY.—*The calculation of calcium orthosilicate in the norm of igneous rocks.* HENRY S. WASHINGTON, Geophysical Laboratory.

When the calculation of the norm from the analysis of an igneous rock was first worked out some fifteen years ago in connection with the Quantitative System, provision had to be made for magmas so low in silica that there remained a deficit for the femic minerals, after salic potash, soda and lime had been assigned their minimal amounts to form leucite, nephelite and anorthite respectively. Nearly all melilite-bearing rocks and some nephelinites fall under this category. At that time the physical chemistry of the calcium silicates had been scarcely studied and, though the use of calcium orthosilicate was considered, the normative calcium silicate molecule selected was $4CaO.3SiO_2$, as it corresponded to the slag mineral akermanite of Vogt, which is apparently isomorphous with and related to melilite. Equations for the calculation of this molecule in the norm were accordingly given in the publication of the quantitative system.

Subsequently, investigations in the Geophysical Laboratory[1] showed the non-existence of $4CaO.3SiO_2$ but the existence of a compound of the formula $3CaO.2SiO_2$. It seemed probable that this last formula, rather than Vogt's, represented the composition of akermanite. Consequently the new formula was adopted, and a corresponding modification of the norm and its calculation was proposed.[2]

Very recently the study of the ternary system $CaO-Al_2O_3-SiO_2$ has been completed by Rankin and Wright,[3] who show that the compound $3CaO.2SiO_2$ is unstable and occupies only a small field, while the orthosilicate, $2CaO.SiO_2$, exists in three stable forms, depending on the temperature, and occupies a large field; that is, the orthosilicate may be formed within a much wider

[1] A. L. Day, E. S. Shepherd and F. E. Wright, Am. J. Sci. (4) 22: 280. 1906; E. S. Shepherd, G. A. Rankin and F. E. Wright, J. Ind. Eng. Chem., 3: 214. 1911.
[2] Cross, Iddings, Pirsson, Washington, J. Geol., 20: 558. 1912.
[3] G. A. Rankin and F. E. Wright, Am. J. Sci., 39: 1. 1915.

range of conditions than the 3:2 silicate. It has therefore been thought best by the authors of the quantitative system to substitute the calcium orthosilicate molecule for that of $3CaO.2SiO_2$. This seems the more advisable, since calcium orthosilicate exists in the mineral monticellite, and is analogous chemically to the ferrous and magnesium orthosilicates, fayalite and forsterite, while $3CaO.2SiO_2$ is unknown in nature.

This change necessitates new equations for the calculation of the norm, and, though these may be figured out by anyone acquainted with the principles involved, it would seem to be advisable to present them. It will, however, be rarely necessary to use them, for among nearly six thousand rock analyses already assembled for a new edition of the *Collection of Rock Analyses*, of which the norms have been calculated, only about 80 are of such low silicity and other chemical characters as to demand the calculation of calcium orthosilicate. It may be remarked that, judging from the cases in which I have had to calculate calcium orthosilicate, the substitution here proposed changes the classificatory position of very few rocks. This is to be expected, as it amounts only to the shifting of a very small amount of silica, and affects only the relation of pyric to olic normative minerals. The present opportunity also permits the illustration of a simplified procedure in calculating the norm which I have finally adopted as most economical of time and labor.

It will be assumed that a preliminary study of the mol numbers and successive trials have shown a deficiency in silica, that is, an amount insufficient to form leucite, nephelite, anorthite, acmite, diopside, and olivine, so that there must be a readjustment of the silica assigned to diopside (and wollastonite), and a certain amount of calcium orthosilicate must be calculated.

The most frequent case is that in which there is no wollastonite, or its amount is insufficient to satisfy the deficit in silica. Here, after allotting SiO_2 to form leucite, nephelite, anorthite, and possibly acmite, the amount thus used is deducted from the total (molecular) amount, the residue being the "available silica." Letting d = molecules of diopside $(CaO.(Mg,Fe)O.2SiO_2)$, f = molecules of olivine $(2(Mg,Fe)O.SiO_2)$, and c = molecules of calcium orthosilicate $(2CaO.SiO_2)$,[4] we have the equations:

(1) $2d + f + c$ = available silica.

(2) $d + 2f$ = amount of MgO and "residual" FeO.[5]

(3) $d + 2c$ = amount of "residual" CaO.[6]

These equations can be solved, of course, in several ways, but. that which I have adopted is as follows: Subtracting (1) from the sum of (2) + (3), we get the value of $f + c$. Substituting this in (1) d is found and then from (2) and (3) f and c are found successively.

In the second case, where there is sufficient tentative wollastonite to meet the deficiency in SiO_2, the total amount of silica in the rock is subtracted from the sum of the silica which has been allotted to leucite, nephelite, anorthite, diopside, and to tentative wollastonite. The deficit thus shown is the number of molecules of necessary $2CaO.SiO_2$, and also the amount of silica to be assigned for it. This requires twice as much CaO. The rest of the CaO remains in wollastonite and takes an equal amount of SiO_2, while the diopside remains unchanged.

Two examples will be given of the calculation of norms containing calcium orthosilicate, the figures being placed in the positions which they uniformly occupy on the backs of the cards on which the analyses of my collection are written (pages 348, 349).

Regarding the mechanical procedure of calculation, it may be observed that a columnar arrangement and the writing down of all the constituent oxides in the minerals of fixed composition, the feldspars and lenads, acmite, magnetite and ilmenite, recommended in the original publication on the Quantitative System, are time-consuming, and needless after a little practice. I have also, to save time, slightly altered the order of procedure, though this does not depart, in any respect, from the principles on which the calculation of the norm is based. The various molecular

---

[4] This is represented by the symbol cs, and has a molecular weight of 172.

. [5] This is the FeO + MnO remaining after the formation of magnetite and ilmenite.

[6] This is the CaO remaining after the formation of anorthite and apatite (and rarely perofskite).

amounts of the minerals (mostly minor constituents), of fixed composition, as apatite, acmite, magnetite and ilmenite, are first written down, and then the salic K_2O, Na_2O and CaO are assigned to orthoclase, albite and anorthite. Diopside is then formed from the balance of the CaO with an equal amount of MgO + FeO, and the rest of these last two oxides, which are usually in excess over CaO, are assigned to hypersthene, care being taken to have their relative proportions the same in both femic minerals. A slide rule is very useful for this, and for obtaining other ratios. It is to be remembered that only the FeO (+ MnO) remaining after the formation of magnetite and ilemite is to be used, as is seen in the lower left hand corner.

The various amounts of SiO_2 assigned for these various molecules are written down on the right and the sum is compared with the total SiO_2 of the rock. If there is an excess it is calculated as quartz and the other mineral molecules are calculated directly from their molecular amounts by the use of the regular tables. If there is a deficit in SiO_2, the SiO_2 of the tentative hypersthene is subtracted from the sum total of used SiO_2, the balance subtracted from total SiO_2, and hypersthene and olivine formed by

	A	Aa	B	Ba
SiO_2	38.35	0.639	40.15	0.669
Al_2O_3	12.02	0.118	17.32	0.170
Fe_2O_3	3.20	0.020	7.25	0.045
FeO	8.32	0.115	4.00	0.056
MgO	18.70	0.468	4.43	0.111
CaO	9.11	0.163	11.78	0.210
Na_2O	3.15	0.051	5.99	0.097
K_2O	0.84	0.009	3.78	0.040
H_2O	3.26		1.18	
TiO_2	3.02	0.038	3.21	0.040
P_2O_5	0.43	0.003	0.71	0.005
MnO			0.08	0.001
Etc.			0.50	
	100.40		100.38	

A. Nephelinite, Vosges, France.   A. Michel-Lévy, C. R., CXLVIII, p. 1530, 1909.   Aa = mol numbers.

B. Nephelinite, Etinde, Kamerun.   E. Esch, Sb. Pr. Ak. W., 1901, p. 415. Ba = mol numbers.

A

an 58 = 16.12

$ap \begin{cases} P_2O_5 & 3 \\ CaO & 10 \end{cases} = 1.01$

mt 20 = 4.64

lc 9 = 3.92

ne 51 = 14.48

il 38 = 5.78

SiO_2

di	ol		116

CaO 75 = 8.70   MgO 401 = 28.07   36

102

MgO 67 = 6.70   FeO   49 = $\underline{5.00}$ 254

33.07   639

FeO   8 = $\underline{1.06}$ SiO_2 225   385

16.46

SiO_2 150

2 d + f + c = 385

cs

d + 2 f   = 525

CaO″ = 95 $CaO\ 20 \atop SiO_2\ 10$ } = 1.72 $\underline{d + 2\ c\ \ \ =\ \ 95}$

MgO = 468   2d + 2f + 2c = 620

FeO = $\underline{57}$ 2d + f + c = 385

525   f + c = 235

d = 75, f = 225, c = 10

B

an 33 =   9.17

$ap \begin{cases} P_2O_5 = 1.68 \\ CaO\ \ 17 \end{cases}$

mt 17 = 3.94

lc 40 = 17.44

ne 97 = 27.55

il 40   6.08

hm 28 . 4.48

di   wo SiO_2

CaO 111 = 12.88 $CaO\ 5 \atop SiO_2\ 5$ } = 0.58   66

160

MgO 111 = $\underline{11.10}$ 194

23.98   222

SiO_2 222   cs $\underline{49}$

691

$CaO\ 44 \atop SiO_2\ 22$ } = 3.78   669

CaO for wo = 49 $\overline{-22}$

the equations on page 194 of the book on the system. If there is still a deficit, all the remaining FeO and MgO are assigned to olivine, and the salic Na_2O_2 and SiO_2 divided between albite and nephelite by the equations in (a) on the same page. If there is still not enough SiO_2 to form albite, orthoclase and leucite are calculated, the salic Na_2O being all assigned to nephelite; and if there is not enough SiO_2 for orthoclase, the equations described above are resorted to.

This procedure may seem to be lengthy and complicated, but in reality, after a little experience, knowing the mineral composition of the rock and the amount of SiO_2, it will often happen that a simple inspection will lead one to adopt at once the correct stage of process. Excess SiO_2 is present in the norm of most rocks, except those with modal lenads, occurring not infrequently in those with modal olivine, so that its presence can usually be assumed in such rocks as diorites, andesite, and even not a few basalts. But if, for example, the rock is a nephelite-syenite, tinguaite or tephrite, the presence of normative nephelite may be assumed as probable, and all the excess MgO and FeO assigned at once to olivine. Such facts permit short cuts in the calculation of the norm, and any errors in the assumptions are detected in the calculation.

A table is here given for the calculation of calcium orthosilicate which may be cut out and pasted over that for akermanite in the book, which it replaces.

Calcium orthosilicate, 2 CaO. SiO₂. molecular weight, 172

(Unit of calculation is one-half molecular proportion of CaO)

MOL.	0.000	0.001	0.002	0.003	0.004	0.005	0.006	0 007	0 008	0.009	MOL.
0.00	0.00	0.17	0.34	0.52	0.69	0.86	1.03	1.20	1.38	1.55	0.00
0.01	1.72	1.89	2.06	2.24	2.41	2.58	2.75	2.92	3.10	3.27	0.01
0.02	3.44	3.61	3.78	3.96	4.13	4.30	4.47	4.64	4.82	4.99	0.02
0.03	5.16	5.33	5.50	5.66	5.85	6.02	6.19	6.36	6.54	6.71	0.03
0.04	6.88	7.05	7.22	7.40	7.57	7.74	7.91	8.08	8.26	8.43	0.04
0.05	8.60	8.77	8.94	9.12	9.29	9.46	9.63	9.80	9.98	10.15	0.05
0.06	10.32	10.49	10.66	10.84	11.01	11.18	11.35	11.52	11.70	11.87	0.06
0.07	12.04	12.21	12.38	12.56	12.73	12.90	13.07	13.24	13.42	13.59	0.07
0.08	13.76	13.93	14.10	14.28	14.45	14.62	14.79	14.96	15.14	15.31	0.08
0.09	15.48	15.65	15.82	16.00	16.17	16.34	16.51	16.68	16.86	17.03	0.09

MINERALOGY.—*Bornite as silver precipitant.*[1] CHASE PALMER, Geological Survey.

In an introductory chapter of their studies in silver enrichment Palmer and Bastin[2] by quantitative experiments have shown that chalcocite (Cu_2S) is decomposed completely by a dilute solution of silver sulphate. As a result of this reaction all the copper of the chalcocite enters the solution as cupric sulphate, while free silver and silver sulphide in equivalent amounts are deposited. Many years ago R. Schneider[3] recorded a similar observation on the conduct of cuprous sulphide (Cu_2S) with dilute silver nitrate solution, but inasmuch as other observers have issued conflicting statements concerning the products of the reaction, it seemed advisable to study the reaction anew with silver sulphate solution. According to these recent experiments the proportions of the substances appearing in the reaction between chalcocite and silver sulphate solution may be expressed by the abbreviated equation:

$$Cu_2S + 2Ag_2SO_4 = 2CuSO_4 + 2Ag + Ag_2S.$$

Anthon[4] had observed that by interaction with silver nitrate solution pure cupric sulphide (Cu_nS_n) is changed completely to silver sulphide and soluble cupric nitrate without deposition of free silver and this observation has been repeatedly confirmed by others. As a precipitant of silver ore, therefore, one gram of pure covellite is capable of depositing 2.26 grams of silver in the form of silver sulphide. On the other hand, one gram of pure chalcocite is capable of precipitating 2.7 grams of silver, one-half of which is combined with sulphur as silver sulphide and the other half is free silver.

Conspicuous among the more complex sulphides commonly associated with native silver is bornite. The mineral contains copper, sulphur and iron, but its chemical composition has

[1] Published by permission of the Director of the United States Geological Survey.
[2] Palmer, Chase, and Bastin, Edson S., Metallic minerals as precipitants of silver and gold. Economic Geology, **8**: 140–170. 1913.
[3] Pogg. Annalen der Physik, **152**: 471. 1874.
[4] Journal f. prak. Chemie, **10**: 353. 1837.

not been definitely settled.   Analyses of bornite from different sources have led to several empirical formulas for it, such as,

$$Cu_3FeS_3, \ Cu_5FeS_4, \ \text{and} \ Cu_{12}Fe_2S_9.$$

The constitution of bornite has been a favorite subject of speculation.   The views of Rammelsberg and Groth illustrate the vacillations and uncertainties likely to follow sole reliance on composition as indicative of constitution.   In 1841 Rammelsberg assigned to bornite the constitutional formula, $3Cu_2S.Fe_2S_3$, by which all the copper is represented as present in the cuprous state.   Later he considered all the iron of bornite to be ferrous iron and the copper to be partly cuprous and partly cupric, and to express these supposed conditions he ascribed to bornite the constitutional formula, $Cu_2S.CuS.FeS$.   Groth has considered bornite to be strictly a cuprous substance and has adopted the formula, $3Cu_2S.Fe_2S_3$ which Rammelsberg had abandoned.

It has been known for a long time that bornite immersed in a silver nitrate solution quickly develops on its surface a crop of silver crystals, but beyond the mere appearance of silver on bornite this striking phenomenon seems to have received no attention from mineralogists.   Believing that a study of the capacity of bornite as a silver precipitant might throw light not only on the chemical composition of the mineral, but also on the intramolecular relations of its constituents, the reaction of a specimen of bornite from Virgilina, Virginia, and dilute silver sulphate solution has been studied quantitatively.   The specimen was massive, its freshly broken surfaces having a uniform color.   Metallographic examination of polished surfaces showed the presence of a few small grains of chalcopyrite and a few gashes of a dark grey mineral suggestive of chalcocite.   The mineral was broken into small fragments, and from these were chosen only those pieces in which, under the magnifier, no chalcopyrite could be detected.   The granular pieces were washed with alcohol, and from these a second selection of bornite was made.   In this way, it was believed, material representative of the true bornite in the specimen was obtained.   An analysis of the material selected for study gave the content

			Atomic ratios
Copper..........	62.50 per cent	62.50 ÷ 63.4 = 0.986	4.74
Iron............	11.64 per cent	11.64 ÷ 56 = 0.208	1.00
Sulphur........	25.40 per cent	25.40 ÷ 32 = 0.794	3.81
	99.54		

These results agree fairly well with the requirements of the empirical formula Cu_5FeS_4. The relatively high proportion of iron suggests the presence of a small quantity of chalcopyrite which in preparing the sample for study had escaped detection.

EXPERIMENT WITH SILVER SULPHATE SOLUTION

The finely ground mineral (0.5926 gram) was digested first on the steam bath for 6 hours and afterwards at room temperature. After 12 hours the solution was filtered from the insoluble material. From the deposit were obtained 0.5983 gram of free silver and 0.6037 gram of combined silver. Traces of copper were present in the residue which also yielded

0.0643 gram iron   = 10.85 per cent of the mineral.
0.1478 gram sulphur = 24.94 per cent of the mineral.

and from the solution were obtained

0.3615 gram copper = 61.00 per cent of the mineral.
0.0053 gram iron   = 0.89 per cent of the mineral.

Atomic proportions of the copper dissolved by the silver solution and the iron and sulphur recovered from the residue:

	Per cent
Copper..	61.00 ÷ 63.4 = 0.962
Iron..	10.85 ÷ 56.0 = 0.193
Sulphur......................................	24.94 ÷ 32.0 = 0.780

and

$$\underset{\text{Cu}}{0.962} : \underset{\text{Fe}}{0.193} : \underset{\text{S}}{0.780} = 4.98 : 1.0 : 4.04.$$

The results obtained by this chemical reaction approximate the requirements of the empirical formula, Cu_5FeS_4, more closely than do the results obtained by a gross analysis of the sample.

Atomic proportions of the dissolved copper and the precipitated silver products:

Per cent
Dissolved copper.............................. 61.00 ÷ 63.4 = 0.962
Free silver.................................100.9 ÷ 107.9 = 0.935
Combined silver.............................101.8 ÷ 107.9 = 0.943

and

				Copper	Free silver	Combined silver
0.962	:	0.935	:	0.943 = 1.00	: 0.97	: 0.98

This experiment shows that for every atom of copper dissolved by the silver sulphate solution one atom of free silver and one atom of combined silver in the residual material are deposited. It is apparent, therefore, that the copper of this bornite is cuprous just as it is in chalcocite and to express the cuprous nature of the copper it is convenient to use for this bornite the formula $5Cu_2S.Fe_2S_3$ after the dualistic system. This formula may be considered a constitutional formula for the mineral under examination, and its corresponding molecular formula becomes $Cu_{10}Fe_2S_8$.

The proportional amounts of the substances participating in this reaction of bornite may, therefore, be expressed by the equation:

$$Cu_{10}Fe_2S_3 + 10Ag_2SO_4 = 10Ag + Ag_{10}Fe_2S_8 + 10CuSO_4$$

Thus one gram of this bornite is capable of precipitating 2.15 grams of silver as silver and silver sulphide. In strong contrast with the reactivity of its cuprous constituent is the inertness of the sulphoferric portion of the bornite.

Inasmuch as the group, Fe_2S_3, is not known to exist as an independent mineral, the formation of a silver ferric sulphide as one of the products of the reaction of bornite with silver sulphate solution may be presumed. Moreover, from the stability of the compound residual products it seems not improbable that in regions abounding in silver deposits associated with bornite some silver sulphoferric mineral as a secondary product may yet be found. It is hoped that further study of the conduct of copper iron sulphide minerals with silver salt solutions will shed light on the chemical relations which sternbergite and its allied minerals bear to one another.

BOTANY.—*New or imperfectly known species of bull-horn acacias.*
WILLIAM EDWIN SAFFORD, Bureau of Plant Industry.

In 1914 the writer published a preliminary paper on the
myrmecophilous acacias of tropical America commonly called
bull-horns.[1] The present paper is intended as a supplement to
it. Additional material has been received from various sources,
including specimens from the herbarium of the Missouri Botanical Garden collected in Mexico by Dr. Josiah Gregg in 1849,
and others from the Isthmus of Panama, collected recently by
Mr. Henry Pittier.

An undescribed species very closely related to *Acacia Standleyi*
and to *A. hirtipes* must be assigned to the section Clavigerae.
The fact that the large spines of this new species are quite glabrous
makes it advisable that the group name Hebacanthae, which
includes these species, be changed; and the name Mesopodiales
is therefore proposed herewith as a substitute for it. As modified the group may be redescribed as follows:

Group V. MESOPODIALES (*Hebacanthae* Safford, op. cit., p. 366).
Involucel borne at or above the middle of the peduncle of the flower
spike. Interfloral bracteoles not peltate, but composed of a fan-shaped
or ovate limb with a hairy margin, borne upon a slender pedicel and
forming an imbricated pubescent covering over the flowers before
anthesis.

Of the three additional species discussed one belongs to the
group Ceratophysae and two to the Globuliferae.

Acacia dolichocephala Safford, sp. nov. Group Ceratophysae, section Dolichocephalae. A shrub or small tree resembling *Acacia sphaer-
ocephala* Schlecht. & Cham., but readily distinguished by its elongate flower-heads and fusiform receptacle, as well as by the occasional
presence of nectar glands on the leaf-rachis at the base of the terminal
and subterminal pairs of pinnae. Young growth puberulent, at length
glabrate. Stipular spines ivory white, tipped with brown, broadly
divergent and slightly curved outward, terete, tapering gradually to
a point, the bases flattened and more or less cuneate, the spines 4 to
5 cm. long, 10 to 12 mm. broad along the line of union of the connate
bases. Leaves of vegetative branches composed usually of 10 pairs
of pinnae; rachis puberulent, 10 to 14 cm. long, with an elongated

[1] Safford, W. E., "*Acacia cornigera* and its allies." Journ. Wash. Acad. Sci.
4: 356–386. 1914.

crater-like nectar gland on the petiole a little below the first pair of pinnae, often a second, tubular gland below the second pair, and sometimes a gland at the base of the terminal and subterminal pairs of pinnae; leaflets 22 to 26 pairs, assuming a reddish bronze color when dry, oblong-linear, 8 to 10 mm. long, 2 mm. broad, unequal at the base, rounded at the apex and mucronulate, those from which apical food bodies have fallen retuse; midrib prominent beneath, oblique; lateral nerves inconspicuous. Leaves of the flowering branchlets composed of 2 to 5 pairs of pinnae; leaflets 8 to 14 pairs, 3 to 4 mm. long; rachis of leaf with a conspicuous raised nectar gland just below the lowermost pair of pinnae, and frequently a smaller gland at the base of the terminal pair of pinnae. Flowers in ovate-oblong heads or spikes 11 to 15 mm. in length and 8 mm. in diameter at anthesis, usually in clusters of 2 or 3, rarely solitary or in clusters of 4; peduncles graduated in length, thick and fleshy, dark reddish brown; the longest equal in length to the fusiform axis of the head or exceeding it, the shortest less than half as long; involucel 4-toothed, calyx-like, situated at or near the base of the peduncle, puberulent without. Flowers ferrugineous, tubular; calyx 1.9 to 2.1 mm. long, 0.5 to 0.6 mm. in diameter, densely puberulent about the margin, obtusely and shallowly 5- or 6-lobed; corolla scarcely exceeding the calyx; stamens numerous, with ferrugineous filaments and pale tan-colored anthers; pistil filiform. Pedicelled bracteoles between the flowers with obtuse ovate ciliate laminae, these puberulent on the upper surface; pedicels 1.4 mm. long, when young clothed with sparse short diaphanous hairs, at length glabrate. Pods resembling those of other Ceratophysae, inflated, indehiscent, thin-chartaceous, 3.5 to 4 cm. long, 1 cm. in diameter, wine-colored when mature, cylindrical, often slightly oblique, terminating in a sharp spine-like beak, and contracted at the base into a short stipe-like neck.

Type in the herbarium of the Field Museum of Natural History, no. 189552, including flowers and mature seed-pods, collected along the shore north of the city of Vera Cruz, Mexico, January 24, 1906, by Dr. J. M. Greenman (no. 87). A specimen of the type collection with less perfectly developed spines and without seed-pods, is in the United States National Herbarium, no. 692164.

Acacia chiapensis Safford, sp. nov. Group Globuliferae, section Ramulosae. An erect shrub or small tree 3 to 5 meters high, resembling *Acacia Donnelliana* but distinguished from that species by the absence of interpinnal nectar glands on the larger leaves and by the more numerous glands at the base of the leaf rachis (petiole). Young growth puberulous. Flower heads globose, borne in axillary clusters on special flowering branches (only very young flower heads observed in the type specimen), covered before anthesis by the imbricate peltate limbs of the pedicelled interfloral bracteoles. Fruit (immature in the type material) a flat strap-shaped legume, somewhat thickened at the sutures, 7.5 to 7.8 cm. long, 7 to 8 mm. broad, terminating in an obtuse point and narrowing at the base into a stipe-like neck, several legumes ·radiating from the indurated torus; fruiting peduncle 1.5 to 2 cm. long and (in the type) as thick as the flowering branch bearing it; seeds 12 to 14. Large spines dark brown, V-shaped, terete, tapering gradually to a sharp point, minutely puberulous near the base, at length glabrous and glossy, 50 mm. long, 5 mm. thick near the base, usually perforated and inhabited by stinging ants. Small spines scarcely exceeding 1 mm. in length, puberulent at the base, terminating in a polished reddish point, in the type not acicular as in *A. Donnelliana.* Leaves of the vegetative branches composed of 20 to 26 pairs of pinnae, these 46 to 60 mm. long, sometimes subopposite; leaflets 34 to 44 pairs, linear-oblong, approximate or contiguous, 5 to 5.5 mm. long, 1 to 1.4 mm. broad, usually rounded or obtuse at the apex, unequal at the base, puberulent when young, often spreading nearly at right angles with the rachis of the pinna; main rachis grooved above, puberulent, devoid of nectar glands except at the base, the groove here broader and bearing 10 to 12 irregularly disposed nectaries, some of them apparently geminate. Leaves of flowering branches varying greatly in size, the larger ones resembling the vegetative leaves but with fewer pinnae, and like them devoid of interpinnal nectar glands, the succeeding ones sometimes with interpinnal glands between the uppermost pinnae, and the smallest bearing 4 to 6 pairs of more or less rudimentary pinnae, nearly all of them with interpinnal nectar glands; all floral leaves with a row of 4 to 6 prominent nectar glands at the base of the rachis, and with minute stipular spines subtending the calyx-like buds from which issue the flower heads.

Type in the United States National Herbarium, no. 692157, collected near San Fernandino, between Tuxtla and Chicoasen, state of Chiapas, Mexico, January 12, 1907, by Guy N. Collins (no. 164), in association with *Acacia Collinsii* Safford. At the time of collection (the dry season) nearly all the plants were entirely leafless.

This species, which appears to be intermediate between *A. Donnelliana* of Honduras and *A. multiglandulosa* of Panama, has thin flat pods, and its spines are uniformly quite straight. On the specimen collected nearly all the spines were punctured, but very few of them contained ants. Those that were secured occurred not in colonies but as individuals in the spines.

Acacia multiglandulosa Schenck, Repert. Nov. Sp. Fedde **12**: 362. 1913.—Bot. Jahrb. Engler **50**: 480. 1914. Group Globuliferae, section Ramulosae. A shrub or small tree with very long narrow bipinnate leaves, some of them provided with large stout polished dark-colored connate stipular spines, these perforated and inhabited by ants, others with minute inconspicuous subulate spines. Large spines (when living) maroon or dark wine-colored, glossy, widely divergent, straight or very slightly curved outward, stout, terete, somewhat flattened at the base, 40 mm. long, 8 to 10 mm. broad at the base. Small spines at the base of equally large leaves scarcely 2 mm. long, minutely puberulent at the base (when young), glabrous at the blood red point. Leaves of vegetative branches composed of 23 to 31 pairs of pinnae; rachis 20 to 38 cm. long, broadly grooved, with the raised edges of the groove puberulent, and with a single small nectar gland at the base of each pair of pinnae; groove broadening at the base of the rachis and enclosing 20 to 25 small nectar glands, these arranged approximately in 3 rows, truncate-conoid in form, with a central pore-like opening; rachis of pinnae 30 to 58 mm. long, bearing 25 to 31 pairs of leaflets, these linear-oblong, 5 to 7 mm. long, 1 to 1.1 mm. broad, with only the midrib conspicuous beneath, unequal at the base, and usually obtusely pointed at the apex. Leaves of the

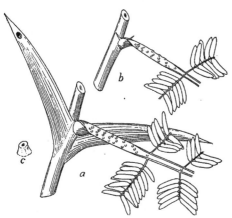

Fig. 1. *Acacia multiglandulosa* Schenck: *a*, enlarged stipular spines, with base of vegetative leaf attached showing numerous extrafloral nectar glands; *b*, leaf base, with minute stipular spines; *c*, nectar gland. Specimen from Panama (*Pittier* 6745). *a* and *b*, natural size; *c*, scale 3.

flowering branches rudimentary, reduced to small bracts about 1 cm. long subtending the peduncles, bearing minute stipular spines and 4 nectar glands but devoid of pinnae.

Flower heads 7 mm. long, 6 mm. in diameter, solitary or in pairs, borne in the axils of the bracts on long erect branchlets composed of many nodes; peduncles 8 mm. long, 0.75 mm. thick, provided with a basal involucre of 4 connate bracts; form of interfloral bracteoles not observed. Fruit lacking.

Type in the Berlin Herbarium, collected at Porto Bello, Panama, in 1825, by J. G. Billberg. It consists of a flowering branch with several flower heads and two disintegrated leaves, but without enlarged stipular spines. Since the publication of Dr. Schenck's paper upon this group fine specimens of vegetative branches with large spines were collected at the head of Gatún Valley, Panama, in 1914, by Mr. Henry Pittier (no. 6745). The latter are now in the United States National Herbarium, sheets no. 716560 and no. 716561.

In its large leaves, composed of many pinnae, this species resembles *Acacia Cookii*; but the presence of many small glands at the base of the rachis separates it at once from that species, and the arrangement of its flower heads on specialized branches instead of in clusters in the axils of large spines places it in the section Ramulosae.

Acacia gladiata Safford, sp. nov. Group Mesopodiales, section Clavigerae. Flower spikes club-shaped, resembling those of *Acacia Standleyi* but much smaller, 10 to 16 mm. long, 4 to 5 mm. thick, densely pubescent before anthesis; peduncles in clusters of 2 to 6, the longest observed 13 mm. in length, pubescent with short straight cinereous hairs both above and below the involucel, the latter normally calyx-like composed of 4 acute ascending teeth, at first densely pubescent on the outside, at length subglabrous and glossy, usually situated at or above the middle of the peduncle; axis of spike not exceeding the peduncle in thickness. Flowers much darker than those of *A. Standleyi*, but apparently yellow after anthesis, on account of the mass of crowded anthers; calyx broadly tubular, shallowly lobed, tan-colored, hairy about the margin and on the sides; corolla maroon or dark wine-colored, obtusely 5- or 6-lobed, about twice as long as the calyx; sta-

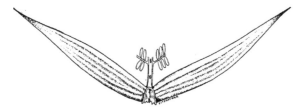

Fig. 2. *Acacia gladiata* Safford. Enlarged stipular spines of vegetative leaf, with base of rachis showing solitary nectar gland. Cotype (*Rose* 3792). Natural size.

mens exserted, very numerous, the filaments ferrugineous, the anthers pale strawcolored; style filiform, longer than the stamens. Fruit not observed. Large spines very long and widely divergent, usually flattened and sword-like, linear-lanceolate in outline, somewhat constricted at the base, resembling certain forms of the spines of *Acacia cochliacantha* H. & B. but connate instead of separate at the base and never split or inflated, gradually narrowed toward the apex to an acute point, 35 to 52 mm. long, 5 to 8 mm. broad, glabrous, reddish or wine-colored when young, at length brown or tan-colored. Leaves with pubescent or minutely hairy rachis and usually with a nectar gland at its base and just below each pair of pinnae, those of vegetative branches 7 to 10 cm. long, composed of about 20 pairs of pinnae, these 23 to 27 mm. long; leaflets about 20 pairs, oblong-linear, 3.5 to 4.5 mm. long and 1 to 1.2 mm. broad, unequal at the base, rounded at the apex, often mucronulate or tipped with a waxy apical body, as in the true myrmecophilous acacias, the margin at first fringed with small stiff hairs, at length subglabrate. Leaves of flowering branches with short subulate stipular spines and 10 to 16 pairs of pinnae; nectar glands circular or oval, with a raised annular margin.

Type, bearing flowers and old spines, in the herbarium of the Missouri Botanical Garden, no. 46838, collected in the vicinity of Rosario, state of Sinaloa, Mexico, in 1849, by Dr. Josiah Gregg (no. 1135). It is mounted on the same sheet with specimens of the spoon-thorn acacia, *A. cochliacantha* H. & B.

Cotype, a young branch with spines and leaves but without flowers or fruit, in the United States National Herbarium, no. 716563, collected near Acaponeta, Territory of Tepic, Mexico, July 30, 1897, by Dr. J. N. Rose (no. 3792.)

This species is closely allied to *Acacia Standleyi* and to *A. hirtipes*, but differs from them both in its smooth, flattened, sword-shaped spines, and in the form and color of its flowers. Though many of the leaflets of the flowering branches are tipped with food bodies, as in the true myrmecophilous acacias, the spines are much compressed and, in the specimens observed, not inhabited by ants.

ECONOMICS.—*Efficiency as a factor in organic evolution. I.*[1]
ALFRED J. LOTKA.

In an earlier issue of this JOURNAL[2] the writer published a paper on *Evolution in discontinuous systems*.   In the first portion of this paper the treatment of the subject was quantitative, and made use of analytical methods.   In the concluding section certain phases of the subject were touched upon, for which at that time no method of quantitative analytical treatment could be suggested.

In the present paper it is proposed to resume the thread of the former discussion, and to show how the qualitative analysis of the problem then suggested has since fulfilled the author's hopes in furnishing the basis for quantitative treatment.

To recall briefly the point of view adopted in the paper cited, we note that r, the rate of increase per head of a given type or species of organisms, under given conditions, may be regarded as a quantitative *index* of the *fitness* of such species, or of its *adaptation* to the conditions given.

The value of this index r of the fitness, depends, of course, on the one hand, on the external conditions; on the other hand

[1] Paper read before the Washington Philosophical Society on February 13, 1915.

[2] This Journal, 2: 2, 49, 66. 1912.

it depends on the properties or characteristics of the type of organism.

These properties may be divided into two classes, viz., those which influence r through b, the birthrate per head, and those which do so through d, the deathrate per head.

The latter set of properties can be further subdivided into a class which we may group together collectively as constituting the means of *passive resistance* of the organism,[3] as exemplified, for instance, by such defensive structures as the shell of the tortoise; and another class which we may similarly denote collectively as the means of *active opposition* to circumstances unfavorable to the life of the individual and the species.   These latter means comprise that system of sense and motor organs, with a controlling and coördinating nerve-apparatus, which is characteristic of animals, especially of the higher animals, and notably of man.

These facts are summarized in tabular form below:

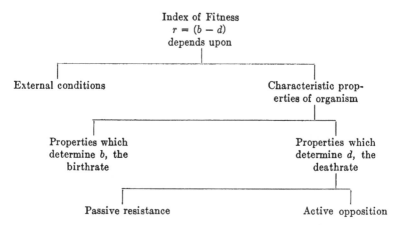

For the purposes of our present discussion we shall regard the external conditions as given, and shall concern ourselves only with the properties of the type of organism under consideration.

---

[3] For details the reader must be referred to the previous paper cited.

Moreover, we shall not, on this occasion, discuss those properties which relate to the birthrate.[4]

And again, of the properties which determine the deathrate, we shall suppose the *passive resistance* of the type of organism under consideration as given, and shall devote our attention solely to the analysis of that *mechanism* or, to use a phrase that does not invite fruitless controversy, that *system*, which constitutes the individual's means of active opposition to unfavorable influences. We shall study the relation which the *efficiency* or *precision* of this mechanism or system bears to the fitness (gauged by r) of a given type of organism.

As regards this mechanism or system, it was pointed out in the paper cited above, that all the actions of the organism form part of a cycle, the so-called sensory-motor cycle, or, better, receptor-effector cycle.

For, every action is more or less directly conditioned by sense impressions received by the organism. Between the impression or impressions received and the action or actions conditioned thereby various steps may intervene. In the simplest case a reflex action may be the direct and immediate result of a sense impression. In other cases the action may lag far behind the impression or impressions to which it is referable, and among the intervening steps that lead from the impression to the action may be certain phenomena which form objects of the individual's consciousness, phenomena of will[5] (desire, choice or selection) and phenomena of mentation (logical deduction, etc.)

The efficiency of the receptor-effector system, and hence the

[4] It is hoped to develop this phase of the subject at a later date along lines which have been suggested by the method here laid down.

[5] It is not intended here to open up a discussion regarding the question of free will. All that is meant to be implied by the expression "selection" is that the individual has a *consciousness*, a *sensation* or a *belief* of making use of a specific faculty commonly denoted by the word *will*, in determining which of two or more seemingly possible courses presented to him is to be followed. We are not here concerned with the nature of this faculty of will, but only with the comparison, as regards their *fitness*, of two or more types of organisms, alike in all other respects, but differing in the particular manner in which they effect their *selection;* that is to say, differing in the particular type of their will; or, in other words, differing in their *sense of value.*

fitness of the individual, it was pointed out, depends on the various errors to which he is prone in each of the three fundamental steps of the receptor-effector cycle:

1. In the receptor step: Errors of observation.
2. In the intermediate step: a. Errors of mentation (errors against logic, etc.)
                                     b. Errors of valuation, i.e., errors in the *choice* among several (seemingly) possible actions, i.e., departures from that choice which would make r a maximum.[6]
3. In the effector step: Errors of operation.

Qualitatively our analysis may be said to be completed when we have thus recognized the several factors that enter into

[6] On this point the reader is referred to the author's paper "An Objective Standard of Value Derived from the Principle of Evolution," this Journal, volume IV, 1914, pp. 409, 447, 499.

The writer wishes to take this opportunity to correct an error which has crept into the paper cited—an error which does not, however, in any way affect the main conclusions of that paper, as applied to our present purposes.

A constant has by an oversight been dropped out of equation (27), pp. 448 and 449. For, after k' had arbitrarily been made equal to unity (equation (20)) we were no longer at liberty to select *labor* as the standard commodity; or, vice versa, if it is deemed convenient so to select our standard commodity, then k' cannot be made unity, but must appear in equation (27), which should thus read

$$v_L = k' \frac{\partial r}{\partial L} = -1 \qquad (27a)$$

This unfortunately means that the indirect method suggested in the paper cited, for establishing the actual numerical ratio between the theoretical (objective) and the practical standard of value, fails, and we are driven back to the resort of actually determining $\frac{\partial r}{\partial x}$ for at least one commodity. The prospects of this being accomplished in the near future seem somewhat slender, though there is one special case in which something can perhaps be done. The writer may have occasion to return to this point in a later communication.

In point of fact it is more convenient to adopt the first of the two alternatives mentioned above, to discard the use of labor as the standard commodity, and to put $k'=1$, so that

$$v_x = \frac{\partial r}{\partial x} \qquad (27b)$$

This is the convention here followed.

play in the operation of the receptor-effector system, and have grasped their bearing upon the fitness of the organism.

Quantitatively our problem may be stated in this form:

If r is the rate of increase per head per annum of a given type or group of organisms, it is required to find a mathematical expression, in terms of suitably chosen characteristic properties of the organism and of the system of which it forms part, for

$$\frac{\partial r}{\partial \epsilon} \tag{1}$$

where ϵ denotes an error of a specified kind, either of observation, operation, mentation or valuation.

At the time when the tabular statement of the qualitative analysis recapitulated above was first given, this was done in the hope that such a provisional analysis might be found to furnish the basis for a quantitative treatment of the subject. This hope has since been realized, although it has been found that in a sense the analysis had been carried too far. In order to make any headway we must now in a measure retrace the steps of our analysis, and recombine some of the threads which we had unraveled.

Let us note first of all that it is not so much isolated and perhaps peculiar actions which interest us, but rather those systematic actions which are of a more or less regular or routine occurrence and which are aimed to meet some more or less permanent demand. In such case, we can say in mathematical terms that the actions in question serve to maintain a certain parameter X_j at a value x_j (for example x_j may be the annual production and consumption of wheat, or the deathrate from malaria etc., etc.).

Disregarding, then, isolated and peculiar actions (which upon reflection are found to constitute at most only a small proportion of the activities of the organism), we may describe in a clear quantitative way the general scope of the activities of a given type of organism, such as man, by stating that the representative individual of that type so distributes his labor, that

labor L_1 is spent in maintaining a parameter X_1 at the
value x_1

labor L_2 is spent in maintaining a parameter X_2 at the
value x_2

$\qquad$ etc., etc., etc., etc., etc.

labor L_j is spent in maintaining a parameter X_j at the
value x_j

$\hspace{8cm}$ (2)

Now it will immediately be seen that the *fitness* of the individual, his adaptation to his environment, in so far as it depends upon the activities defined as above, will depend on two factors:

1. On the manner in which the individual distributes his labor among the several pursuits indicated or, in other words, on the proportion

$$L_1 : L_2 : \quad . \quad . \quad . \quad : L_j \qquad (3)$$

2. On the *productivity* or *productive efficiency* of the individual in each pursuit, as measured by

$$E_j = \frac{x_j - C_j}{L_j} \qquad (4)$$

$x_j - C_j$[7] being the increment in x_j produced by labor L_j per unit of time.[8]

It will be seen that the factors (1) and (2) correspond in a way to certain points in our tabular analysis of the influence of various errors on the efficiency of the individual. But instead of considering individual errors we have lumped them together in a statistical way, so that errors of observation and operation find their expression in the corresponding values of the productive efficiencies (which are of course diminished by every such error), while errors of valuation find their expression in the proportion

$$L_1 : L_2 : \quad . \quad . \quad . \quad : L_j$$

---

[7] The constant C_j is introduced because for some commodities (and for most discommodities) x_j is not zero when L_j is zero, i.e., some of the commodity "grows" spontaneously without the intervention of the interested individual.

[8] In case X_j is of the nature of a "discommodity," E_j is of course negative, as in the case of the example cited above, namely, if X_j is the deathrate from malaria.

While we have thus lost something of the detail of our first analysis, we have gained this point, that the quantities with which we are now dealing are clear cut, measurable and, in principle at least, determinable by statistical methods. By their aid we can attack the problem before us by analytical methods; and furthermore, when we have taken the first steps in this direction, we can, if we wish, restore to our analysis some of the detail which we had temporarily sacrificed.

ERRORS OF OBSERVATION, OPERATION, AND MENTATION

We shall deal with these three types of error under one general head, since they have this in common: that they all exert their influence upon r through the *productivity* or *productive efficiency* of the individual.

We have, quite generally,

$$r = r(x_1, x_2, \cdots x_j, \cdots)$$
(5)

so that

$$\frac{\partial r}{\partial E_j} = \frac{\partial r}{\partial x_j} \cdot \frac{\partial x_j}{\partial E_j}$$
(6)

In the particular case that the parameter X_j is of the nature of mass produced (and consumed) per unit of time (e.g. the annual production and consumption of wheat), $\dfrac{\partial r}{\partial x_j}$ is the objective value[9] v_j per unit mass of the commodity X_j. In any case, we can, with obvious economic significance, write

$$\frac{\partial r}{\partial x_j} = v_j$$
(7)

Also, from (4) we have

$$\frac{\partial x_j}{\partial E_j} = L_j$$
(8)

so that (6) becomes

$$\frac{\partial r}{\partial E_j} = v_j L_j$$
(9)

[9] This Journal, 1914, loc. cit.

We have obtained this result by lumping together in a statistical way errors committed by the individual, and dealing not directly with variations in these errors but with corresponding variations in the productive efficiency E_j. There is now no difficulty in carrying our analysis farther, so as to make it correspond in matter of detail more nearly with the qualitative analysis from which we started. We may proceed as follows:

Let I be some suitable parameter which can serve as an index of the imprecision of a particular type of observation or operation. (Thus I may be the mean error made in a particular type of observation or operation; or it may be, for example, the strength of the correcting lens worn by a short-sighted person; or yet again it may be a suitable index measuring the acuity of the logical faculties of the type under consideration, say, something of the nature of a refined Binet test).[10]

Then if i is the value of the parameter I, we have

$$E_j = \varphi(i) \tag{10}$$

$$\delta r = \frac{\partial r}{\partial i}\,\delta i \tag{11}$$

$$= \sum \frac{\partial r}{\partial E_j}\cdot\frac{\partial E_j}{\partial i}\,\delta i \tag{12}$$

the summation being carried over all those parameters X, for which the productive efficiency is affected by the imprecision I. Hence, by (9)

$$\delta r = \sum v_j\, L_j\, \frac{\partial E_j}{\partial i}\,\delta i \tag{13}$$

or

$$\frac{\partial r}{\partial i} = \sum v_j\, L_j\, \frac{\partial E_j}{\partial i} \tag{14}$$

which we interpret, in view of (7) as

$$v_i = \sum v_j\, L_j\, \frac{\partial E_j}{\partial i} \tag{15}$$

[10] Compare C. B. Davenport, Heredity in Relation to Eugenics, 1911, p. 9.

The quantity v_i in equation (15) has an interesting economic significance. It is the (negative) value, per unit, of the *imprecision* denoted by the parameter I. Thus if I is short-sightedness, measured, say, in dioptries of the correcting lens, then $v_i \, \delta i$ is the (annual) loss in values (commodities) which would be suffered, per head, if all individuals had their short-sightedness increased by a small increment δi, all other things remaining the same.

Or, putting it in another way, $v_i \, \delta i$ is the *fair compensation*[11] which should be paid, per head, to a community in which each individual had his eyesight injured by the (infinitesimal) increment δi, in order to restore to them the total earnings (measured in real commodities) which they made prior to the injury.

Equations (9), (14), and (15) represent the solution of the problem of finding an expression for the differential coefficient (1), so far as errors of observation, operation and mentation are concerned.

---

[11] To prevent any possible misunderstanding, it must here be pointed out that we cannot, along the lines here given, establish an exact expression for the *fair compensation* corresponding to an injury δi for the case of one individual so injured and competing with others not injured.

ABSTRACTS

Authors of scientific papers are requested to see that abstracts, preferably prepared and signed by themselves, are forwarded promptly to the editors. Each of the scientific bureaus in Washington has a representative authorized to forward such material to this journal and abstracts of official publications should be transmitted through the representative of the bureau in which they originate. The abstracts should conform in length and general style to those appearing in this issue.

GEODESY.—*Triangulation in Alabama and Mississippi.* WALTER F. REYNOLDS, U. S. Coast and Geodetic Survey Special Publication No. 24. Pp. 71. 1915.

This publication contains the positions and descriptions of nearly 600 triangulation stations in Alabama and on the Gulf coast of Mississippi. The primary stations included in the volume are a part of the Eastern Oblique Arc, the field work of which was completed in 1898. The results of that triangulation appeared in Special Publication No. 7 in 1901, the positions being on the same datum as that used for the Transcontinental Triangulation, the results of which appeared in Special Publication No. 4. Since that time the United States Standard Datum, now called the North American Datum, was adopted and it became necessary to change the old positions to that datum.

The field work of the triangulation was done between the years 1848 and 1911. Many of the stations of the early surveys are lost, but from time to time tertiary triangulation has been done along the coast to supplement the triangulation of the Oblique Arc.

The elevations of the triangulation stations in Alabama appeared in Special Publication No. 7, but the elevations of several of the stations have since been determined by precise leveling and are now held fixed in a rigid adjustment since made of all the elevations. In this adjustment are also included the elevations of a number of stations in Georgia and Tennessee. On account of the new adjustment of the net, the elevations appearing in this publication will differ slightly from those in Special Publication No. 7.

As a full discussion of the errors and the accuracy of the triangulation of the Eastern Oblique Arc appeared in Special Publication No. 7, it was not considered necessary to give any discussion of these subjects in the new work. There is a table comparing the accuracy of the triangulation in this volume with that of the entire Oblique Arc.

Aside from its scientific interest this volume has a large practical value, as it offers to the engineer a large number of points determined trigonometrically and correlated on one geodetic datum. If the engineer wishes to extend this triangulation or to base other surveys upon it, the positions, descriptions, and sketches given in this volume will supply the data that he will need. W. F. R.

GEOLOGY.—*A gold-platinum-palladium lode in southern Nevada.* ADOLPH KNOPF, U. S. Geol. Survey Bull. 620-A. Pp. 1-18. 1915. The ore of the Boss gold mine in the Yellow Pine mining district, Clark County, Nevada, has recently been shown to be rich in platinum and palladium. The deposit consists of a fine-grained quartz mass, which constitutes an irregular siliceous replacement of Carboniferous dolomites along a series of vertical fractures. The main ore shoot, in which from 1000 to 2000 tons had been developed at the time of visit, averaged in ounces to the ton: Gold, 3.46; silver, 6.4; platinum, 0.70; palladium, 3.38. The precious metals are especially associated with the rare mineral plumbojarosite, Pb $[Fe (O H)_2]_6$ $(SO_4)_4$; pockets of this mineral carry 100 or more ounces of palladium and platinum and several hundred ounces of gold to the ton. The only sulphide so far found in the mine is chalcocite, and this is probably of secondary origin. The occurrence of platinum and palladium in this Nevada gold ore is of some interest, inasmuch as a review of the known distribution of platinum in veins shows that the Boss vein is one of the few primary deposits in which metals of the platinum group are present in more than traces, and, with one possible exception—the New Rambler deposit in Wyoming—is the only primary deposit of economic importance in which these metals are the constituents of predominant value. A. K.

ZOOLOGY.—*The crinoids collected by the Endeavour between Fremantle and Geraldton (Western Australia).* AUSTIN HOBART CLARK. Records of the Western Australian Museum and Art Gallery, **1**[3]: 113-129. 1914. A detailed description is given herein of the specimens of each of the twelve species of crinoids which were obtained by the "Endeavour" off southwestern Australia. Of these twelve species one (*Capillaster sentosa*) was not previously known from Australia, while two (*Neometra gorgonia* and *N. conaminis*) represent a family (Calometridae) heretofore not reported south of the Sunda Islands. A. H. C.

PROCEEDINGS OF THE ACADEMY AND AFFILIATED SOCIETIES

THE BIOLOGICAL SOCIETY OF WASHINGTON

The 539th meeting of the Biological Society of Washington was held at the Cosmos Club, Saturday, April 3, 1915, with President BARTSCH in the chair and 65 persons present.

On recommendation of the Council, Mr. Ben Miller was elected to active membership.

Under heading Brief Notes, L. O. HOWARD called attention to a wasps' nest he had lately seen which was marked by a conspicuous blue streak. In making this nest the wasps had evidently made the blue streaked part out of a blue building paper, instead of making their pulp from the natural wood. Messrs. BARTSCH and LYON referred to the red-headed woodpeckers in the grounds of Freedmen's Hospital, stating that a few birds had remained during the winter of 1914–15, though none had wintered during 1913–14. The species is abundant in the hospital grounds this spring. Messrs. BARTSCH and BAILEY commented upon the scratching of the gray squirrels in the city parks, which Mr. BAILEY said was due to infestation with fleas from their winter boxes. Suitable insect powder placed in the boxes would drive out the fleas but was not relished by the squirrels.

The first paper on the regular program was by Dr. A. H. WRIGHT, of Cornell University. *The snakes and lizards of Okefinokee Swamp.*

Seven snakes of the dry open sandy fields or pine forests of southeastern United States were absent on the Okefinokee Swamp islands. None of the truly Floridan ophidians and saurians were represented. Some forms occurred on the outskirts of the swamp but were wholly wanting within the swamp. The 21 species of snakes and 6 lizards were very variable in scutellation and coloration. Whether the restricted quarters and the incessant warfare and struggle for place caused the wide range of variation is not yet answerable. We had expected to find fixed peculiar stable races or subspecies because of the isolated nature of some of the islands, but segregation has not yet placed a local stamp on any of the reptilian forms. The swamp is the common source of the Atlantic coastal stream, the St. Mary's, and the Gulf affluent, the Suwannee. This factor may have had its influence on the turtles and possibly on the snakes and lizards. The swamp does not appear to be a barrier or boundary line between two decided faunal areas. It is rather a melting pot for many of the supposed cardinal characters of distinction in snakes and lizards.

Some of the interesting systematic observations are: the non-trustworthiness of the temporal scutellation and coloration in the *Elaphe* group; the need of further study in the *Tropidonotus fasciatus* assemblage; the presence of the *Osceola elapsoidea* and the: *Lampropeltis doliatus coccineus* characters in one and the same specimen; the reduction of *Diadophis amabilis stictogenys* to *D. punctatus*: the non-recognition of *Ophisaurus ventralis compressus*; the presence of white-bellied adults and young of *Farancia;* the possibility of *Heterodon niger* as an end phase of coloration and a query as to the loss of the azygous in *Heterodon browni;* the overlapping in scale rows and ocular formulae in *Storeria occipitomaculata* and *S. dekayi*; the fact that no two heads of the *Sceloporus undulatus* specimens had the same plate arrangements; and the unreliability of the mental characters in *Plestiodon*, our specimens of *P. quinquelineatus* falling into two of Cope's major groups, if determined on mental scutellation. (*Author's abstract*.)

Dr. WRIGHT's paper was illustrated by lantern slides showing views of the swamp, of its reptile inhabitants, and of the variations found in certain of the species. His communication was discussed by the Chair and by Messrs. WM. PALMER and HUGH SMITH.

The second and last paper of the program was by Dr. ARTHUR A. ALLEN, of Cornell University, *The birds of a cat-tail marsh.*

Observations on the food, nesting habits, and structure of marsh birds showing the limitations of specialized species as to food, distribution, and power of adaptability and the dominance of generalized forms were made.

Specialization in birds goes hand in hand with a high development of the instincts but with a low degree of intelligence and little adaptability. Generalization of structure on the other hand, occurs with a weaker development of the instincts, greater intelligence, and greater adaptability. The generalized, adaptable species persist through the ages while the specialized, non-adaptable are first to go. This is seen in the birds of a cat-tail marsh.

Seven stages are recognized in the formation of a marsh, represented in the mature marsh by zones of typical vegetation or plant associations, these associations following one another in regular succession. Similar associations and succession can be recognized among the birds, if we group them according to their nesting range in the marsh. Most species are not confined to one association, although reaching their maximum of abundance in it. The generalized, adaptable species have the widest range.

The various associations with their typical birds follow:

I. The Open-water Association: important in supplying forage but with no nesting birds.

II. The Shoreline Association, with the pied-billed grebe, a specialized non-adaptable species.

III. The Cat-tail Association, with the least bittern, coot, Florida gallinule, Virginia rail, sora rail, and red-winged blackbird finding optimum conditions.

IV. The Sedge Association, with the long-billed marsh wren, bittern, swamp sparrow, short-billed marsh wren, and marsh hawk.

V. The Grass Association, with the song sparrow and Maryland yellowthroat.

VI. The Alder-Willow Association, with the green heron and alder flycatcher.

VII. The Maple-Elm Association, with the black-crowned night heron and great blue heron, of the marsh birds, and a great variety woodland species.

Of all these species the most generalized in habit and structure is the red-winged blackbird. It, too, is the most adaptable and is the dominant species in the marsh. (*Author's abstract.*)

Dr. ALLEN's paper was illustrated by numerous lantern slides from photographs of the marsh, its bird inhabitants, and their homes, and by motion pictures of the least bittern and of the canvas-back and other ducks. It was discussed by Dr. L. O. HOWARD.

M. W. LYON, JR., *Recording Secretary.*

THE ANTHROPOLOGICAL SOCIETY OF WASHINGTON

At the 481st meeting of the Society, held January 19, 1915, at the Public Library, an address on *The ancient civilization of India* was delivered by SARATH KUMAR GHOSH, a member of the ancient princely house of Ghoshpara, India. About 260 persons were present. The lecturer said that the Aryans settled in India between 6000 and 4000 B. C. There, shut off from hostile neighbors by the mountains on the north and finding a fertile soil, they adopted agriculture, the beginning of civilization. Aryan civilization first began in India. In Europe, much later, the Greeks were the first to become civilized, because they too were protected by mountains. Primitive man had no distinct domestic life. A woman was not even the chattel of a particular man, but common to the community. Later, the man accepted the responsibilities of husband and father. That stage had been already reached when the Aryan race came to India, but it was there that the family became a distinct unit. The mode of government was patriarchal. Later, the heads of families made the laws; the community became a republic. Next, a group of elders were acknowledged as the leaders of the community, constituting an oligarchy. Still later, a man of supreme valor and ability was elected as king, probably at some crisis. Finally, monarchy became hereditary when the Aryans evolved a caste system.

Man first worshipped his tools and weapons; later, the forces of nature. The worship of nature was intensified when the Aryans became agriculturists, as their food depended upon the clemency of nature. The Aryans of the West, even the Greeks and Romans, never progressed beyond this stage. The Hindus, however, evolved a higher religion, worshipping a supreme and omnipotent Deity above the forces of nature. This was about 2500 B. C. By this time the Hindus had brought their language to the highest perfection. The Vedas, or hymns in praise of the Deity which were then composed, still remain the most exalted poetry in all literature. Some of the composers of the Vedas were women. The Hindus, seeing the dual form, male and female, pervading all the works of Deity, attributed a dual form to Deity itself, and regarded all its gentle qualities as feminine, such as the joy of creation. That was the apotheosis of womanhood. Not only was marriage exalted to a sacrament, but woman's part in it was greater than man's. Upon woman's good will were made dependent man's good deeds (karma), hence, his very salvation. The building of the temple was the beginning of architecture. The priest designed his altar stones after the regular forms in nature—which was the beginning of geometry. Astronomy began when the priesthood designed some star-deity to shine on the altar stone through an orifice in the roof at the moment of sacrifice. In Sanscrit literature the age of life on the earth is estimated to be four million years. Because of this habit of "thinking in millions" European critics brought the charge of gross exaggeration against the Hindus. A code of war was enunciated in the Mahabharata which enjoins upon a combatant to discard a superior weapon if his enemy has an inferior one, and forbids him to take advantage of an enemy in toil—in comparison with which the Hague Conference itself is but a code of savage warfare. Hindu civilization reached its zenith about 600 B. C. Thereupon Manu codified the laws, customs, institutions, and even the canons of art, thus unconsciously sowing the seeds of stagnation and decay.

The Aryans found in India several Turanian races whom they conquered and ultimately allowed to enter their political and social system as a subordinate caste. Only the high-caste Hindus of today are of pure Aryan descent; the masses are generally of mixed descent, in the South, almost entirely Turanian (Dravidian). Long continued immigration from Europe has caused a mixture of blood among the higher castes. Megasthenes, an early Greek ambassador, accorded the highest testimony to Hindu civilization. He noted with admiration the chastity of the women, the valor of the men, and the three stupendous facts that slavery, locks, and falsehood were unknown in India. Still later India taught the arts, philosophy, and religion from Java to Japan. Java and Siam elected Hindu princes as their kings. The present king of Siam is of direct Hindu descent. In the Philippines many words of higher meaning are of Sanscrit origin. There is a possibility of early Hindu influence having reached America, or Patal Desha, the Land of the Antipodes. Further research in Central America and Peru is needed to establish this point.

At the 482d meeting of the Society, held February 2, 1915, Dr. C. L. G. ANDERSON, of the Medical Reserve Corps, U. S. A., read an obituary on Dr. A. F. A. KING, a member of the Anthropological Society, who died in Washington December 13, 1914. Dr. KING was born in Oxfordshire, England, January 18, 1841, and came to Virginia with his parents when but ten years of age. He received degrees in medicine from the National Medical College, now merged with the George Washington University, and from the University of Pennsylvania. Beginning practice in Virginia, he helped treat the Confederate wounded after the battle of Bull Run. Soon after, he served as Acting Assistant Surgeon, U. S. A., at the Lincoln Hospital, in Washington. In 1870 he became assistant, and later, professor in obstetrics in the National Medical College, and in the University of Vermont, which positions he filled until his death, through a period of 43 years. He is survived by his widow and three children. He belonged to the Anthropological, the Medical and other scientific societies of Washington and also to foreign societies, and made many contributions to medical and scientific literature. His best known work is *A manual of obstetrics.* Among his papers of interest to anthropologists are those on *Hysteria* and *functional reversion.* He read a paper before the Anthropological Society in 1881 on *The evolution of marriage ceremony and its import.* The following year he was elected a member of the Council. He was a man of charming personality, and lived an exceptionally happy, normal, and complete life.

At the 483d meeting of the Society, held February 16, 1915, at the Public Library, a paper was read by Mr. WILLIAM H. BABCOCK on *The races of Britain,* and brief reports were made by Messrs. W. H. HOLMES, J. W. FEWKES, TRUMAN MICHELSON. and J. N. B. HEWITT on *Recent field research in anthropology and ethnology.* Mr. BABCOCK pointed out that three native languages are spoken in the island of Great Britain—English over the greater part of it, Welsh in parts of the western mountains, and Gaelic in the northern mountains—a situation which was the same in the latter part of the sixth century, excepting differences in the area of each. These languages represent three distinct waves of invasion by people who were blond when of pure blood; yet the present population contains a great number of brunets or persons of medium tint, and brunetness seems to be gaining on blondness. The best explanation seems to be that the blond conquerors found in Britain a long established and thoroughly acclimated darker population, which perhaps remained more numerous than the newcomers and certainly was better adapted to permanently transmit its characteristics. This was composed mainly of a fairly advanced neolithic race, probably from southern Europe, with whatever paleolithic stocks may have been absorbed by them. The historic conquests of Great Britain—Roman, Saxon, Danish, and Norman—have not changed the essential result, which consists of a darker substratum gradually gaining on superimposed Celtic and Teutonic layers.

Professor HOLMES outlined the work done recently in California by himself and Dr. ALEŠ HRDLIČKA. The Panama-California Exposition had assigned funds to Dr. HRDLIČKA for the preparation of an exhibit illustrating the physical history and present status of man, and to Professor HOLMES for another illustrating the practice of certain industries of the American aborigines. The materials gathered by Dr. HRDLIČKA form, it is believed, the most important exhibit within this particular field that has ever been brought together. They were collected largely through expeditions conducted by Dr. HRDLIČKA personally. The exhibits cover, in as many halls, man's evolution, the life cycle of man, man's variations, and human pathology, with dissolution. A large room is fitted out as an anthropological laboratory, lecture room, and library. The exhibit prepared by Professor HOLMES includes six lay-figure groups illustrating: Copper mining on Isle Royal, Michigan; iron and paint mining in Missouri; quarrying and working of soapstone and of obsidian in California; flint arrow makers; and stone cutters of Mitla, Mexico. These are supplemented by collections of the products of aboriginal handiwork and by two cases of casts of the sculptural work of North and South America. The exhibits, which are shown in the Arts and Crafts Building, will probably become part of a permanent museum in San Diego.

Dr. FEWKES made a trip last month primarily to examine two of the possible trails by which prehistoric cultural interchanges between Mexico and our Southwest were effected. These were the valleys of the Santa Cruz in Arizona and of the Mimbres in New Mexico, both extending north and south. The ruins from Tucson to the Mexican border along the Santa Cruz are of the Casa Grande type. The old mission of Tumacacori, south of Tucson, preserved as a national monument, must be attended to within a few years or its walls will fall. The Papagueria, or desert home of the Papagos, is one of the most instructive unexplored regions in the Southwest. In the valley of the Mimbres are ruins showing cultural resemblances between Old and New Mexico. From this valley he brought back a collection of more than 800 specimens, including 250 pieces of painted pottery which, together with specimens brought back last year, open up a new culture area, the character of which was practically unknown before.

Dr. MICHELSON gave an account of his researches among New England Indians now in Wisconsin. There are 600 Stockbridges adjoining the Menominee reservation, for the most part showing mixture of white or negro blood. Perhaps a dozen of these know genuine Stockbridge words. One old man could dictate texts. The material obtained showed that Stockbridge belongs to the Pequot-Mohegan and Natick division of Central Algonquian dialects, sharing one or two points with Delaware-Munsee. Their ethnology is forgotten. Among the 250 or more Brothertowns near Lake Winnebago, not one was found who could remember a word of his own language. No full bloods were found.

Mr. HEWITT reported concerning his trip last December to Canada on which only one survivor was found who preserved any knowledge of the Nanticoke dialect, a woman taken from the eastern shore of Chesapeake Bay. A particular investigation was made of the purpose and part of song in the ceremonial of an Iroquois lodge.

DANIEL FOLKMAR, *Secretary.*

JOURNAL

OF THE

WASHINGTON ACADEMY OF SCIENCES

Vol. V   JUNE 4, 1915   No. 11

PHYSICS.—*The emissivity of metals and oxides. IV. Iron oxide.*[1] GEORGE K. BURGESS and PAUL D. FOOTE, Bureau of Standards.

This paper is a continuation of the study of the radiometric properties of metals and oxides. By the use of radiation pyrometers and the method of microscopic melts described in the earlier papers, the total and monochromatic emissivity ($\lambda = 0.65\ \mu$) of iron oxide formed by heating iron in air has been determined at high temperatures.

Iron oxide in the spectral region $\lambda = 0.65\ \mu$ is almost "black," having an emissivity varying from 0.98 to 0.92 in the range 800° to 1200°C. The corrections necessary to apply to the readings of an optical pyrometer in this temperature range vary from 0° to 10°C. The total emissivity of iron oxide increases from 0.85 at 500°C. to 0.89 at 1200°C. The corrections necessary to apply to the readings of a radiation pyrometer in this temperature range vary from 30° to 50°C.

The temperature of the outside of the oxide layer is considerably different from that of the inside in contact with the metal, as a result, in part, of the low thermal conductivity of the oxide and, in part, undoubtedly, of the actual separation of the outside oxide layer from the metal, thus forming an air gap between the two surfaces or between two surfaces of oxide, the outer one thick and the inner one thin. The drop in temperature through

[1] To appear in full in the Bulletin of the Bureau of Standards.

the oxide layer is approximately constant for various sized samples from small iron tubes to 100 pound rails, and increases rapidly with temperature, rising to about 100° at an outside temperature of 1100°C.

PHYSICAL CHEMISTRY.—*A study of the quality of platinum ware.*[1]   GEORGE K. BURGESS and P. D. SALE, Bureau of Standards.

There has been devised a simple, thermoelectric method suitable for the determination of the purity of platinum ware.[2] This method of analysis does not mar the article tested and gives data for the classification of platinum in terms of its equivalent iridium (or rhodium) content.

There were examined by this thermoelectric method 164 pieces of platinum ware of which 26 per cent contained less than 0.5 per cent iridium and 67 per cent less than 2 per cent of iridium. Of 84 crucibles 36 per cent contained less than 0.5 per cent iridium and 87 per cent less than 2 per cent iridium.

A method has been developed for determination of the exact loss on heating of platinum crucibles, by means of a suitable electric furnace containing no heated metal parts.

Fourteen crucibles of various makes and grades were examined for loss in weight on heating and after acid treatment following each heating. Their magnetic susceptibilities were also determined. The susceptibility of pure platinum is zero and the range of susceptibility of seven "platinum" crucibles was found to be 1 to 125. The value usually given for the magnetic susceptibility of pure platinum is about 20 in the same units.

A summary of the results on losses in weight of a series of crucibles is shown in figure 1 in which each letter refers to a crucible. As abscissae, are plotted the losses in mg. per 100 cm.^{2} for 6 hours at 1200°C. and as ordinates the EMF developed against pure platinum at 1100°C.; there is also indicated on the

---

[1] To appear in full as a Scientific Paper of the Bureau of Standards. Read before the American Chemical Society, April 2. 1915.

[2] This Journal, **4**: 282. 1914.

scale of ordinates the iridium and rhodium contents of platinum corresponding to these EMF's. It is seen that for practically pure platinum the loss in weight is about 1 mg. per hour per 100 cm² at 1200° (crucibles a, b, c, d, e). For platinum containing 7.5 per cent rhodium (crucibles m and n) the loss is about 0.5 mg. per hour, while 2 per cent iridium in platinum (crucible i) increases this loss to 2.5 mg. As shown, the heating losses may be taken as approximately proportional to the iridium or rhodium content for crucibles that are practically free from iron.

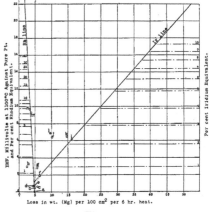

Fig. 1

Iron appears to lessen somewhat the loss of weight on heating (see crucibles g, h, j, k, l, of Fig. 1) but its presence is objectionable on account of the soluble oxide formed on the crucible surface. The chemical analysis and magnetic measurements place the crucibles in only approximately the same order as to iron content; the magnetic susceptibility is not, however, proportional to the iron content.

A microscopic examination of a crucible that has been heated will oftentimes aid in deciding whether it contains rhodium or iridium as the principle impurity, the latter usually showing heavier crystal boundaries and the former imparting a characteristic skew structure.

It appears, therefore, to be possible, from thermoelectric and microscopic examinations of a crucible, to predict its probable loss of weight on heating within limits close enough for analytical purposes.

Whether crucibles have been long in use or not, after the first two or three heatings and acid washings, appears to make little or no difference on their behavior as to losses on heating and washing.

The nature of the process of disintegration of platinum and its alloys is briefly discussed in the complete paper, and suggestions are there offered concerning the specifications of highest grade platinum crucibles, including the substitution of rhodium to 5 per cent for iridium, and the practical elimination of iron.

GEOLOGY.—*The Paleozoic section of the Ray quadrangle, Arizona.* F. L. RANSOME, Geological Survey.

Introduction. The geologic mapping of the Ray quadrangle, for folio publication as part of the Geologic Atlas of the United States, was completed in 1911. A year or more is likely to elapse, however, before the folio can be published, and as in the meantime there will be occasion in other publications to refer to the Ray geologic section, it appears desirable that a brief preliminary statement regarding this section and its nomenclature should be placed on record.

Pre-Cambrian. The fundamental rocks of the region are the Pinal schist, commonly a thinly laminated sericitic variety, and granitic rocks intrusive into the schist. The Pinal schist consists in the main of metamorphosed sedimentary rocks. Both the schist and the granitic rocks are pre-Cambrian. Whether they should be classed as Algonkian or Archean is a question as yet undecided.

Scanlan conglomerate. Resting as a rule directly on the worn surface of the pre-Cambrian crystalline rocks is the Scanlan conglomerate. The first description of this basal conglomerate appeared in the Globe report[1] where it was assigned a thickness of from 1 to 6 feet and was characterized as being composed of imperfectly rounded pebbles of white quartz, with occasional flakes of schist, in a pink arkosic matrix. The name was derived from Scanlan Pass in the northwestern part of the Globe quadrangle. The conglomerate has since been found to present considerable variation in character and thickness. In parts of

[1] U. S. Geol. Survey, Prof. Paper No. 12, pp. 30–31. 1903.

the Ray quadrangle it is 15 feet thick and contains abundant well-rounded pebbles, some of which are quartzite. In the vicinity of Roosevelt, 35 miles northwest of Ray, the conglomerate rests on granite and is 30 feet thick with well-rounded pebbles up to 9 inches in diameter. The same conglomerate has been recognized in the Santa Catalina Range about 45 miles south-southeast of Ray, where its thickness at one locality was estimated at about 12 feet. The original distribution of this basal conglomerate over an area at least 85 miles from northwest to southeast and at least 40 miles wide is well established. In some places weathered, disintegrated, and recemented granitic detritus, or arkose, lies between the conglomerate and the pre-Cambrian granite.

Pioneer shale. Overlying the Scanlan conglomerate conformably is the Pioneer shale, its type locality being Pioneer Mountain in the northeastern part of the Ray quadrangle, although the name was first applied in the Globe report.[2]

As a rule the Pioneer formation consists of dark reddish brown, more or less arenaceous shale composed largely of fine arkosic detritus with little or no calcareous material. At many places the shale grades downward into arkosic sandstone and in the Apache Mountains, northeast of Globe, 200 feet of this sandstone intervenes between the Scanlan conglomerate and the typical shale. Near Roosevelt the lower part of the formation consists of alternating beds of sandstone and shale. Abundant round or elliptical spots, of light-buff or greenish color, are highly characteristic of the shale. The average thickness of the Pioneer formation in the Ray quadrangle is about 150 feet. It is 200 feet thick, however, in the northeastern part of the quadrangle. In the canyon of Salt River, below the Roosevelt dam, the formation has an estimated thickness of 250 feet.

Barnes conglomerate. The Barnes conglomerate, first described in the Globe report[3] takes its name from Barnes Peak in the northwest part of the Globe quadrangle. In its typical development it consists of smooth pebbles of white quartz and of hard

[2] Op. cit., p. 31.
[3] Op. cit., p. 31.

vitreous quartzite, in an arkosic matrix. The pebbles are generally less than 6 inches in diameter although there are some 8 inches across. Although beautifully rounded, they are not rotund but are flat ellipsoids or round-edged disks. Small fragments or pebbles of bright red jasper, while nowhere abundant, are a very characteristic and constant feature of this conglomerate. The only rocks known that might have furnished these red fragments are certain hematitic jaspers associated with schist in the northern part of the Mazatzal Range, about 70 miles north-northwest of Ray. The matrix of the conglomerate pebbles is arkosic.

In the Ray quadrangle the Barnes conglomerate varies from 10 to 40 feet in thickness. Near Roosevelt it is from 15 to 20 feet thick.

This conglomerate is very constant in character and has a wide distribution. It has been identified in the Sierra Ancha to the north, and in the Santa Catalina Range to the south, the two localities being about 80 miles apart.

Th˙ occurrence of a deposit of this character overlying shale is itself indicative of unconformity. Beyond the inference that may be drawn from this relationship however, no evidence of unconformity has been detected.

Dripping Spring quartzite. Conformably overlying the Barnes conglomerate is a formation of quartzite and quartzitic sandstone from 400 to 500 feet thick in the Globe-Ray region. In the Globe report the name Dripping Spring quartzite was applied not only to this formation but also, through error, to a similar stratigraphically higher quartzite whose distinctness from the lower quartzite was not recognized in the intricately faulted area of the Globe quadrangle. The name Dripping Spring quartzite is here redefined as that formation which overlies the Barnes conglomerate and underlies what will presently be described as the Mescal limestone.

In the Ray quadrangle, approximately the lower third of the formation consists of hard fine-grained arkosic quartzite which, as seen in natural sections, shows no very definite division into distinct beds but does exhibit a pronounced striping, due to the alternation of dull red and dark gray or nearly black bands parallel with the planes of stratification. These as a rule are less than one foot thick. About midway between the top and bottom of the formation the striped beds are overlain by fairly massive beds, up to 6 feet thick, of even-grained buff or pinkish quartzite associated with flaggy, variegated, red, brown and gray beds and with some layers of red and grayish shale that are suggestive of the Pioneer shale. In the upper part of the formation the beds become thin, flaggy, and rusty. The Dripping Spring quartzite, as may be seen from fossil ripple-marks, sun-cracks, and worm-casts, visible on exposed surfaces of the beds, was deposited in shallow water. It contains, however, no pebbles in the Ray quadrangle, and their absence, together with the banding of the lower beds as seen in section, serves to distinguish it from the pebbly cross-bedded Troy quartzite to be described later. The formation is in most localities in the Ray quadrangle closely associated with intrusive masses of diabase, usually in the form of sheets. Some of the characteristics of the quartzite are probably due to the effect of these intrusions.

Mescal limestone. The Mescal limestone conformably overlies the Dripping Spring quartzite and in the Ray quadrangle is well exposed in the Mescal Mountains from which the formation takes its name. It is represented in the Globe quadrangle in a number of small fault blocks and as inclusions in diabase, but when the Globe report was written the limestone of these isolated masses was not known to be distinct from and older than the Devonian and Carboniferous limestones. It was consequently included in the "Globe limestone" of that report.

The Mescal is composed of thin beds that have a varied range of color but are persistently cherty, the siliceous segregations as a rule forming irregular layers parallel with the bedding planes. On weathered surfaces these layers stand out in relief and give to the limestone the rough gnarled banding that is its most characteristic feature. The general hue of the formation is gray or white, but some beds are yellow, some buff and some rusty brown. Most of the Mescal limestone is magnesian and a part of the formation is dolomite, as may be seen at the Roosevelt dam where the beds are well exposed in the spillway cuts.

Between the limestone and the overlying Troy quartzite is a layer of decomposed vesicular basalt whose maximum observed thickness is from 75 to 100 feet. Although the basalt in places is much thinner than this, the flow was apparently coextensive with the Mescal limestone throughout the Ray and Globe quadrangles, and has been recognized as far north as Roosevelt. This basalt, owing to its small thickness, has been mapped with the Mescal limestone in the Ray quadrangle although it is not included in the definition of that formation. The average thickness of the Mescal limestone is about 225 feet in the Ray quadrangle.

The Mescal limestone has been recognized in the Sierra Ancha and in the Santa Catalina Range. It is in part lithologically identical with and is probably the stratigraphic equivalent of the Abrigo limestone of Bisbee and Tombstone, which contains Middle Cambrian fossils. This correlation, however, is not regarded as sufficiently well established to justify definite application of the name Abrigo in the Ray area.

In all of the regions where it has been identified the Mescal limestone has been extensively invaded by intrusive sheets of diabase and has suffered dismemberment as an effect of the intrusion. In parts of the Ray quadrangle the formation is represented only by detached masses of strata included in diabase.

Troy quartzite. The name of this formation, which lies above the Mescal limestone, is derived from Troy Mountain in the Dripping Spring Range. Everywhere in the Ray quadrangle it is separated from the limestone by the basalt flow and this may possibly indicate some slight unconformity. No evidence of erosion, however, has been detected either below or above the basalt, which may have flowed under water.

The beds of the Troy quartzite range from thin flaggy or shaly layers to cross-bedded pebbly strata from 25 to 50 feet thick. On the whole the thicker beds are characteristic of the lower and middle portions of the formation. The upper part is invariably composed of thin generally yellowish to rusty, worm-marked, shaly quartzite indicative of a change in sedimentation preparatory to the deposition of the succeeding Devonian lime-stone. The most characteristic material of these upper beds is a fine-grained, unevenly colored, pink and green quartzite in layers an inch or two thick separated by films of olive-gray shale, whose cleavage surfaces are ridged and knotted with numerous worm casts. The most noteworthy features of the thicker beds are their generally pebbly character, which is a use-ful means of distinguishing isolated exposures of the Troy quartz-ite from the, locally at least, pebble-free Dripping Spring quartzite, and their conspicuous cross bedding. While the Dripping Spring quartzite is arkosic the Troy quartzite shows little or no feld-spar. In the Ray and Globe quadrangles the name quartzite is generally applicable to this formation, but farther north, near Roosevelt and in the Sierra Ancha, it is essentially a sandstone.

The average thickness of the Troy quartzite in the Ray quad-rangle is estimated at 400 feet.

General comment on preceding formations. The formations just described, from the Scanlan conglomerate at the base to the Troy quartzite at the top, constitute an apparently conformable series. The name Apache group was applied to these beds in the Globe report, although at that time the Troy quartzite was not distinguished from the Dripping Spring quartzite and con-sequently did not figure as an individual unit in the group. Moreover, the Mescal limestone, supposed then to be above all of the quartzite, was grouped with the Devonian and Car-boniferous limestones of the "Globe limestone." As revised the Apache group now includes, from the base up, the Scanlan conglomerate, the Pioneer shale, the Barnes conglomerate, the Dripping Spring quartzite, the Mescal limestone, and the Troy quartzite.

No identifiable fossils have been found in the beds of the Apache group, but from the facts that it underlies the Devonian, overlies schists and granitic rocks, and appears to be equivalent at least in part to the known Cambrian of the Bisbee District and of the Grand Canyon, it is provisionally classed as Cambrian.

If the Mescal limestone is the same as the Abrigo limestone, the Troy quartzite of course may represent Ordovician or Silurian time, but in the absence of fossils or distinct unconformities it appears safer to consider this quartzite as provisionally of Cambrian age. The entire group has been considered Algonkian,[4] partly because of a supposed resemblance to the Algonkian rocks of the Grand Canyon and partly because the quartzites at Roosevelt were erroneously thought to be unconformably overlain by the Carboniferous limestone. A. B. Reagan[5] also appears to have included a part of the group in the Algonkian while calling what is here designated the Troy quartzite, Tonto (Cambrian).

It is possible of course that a part of the group may be pre-Cambrian, but the apparent conformability of the whole group with the overlying Devonian, taken in connection with the great unconformity between the basal Cambrian of the Grand Canyon with the Algonkian (Unkar and Chuar), lends little support to this view. Additional improbability is cast upon it by the discovery in 1914 that a series of quartzites and shales in the northern part of the Mazatzal Range, hitherto undescribed, are unconformably overlain by some of the formations of the Apache group. The results of this reconnaissance will be brought out more fully in another paper. The hard quartzitic pebbles in the Barnes conglomerate evidently came from the erosion of these older quartzites of the Mazatzal Range. As at present defined therefore the Apache group embraces the apparently conformable series of supposedly Cambrian sedimentary rocks of central Arizona. Should some of the beds turn out to be other than Cambrian the group name will have to be correspondingly restricted or may perhaps be abandoned as no longer a convenient designation for a major stratigraphic unit.

Martin limestone. Conformably overlying the Troy quartzite is a series of limestone beds, some of which carry abundant and

[4] Lee, W. T., Underground waters of Salt River Valley, Arizona. U. S. Geol. Survey, Water-Supply Paper No. 136, p. 96, and fig. 11 on page 97. 1905.

[5] Geology of the Fort Apache region, Arizona. Amer. Geologist **32**: 277. 1903.

characteristic Devonian fossils. These link the formation so closely with the Martin limestone of the Bisbee region as to warrant the extension of the name Martin limestone into the Ray-Globe region.

In the Ray quadrangle the formation is comparatively thin-bedded and is divisible into two nearly equal parts, recognizable in natural sections by a difference in color. The prevailing hue of the lower division is light yellowish gray, while the upper division, less uniform in tint, displays alternations of deeper yellow and darker gray. No identifiable fossils have been found in the lower division which consequently can not be regarded as unequivocably Devonian. The top bed of the formation is a yellow calcareous shale, which breaks up on exposure into minute thin flakes and which consequently has no prominent outcrops. The yellow color is characteristic of all natural exposures, although before weathering the shale is gray. Being overlain by thick-bedded cliff-making Carboniferous limestone, the bed of shale is in many places concealed by talus and its thickness has not been exactly determined. It may be from 15 to 20 feet.

The average thickness of the Martin limestone in the Ray quadrangle is 325 feet, which compares closely with the 340 feet found at Bisbee.

Devonian, presumably the Martin limestone, has been found by Prof. C. F. Tolman Jr.,[6] in the Santa Catalina Range. The presence of the Martin limestone has been fully established also in the Roosevelt section by the finding, in 1914, of sufficient fossils to confirm a lithologic and indecisive paleontologic identification made a year earlier. A list of the fossils, as determined by Dr. Edwin Kirk, and a fuller discussion of the extent and correlation of the Devonian will be published later.

Tornado limestone. The Devonian Martin limestone is conformably overlain by thick-bedded light gray limestone that is nearly everywhere a prominent cliff-maker in the Ray-Globe region. The name here used is derived from Tornado Peak, in the Dripping Spring Range. The Tornado limestone as exposed

[6] Unpublished manuscript of Tucson folio.

in the Ray quadrangle has a maximum thickness of at least 1000 feet. As its upper limit is a surface of erosion dating in part from early Mesozoic time, the limestone was probably at one time much thicker than at present. It is of Carboniferous age. The basal division is about 75 feet thick and forms the lower part of the scarp that in this region is so prevalent a feature of the Carboniferous outcrop. Under the action of erosion this division behaves as a single massive bed, but in reality it is made up of alternating dark and light gray layers, a foot or two thick, which in cliff faces give a banded appearance. This member with a few transitional beds at its top is succeeded by a very massive member, fully 100 feet thick, within which, as exposed in cliffs, there is as a rule scarcely more than a suggestion of divisional bedding planes. These two members together constitute the principal cliff-forming part of the Carboniferous limestone. The third division consists of beds generally thinner than those in the other two divisions but not separable from them by any marked lithological distinction. Thin layers of calcareous shale separate some of the beds but these are a very subordinate part of the formation.

The beds of the two lower divisions carry many fragments of crinoid stems and less abundant rugose corals, with long-winged spirifers and *Rhipidomella*. In the upper division appear different species of *Productus* and *Spirifer*, *Derbya crassa*, *Composita subtilita*, and *Fusulina*. According to Dr. George H. Girty two faunas are represented, one Mississippian and the other early Pennsylvanian. Had it proved practicable to map separately the Mississippian and Pennsylvanian portions of the formation the corresponding names Escabroso limestone and Naco limestone, used in the Bisbee quadrangle, might have been appiicable in the Ray quadrangle.

By far the greater part of the formation as exposed in the Ray quadrangle belongs to the Mississippian.

MINERALOGY.—*Nephelite crystals from Monte Ferru, Sardinia.* H. S. WASHINGTON and H. E. MERWIN, Geophysical Laboratory.

A trachytic phonolite forms the upper part of a rounded hill immediately south of Monte Enzu, the culminating point of Monte Ferru.[1] This rock is dense, light gray, aphyric, and composed essentially, as shown by the microscope, of tables of soda-orthoclase, with interstitial nephelite, and small amounts of minute diopside crystals. There are numerous small miarolitic cavities, in which are found small (1–2 mm.) well-formed nephelite crystals, the walls being lined with minute tables of orthoclase and crystals of pyroxene and titanite.

More than one hundred crystals were picked out for examination, twenty-five being selected for the crystallographic and optical examination, and the balance for chemical analysis, the former being undertaken by Merwin and the latter by Washington.

The nephelite crystals are stout, almost equant, prisms, from 1 to 2 mm. in diameter and weighing, on the average, 3 mg. each. They are fresh and clear, except for inclusions of minute augite and titanite crystals.

Usually not more than 4 faces giving satisfactory signals were found on a crystal. The prism appeared vertically striated; the base in all cases gave multiple signals, possessed a pearly luster, and showed grooves parallel to the edges in some cases. The unit pyramid $(10\bar{1}1)$, and the pyramids $(10\bar{1}2)$ and $(20\bar{2}1)$ gave good signals. 12 angles $(10\bar{1}0) \wedge (10\bar{1}1)$ from excellent signals varied between 45°39′ and 45°58′, average 45°49′. 13 other angles from less accurate settings varied between 45°30′ and 46°15′, average 45°51′. 7 angles $(10\bar{1}0) \wedge (10\bar{1}2)$ varied between 26°55′ and 27°18′, average 27°10′. Between $(10\bar{1}0)$ and $(20\bar{2}1)$ 4 angles varied between 63°30′ and 64°20′, average 64°10′. The complements of these observed angles and the corresponding calculated crystallographic constants appear below. With them are placed those for nephelite from Monte

---

[1] For a description of the lavas of this volcano, see H. S. Washington, Am. J. Sci., **39**: 513. 1915.

Somma (Vesuvius), the only other nephelite for which crystallographic constants have been established; and also 4 angles which are fairly consistent with each other measured by Strüver[2] on two crystals from the Alban Hills.

	Monte Ferru		Monte Somma	Alban Hills
	obs.	*calc.*		
$c(0001) \wedge p(10\bar{1}1)$ =	44°10′	44°11′	44° 4′–	40° 1′ 43°51′
" $\wedge q(10\bar{1}2)$ =	62°51′	62°47′	62°42′–	·62°39′
" $\wedge z(20\bar{2}1)$ =	25°50′	25°55′	25°50′ ·	25°41′
$\dot{c}$ =	0.841		0.8386[3]	0.834

Differences in $\dot{c}$ are not surprising in view of the differences in composition shown later.

Refractive indices were determined on fragments of several crystals of the nephelite. $\epsilon = 1.529$, $\omega = 1.532$–3· From independent measurements on two crystals $\omega - \epsilon = 0.0026$. Comparison with other nephelites of determined composition is made in Table 1. The refractive indices are considerably lower than have been observed in other nephelites. A systematic investi-

TABLE 1

	ϵ	ω
Monte Ferru..	1.529	1.532–3
Artificial Soda Nephelite[4].........................	1.533	1.537
Artificial Soda-Lime Nephelite[4]....................	1.539	1.537
Monte Somma[5]......................................	1.5376	1.5421
Magnet Cove, Ark.[6].·..............................	1.5420	1.5468

gation of the relation of composition to optical properties is being undertaken. Available results are as yet too few for discussion.

A complete chemical analysis was made on a batch of 60 crystals weighing in all 0.1865 gram. These were dried at 110°

[2] Zeitschr. Kryst. **1**: 240.

[3] Koksharov, quoted by Dana, gives 0.8389; Baumhauer gives 0.8383, Zeitschr. Kryst., **18**: 613.

[4] N. L. Bowen, Am. J. Sci. **33**: 566. 1912.

[5] Average of 4 accordant determinations. See "Rock Minerals," Iddings; and Zeitschr.. Kryst., **22**: 333; **53**: 426.

[6] See "Rock Minerals," Iddings.

and dissolved in hydrochloric acid, and the analysis was conducted by the ordinary methods. Magnesia was not determined owing to lack of material. The optical study of the insoluble portion showed that the augite and titanite crystals had not been attacked, so no correction is needed for impurities introduced from this source. The results are as follows, an average of four out of many fairly accordant analyses of Vesuvian nephelite being given for comparison.

	A	B	C	Ba		
SiO_2	40.27	43.34	42.93	0.722	0.722	2.26
Al_2O_3	31.05	33.45	33.84	0.320	0.320	1.00
Fe_2O_3	2.42	2.60	0.40	0.016		
MgO	–	–	0.15			
CaO	0.81	0.87	2.08	0.015		
Na_2O	15.11	16.28	15.39	0.263	0.315	0.99
K_2O	3.22	3.46	5.08	0.037		
H_2O	–	–	0.18			
Insol	7.51	–	0.12			
	100.39	99.99	100.17			

A. Nephelite. Monte Ferru, Sardinia. H. S. Washington analyst.
B. Same, calculated free from insoluble.
C. Nephelite. Monte Somma. J. Morozewicz, analyst. Bull. Acad. Sci. Crac. **8**: 979–983. 1907.
Ba. Molecular ratios of B.

BOTANY.—*The North American tribes and genera of Amarantha-ceae.*[1] PAUL C. STANDLEY, National Museum.

The North American representatives of the family Amaranthaceae have received little attention from American botanists in either early or recent years. This may have resulted from the unattractive aspect of most of the plants composing the group, but more probably from the circumstance that their generic and specific characters are based chiefly upon very minute floral structures. Because of the small size and often complicated structure of their flowers the plants have, indeed, been considered a "difficult" group, when, as a matter of fact, they are remarkably easy of recognition, and of disposition, provided that generic limits are agreed upon. The species, as a rule, are sharply differentiated. Confusion as to generic limits

[1] Published by permission of the Secretary of the Smithsonian Institution.

has resulted largely from an attempt to recognize in certain tribes too large a number of genera, these based upon vegetative or inconstant characters.

The only monograph of the North American Amaranthaceae is that of Uline and Bray, which appeared about 20 years ago in the *Botanical Gazette*.[2] The conclusions reached by these authors need scarcely be modified now except for certain changes of names necessitated by modern systems of nomenclature. The species treated, however, included only a small part of those found in tropical North America. Moquin had in 1849[3] described all the North American Amaranthaceae then known, in his monograph of the whole family, but naturally many additional species have been discovered in the intervening 66 years, about 155 species being known in North America at the present time. Several of the tribes, particularly the Amarantheae, reach their highest development on this continent. The family being chiefly tropical, South America possesses a larger number of species than North America. Many species are to be found also in Africa and Australia, and a few in Europe and Asia.

The following arrangement of tribes and genera is proposed by the writer for use in a monograph of the family now in preparation for the North American Flora:

I. CELOSIEAE. Differentiated from all other tribes of the family by the presence of 2 or more ovules in the ovary, instead of a single ovule. Only ône genus, Celosia, occurs in North America, being represented by 6 species.

II. AMARANTHEAE. Five genera are represented in North America: Lagrezia, Chamissoa, Amaranthus, Acnida, and Acanthochiton. .

1. Lagrezia has not been reported previously from outside of Africa, nor has it always been referred to the Amarantheae. Moquin placed it in this tribe, but Dr. Schinz in his treatment of the famly in Engler and Prantl's *Natürlichen Pflanzenfamilien* considered it a synonym of Celosia. There is no doubt that Lagrezia is closely related to that genus, but it seems to be quite distinct in having only a single ovule in the ovary. If the Celosieae and Amarantheae are to be maintained

[2] 19: 267-272. 1894; 20: 155-161, 337-344, 449-453. 1895; 21: 348-356 1896.
[3] In DC. Prodr. 13[2]: 231-424.

as separate tribes, Lagrezia must be therefore placed in the latter.   In Dr. Schinz's key to the tribes there is no means of telling to which of them a plant with a 1-seeded utricle should be referred.   In 1895 Dr. J. N. Rose described a new plant from Manzanillo, Mexico, which he called *Celosia ? monosperma*.[4]   This should be referred to the genus here discussed, and may be known as **Lagrezia monosperma**.   The few other species of the genus are natives of Madagascar and southern Africa.

2. Chamissoa is represented in tropical North America by two species, the widely distributed *Chamissoa altissima*, and *C. maximiliani*, known within our limits only from Costa Rica.   *Chamissoa macrocarpa* H. B. K. has been reported frequently from the West Indies and Central America, but the specimens so determined are *C. altissima*.

3. Amaranthus seems to have its center of distribution in the southwestern United States and northern Mexico.   A large number of species are found in the somewhat similar règion of Argentina, a number that doubtless will be increased when that country is better explored botanically.   About 40 species are known from North America.   Most of these are common weeds of cultivated land, but several species are known only from the southwestern mesas and foothills.

Several segregates from Amaranthus have been proposed by different authors, notably Mengea, Euxolus, and Scleropus.   With our present knowledge of the group it seems impossible to maintain any of these genera, for the characters depended upon to separate them will not hold when all the species of the genus are taken into consideration.

4. Acnida is a wholly North American genus.   Five species are found in salt marches along the eastern and southern coasts of the United States, on the southwest coast of Mexico, and in the West Indies.   Three others occur in the central and southwestern United States.   The genus is very closely related to Amaranthus, differing only in the absence of a perianth in the pistillate flowers.   *Acnida tuberculata* is so closely allied to *Amaranthus torreyi* that it is practically impossible to distinguish staminate plants of the two species, whose ranges largely overlap.

5. Acanthochiton consists of a single species, a native of the sandhills of western Texas, New Mexico, Arizona, and northeastern Mexico. It is distinguished from Acnida only by a vegetative character—the large size and peculiar form of the bracts; but it has always been accepted as a valid genus.

[4] Contr. U. S. Nat. Herb. **1**: 352.

III. Centrostachydeae. Two genera of this tribe occur in North America, Centrostachys and Cyathula. The group has always been known as the Achyrantheae; but since the name Achyranthes must be applied to a genus of the Gomphreneae, as explained recently by the writer,[5] it is necessary to form a new tribal name, typified by the best known genus of the group.

The Centrostachydeae reach their highest development in Africa, the East Indies, and Australia. Two Old World species of Centrostachys have become established in tropical and subtropical North America. Two species of Cyathula are found in the same region, *C. prostrata*, a native of the Old World, being established in Jamaica and Panama; while *C. achyranthoides*, an American species, occurs in the Greater Antilles, where it may be adventive, and ranges from southern Mexico to Panama, Brazil, and Chile.

IV. Brayulineae. This is a new tribe, here proposed for the genus Brayulinea, better known by the name Guilleminea, which, unfortunately, is a homonym. The genus is related to the Gomphreneae, with which it has usually been placed, but is distinguished by the perigynous androecium. Apparently Dr. Schinz at one time considered this segregation, for in his key to the tribes of the Amaranthaceae in Engler and Prantl's *Natürlichen Pflanzenfamilien*[6] he separates the tribe Guillemineae. When the text for this part of the family appeared, at a later date than the key, we find no mention of such a tribe, the genus Guilleminea being referred to the Gomphreneae.

In general appearance the species of Brayulinea are quite similar to those of Gossypianthus. One species is found in North America.

V. Froelichieae. It seems desirable to place the genus Froelichia. in a tribe separate from the Gomphreneae, to which it has always been referred. The group is characterized by the gamophyllous perianth which becomes indurated and variously appendaged in fruit, characters which are not found in any Gomphreneae.

The genus is an American one, seven species occurring in southern North America, with others in South America. Most of the species are closely interrelated and are separated with difficulty. It is still a matter of doubt how specific limits are to be determined with precision in the genus.

VI. Gomphreneae. Half of the North American genera of the family fall into this tribe, which is, however, best represented in north-

[5] Journ. Wash. Acad. Sci. **5**: 72–76. 1915.
[6] **3**[1a]: 97. 1893.

ern South America. Different authors have proposed very different divisions of genera for the group, but the characters used often have been vegetative or else they proved unreliable as additional species have been discovered. Martius, who was perhaps the most careful student of the group, proposed a large number of genera, based chiefly upon Brazilian species, but scarcely any of his genera are recognized today. The treatment here proposed follows closely that suggested by Otto Kuntze,[7] which was later adopted by Dr. Schinz, and very recently by Dr. Stuchlík.[8] It is based almost wholly upon flower structure, and chiefly upon the characters of the gynoecium and androecium. The North American genera are ten in number, as follows.

1. Cladothrix is closely related to both Gossypianthus and Achyranthes and is distinguished principally by the form of the inflorescence, the flowers being glomerate rather than spicate or capitate. Three species occur in the southwestern United States and in northern Mexico.

2. Gossypianthus is wholly North American, four species being known. One is confined to Cuba, a second is common to Hispaniola, the southwestern United States, and northeastern Mexico, while the other two are found in Texas and Oklahoma.

3. Pfaffia consists of a large number of South American species of diverse habit, some of them resembling the better known species of Gomphrena, while others are tall shrubs or vines. In Mexico and Central America there is a single species which closely resembles some of the species of Iresine. Hebanthe of Martius must be considered a synonym of Pfaffia, although not all the plants described under Hebanthe are true Pfaffias. One plant described by Hemsley as a Hebanthe is to be referred to an older species of Iresine. The proper place of two other Mexican species described by Hemsley is still uncertain. Dr. Watson in 1883 applied the name *Hebanthe palmeri*[9] to another Mexican plant which is not a Pfaffia, but should be known as **Iresine palmeri.**

4. Achyranthes has been discussed by the writer very recently[10] and need not be treated further here.

5. Woehleria is one of the so-called "monotypic" genera. It is endemic in Cuba and is apparently very rare. In general appearance

[7] Rev. Gen. Pl. **2**: 534–545. 1891.

[8] Repert. Sp. Nov. Fedde **12**: 350–359. 1913.

[9] Proc. Amer. Acad. **18**: 144.

[10] Journ. Wash. Acad. Sci. **5**: 72–76. 1915.

the plant is similar to some species of Achyranthes, but the androecium consists of only a single stamen, and the stigma is bilobate rather than capitate.

6. Gomphrena is represented in North America by some fifteen species. Thirteen of these are low plants, with usually large, sessile, and globose heads, closely related to the cultivated globe amaranth, *Gomphrena globosa*. The other two are tall plants with narrow, long-pedunculate, cylindric heads, closely simulating certain forms of Achyranthes. A large number of species of Gomphrena have been described from South America, no less than 66 being reported from Brazil 40 years ago.

7. Iresine is one of the most interesting genera of the Amaranthaceae, chiefly because the plants are of an attractive rather than a "weedy" appearance. About 30 species are known within our limits. The segregates Trommsdorffia and Rosea were proposed by Martius, but it seems impracticable to maintain them as distinct genera.

8. Dicraurus is distinguished from all other genera of the Gomphreneae by the alternate leaves; otherwise it is too closely related to Iresine, and, indeed, it seems probable that ultimately it may be united with that genus. Two species are known, *D. leptocladus* and *D. alternifolius*. The first, a plant of western Texas and northeastern Mexico, has all its leaves alternate; but in the second, a native of Lower California, while most of the leaves are alternate, the lower ones frequently are opposite.

9. Lithophila was based by Swartz upon a plant which is common on the seashores of the West Indies. Some authors have referred the genus to Iresine, but it may be maintained because of the strongly compressed perianth and 2 rather than 5 stamens. Besides the type species, three others, of somewhat diverse habit, are known, all inhabitants of the Galapagos Islands: **Lithophila radicata** (*Alternanthera radicata* Hook. f., 1847), **L. rigida** (*Alternanthera rigida* Rob. & Greenm., 1895), and **L. subscaposa** (*Alternanthera subscaposa* Hook. f., 1847).

10. Philoxerus was proposed by Robert Brown in 1840. The plants of this group have usually been referred to Iresine and Lithophila. Philoxerus seems, however, a valid genus, distinguished from Iresine not only by habit but by the compressed perianth, and from Lithophila by the different structure of the androecium and by the stipitate flowers. Many species of the genus have been proposed, but how many of them are valid is an unsettled question. In North America only a single one is known.

ECONOMICS.—*Efficiency as a factor in organic evolution. II.*[12]
ALFRED J. LOTKA.

ERRORS OF VALUATION

There remains to be discussed the effect upon r or errors of the sense of values, or errors of valuation. We must here apply a different method from the one employed in the case of errors of observation, operation, and mentation, since errors of valuation influence r not through the productive efficiencies of the individual in several activities but through the manner in which the individual distributes his efforts among different activities.

We may proceed as follows:

If an individual had a perfect sense of values he would arrange his affairs, distribute his labor, so that r, the rate of increase per head of the race, were a maximum.[13]

$$\left.\begin{array}{ll} \text{Let } x_1, x_2 \quad . \quad . \quad . & \text{be quantities of commodities produced and consumed per head per unit of time} \\[1em] L_1, L_2 \quad . \quad . \quad . & \text{the labor spent on each commodity per head per unit of time} \\[1em] f_1, f_2 \quad . \quad . \quad . & \text{the fatigue produced per head per unit of time by labor } L_1, L_2 \text{ per unit of time.} \end{array}\right\} \quad (16)$$

Then the individual with a perfect sense of values would, for each commodity, make

$$\left(\frac{\partial r}{\partial x_j} \cdot \frac{\partial x_j}{\partial L_j} + \frac{\partial r}{\partial f_j} \cdot \frac{\partial f_j}{\partial L_j} \right) dL_j = 0 \qquad (17)$$

for any arbitrary small dL_j.

$$\left(\frac{\partial r}{\partial f} \text{ is in general a minus quantity} \right).$$

[12] Part I of this paper appeared in this Journal, Vol. 5, no. 10, May 19, 1915, pp. 360-368.
[13] Compare this Journal, 1914, loc. cit.

Let us write (17) in the form

$$(vE + v'E')dL = 0 \qquad (18)^{14}$$

$$vE + v'E' \quad = 0 \qquad (19)$$

The problem before us is, Suppose the individual values the commodity not at v per unit, but at $v + \delta\epsilon$, what will be the effect upon r?

We have:

$$\delta r = \frac{\partial r}{\partial \epsilon}\, \delta\epsilon \qquad (20)$$

$$= \frac{\partial r}{\partial x} \cdot \frac{\partial x}{\partial \epsilon}\, \delta\epsilon \qquad (21)$$

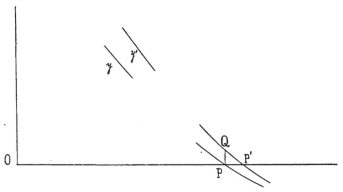

Fig. 1

Consider a graph (see figure 1):

$$y = vE + v'E' \qquad (22)$$

$$y' = (v + \delta\epsilon)\, E + v'E' \qquad (23)$$

If the individual acted in accordance with the curve y, the *true* curve, he would consume

$$x = OP \qquad (24)$$

[14] The quantity $E = \frac{\partial x}{\partial L}$ in equation (18) measures *marginal* efficiency and thus differs from E_j in equation (4), which measures total efficiency.

Instead of this he acts in accordance with the slightly erroneous curve y', and hence consumes

$$x' = OP' \tag{25}$$

so that we may write

$$\delta x = x' - x = OP' - OP = PP' \tag{26}$$

This, because he makes an error in

$$y = vE + v'E' \tag{22}$$

making it

$$y' = (v + \delta\epsilon) E + v'E' \tag{23}$$

so that

$$y' - y = E \, \delta\epsilon = PQ \tag{27}$$

$$\delta\epsilon = \frac{PQ}{E} \tag{28}$$

$$\frac{\partial x}{\partial\epsilon} = \frac{PP'}{PQ} E = - E \bigg/ \frac{dy}{dx} \tag{29}$$

Substituting in (21) we have:

$$\frac{\partial r}{\partial\epsilon} = - \frac{\partial r}{\partial x} E \bigg/ \frac{d}{dx} (vE + v'E') \tag{30}$$

$$= - vE \bigg/ \frac{d}{dx} (vE + v'E') \tag{31}$$

which is the desired expression for the differential coefficient $\frac{\partial r}{\partial\epsilon}$ for the case that ϵ denotes an error of valuation.

LIMITATIONS OF THE METHOD HERE DEVELOPED

In conclusion the writer wishes to consider the limitations of the method presented above and to point out their significance and to indicate at what points there is room for further development.

1. We have restricted our attentions to routine or habitual activities, in particular to such as have a definite economic significance.

On reflection it is found that this restriction in practise is almost no restriction at all, that only a vanishingly small proportion of our activities fall outside the scope thus circumscribed. If we actually consider one by one our various activities of a common working day, or for the matter of that of a holiday, we find that, almost without exception, even the most trivial of them are either bought or sold. My breakfast is bought at the butcher's and grocer's. I pay rent for the privilege of sitting at table in my dining room. I pay carfare to be conveyed from my house to my office. Every hour spent at the office is paid for in salary. At night there is again the item of carfare, food, rent, amusements, etc. It is difficult or impossible to find an action ever so trivial which has not a definite money value.

2. A seemingly more serious limitation than the one just considered might seem to lie in the fact that much of the argument presented has been sketched out on a background of examples taken from the special case of the human species. A well developed economic system among living organisms is peculiar to civilized man. It might therefore appear at first sight as if arguments and conclusions involving economic concepts could in no sense be applied to such organisms as those higher animals which in their general habits and characteristics do more or less resemble man.

It must be admitted that in practise this restriction has a real significance. But the difference between the actions of man and those of some of the highly developed species of animals is not so much that the one possesses a sense of values and the others do not, as, that in the case of the one—man—we have in market prices a definite and readily accessible standard of measurement of the values attached by him to various commodities, while in the case of the others—the animals—we have no such readily accessible standard of measurement. To argue that because we have at present no ready means of ascertaining the value set by a given animal upon a given material of consumption, therefore no such value exists, would be parallel to the contention that because men were at one time unable to measure the distance from the earth to the moon, therefore there was no such distance. In the matter of the measurement of values we have not yet reached the epoch where the means for measuring values of materials to animals have been devised. But there is nothing inherently impossible about the solution of the problem of measuring these values, and, in fact, if it seemed worth while, suggestions could be made at this juncture as to how the first crude steps at any rate in this direction might be taken.

Furthermore, since an objective standard of value has been furnished in a previous communication, a standard which is quite independent of the subjective estimate of values and which applies with absolute impartiality to any species, there is in principle no difficulty whatever involved in extending our argument from man to other members of the animal kingdom. The difficulties which arise are only those of translating our results into concrete practical examples.

3. Several restrictions in the scope within which our arguments are strictly applicable are introduced through the fact that we have made use of Jevons' equation for the distribution of labor in different pursuits, or its equivalent. The first of the limitations thus introduced is that our arguments strictly apply only to a community in which there is absolutely free competition and no kind of a monopoly.

In the case of animals this condition is probably in most cases approximately fulfilled.

In the case of a highly developed industrial community of the human species this assumption is very far from the truth. The case of such a community requires special consideration by more complicated methods, and further work in this direction will have to be done to complete the discussion. The writer hopes that perhaps he may be able to take up this phase of the problem on another occasion. In the meantime the simple case here considered illustrates the principles at work just as well as a more complicated case.

4. Another limitation introduced by the use of Jevons' equation is the fact that our arguments apply only to a steady state, in which consumption equals production.

As a matter of fact conditions in nature in all probability approach a steady state in most cases. This is almost inevitable, since a persistent excess of production over consumption would lead to an ultimately unbounded accumulation of stock. It is of course imaginable that there might be periods of excessive production alternating with periods of excessive consumption. But there are good reasons to believe that such fluctuations, in so far as they do occur, do not exceed certain limits, so that as a first approximation, at any rate, conditions may be regarded as steady. The steady state is a permanent state. Other states in general are transient. For this reason a particular interest attaches to the steady state, which fully justifies any *special* attention paid to it. At the same time it presents the simplest problem and should therefore receive *first* attention. A precisely similar state of affairs to that which confronts us here is familiar to every student of thermodynamics in connection with the theory of Change of State.

5. Certain limitations are introduced by an incompleteness of the Jevons' equation. This equation takes account of only two kinds of terms, those relating to pleasure derived from consumption, and those derived from displeasure bound up with production. Many activities are sufficiently covered by two such classes of terms, but there are certain notable exceptions.

For the individual may labor without any definite calculation of reward, for the mere love of the labor, under the impulse of the *instinct of workmanship*, production itself being a source of pleasure. A flippant disciple of modern industrialism might perhaps remark that cases of this kind are so rare that little error is introduced in leaving them out of account. The writer believes that this is a misconception; that the *instinct of workmanship* fulfils a very definite function in the scheme of nature:

The individual can assist in preserving the species by acts aimed at self preservation; certain egoistic instincts take care of that.

Or, he may assist in preserving the species by acts of service to other individuals of his species. Another set of instincts, altruistic instincts, have been evolved to take care of this. They take various shapes and manifest themselves in different phases of the life of the individual. One of them is the *instinct of workmanship*, which is found not only in man, but also in other species possessing a definite social system, such as the bee.

There would probably be no difficulty in overcoming this limitation of the Jevons' equation by introducing additional terms into it. We shall not carry this out on the present occasion.

6. Lastly, Jevons' equation is built up on a plan which seems to involve the assumption that the individual is a perfectly rational being, weighing all his actions and selecting some definite course after having considered all avenues open to him and the consequences to which they lead.

In point of fact this is far from being the truth even for far-seeing man. Not only are there many circumstances beyond our ken which would enter into the determination of the actions of a more perfect being, but even many of the facts plainly known to the individual may fail to be weighed by him in framing his actions, simply because no man can possibly have the entire contents of his mind consciously before him at all times, or even at any time. In other cases the individual may be aware of certain remote consequences of his actions, but the lure of the immediate gratification derived from such actions may so completely outweigh the promptings arising from a consideration of remote consequences as to induce him to follow a course which yields him a net result of pain rather than pleasure, loss rather than gain. Indeed, nature tricks us into actions of this kind to fulfil her own ends, which are to benefit the species, at the cost of the individual if need be.

Without going into details it may be suggested that this limitation also is, in principle, at least, not as serious as at first sight appears.

In so far as it relates to the inability of the individual to fully realize all the factors which might with advantage be taken into account in framing his actions, it can probably be taken care of under the heading of errors of observation, mentation, and operation.

On the other hand those errors which a man commits in giving undue weight to immediate gratification when in conflict with the prospect of more remote benefits these are plainly errors of valuation and as such fall within the scope of the method here developed.

REFERENCES

Under this heading it is proposed to include, by author, title, and citation, references to all scientific papers published in or emanating from Washington. It is requested that authors coöperate with the editors by submitting titles promptly, following the style used below. These references are not intended to replace the more extended abstracts published elsewhere in this JOURNAL

ZOOLOGY

HANSEN, H. J. *The Crustacea Euphausiacea of the U. S. National Museum.* Proceedings of the U. S. National Museum **48**: 59-114, plates 1-4. January 19, 1915. (Primarily an enumeration of the localities with remarks on distribution for every species represented; with descriptions, and in some cases figures as well, of several forms.—W. S.)

HARRING, H. K. *Report on Rotatoria from Panama, with descriptions of new species.* Proceedings of the U. S. National Museum **47**: 525-564, plates 16-24. December 15, 1914. (Describes nineteen new species; also contains notes on distribution, and hints on preservation.—W. S.)

KOEHLER, R. *A contribution to the study of ophiurans of the U. S. National Museum.* Bulletin 84, U. S. National Museum. Pp. i-vii, 1-173, 18 plates. April 9, 1914. (Deals chiefly with littoral and deep-sea forms from the Caribbean Sea; twenty-four new species are described; an extended and well illustrated treatment of the genera Amphiura and Ophiacantha is included; also, "to complete the published records of West Indian ophiurans in the National Museum, a list is appended of specimens identified by the Hon. Theodore Lyman, but never reported on."—W. S.)

OSHIMA, H. *Report on the holothurians collected by the U. S. Fisheries Steamer "Albatross" in the Northwest Pacific, during the summer of 1906.* Proceedings of the U. S. National Museum **48**: 213-291, plates 8-11. February 11, 1915. (Describes forty-six new species, and extends the range of eleven others.—W. S.)

PEARSE, A. S. *Habits of fiddler crabs.* Smithsonian Report for 1913, pp. 415-428, 10 text figures. 1914. (With bibliography.)

RATHBUN, MARY J. *A new genus and some new species of crabs of the family Goneplacidae.* (*Scientific results of the Philippine cruise of the Fisheries Steamer "Albatross," 1907-1910, No. 32.*) Proceedings of the U. S. National Museum **48**: 137-154. December 16, 1914. (A new genus *Homoioplax* is founded on an old species; eighteen new species are described.—W. S.)

RATHBUN, MARY J. *New fresh-water crabs (Pseudothelphusa) from Colombia.* Proceedings of the Biological Society of Washington **28**: 95-100. April 13, 1915. (Describes four new species.—W. S.)

RATHBUN, MARY J. *Stalk-eyed crustaceans collected at the Monte Bello Islands.* Proceedings of the Zoological Society of London, pp. 653-664, plates 1 and 2, September, 1914. (Describes three new species and gives one new name; makes discovery that at least one of the marine crabs, *Naxioides serpulifera,* undergoes transformation to adult form while still within the brood pouch of the mother.—W. S.)

WILSON, C. B. *North American parasitic copepods belonging to the Lernaeopodidae, with a revision of the entire family.* (Describes twelve new genera and twenty-one new species; gives full notes on ecology and morphology.—W. S.)

ENTOMOLOGY

BARBER, H. S. *The breeding place of* Dermestes elongatus *Leconte.* Proceedings of the Biological Society of Washington **27**: 146. July 10, 1914. (Records the species breeding in the nest of the black-crowned night heron, in the vicinity of Washington, D. C.—J. C. C.)

BÖVING, A. *On the abdominal structure of certain beetle larvae of the campodeiform type: A study of the relation between the structure of the integument and the muscles.* Proceedings of the Entomological Society of Washington **16**: 55-61, pls. 3-6. June 12, 1914. (In this paper the author defines the various areas and sclerites and also gives the muscles causing the boundary lines of the different areas in these larvae.—J. C. C.)

BUSCK, A. *Seven new species of Ethmia from tropical America.* Insecutor Inscitiae Menstruus, **2**: 53-57. April 24, 1914.

BUSCK, A. *New genera and species of Microlepidoptera from Panama.* Proceedings of the U. S. National Museum **47**: 1-67. April 30, 1914. (Describes the new genera Fortinea, Atoponeura, Belthera, Besciva, Galtica, Aroga, Pavolechia, Promenesta, in the Gelechiidae; Hamadera, Costoma, Rhindoma, Ancipita, in the Oecophoridae; and Harmaclona in the Tineidae, together with 123 new species.—J. C. C.)

BUSCK, A. *On the classification of the Microlepidoptera.* Proceedings of the Entomological Society of Washington **16**: 46-54, pl. 2. June 12, 1914.

CAUDELL, A. N. *Some bromeliadicolous Blattidae from Mexico and Central America.* Insecutor Inscitiae Menstruus **2**: 76-80. June 8, 1914. (Describes three new species from Panama and gives notes on other species found in Bromeliaceae. —J. C. C.)

CAUDELL, A. N. *The egg of* Pseudosermyle truncata *Caudell.* Proceedings of the Entomological Society of Washington **16**: 96, *fig. 1.* June 12, 1914. (Illustrates this egg from material collected in Arizona.—J. C. C.)

COOK, F. C., HUTCHINSON, R. H., and SCALES, F. M. *Experiments in the destruction of fly larvae in horse manure.* Bulletin of the U. S. Department of Agriculture, No. 118, Pp. 1-26, pls. 1-4. July 14, 1914. (A professional paper giving details of experiments and suggesting the use of borax as satisfactory in the destruction of the fly larvae.—J. C. C.)

CRAWFORD, D. L. *A monograph of the jumping plant-lice or Psyllidae of the New World.* U. S. National Museum Bulletin 85. Pp. 1-186, pls. 1-30. June 3, 1914. (In this paper the author describes the new genera Aphalaroida, Heteropsylla, Leuronota, Hemitrioza, Uhleria, Tetragonocephala, Katacephala, Mitrapsylla, and the new subgenus Anomoura, together with 62 new species. —J. C. C.)

CRAWFORD, J. C. *Hymenoptera, superfamilies Apoidea and Chalcidoidea, of the Yale-Dominican Expedition of 1913.* Proceedings of the U. S. National Museum **47**: 131-134. April 30, 1914. (Four new species of bees are described.—J. C. C.)

PROCEEDINGS OF THE ACADEMY AND AFFILIATED SOCIETIES

THE GEOLOGICAL SOCIETY OF WASHINGTON

The 293d meeting was held in the lecture room of the Cosmos Club, on March 10, 1915.

INFORMAL COMMUNICATIONS

J. W. SPENCER: *Results of recent soundings at Niagara, and their interpretation.* In October, 1914, the speaker made a re-survey of the crest-line of the Falls and made additional soundings. In the light of these and of previous work an analysis of certain conclusions in the Niagara Folio of the U. S. Geological Survey was given. The folio adopts, in finding the rate of recession, a condition where most of the water temporarily passes over about two-thirds the width of the Falls. This is used as the mean rate for the full breadth. This factor underlies all calculations. The Falls were lately higher than now, as shown by soundings, by borings at the Whirlpool Rapids Narrows, and from the historic records (of Kalm in 1750); and this increased the rate of recession. While the errors made by neglecting these factors are opposing, they do not lead to the correct determination of the age of the Falls. A vertical section under the Falls is given in the folio, showing a depth of water in the gorge of about 200 feet, although the evidence mentioned proves it to be less than 100 feet. Nearly the same amount of work should be performed by the same volume of water, acting on the same set of rocks (height and breadth of the Falls being the same) in the five sections adopted. Yet from the speaker's interpretation, one-quarter the volume (in descending the same height) is made to dig four times as deeply at one point as the full volume at another—a variation in efficiency of 1600 per cent. Between other sections, similar variations appear, while not more than 10 to 25 per cent would be admissible. The age of the Falls as estimated by the speaker is believed to be based on an excessive rate of recession, modified by unsupported opinions to avoid implication of attempts at precision. Thus if we apply calculations alone to his data, the age would be 26,100 years, yet the speaker gives as the sum of his components 19,500 to 30,000 years. The effects of the variable height of the Falls are not considered by him; if these be taken into account the time would be reduced to 14,700 years. The great importance of the age of Niagara lies in its being a chronometer of many geological events, and therefore it should be determined with the greatest precision. The re-survey of the crest-line made by the speaker reduced the estimated rate of recession from the former figure of 4.2 feet a year to 4 feet.   This rate would increase the age of the Falls to 41,000 years.

DAVID WHITE: *The occurrence of transported bowlders in coal beds.* The discovery of stray bowlders in the midst of coal seams is a rare event, but often where one is discovered others are found in the same locality.   Several occurrences in the Appalachian field were mentioned, in Tennessee, Pennsylvania, etc.   A late discovery in the New River coal field of West Virginia has been reported to the Survey, and a specimen from this find was exhibited.   The bowlder was of quartzite, well rounded, and lacquered with coal.   The speaker suggested that the character of the rounding seemed to indicate fluviatile action.   In explanation of the occurrence of the bowlders it was considered probable that a more or less open lane through the coal swamp had existed, permitting the transportation of bowlders by floating drift.

REGULAR PROGRAM

B. S. BUTLER: *Relation of ore deposits to different types of intrusive bodies in Utah.*   The larger intrusive bodies of Utah are of two types, laccoliths and stocks.   The laccoliths occur in the sandy and shaly sediments in the southeastern part of the state; the stocks in the quartzites and limestones in the western part of the state.   The stocks may be subdivided into those truncated near the apex and those truncated at greater depth.   The deeper truncated stocks are uniformly more siliceous.   The apically-truncated stocks are monzonitic to diorritic in composition, the deeper truncated stocks have the composition of granodiorite to granite.   The ore deposits associated with the laccoliths and deeper truncated stocks have been of comparatively slight commercial importance, while associated with the apically-truncated stocks are deposits of great value.   It is believed that the lack of large deposits associated with the laccoliths is due to the fact that after intrusion they were sealed off from their deep-seated source and that the amount of material in the laccoliths themselves was too small and the differentiation on solidifying too incomplete to furnish large deposits.   It is believed that in the stocks the differentiation was greater at depth and that the mobile constituents of the magma, as the water and other mineralizers, with silica, metals, sulphur, etc., in solution, rose toward the surface, while the heavier minerals that crystallized early sunk to greater depth.   When the mobile constituents reached a point where the magma was sufficiently solidified to fracture they were guided by the fractures or fissures, and on reaching favorable physical and chemical environments began· to deposit the metals in solution.   The deeper truncated stocks are regarded as probably remnants from which the portion in which the metals were concentrated has been eroded.

Discussion: SIDNEY PAIGE said he was interested in the speaker's views regarding mineralization around laccoliths.   In the Black Hills the laccoliths had been fractured vertically, and these fractures ("pipes") had been *loci* of rich mineralization. There was reason to suppose that a large batholith underlay the region, from which, Paige believed, the ore-minerals had been distilled. S. R. CAPPS inquired regarding the field criteria for distinguishing between the several forms of intrusive bodies; laccoliths, apically truncated stocks, and medially truncated stocks. Butler replied that this would be difficult in some cases, but in the region he had described the stocks show distinct cross-cutting characteristics, while the laccoliths had produced evidences of doming in the associated sedimentaries. The boundary between apically and medially truncated stocks is somewhat arbitrary, but often the age of the associated formations gives a basis for judgment as to the depth to which erosion has been carried. For example, if the wall-rocks are of pre-Cambrian strata, erosion is believed to have reached a great depth in the stock. A. C. SPENCER thought Butler's ideas regarding association of minerals with character of stock and depth of truncation very valuable. He believed that analyses of small, undifferentiated sills or laccoliths for ore minerals should give basis of estimation of the original content of the magma in such minerals, before the differentiation which had been effective in larger bodies had resulted in concentration in some parts and impoverishment in others. F. L. RANSOME was inclined to differ with Spencer's opinion on this matter and doubted if such analyses would be of value in drawing conclusions. J. B. UMPLEBY referred to the Idaho districts with which he was familiar. They did not seem to conform with Butler's ideas regarding relation between mineral deposition and depth of truncation. J. T. SINGEWALD, JR., referred to the tin deposits of the Erzgebirge. There was a similar association there to what Butler had described. Tin veins were found around the apices of granitic stocks, while more deeply eroded stocks showed no accompaniment of veins. N. L. BOWEN brought up the question of the probable degree of solidification supposed to have been reached in the stocks at the time of ore-deposition. If the apices had reached a condition of complete solidification there was no apparent reason why they should serve as channels for ore-bearing solutions. Umpleby thought that in such cases solidification had not been complete at time of ore-deposition.

BAILEY WILLIS: *Physiographic provinces of South America.* The speaker described in some detail the broader physiographic features of the continent, such as the delta of the Amazon, the chain of the Andes, the pre-Andean depression, and the plains of Argentina, and explained the processes to which their origin and present condition are due. In many places over broad areas very recent movements of depression or elevation have occurred and may still be continuing.

Discussion: KEITH inquired whether the Argentine plain which had been described was simple or whether it was made up of two or three or several plains which were more or less distinct. Willis replied that in the broad expanse from the pre-Andean depression to the Atlantic there is no evidence of faulting, but warping has produced irregularities of surface. C. H. WEGEMANN inquired as to conditions of sedimentation in the great, down-warped, synclinal areas in South America in comparison with similar areas of the United States. Willis thought them very similar. In many places the areas are covered with woody or reedy vegetation and in some instances the conditions are apparently favorable for the formation of flat deposits. A. H. BROOKS inquired whether the sketch of the southern Andes made by Willis was intended to imply the presence of a peneplain on top of the Andes. Willis thought that a moderately developed peneplain had existed, although it had not been brought to such a stage but that considerable irregularity had survived. Moreover, a good deal of warping had occurred during elevatory doming. SIDNEY PAIGE referred to Lowthian Green's theory of a tetrahedral earth, and thought that the general unit character of elevation recently undergone by South America tended to support Green's view. A. H. BROOKS inquired as to the origin of fiords along southern coasts. Willis thought they were located in zones of softer rocks which had been cut into by rivers and glaciers. DAVID WHITE inquired whether continental shelves were a marked feature along the southeastern coast where Willis had spoken of recent warping. Willis replied that they were present in some degree of development.

C. N. FENNER, *Secretary.*

THE BIOLOGICAL SOCIETY OF WASHINGTON

The 540th meeting of the Society was held in the Assembly Hall of the Cosmos Club, Saturday, April 17, 1915, with Vice-President ROSE in the chair and 50 persons present.

Under the heading Brief Notes, L. O. HOWARD called attention to the development of mosquito larvae and adults in pools of water formed by melting snow in the mountains of New York state, the eggs having been laid on the ground the previous summer in places where pools would be formed.

The first paper of the regular program was by J. D. HOOD, *Some features in the morphology of the insect order Thysanoptera.* Mr. HOOD gave a general account of the Thysanoptera, called attention to the large amount of systematic work that had been done in it during recent years, and said that it was estimated that about 25,000 forms would be found to exist in the order. He called particular attention to the structure and mechanics of the foot, and to the asymmetrical mouth parts, illustrating the peculiarities of each by diagrams. Mr. HOOD's paper was discussed by Dr. HOWARD.

The second paper was by E. A. GOLDMAN, *Biological explorations in eastern Panama.* Mr. GOLDMAN gave an account of his work in connection with the Smithsonian Biological Survey of the Panama Canal Zone, in 1912, in extreme eastern Panama with a view to determining the faunal relations of that section to the Canal Zone and to western Panama. Very little zoological collecting had previously been done in this region which was scarcely better known than in the 16th Century, at the time of the Conquest. It proved to be mainly Southern American in faunal characters, with a slight admixture of North and Middle American elements. Many South American species apparently reach their northern limits here. The collections of birds and mammals have been identified, and about 40 of the mammals and 30 of the birds have been described as new. Among the birds are three new genera, two of them of humming birds. No new genera of mammals were taken, but several had not previously been reported from Panama. A new species of *Capybara* was among the more notable mammals. Spiny rats of the genus *Proechimys* were found to be common. The tail, normally long in this animal, is lost through some pathological condition in many individuals, and owing to this circumstance the natives believe in the existence of two species.

GOLDMAN's paper was illustrated by lantern slide views of the country explored, and of objects pertaining to its natural history. It was discussed by Messrs. WETMORE and LYON.

The third paper was by VERNON BAILEY, *Notes on variation, distribution, and habits of the pocket-gophers of the genus Thomomys.* Mr. BAILEY said these rodents, constituting a genus of the peculiar American family Geomyidae, are distributed over the western United States, extending from Alberta and British Columbia to southern Mexico. They range from the Arctic-Alpine to the Tropical zonal areas and are generally abundant in the regions they inhabit. They are burrowers, live almost entirely underground, and are probably more restricted in their individual habitats than any other of our native mammals. This to some extent accounts for their great range of variation and the large number of recognizable forms, nearly 90. Almost every change in climate, soil, and environment is reflected by some change in the color, size, proportions, or cranial characters. There is wonderful adaptation in their color to that of the soil inhabited by them, varying from creamy white on the light sands of the lower Colorado River flats to dark browns on the volcanic plateaus of Mexico and Arizona, and almost black along the humid Pacific coast region of northwestern California. There is also a pure black form on the coast of Oregon which may be an extreme case of dichromatism, as there are several species with a well marked black phase.

Their habit of burrowing enables the gophers to escape many enemies and to adapt themselves to rigorous climatic conditions. In the past this habit was useful in keeping the soil upturned and "ploughed," but under artificial cultivation by man this habit renders the animals a pest. They are very destructive to root crops, clover, alfalfa, and grain. By cutting roots they often do much damage to orchards, nurseries, and vineyards. They may be destroyed by trapping or on a large scale by placing poisoned food in their burrows. In a revision of the genus just submitted for publication as a number of the North American Fauna a general discussion of the habits is given, as well as descriptions of species and subspecies, and maps showing distribution.

Mr. Bailey's communication was illustrated by lantern slides from photographs of living animals and of their work. Messrs. Cooke, Wilcox, Howard and others took part in the discussion.

The 541st meeting of the Society was held in the Assembly Hall of the Cosmos Club, Saurday, May 1, 1915, with Vice-President Rose in the chair and 26 persons present.

On recommendation of the council, Admiral G. W. Baird was elected to active membership.

Under the heading of Brief Notes and Exhibition of Specimens, Dr. O. P. Hay made remarks on the extinct ground sloths of America and called attention to the existence of a specimen of *Nothrotherium* from North American Pleistocene, in Baylor University, Texas. Wm. Palmer announced that he had lately seen an apparently wild specimen of the European skylark in nearby Virginia. He also exhibited the jaws of a ray, *Rhinoptera bonasus*, collected at Chesapeake Beach, Maryland. E. W. Nelson called attention to the newspaper notoriety attained by the San Antonio (Texas) bat roost erected under the misconception that bats were destructive to mosquitoes. He said there was no evidence that the species of bats (*Nyctinomus mexicanus*) in these roosts consumed mosquitoes, and that they foraged so far from these roosts that there would be little likelihood of their consuming insects in the vicinity of San Antonio.

The first communication of the regular program was by C. W. Gilmore, *Observations on new dinosaurian reptiles.* The speaker discussed briefly some of the more important discoveries of dinosaurian fossils made in North America during the past two or three years, referring especially to the explorations conducted by the American Museum of Natural History and Canadian Geological Survey in the Edmonton and Belly River formations in the province of Alberta, Canada. He stated that the recent finding of several specimens, with which were preserved impressions of considerable parts of the epidermal covering, leads us to hope that the time is not far distant when the external appearance of these animals will be as well known as the internal skeleton.

Lantern slides of many of the more striking specimens were shown, the speaker confining himself to brief explanatory remarks regarding their systematic position and their more striking characteristics. The following forms were discussed: *Saurolophus* and *Corthyosaurus* of the trachodont dinosaurs; *Ankylosaurus*, an armored reptile; *Monoclonius*, *Anchiceratops*, *Ceratops*, *Styracosaurus*, and *Brachyceratops*, all of the Ceratopsia or horned dinosaurs. In conclusion, life restorations of *Brachyceratops*, *Thescelosaurus*, and *Stegosaurus*, modelled by the speaker, were exhibited for the first time. (*Author's abstract.*)

Mr. Gilmore's communication was discussed by Messrs. O. P. Hay, Nelson, and Lyon.

The second paper was by William Palmer, *The basic facts of bird coloration.* The complex and varied coloration of birds was explained as due to several causes which were grouped as pigmental, structural, chemical, and a mixture of two of these. The basic pigmentation was considered as composed of blackish, reddish, and yellowish cells, the latter being much subdued and principally diluting the others. This coloration group was classed as physiological, in contradistinction to all other tints, colors, and glossiness, which were considered as psychological results due to semi-consciousness, especially to eyesight, food, and certain phases of light.

This arrangement was based on the experience of the speaker on the forest slopes of Mt. Gede, in western Java, where it was found that non-glossy, dark and dingy colored birds were confined almost entirely to a habitat of damp dense ground-cover vegetation, while those clothed in more or less brilliant colors were inhabitants of the intermediate areas above the ground cover and below the dense canopy of the branches of the tall forest growth.

In the tops of the forest trees a different type of coloration was evident; glossy blacks, whites, and grays were exclusively characteristic, or predominant. These types of coloration were continued down into the lowlands in the same order but with different species or genera, and with the tree-top spreading through the more open and drier areas of the lowlands to near and on the ground.

Less definite intermediate areas between the ground cover and the tree tops, less dense, or with a different vegetation, were shown to be habitats of birds largely green or yellow, the result being that the general and special coloration of a bird clearly indicates its habitat, apparent exceptions having been greatly influenced by other factors.

A correlation was made of these distributional results with the birds of eastern North America, which were considered as governed by the same influences, though forest changes in recent times have complicated the question.

The coloration of other animals is governed by the same laws with similar results, so that where white, glossy black, bright and highly colored areas exist on animals, it is due to psychological progressive adaptations, based on a less complex and simpler dull coloration to be considered as basic, primitive, and thus more purely physiological in contrast. (*Author's abstract.*)

Mr. PALMER's communication was discussed by E. W. NELSON and Hon. GEORGE SHIRAS 3d.

M. W. LYON, JR., *Recording Secretary.*

JOURNAL

OF THE

WASHINGTON ACADEMY OF SCIENCES

Vol. V   JUNE 19, 1915   No. 12

GEOLOGY.—*Factors in movements of the strand line.*[1] JOSEPH BARRELL, Yale University.

Within recent years new points of view in regard to present and recent movements of the sea level have been developed by a number of geologists. Johnson, Daly, Vaughan, and Davis have made important contributions. The writer has not entered upon this subject as a special problem for research but in the pursuit of other investigations has several times come into contact with it. But coming unexpectedly upon a subject from an angle is apt to give new suggestions and somewhat novel points of view. In the brief treatment which is necessary here, the purpose is to outline controlling factors, putting the emphasis upon those aspects which have presented themselves as somewhat novel. It is not the plan to demonstrate fully any single thesis, nor to treat in proper proportion all the composite factors.

The interpretation of composite rhythms. The movements of the strand show a rhythmic character. Smaller undulations are superposed upon larger oscillations. In the interpretation of these rhythms attention has generally been focused upon the marks of previous inroads of the sea, not upon the limits of its retreats, for these are now concealed. The record of a descending series measures only the sequence from the last maximum of a greater rhythm and does not in itself tell the present trend of the oscillations.

---

[1] Abstract of a paper presented before the Geological Society of Washington, March 24, 1915. To be published in full in the American Journal of Science.

Since the Oligocene the strand line has, on the whole, been retreating, the continents rising higher, the climates growing colder.   In the Pleistocene there seems to have been a culmination of crustal and climatic oscillations, followed by a descending series.   From these facts the ice age has been looked upon as past and the Quaternary revolution as closing, but at several times within the Pleistocene that view would have been better justified on the basis of a descending series than it is at the present moment.

Indications of oscillations given by subaqueous profiles.   From a study of present shore action made some years previously as a basis for the development of "Some distinctions between marine and terrestrial conglomerates,"[2] it appeared that recent movements of the strand line may be elucidated by a method of study which analyzes the place and character of marine erosion and sedimentation.   Both rivers and sea work with respect to a base level.   Their first effort is to bring a profile to a graded slope and the nature of the work shows the direction, amount, and relative duration of recent changes of level.   In order to study the water bottom the writer has made use of hydrographic charts of soundings.   Profiles at right angles to the submarine contours have been obtained by projecting upon the given section all soundings within a certain width.   A smoothed curve is then drawn through the soundings.   Thus minor irregularities and possible errors tend to be eliminated.   Such profiles show for many coasts that the present profile of wave-action is about 20 fathoms above a previous stand, this conclusion being in accord with the results reached by both Daly and Vaughan. Professor Daly has been following independently the same line of investigation and he states in a personal communication that he has reached the conclusion that effective wave-action stops much above the conventionally accepted 100-fathom line. With this conclusion the writer is in accord, and as an implication it appears that the outer flats of continental shelves are wave-built terraces constructed mostly from river detritus and laid down during lower stands of the sea.   Drowned river val-

[2] Abstract, Bull. Geol. Society of America, 20: 620.   1908.

leys point in the same direction, but the method of investigation here suggested is of independent value and should give much information for regions such as oceanic islands where the embayments do not give the depth nor duration of submergence.

Pliocene and Pleistocene marine terraces. A second line of investigation which has brought the writer to an intersection with the problem of recent movements was in connection with areal geologic work in southern New England. The topography in this region indicated a series of descending base levels. The methods applied in their study and the results have been published in abstract.[3] Each base level would be recorded in the interior by surfaces of subaerial denudation, on the seaward side by surfaces of marine planation. The latter were cut as benches across the harder rocks and are consequently better preserved than the former. A method of projected profiles, looking along the line of the shore, restores these ancient levels, gives the appearance of a wide flight of giant stairs, and hides the effects of later dissection. It is thought that the Goshen level, reaching to the height of 1380 feet in western Connecticut, dates from the earlier Pliocene. The terraces below descend by steps many miles broad and lying approximately at 1140, 920, 730, and 520 feet. The Pleistocene terraces below were, in comparison, very imperfectly developed, but a number can be traced. They show briefer periods of crustal rest and appear to represent an acceleration of the diastrophic rhythm in Pleistocene time. This crustal unrest is continued to the present, and the present is diastrophically as well as climatically a part of the Pleistocene. •

The broader Tertiary rhythm shown by these wide terraces must have been complicated in the Pleistocene by special effects, such as the weight of the ice-sheets, the changes in volume of ocean water related to glaciation, and minor diastrophic movements. These complications, however, do not hide the facts which lead to the conclusion that on the Atlantic coast an abnormal crustal unrest beginning in the Pliocene has marked especially the entire Pleistocene period.

[3] Bull. Geol. Society of America, **24**: 688–696. 1913.

Turning attention next to the other side of the rhythm of movement, that of the record of submergences, we are led to the conclusion that the emergent phases of the oscillations are relatively rapid and brief, the submergent phase prolonged, and marked by a slowly rising level of the sea.

The combination of evidence from Maryland and New Jersey suggests strongly that certain early Pleistocene stages of cold climate and glaciation occurred when the ocean level stood at the higher parts of the phases of cyclic oscillation. The important point is that the development of the cold climates culminating in glaciation does not appear to have required a low level of the sea or high elevation of the land of this region. The evidence of the region marginal to glaciation leans toward the view that the amount of water abstracted for the formation of the ice-sheets was not a major factor in the control of Pleistocene sea levels. It would seem necessarily to have been an important factor, but the diastrophic rhythm continuing with accelerated movement from the Pliocene constituted apparently a factor of more control.

Post-glacial emergent cycle marginal to the glaciated areas. A third line of investigation is that connected with the Strength of the Crust, a subject now in progress of publication in the *Journal of Geology*. If the hypothesis set forth there is valid— that a thick and strong lithosphere rests upon a thick zone of comparative weakness, an asthenosphere—then the weight of a continental ice-sheet should tend to depress the crust into this weak zone. As this subcrustal zone is not a fluid it can not transmit the excess pressures to unlimited distances. Broad and low pressure ridges would therefore tend to be raised beyond the limits of the ice-sheets. With removal of the ice-load the pressure ridges might rise at first with the central part and then subside.

This theory has been applied to the data regarding water levels during the retreat of the ice, as given by Woodworth for the Champlain and Hudson valleys.[4] The data permit the

[4] New York State Education Department, Bull, **84**. 1905.

determination of the sea level in latitude 40° for each stage of the ice retreat. This represents the movements in a belt beyond the terminal moraines. The figures obtained indicate that the Coastal Plain was higher than at present and rising, the sea sinking, during the retreat of the ice. These effects are of an opposite character to that produced by the addition of water to the ocean during deglaciation.

This argument by itself rests upon a structure of hypothesis and carries but little weight, but independent lines of evidence pointing in this direction will now be considered. Analysis of the data obtained from borings in the channels of the Hudson shows that a cycle of emergence and subsidence has occurred since the retreat of the ice, but not over 200 feet as a maximum above present level. Evidence that a minor cycle of emergence and submergence has occurred along the shores of southern New England and the South is also found. The evidence for a rapid cycle of post-glacial emergence of considerable amount, involving a tract beyond the limits of glaciation, now drowned, is perhaps best given by the distribution of plants along the Atlantic shore from New Jersey to Newfoundland. From the work of Britton, Hollick, and especially Fernald, it is shown that 118 species of plants belonging to the southern Coastal Plain floras are known from widely isolated outlying stations along the coastal strip of New England and the Maritime Provinces. Newfoundland, however, furnishes the most remarkable and convincing evidence. Fernald shows that neither winds nor currents nor migrating birds can be competently invoked in explanation. A remaining hypothesis is that for a time after the last retreat of the ice the Coastal Plain stood higher, margined the continent as far at least as Labrador, and permitted the spread of the Coastal Plain flora. The character of the flora suggests that the migration to the present isolated localities must have taken place during a period of climate even warmer than the present and therefore at a time after the ice-sheets had given up their water. The hypothesis that the emergence was due to withdrawal of water during glaciation must therefore be ruled out.

Somewhat similar evidence is found, on the shores of north-western Europe, of land emergence above the present level involving regions beyond the limits of glaciation and occurring in a warm stage following the retreat of the ice. Submergence to a level a little below the present stand of the sea then took place. This is presented in comprehensive form by W. B. Wright, of the Geological Survey of Ireland, in his recent book on the *Quaternary Ice Age*. Wright considers the breadth of this movement as indicative of a general lowering of sea level, possibly by a recrudescence of the Antarctic ice-sheets, but either of two other hypotheses is preferable.

One of these is that the movements represent a diastrophic cycle entirely unrelated to glaciation. The other hypothesis is that the weight of the ice-sheets caused crustal depression directly below the load, but moderate elevation in a wide zone beyond. Upon the removal of the ice-load the first isostatic upwarping carried up higher this marginal upwarped zone with it. This broad regional movement carried it up to a level where it became unstable and a slow settling-back occurred as an after-effect. The close association of these movements with the close of glaciation appears to favor a genetic connection with deglaciation.

Possible effects of radial shrinkage. Calculations made by the writer as to the quantitative effect of earth shrinkage in producing an increased speed of rotation, and consequently a rise of ocean waters toward the equator and a depression in the polar regions, suggest that it may be a very real factor. A shrinkage of a mile, if taken up wholly by adjustment of ocean level and not by internal earth adjustment (a supposition which can be true to only a limited degree), would raise the water level at the equator about 35 feet and depress it at the poles about 60 feet.

Such great folding and thrusting movements as have occurred in the later Tertiary suggest that earth shrinkage is an important factor. Schuchert has called attention to the greater persistence of equatorial epeiric seas and the readvance of waters more frequently from lower toward higher latitudes. It is possible also that a slight change in slope of the sea level at the time that river courses were established on a newly emerged coastal plain may be at least a partial cause of the southward deflections of rivers which were established along the Atlantic margin in late Tertiary time.

Conclusions. First, we must recognize the special factors connected with Pleistocene climates. These consist in the abstraction of vast quantities of ocean water during the development of the ice-sheets; the direct depression under the load of ice; a possible compensatory elevation in a broad zone beyond; a deferred, intermittent, and possibly oscillatory readjustment upon the removal of the burden of ice.

But these factors must not be used alone. The second group of causes includes the isostatic factors. They tend to maintain the equilibrium of large sections of the crust, affect the whole ocean level, and locally warp the lands, but do not involve earth shrinkage. The general rise of lands which has marked the later geologic times may most probably be placed in this category. The movements are due either to changes of external load or to changes in crustal density. Continental rejuvenation is the chief effect, but they include a possible enlargement or deepening of portions of the ocean basins.

The third group of causes is thought to be found in great compressive movements in the lithosphere which seem to be due in turn to a shrinkage of the centrosphere. Locally they may work against isostasy, more broadly they may start isostatic movements. As their ultimate expression is in mountain building along lines of weakness, they may be classed as orogenic causes.

Fourth are the planation factors, working in opposition to isostasy. They tend to erode the lands, fill the seas with sediment, and raise their surface level. The combination of isostatic and compressive forces has operated through geologic time. The causes are complex and the result is seen in the composite diastrophic rhythms.

To sift apart the factors comprehensive investigations must be prosecuted over different parts of the earth. The sequence and amount of oscillations in the tropics must be linked to those of higher latitudes. Changes of sea level must be separated from local changes in the level of the crust. Multiple working hypotheses must be tested by the application of new and significant facts.

BOTANY.—Merope angulata, *a salt-tolerant plant related to Citrus, from the Malay Archipelago.* WALTER T. SWINGLE, Bureau of Plant Industry.

In the course of a survey of the wild relatives of the commonly cultivated citrous fruits, in the hope of finding new material for use in breeding, the writer was struck by accounts of a curious thick-leaved plant said to grow in tidal swamps in the Malay Archipelago at Noessa Kambangan, in southern Java, where it is called "kigerukkan." A search for descriptions has revealed a curious and involved nomenclatorial history, and a surprising lack of information as to the occurrence, nature, and possible economic value of this curious salt-tolerant plant. As early as 1801 it was described by Willdenow as *Citrus angulata*, with a citation of Rumphius' illustration of *Limonellus angulosus* in the Herbarium Amboinense (1741). In 1834 Wight and Arnott noted that the *Citrus angulata* of Willdenow was undoubtedly a Limonia, and Miquel later (1859) made the transfer as *Limonia angulosa*. In 1872 Kurz described this same plant as a new species under the name *Atalantia longispina*. Two years later he decided to create a genus, Gonocitrus, for the *Citrus angulata* of Willdenow, making his *Atalantia longispina* a synonym. In 1875 Hooker described the plant as *Paramignya longispina;* and in 1876 Kurz abandoned his genus Gonocitrus and transferred the *Citrus angulata* of Willdenow to Paramignya as *P. angulata.*

The nomenclatorial vicissitudes outlined above, however, tell only half the story!

In 1825 Blume created a new genus, Sclerostylis, to receive five species, regarded by him as new. Among them was the kigerukkan, which received the name *S. spinosa.* Although it is the first species listed by Blume, it cannot properly be considered the type of the genus. The name *Sclerostylis*, meaning hard style, must of course have applied to some species the styles of which were seen, whereas the type specimen of *Sclerostylis spinosa* has no flowers,[1] and the original description does not describe the flowers. Very probably Blume had only a single specimen of this plant from which to draw his description of the species. He had, however, flowering specimens of some, if not all, of his other species of Sclerostylis, now considered as belonging to Glycosmis, which have very short, thick styles that might easily have given occasion for the generic name. Material of *S. trifoliata* and *S. lanceolata* in the herbarium of the Muséum in Paris, labeled in Blume's hand, shows styles characteristic of Glycosmis and suggestive of the name Sclerostylis.

Finally, characteristically spiny material from the type locality (it should be noted that the other four species of Blume's Sclerostylis are inermous) shows the plant in question to be very different from Blume's genus in flower and especially in style characters.

Sprengel, in 1827, referred the *Sclerostylis spinosa* of Blume to the genus Limonia, and Dietrich in 1840 referred it to Glycosmis. In 1846 Roemer created a new monotypic genus, Merope, based on Blume's *Sclerostylis spinosa*. There is every reason to believe that Roemer did not see actual specimens of the plant, but drew the characters of his new genus exclusively from Blume's description. In 1912 Koorders[2] records this plant from Noessa Kambangan under the name *Atalantia spinosa*, giving "Hook., Index Kew. II. 849" as authority.[3]

A photograph of Blume's original type specimen at Leiden, obtained through the kindness of Dr. Th. Valeton, and a subsequent study of the specimen itself show beyond question that the *Sclerostylis spinosa* of Blume is the same as Willdenow's

---

[1] "Comme vous voyez le spec'men (l'original de *Sclerostylis spinosa* de Blume) n'a ni fleurs ni fruits." Valeton, Th. Letter dated Leiden, 10 October, 1910. In February, 1912, I had an opportunity of seeing the specimen myself in the Rijks Herbarium at Leiden.

[2] Exkursionsfl. Jav. 2: 427.

[3] The reference in Kew Index under Sc'erostylis is as follows: "*spinosa* Blume, Bijdr. 134 (Atlantiae sp.)"

Citrus angulata.   Under the name *Paramignya angulata* Kurz, Valeton in 1912[4] published a Latin description of this plant, accompanied by an excellent figure, giving fruits and flowers. Here, as a result of a suggestion made by the writer to Dr.

Valeton in 1909, attention is first called to the identity of *Sclerostylis spinosa* and *Citrus angulata.*   At the request of the writer a native collector was sent by Dr. Valeton to Noessa Kambangan on the south side of Java in 1910 and he succeeded in securing specimens of the kigerukkan and later on a considerable quantity of viable seeds.

A study of these specimens and of living plants growing in the greenhouses of the U. S. Department of Agriculture at Washington, D. C., has convinced the writer that this plant cannot be referred to Paramignya but constitutes a distinct genus (figs. 1 and 2).   Since Sclerostylis must be considered a synonym of Glycosmis, as shown above, the oldest available name for this plant

Fig. 1. *Merope angulata.* Flowering branch. Scale one-half.

is Roemer's Merope. This genus differs rather widely from any other plant in the subfamily Citratae, but is doubtless most nearly related to Paramignya and Lavanga, which also have fruits lacking in pulp vesicles.   It differs from Paramignya in the character of the seeds, which are very long and flattened, in the triquetrous fruit (see fig. 2), the paired spines, the simple, short petiole (not long and twisted), and the thick, leathery leaves.   It differs from Lavanga in the simple (not trifoliate) leaves, the simple, short petiole, and the straight (not curved) spines.

[4] Icones Bogorienses, **4:** 159–161. *pl. 348.* 1912.

The name of the kigerukkan, the only species known in this genus, becomes:

Merope angulata (Willd.) Swingle, comb. nov.[5]
Citrus angulata Willd. Sp. Pl., ed. 4, 3^2: 1426. 1801.
Sclerostylis spinosa Blume, Bijdr. Fl. Ned. Ind. **1**: 134. 1825.
Limonia spinosa Spreng. Syst. Veg., ed. 16, 4^2: 162. 1827.
Glycosmis spinosa Dietr. Syn. Pl. **2**: 1409. 1840.
Merope spinosa Roem. Syn. Mon. Hesp. **1**: 44. 1846.
Limonia angulosa Wight & Arnott; Miq. Fl. Ind. Bat. 1^2: 521. 1859.
Atalantia longispina Kurz, Journ. As. Soc. Bengal, 41^2: 295. 1872.
Gonocitrus angulatus Kurz, Journ. As. Soc. Bengal, 42^2: 228, *pl. 18.* 1874.
Paramignya longispina Hook. f. Fl. Brit. Ind. **1**: 511. 1875.
Paramignya angulata Kurz, Journ. As. Soc. Bengal, 44^2: 135. 1876.
Atalantia spinosa Hook. f. Index Kew. **4**: 849. 1895. (vide Koorders, Exkursionsfl. Jav. **2**: 427. 1912.)

Leaves coriaceous, inconspicuously veined, alternate; petioles simple. Twigs with very strong spines, often in pairs. Flowers borne singly or in pairs (rarely in few-flowered clusters) in the axils of the leaves; ovary stalked on a rather tall disk, 3–5-celled, with 2–4 pendulous ovules in each cell; stamens 10, free; anthers linear oblong. Fruits strongly angled, triangular in cross section; cells filled with a sticky mucilaginous fluid (without true pulp vesicles); seeds very large, flattened, reniform, caudate at the tip where attached. Cotyledons in germination aerial, not increasing in size; first foliage leaves alternate, broadly ovate.

A large shrub or small tree (not a climbing shrub), growing on the seashore in tidal forests or mangrove swamps from the mouth of the Ganges to the Moluccas.

MEROPE RESISTANT TO SOIL SALINITY

This plant, which has not received the attention it merits, either from botanists or horticulturists, was discovered in the Moluccas and has since been found in Java, at Malacca, in upper Tenasserim and lower Pegu (Burma), and in the Sunderbuns (the mouth of the Ganges in India). These regions represent a range of nearly 3000 miles, and it will doubtless be found to be widely distributed throughout the Malay Archipelago. It is likely to have escaped most collectors, however, because of its restriction to inaccessible coastal swamps.

The fact that *Merope angulata* grows only along the seashore

[5] The following pre-Linnaean name is referable to this species: *Limonellus angulosus* Rumph. Herb. Amboin. **2**: 110. *pl. 32.* 1741.

in mangrove swamps and tidal forests would naturally lead us to expect that it possesses high powers of "alkali resistance," since sea water contains over 3 per cent of dissolved salts and the mangrove and other plants growing in the mangrove swamps are_able to withstand large quantities of dissolved salts in the

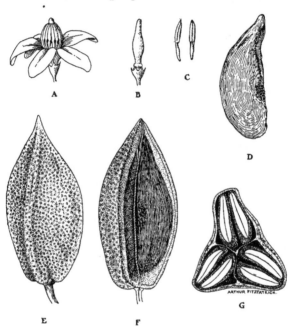

Fig. 2. *Merope angulata.* A, flower; B, pistil; C, stamens; D, seed; E, fruit; F, longitudinal section of fruit; G, cross section of fruit. A–C, scale 1.5 ; D–G natural size.

substratum. Experiments carried. on with seedling plants in the greenhouses of the Department of Agriculture at Washington have shown that it is indeed very resistant to salt. One plant which was watered exclusively with a normal salt solution showed no ill effects for two months. The treatment was continued and the plant finally died, the soil containing at the time of its death 1.34 per cent salt (computed from readings by electrolytic bridge). Another plant was given 1.5 oz. normal salt solution every fourth day (ordinary water being used in addition for any further moisture needed by the plant) from August 31, 1914, to January 20, 1915. At this latter date the foliage was yellowing and the roots were beginning to decay. Other plants of this species, however, which were given small amounts of normal salt solution from time to time, actually made better growth than those not receiving any salt.

POSSIBLE UTILIZATION OF KIGERUKKAN FOR STOCKS

When we remember that the orange is one of the most sensitive to alkali among the fruit trees, it can readily be seen that *Merope angulata* is a plant of decided interest for trial as a stock for other citrous plants, and experiments are now being carried on under greenhouse and field conditions to determine whether it can be so used. So far Citrus has not been grafted success-fully on this stock; but a seedling kigerukkan grafted on a seedling grapefruit grew rapidly and after some months flowered, having developed a strong swelling at the point of union of the stock and scion in the meantime. It is therefore hoped that recipro-cal grafting of the kigerukkan and the cultivated species of Citrus will ultimately be successful.

ZOOLOGY.—*The relationship between phylogenetic specialization and temperature in the recent crinoids.*[1] AUSTIN H. CLARK, National Museum.

In a previous paper[2] I discussed the relationship between phylogenetic specialization and bathymetrical distribution in the recent crinoids. In the present paper I shall consider in the same way the relationship between phylogenetic specialization and the temperature of the habitat.

Unfortunately temperature records for the crinoids are com-paratively few, and for many of the families very unsatisfactory; yet, incomplete as they are, they bring out certain features which are not without interest.

[1] Published by permission of the Secretary of the Smithsonian Institution.
[2] Journ. Wash. Acad. Sci. 5: 309–317, May 4, 1915.

The frequency of the characters in the contrasted pairs (which are the same as those described in the preceding paper) at different temperatures are as follows; as before, the columns headed "1" represent the more primitive characters, those headed "2" the more specialized.

TABLE 1

Degrees Fahrenheit	Calyx		Column		Disk		Arms		Pinnules		General	
	1	2	1	2	1	2	1	2	1	2	1	2
80–75	2	8	1	5·	5	5	6	8	5	5	1	1
75–70	12	18	8	11	7	9	14	20	14	6	1	3
70–65	10	13	5	8	5	7	11	14	10	5	1	2
65–60	10	13	5	8	5	7	11	14	10	5	1	2
60–55	10	13	5	8	5	7	12	14	10	5	1	2
55–50	10	13	5	8	5	7	12	14	10	5	1	2
50–45	10	14	5	8	4	7	11	15,	10	5	1	2
45–40	19	19	11	9	9	7	19	16	15	5	1	3
40–35	28	30	20	16	12	10	30	20	23	7	1	5
35–30	10	18	11	9	7	7	17	11	13	4	1	3
30–25	7	14	5	8	2	7	7	10	6	4	1	1

Expressed as percentages of the whole number in each category these figures are as follows:

TABLE 2

Degrees Fahrenheit	Calyx		Column		Disk		Arms		Pinnules		General	
	1	2	1	2	1	2	1	2	1	2	1	2
80–75	3	12	2	12	18	18	8	12	14	14	14	14
75–70	18	26	19	26	25	32	22	32	40	17	14	43
70–65	15	19	12	19	18	25	17	22	29	14	14	29
65–60	15	·19	12	19	18	25	17	22	29	14	14	29
60–55	15	19	12	19	18	25	19	22	29	14	14	29
55–50	15	19	12	19	18	25	19	22	29	14	14	29
50–45	15	21	12	19	14	25	17	24	29	14	14	29
45–40	28	28	26	21	32	25	30	25	43	14	14	43
40–35	41	44	48	38	43	36	48	32	66	20	14	71
35–30	15	26	26	21	25	25	27	17	37	11	14	43
30–25	10	21	12	19	7	25	11	16	17	11	14	14

The average for all the columns headed "1" and for all of those headed "2" with and without the column headed "General," are as follows:

TABLE 3

Degrees Fahrenheit	Average, including the figures under the heading "General"		Excess		Average, without the figures under the heading "General"		Excess	
	1	2	1	2	1	2	1	2
80–75	10	14	–	4	9	14	–	5
75–70	23	29	..	6	25	27	–	2
70–65	17	21	–	4	18	20	–	2
65–60	17	21	–	4	18	20	–	2
60–55	18	21	–	3	18	20	–	2
55–50	18	21	–	3	18	20	–	2
50–45	17	22	–	5	18	21	–	3
45–40	29	26	3	–	32	23	9	–
40–35	43	40	3	.	49	34	15	.
35–30	24	24	0	–	26	20	6	–
30–25	12	18	–	6	12	18	–	6

Plotting the averages of all the less specialized (1) and the more specialized (2) characters with and without the averages under the heading "General" (fig. 1), we find that the more

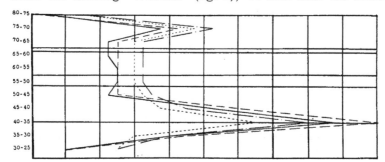

Fig. 1.

specialized characters predominate above 45°, and the less specialized below, down to 30°–25°, where the more specialized are again in the majority.

Plotting the excess of the more primitive (1) or of the more specialized (2) at different depths (fig. 2), we find that the more specialized predominate above 45°, and the more primitive between 45° and 30°, while below 30° the more specialized again predominate.

Within the optimum temperature range (55°–65°) we find a region of conservative phylogenetic advance, where the specialized characters, though predominant over the primitive, are not markedly so. The greatest predominance of specialized over primitive characters occurs equally in very warm and in very cold water, representing an acceleration of phylogenetic degeneration induced by phylogenetically unfavorable conditions.

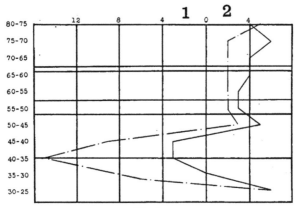

Fig. 2.

A statistical study of the crinoid characters on the basis of contrasted pairs thus bears out what I wrote in 1914 (Bull. No. 294, Institut Océanographique, Monaco): "Les espèces de l'eau très froide ressemblent pour cela aux espèces de l'eau très chaude par la possession d'une construction fondamentalement aberrante, car elles conservent et exagèrent certains caractères très primitifs, mais en même temps elles montrent une condition de développement très grande le long de lignes differentes. . . . Quelque extraordinaire que cela paraisse, dans tout ce grand développement les comatules de l'eau la plus froide se mettent d'accord plus intimement avec les espèces d'eau très chaude, qui appartiennent toutes à l'autre sous-ordre Oligophréata, qu'avec aucune des espèces des eaux intermédiares."

ENTOMOLOGY.—*A new genus of scolytoid beetles.*[1] A. D. HOPKINS, Bureau of Entomology.

There is in North America a group of beetles which inhabits the young cones and, in rare cases, the twigs or shoots of different species of Pinus. A representative of this group has been in the Fitch collection since 1850; another in the Hubbard and Schwarz collection since 1877; two species in Dr. W. H. Harrington's collection, Ottawa, Canada, since 1885; one species in the collection of Dr. J. Hamilton, Allegheny, Pa., since 1893; and during the past thirteen years many species have been added to the Forest Insect Collection of the Bureau of Entomology,· in the U. S. National Museum. It has been found that some of the species are exceedingly common and often so destructive to the young cones of *Pinus strobus* in the East, *Pinus scopulorum* in the Rocky Mountain region, and *Pinus ponderosa* and *Pinus lambertiana* on the Pacific Slope, as to reduce the crop of seed fifty per cent or more below the normal during a single year. The species which inhabits the cones of *Pinus strobus* was described by Mr. E. A. Schwarz[2] as *Pityophthorus coniperda.*

The first reference to the habits of a representative of the group was published by A. S. Packard in the fifth report of the U. S. Entomological Commission, 1890, page 810, under the name *Dryocoetes affaber* Mann., and later Dr. Harrington[3] and Dr. Hamilton[4] published notes under the names *Dryocoetes affaber, D. autographus,* and *Pityophthorus coniperda.*

The other species, while recognized by the writer as new and as representing an undescribed genus, have not been described, because it was intended to include them in one of the parts of a monograph.[5]

[1] Contribution from the Branch of Forest Insects, Bureau of Entomology U. S. Department of Agriculture.

[2] Proc. Entom. Soc. Washington, **3**: 143–145. March 28, 1895

[3] Canad. Entom. **23**: 26–27. 1891. Also, Ibid. **34**: 72–73. 1902.

[4] Ibid. **25**: 279. 1893.

[5] Contributions toward a monograph of the scolytoid beetles, of which have been published: Tech. Series No. 17, Part I, 1909, and Part II, 1915, Bureau of Entomology, U S. Dept. Agric.; Proc. U. S. National Museum, Vol. 48, pp. 115–136, 1914; and Report 99, Office of the Secretary, U. S. Dept. Agric., 1915.

A bulletin (No. 243) of the U. S. Department of Agriculture is now in press giving the results of investigations on the habits and seasonal history of two of the undescribed species, which renders it necessary to publish these brief descriptions without further delay.

Conophthorus Hopk., gen. nov.

(Order *Coleoptera*, Superfamily *Scolytoidea*)

Pronotum with sides broadly rounded from near base to apex, slightly constricted beyond middle with the base margined; antennal club compressed, not thickened at base; abdominal sternite 7 with posterior margin procurved; pygidium vertical when in contact with posterior margin•of sternite; pronotal rugosities extending toward or to lateral margin; tarsi with joint 5 not as long as joints 1 to 4 united; antennal club with three sutures on anterior and two on posterior face, sutures 1 and 2 without septum; eyes acutely emarginate.

Type of genus, *Pityophthorus coniperda* Schwarz, from Marquette, Michigan, Hubbard and Schwarz, collectors. Type in U. S. National Museum.

The genus Conophthorus is at once distinguished from Pityophthorus Eichh. by the absence of sutural septa in the antennal club.

SYNOPSIS

Elytral declivity with striae 1, 2 and 3 punctured; interspace 3 smooth.
Division I.
Elytral declivity with stria 1 not punctured, 2 and 3 approximate and faintly punctured; interspace 3 rarely without granules...Division II.

DIVISION I

Head, prothorax, base of elytra, and ventral area dark; remainder of elytra red. Trinidad, Fort Garland, and Buena Vista, Colorado and Las Vegas, New Mexico, in cones of *Pinus edulis*. Length, 1.25–2.75 mm. Length, female type, 2.65 mm.; Las Vegas Hot Springs, New Mexico, on *Pinus edulis*, August 13, 1901, Barber and Schwarz, collectors. Type, Cat. No. 7472, U. S. N. M....**C. edulis,** sp. nov.

DIVISION II •

Elytra with strial and interspacial punctures equal or subequal in size and density on dorsal and lateral areas..........Subdivision A.
Elytra with strial and interspacial punctures unequal in size and density, those of the interspaces smaller and sparsely placed, especially on the dorsal area.......................Subdivision B.

SUBDIVISION A

Elytral punctures fine, not impressed.
  Black, shining; declivity with interspaces 1 granulate. Norfolk,
  Virginia, probably in cones of *Pinus taeda*. Length, type, 2.70 mm.,
  (head missing); Hubbard and Schwarz Collection; Fortress Mon-
  roe, Virginia. Type, Cat. No. 7473, U. S. N. M.
                            Section a1; **C. taedae**, sp. nov.
Elytral punctures coarse, impressed....................Section a2.

SECTION a2

Interspaces 3 of elytral declivity with distinct granules, the declivity
  not strongly impressed.........................Subsection b1.
Interspaces 3 of the elytral declivity without granules, or obscure......
                                        Subsection b2.

SUBSECTION b1

Elytra with strial punctures confused on dorsal area..........Series c1.
Elytra with strial punctures in obscure to distinct rows on dorsal area.
                                        Series c2.

Series c1

Declivity with interspace 1 granulate:
  Light to dark brown, West Virginia, in cones of *Pinus virginiana*.
  Length 2.70–3.05 mm. Length, female type, 2.70 mm.; Huttons-
  ville, West Virginia, in *Pinus virginiana*, September 20, 1910,
  author, collector; Hopk. U. S., No. 8644a. Type, Cat. No. 7482,
  U. S. N. M.............................**C. virginianae**, sp. nov.
  Dull black. Maine, New Hampshire, Ontario, Canada, in cones
  and shoots of *Pinus resinosa*. Length, 2.75–3.25 mm. Length,
  female type, 3.15 mm.; in cones of red pine; Harrington Collection.
  Type, Cat. No. 7483, U. S. N. M..........**C. resinosae**, sp. nov.

Series c2

Declivity with interspaces 1 smooth, 3 granulate.
  Pronotum dark, elytra reddish. Oregon, in cones of *Pinus ponder-
  osa*. Length, 3.50–3.85 mm. Length, female type, 3.62 mm.;
  Ashland, Oregon, in *Pinus ponderosa*, May 29, 1913, P. D. Sergent,
  collector; Hopk. U. S., No. 10807a. Type, Cat. No. 7479, U. S.
  N. M...............................**C. ponderosae**, sp. nov.

SUBSECTION b2

Elytral declivity not strongly impressed.
  Pronotum dark; elytra reddish brown; front broad. Colorado,
  New Mexico, and Arizona, in cones of *Pinus scopulorum*. Length,
  3.2–3.55 mm. Length, female type, 3.55 mm.; Flagstaff, Arizona,
  in *Pinus ponderosa*, May 26, 1904, author, collector; Hopk. U. S.,
  No. 2740b. Type, Cat. No. 7480, U. S. N. M.
                            C. scopulorum, sp. nov.

Elytral declivity strongly impressed.
Pronotum dark; elytra dark reddish. Chiricahua Mountains, Arizona, in cones of *Pinus apachecae* (?)   Length, 3.50–3.90 mm. Length, male type, 3.90 mm.; Chiricahua Mountains, June 6, Hubbard and Schwarz Collection.   Type, Cat. No. 7484, U. S. N. M..................................**C. apachecae**, sp. nov.

SUBDIVISION B

Elytra with strial punctures in obscure rows on lateral area
Section a3.
Elytra with strial punctures in distinct rows on lateral area
Section a4.

SECTION a3

Pronotum with punctures of posterior area fine......Subsection b3.
Pronotum with punctures of posterior area coarse.....Subsection b4.

SUBSECTION b3

Punctures of elytra fine, obscure and sparse..............Series c3.
Punctures of elytra distinct, those of the striae rather dense...Series c4.

Series c3

Declivity with interspace 1 obscurely granulate.
Black; length 3 mm.   Fitch collection.........**C. clunicus**, sp. nov.

Series c4

Declivity with interspaces 1 granulate; pubescence moderately long, erect.
Black, shining. front; narrow. Michigan, Ontario, Canada, New Hampshire, Massachusetts, Maine, Rhode Island, and Virginia, in cones and twigs of *Pinus strobus*.   Length 2.50–2.90 mm.
C. coniperda Schwarz.
Black, shining, front broad. Monterey County and Pacific Grove, California, in cones of *Pinus radiata*.   Length 2.40–3.60 mm. Length, female type, 3.45 mm.; Pacific Grove, California. in *Pinus radiata*, November 14, 1913, J. M. Miller, collector; Hopk. U. S., No. 10861a.   Type, Cat. No. 7481, U. S. N. M.
C. radiatae, sp. nov.
Declivity with interspace 1 smooth, except toward apex, pubescence long.
Blackish brown, shining. Newport, Oregon, in cones of *Pinus contorta*.   Length, female type, 3.10 mm.; Newport, Oregon, in *Pinus contorta*, April 30, 1899, author, collector; Hopk. U. S., No. 88.   Type, Cat. No. 7476, U. S. N. M....**C. contortae**, sp. nov.
Pronotum black; elytra black to reddish brown.   Priest River, Idaho, and Cowitche Lake, Canada, in cones of *Pinus monticola*. Length 2.95–3.45 mm.   Length, female type, 3.45 mm.; Priest River, Idaho, in *Pinus monticola*, October 19, 1906, R. L. Fromme, collector; Hopk. U. S., No. 6541a.   Type, Cat. No. 7477, U.S. N. M.
C. monticolae, sp. nov.

SUBSECTION b4

Elytra with punctures of dorsal area fine, not impressed.
Declivity with interspaces 1 smooth; black shining. Ventura
County, California, in cones of *Pinus monophylla*. Length,
2.95–3.20 mm. Length, female type, 2.95 mm.; Ventura County,
California, in *Pinus monophylla*, June 5, 1904, author, collector;
Hopk. U. S., No. 2784. Type, Cat. No. 7474, U. S. N. M.

C. monophyllae, sp. nov.

Elytra with punctures of dorsal area coarse, impressed.
Dull black. Boulder and Manitou, Colorado, in cones of *Pinus
flexilis*. Length 2.95–3.30 mm. Length, female type, 3.15 mm.;
Mount Manitou, Colorado, in *Pinus flexilis*, January 25, 1914,
W. D. Edmonston, collector; Hopk. U. S., No. 12400a. Type,
Cat. No. 7475, U. S. N. M..................**C. flexilis, sp. nov.**

SECTION a4

Black, shining; declivity with interspace 1 smooth. Northern California and southern Oregon, in cones of *Pinus lambertiana*. Length
2.85–3.95 mm. Length, female type, 3.50 mm.; Hilt, California, in
Pinus lambertiana, September 20, 1913, P. D. Sergent, collector;
Hopk. U. S., No. 10833a2. Type, Cat. No. 7478, U. S. N. M.

C. lambertianae, sp. nov.

ENTOMOLOGY.—*Correction of the misuse of the generic name
Musca, with description of two new genera.* CHARLES H. T.
TOWNSEND, Bureau of Entomology.

For almost a century the generic name Musca has, by misuse,
been perverted from its rightful application. It is, nomen-
clatorially, one of the most important in the order of flies, or
Diptera, the superfamily name Muscoidea being derived from it;
hence, the correction of its misuse is especially important. The
present paper deals with the proper application of the name and
includes also descriptions of two new muscoid genera.

In 1810 Latreille[1] designated *Musca vomitoria* F. ($=Musca vomi-
toria* L.)[2] as type of the genus *Musca*. The designation is valid and
can not consistently be set aside. Calliphora RD.[3] (1830) falls to

[1] Consid. 444.
[2] Bezzi & Stein (Kat. Pal. Dipt., 1907) indicate *Musca vomitoria* F. as a synonym
of *Musca mortuorum* L. This is manifestly incorrect. Both the description and
the bibliographic references given by Fabricius under *vomitoria* fix his species
as *vomitoria* L. It must be pointed out that Latreille, in designating genotypes,
customarily accredited Linnean species to Fabricius when such had been treated
by the latter author.
[3] Myod. 433.

Musca; its type is *Musca vomitoria* RD. (nec. L.) = *Musca erythrocephala* Meigen, which species is congeneric with *vomitoria* L.)

Musca domestica L. and the species that have long been classed with it under the name Musca require fresh generic reference. At least three genera have been confused here, outside of Byomya and Plaxemya. The type of Plaxemya is *Musca vitripennis* Meigen, according to well-established synonymy. *Musca violacea* RD.[4] is hereby designated as the genotype of Byomya RD. (1830).[5]

Eumusca Townsend (1911) was founded on *Musca corvina* F. (restricted). The new genus Promusca is here erected for *Musca domestica* L., and the new genus Viviparomusca for *Musca bezzii* Patton & Cragg. *Musca tempestiva* Fallen is not typical of Promusca on external adult characters. It may form an atypical subgenus under Promusca, provided reproductive and early-stage characters are found to agree. Credit belongs to Portchinski[6] for suggesting, from the reproductive standpoint, some thirty years ago, the distinctness of the genotypes of Promusca, Eumusca, and Viviparomusca.

Promusca Townsend, gen. nov.

Genotype, *Musca domestica* Linné, Syst. Nat., ed. 10, no. 54. 1758.
The genus is to be distinguished from all the forms hitherto confused with it by the frontalia of female widening out to fill practically or nearly the whole front, and the eyes of male being widely separated. There are about sixty to eighty ovarioles in each ovary. The uterovagina is provided anteriorly with a pair of inflatable pouches or sacs named by Hewitt the accessory copulatory vesicles. Small macrotype, subcylindrical, unpediceled, unmodified and unincubated eggs are deposited. The ovaries mature simultaneously an egg for each ovariole, the whole product being normally ejected by the fly during one oviposition period. Puparium reddish-brown.

---

[4] Ibid. 393.

[5] Coquillett's designation (Type Spp. No. Amer. Dipt., 1910) of *Musca tempestiva* Fallen as type of Byomya is invalid, since he mentions by name no originally included species. Were we to accept as valid a designation of an originally included species by number with omission of the name, the designation in question would still remain invalid since it designates two of the originally included species. The use of the term "supposed species" does not affect the status of the case. The logical interpretation of the International Code is that one, and only one, of the originally included names of species can be validly designated as genotype, since this is the only course that can insure stable results. Synonymy is always subject to revision. Two names supposed to be synonymous may at any time prove to be distinct.

[6] Hor. Soc. Ent. Ross. **19:** 210–244. 1885.

EUMUSCA Townsend

Genotype, *Musca corvina* Fab.; Towns. restr., Proc. Entom. Soc. Washington, **13**: 167–170. 1911.

Syn. *Musca corvina* F.; Port., 1885–1892 (form depositing two dozen large eggs with pedicel).

Musca ovipara Port., Bur. Entom. Comm. Sc. Minist. Agr. St. Petersburg, **8**, No. 8: 13, footnote. 1910.

Musca corvina F.; Schnabl & Dziedz., Die Anthomyid. 128. 1911.

Parafacialia of female about one and one-half times as wide as third antennal joint, slightly narrowing below; those of male slightly widening below. Parafrontalia of female narrowest in middle, a little over half the width of frontalia at that point. Cheeks of male less than one-third eye-height, those of female not much over two-sevenths of same. Palpi of both sexes only faintly thickened apically, not flattened. Both sexes with only one pair of weak ocellars. Front of female distinctly less than eye-width. Only one discal pair of scutellars in both sexes. Penultimate joint of hind tarsi in both sexes hardly or but slightly longer than broad, the tarsal joints in general shortened. Male claws not heavy, strongly curved, slightly longer than last tarsal joint. Vein M_1 hardly at all or only faintly bent in after origin.

This genus has from one to two dozen ovarioles in each ovary. The uterovagina is without copulatory vesicles, so far as known. The eggs are large macrotype, subcylindrical, with long petiole. The whole product of both ovaries, being one egg for each ovariole, is apparently deposited at one oviposition period. Puparium white.

Musca pattoni Austen, *M. gibsoni* Patton & Cragg, and *M. convexifrons* Thoms. appear to belong in this genus, either as typical or as atypical forms.

Viviparomusca Townsend, gen. nov.

Genotype, *Musca bezzii* Patton & Cragg, Indian Journ. Med. Research, **1**: 9–14, *pls. 4 and 5.* 1913.

Differs from Eumusca as follows: Parafacialia of female very broad, equilateral, fully twice as wide as third antennal joint; those of male much narrower above, broadening conspicuously below. Parafrontalia of female in middle fully three-fourths the width of frontalia at same point. Cheeks of male over one-third eye-height, those of female about two-fifths same. Palpi of female much widened and flattened apically, those of male distinctly enlarged at tip but not much flattened. Female with three or four pairs of rather strong ocellar bristles, male with weak ones behind the front pair. Front of female in middle greater than eye-width. Two discal pairs of macrochaetae on scutellum. Penultimate joint of male hind tarsi fully twice as long as wide, the tarsal joints in general elongate rather than shortened. Male claws long and strong, those of front and middle legs fully as long as last tarsal joint. Vein M_1 usually deeply bent in after origin.

This genus is remarkable for having practically the same type of female reproductive system as Glossina. There is only one ovariole in each ovary. The ovaries mature an egg alternately; one at a time being hatched, and maggot carried to third stage, in the uterus. The uterus is merely the much distended uterovagina, functioning as uterus; it bears no copulatory vesicles anteriorly. Puparium dirty-gray to yellowish.

Musca larvipara Portchinski[7] (syn. *Musca corvinoides* Schnabl & Dziedz.[8]) evidently belongs to this genus.

ANTHROPOLOGY.—*Prehistoric cultural centers in the West Indies.*[1]   J. WALTER FEWKES, Bureau of Ethnology.

When the West Indies were discovered by Europeans the inhabitants of these islands were ignorant of the metals, iron and bronze, which have played such an important part in elevating the condition of prehistoric man in the Old World. Stone, clay, wood, bone, and shell were employed by the natives for utensils and implements; gold and copper for ceremonial purposes or for personal decoration. The Precolumbian aborigines of the West Indies, like those of the rest of America, were practically in what Professor Hoernes has aptly called the infancy of our race culture, to which the name Stone Age is commonly applied.

This period of race history seems to have been universal; it was nowhere of brief duration. Successive steps in cultural advancement were slow and in certain localities were retarded by unfavorable environmental conditions.

It has been estimated that the Stone Age in the Old World lasted from the year 100,000 to 5000 B.C.[2] The American Indian was practically in the Stone Age when he was discovered at the close of the 15th century, and the inhabitants of a few of the Polynesian Islands were still living in this epoch a little over a century ago. There is every reason to suppose that the

[7] Bur. Ent. Comm. Sc. Minist. Agr. St. Petersburg, **8**, no. 8: 13, footnote. 1910.
[8] Die Anthomyid. 128. 1911.
[1] Published by permission of the Secretary of the Smithsonian Institution.
[2] Practically another way of saying that the length of the Stone Age far exceeded the age of metals.

parentage of the American Indian dates as far back as that of the Europe-Asian man, provided both sprang from the same original source. It is known from evidences drawn from differences in implements that during the protracted Stone Age epoch man in Europe passed through distinct phases, which have been designated the Earliest, the Old, and the New stone epochs, before he entered that of metals. The American Indian had developed into the New or polished Stone Age when he came to America, and had not progressed beyond it when America was discovered by Columbus.

Although the Stone Age still survived in America when it was discovered, this epoch in the Old World had long before been superseded by one of metals, showing that the Age of Stone in the Old and New Worlds does not correspond in time; when the New World was discovered Europe had been in possession of metal implements for several thousand years. The highest development of stone technic, other things being equal, would naturally be looked for where it had been practised the longest time, and it is to be expected that the prehistoric stone objects found in America would be superior to the European, known to have been made before the discovery of bronze and iron.

Individual specimens of stone implements from the Old and New Worlds are so similar in form and technic that it is very difficult to determine which continent can show the better ex-. amples, but comparing the majority of implements from the Stone Age in America with those made before the discovery of bronze and iron now exhibited in Europe, it has been found that the former are, as a rule, superior to the latter. In Stone Age architecture we find a like superiority. The buildings constructed in the American Stone Age excel those of the same epoch in Europe, as will appear when we compare the stately temples of Peru, Yucatan, or Central America with the megalithic monuments and other buildings ascribed to the latest Stone Age of Europe.[3]

[3] I have based my judgment on the probable form and character of the ancient houses of the Stone Age in Europe, from "house urns" or burial urns shaped like houses, or from the reconstructions made of walls as indicated by post holes and floors. These buildings of the European Stone Age were certainly inferior to those of the same epoch in America.

Character and decoration of pottery is also a fair indication of cultural conditions reached in the Stone Age in different regions of the globe. The ceramics of this epoch in America reached a higher development than those of the polished Stone Age of the Old World, as may be readily seen by comparisons of the beautiful prehistoric American Stone Age pottery and that of man before the use of metals in the Old World.[4]

It thus appears that, if we base cultural advancement on pottery or house building, America had reached a higher stage of development than Europe, even though man in the former was ignorant of the metals, bronze and iron. The implication is that the human race, found in America in 1500 A.D., had lived in a Stone Age longer than man in Europe, where metals had been introduced fully 6000 years before Columbus.

The implements found in the West Indies are among the highest developed examples of this Stone Age. Many of them are the most perfect of their kind and rank with the polished stones of Polynesia, of Africa and Asia. In architecture, the branch of the American race inhabiting the West Indies in prehistoric times had not made great progress, although the cognate ceramic art was well developed.

While there is little in prehistoric America to show a serial succession of stone implements based on method of manufacture, as indicated by chipping, polishing, or other superficial characters, the variations in their forms are great. They indicate geographical rather than historical cultural distribution. Certain characteristic forms of stone artifacts are confined to certain areas, but these characteristics are not of such a kind as to make it difficult for us to readily arrange them in a sequence. The first step to take in explanation of different types of stone implements is naturally to define the areas that are typical.[5]

[4] These examples show the weakness of relying solely on stone, bronze and iron in classification and the futility of basing the degree of human culture on any one form of artifacts.

[5] The culture historian is concerned with the distribution of archaeological objects in time and space or in history and geography. It is for the geographer to interpret geography in relation to history and of the historian to translate history by the interpretation of the geographer.

While the different known types of stone objects found in the West Indies may be considered geographically rather than historically, this manner of assembling specimens in large collections brings out many facts which will make it possible later to determine a definite chronology, and to associate types of implements with local conditions, thus affording an instructive study of the interrelations of environment and human culture.

We can believe that certain of the stone implements found on these islands are old, but it cannot be proved that the oldest of them extend back to the earliest polished stone epoch. Stone implements made by chipping, or those having unpolished surfaces, are rare in the West Indies; they have not been reported in sufficient numbers to enable us to say that they indicate the former existence in these islands of an epoch when chipped implements were the only ones employed. A few chipped axes have been reported from Santo Domingo and other islands, but neither there nor in other islands are the flint chips numerous enough to afford conclusive proofs of an epoch, notwithstanding these implements and their chips closely resemble similar objects picked up on the sites of work shops in the Old World.

The discoverers of the West Indies early recognized that the aborigines of different islands differed in their mode of life, their culture, and their language. In early accounts we find two groups designated as Arawak and Carib, accordingly as their life was agricultural or nomadic. It was stated by the early travelers that these groups inhabited different islands, the former being assigned to the Greater Antilles, the latter to the Lesser.

The large collection of artifacts characteristic of the aborigines of the West Indies now available shows that the stone tools, pottery, and other objects found on the islands inhabited by the Caribs are radically different from those from islands on which the so-called Arawaks lived. Students of prehistory did not at first connect this difference with any racial dissimilarity, but ascribed all these implements to Caribs. This conclusion does not necessarily follow, for it fails to take into account the significant fact that the stone objects found on the so-called Carib islands may have been made by a people inhabiting them before the Caribs came. Moreover, this interpretation does not give sufficient weight to the evidence furnished by the implements themselves, for they imply a culture quite different from that of the Caribs as made known by historical accounts, as flourishing at an earlier date on the Carib islands. In other words, there is good evidence of a prehistoric race inhabiting the Lesser Antilles before the arrival of the Europeans.

One characteristic of the prehistoric objects found on the islands inhabited by Caribs when discovered may be mentioned in this connection. It is well known that the Arawak, like all agricultural peoples, are great potters, and that the ancient Caribs, like nomads, from necessity were not. The two races probably preserved these characteristics in the West Indies; and the fact that we find pottery objects of high excellence on all the islands inhabited by the Caribs leads to the natural inference that they were made by a people allied to the Arawak who anciently lived on these same islands.

Archæological remains left by the aborigines of the West Indies reveal three cultural epochs, grading into each other, which may indicate a sequence in time or distinct cultural stages. These epochs were the cave dwellers, the agriculturalists, and the Caribs. The most primitive culture is represented by objects found in the floors of caves or in the numerous shellheaps scattered from Cuba to Trinidad. A second stage is more advanced and is agricultural in nature, represented on all the islands but surviving at the time of discovery on the larger— Cuba, Hayti, and Porto Rico; while the third, or Carib stage, had replaced the agricultural in certain of the Lesser Antilles, especially on the chain of volcanic islands extending from Guadeloupe to Grenada.

Although the three stages above mentioned are supposed to follow each other chronologically, not one of them had completely died out when Columbus discovered America. The cave dwellers still survived in western Cuba and in Hayti, and according to some authorities they spoke a characteristic language. The Arawak inhabited Porto Rico, Hayti, Cuba, Jamaica, and the Bahamas.

The customs of the aborigines who left the great sheelheaps found throughout the West Indies were apparently not very different from those of the natives of prehistoric Florida, or northern South America. These people, essentially fishermen, lived on fishes, mollusks, or crabs, eking out their dietary with turtles, birds, and other game captured along the shores; fruits and roots were also probably collected and eaten, but their main food came from cultivated crops of yuca planted in the neighborhood of their settlements. The nature of their food supply confined them to the seashore or to banks of rivers where village sites occur in numbers. It is probable that the shellheap people of the West Indies were likewise cave dwellers and resorted at times to rock shelters for shelter or protection. We know from excavations in caverns that they buried their dead in these caves which later came to have a religious or ceremonial significance.

We may suppose that a life devoted to fishing would make men good sailors, and it is probable that the prehistoric Antilleans manufactured seaworthy canoes, hollowing out logs of wood with the live ember and the stone axe. It is also evident from objects found in the floors of caves that the women of this epoch manufactured pottery, and as reptilean figures in relief or effigy vases representing this animal occur constantly, we may suppose that some reptile as the iguana or turtle was highly prized for food. Some of the bone needles, whistles, and ornaments of shell or wood found in shellheaps show that those who camped in the neighborhood were advanced in culture, while other objects found in the West Indian shellheaps are, so far as technic goes, equal to that of the highest of the Stone Age culture. It is probable that this form of culture reaches back to a very early date in culture development.

One important consideration presents itself in relation to the shellheap life in the West Indies as compared with that of the shellheaps in Florida and Guiana in South America. From the very existence of the shellheap culture on the continents and connecting islands they would seem to shed light on the earliest migrations of West Indian aborigines. Unfortunately, however, the objects manufactured by all primitive people in this stage are so crude that they are not distinctive; there is often a parallelism in their work. For example, pottery from widely separated regions often bears identical symbols, even where the people who manufactured it have had no cultural connection. Consequently, although we find certain common features in decorated coastal pottery of Florida and that of Porto Rico, this similarity implies rather than proves cultural contact.

The highest prehistoric culture attained in the West Indies was an agricultural one. It was based on the cultivation of the yuca (*Manihot manihot*), a poisonous root out of which was prepared a meal, from which the so-called cassava bread was made. At the time of the discovery the cultivation of this plant had attained its greatest development and so completely had it developed that Porto Rico and Hayti are said to have been practically covered with farms of this plant. In fact, when sorely pressed by the Spaniards to furnish them gold for tribute one of the caciques offered to cultivate, for the conquerors, a yuca farm extending across the island of Hayti. Both Porto Rico and Hayti appear to have been densely populated, and the failure of the population to advance into a higher stage of development was limited by the perishable character of the root or food plant cultivated. Corn and other cereals[6] were not extensively used and there was no domesticated animal. It is evident that this culture was built on a root food supply which was clearly a product of environment, and on account of this dependence merits careful study by the culture historian and anthropo-geographer.

The development of this culture varies on different islands or groups of islands, forming cultural centers of which the following can be recognized by the character of the pottery: (1)

[6] Corn (*Zea mays*) was introduced into the West Indies as a food plant shortly before the advent of the Spaniards. If sufficient time had elapsed it would have rep'aced this unique form of cultural development based on root agriculture, unless as in the Lesser Antilles it had been destroyed by Caribs who were pressing in upon it with uch force that it could no: survive.

Porto Rico, (2) Jamaica, (3) eastern Cuba and Bahamas, (4) St. Kitts, (5) St. Vincent, (6) Barbados, (7) Trinidad. The differences in artifacts characteristic of these culture centers of the Antilles are sometimes small; thus, the Porto Rico area, which includes also Hayti and Santo Domingo on the one side and the Danish islands on the other, is clearly allied to the eastern Cuba and Bahama area. In the former we have the three types of stone implements—stone collars, elbow stones, and three pointed idols—none of which has yet been found in Cuba, the Bahamas, or Jamaica. Pottery from these islands, except the last mentioned, bears rectilinear or curved lines end-ing in enlargements,[7] a decorative feature which is absent in Jamaica. This feature does not occur in the Lesser Antilles from St. Thomas to Trinidad, where four different regions of decorated pottery can be differentiated.

An adequate account of the characteristic features that differentiate the seven Antillean culture centers of the West Indies would swell this article to undue proportions, but will be considered at length in a report on the magnificent Heye collection of West Indian antiquities.

Lest the author may be thought to have confused the ancestral cavern culture with a secondary cave life due to an adaptation to environment, it may be added that the former is that discussed in this article.

[7] This characteristic feature of Porto Rican pottery decoration appears on characteristic pottery found by Mr. Clarence Moore in mounds of northern Florida.

PROCEEDINGS OF THE ACADEMY AND AFFILIATED SOCIETIES

THE GEOLOGICAL SOCIETY OF WASHINGTON

The 294th meeting was held in the lecture room of the Cosmos Club on March 24, 1915.

SYMPOSIUM ON THE FACTORS PRODUCING CHANGE IN POSITION OF STRAND-LINE DURING PLEISTOCENE AND POST-PLEISTOCENE

T. WAYLAND VAUGHAN: *Introductory remarks.* Before introducing the speakers, the President of the Society called attention to the geologic importance of the factors producing change in the position of the strand-line, and stated that the subject is perhaps brought more forcibly to the consciousness of those who are studying present-day shore lines. As instances of phenomena which demand explanation, the succession of terraces and the general character of the shore line within the Coastal Plain of the eastern United States between New Jersey and Mexico were mentioned. The so-called "coral-reef" problem was cited as furnishing other instances of phenomena which have not been satisfactorily explained.

It appears safe to say that the coral-reef platforms are due to planation processes, operating partly above and partly below sea-level. It has been possible to make correlations in some of the West Indies between the length of geologic time planation processes have been operative and the width of the platform. The deduction that such platforms were formed and have been submerged is so firmly established that it may be accounted a geologic fact. How were they submerged, why do some show vibratory oscillation while others do not, why has there been in some areas marked tilting or warping while in other areas such phenomena are not exhibited, why does the depth of water in the principal atoll and barrier lagoons of the Pacific so nearly accord, and why is the depth on the extensive platforms in the Caribbean Sea and around many of the West Indian Islands the same as on similar platforms in the Pacific? Are there causes of world-wide as well as others of only local effect? If causes of the two classes are operative, how much of the resultant effect is to be assigned to each? The ultimate answer to these questions largely depends upon detailed investigations of numerous tropical and sub-tropical areas, but definite results can not be expected unless the fundamental principles involved have been ascertained, and unless these principles are properly applied in the elucidation of the phenomena. After referring to the important work of American geologists, geodesists, mathematicians, and physicists in contributing to our knowledge of the fundamentals of geology, he introduced the speakers of the evening.

JOSEPH BARRELL, *Factors in strand line movement and their results during Pleistocene and post-Pleistocene.* (Published in brief in Journ. Wash. Acad. Sci., **5**: 413–420. 1915.)

W. J. HUMPHREYS, *Changes of sea-level due to changes of ocean volume.* Obviously anything that changes the amount of water in the oceans also changes the sea-level at all parts of the world. Hence to this extent changes in the positions of strand lines are not referable to differential crustal movements. It will be interesting, therefore, to consider how greatly and by what means the amount of water in the ocean probably has varied in recent geologic times. There have been at least three factors effecting such changes: (*a*) Annual accumulation and melting of snows,—negligible in its effect on sea-level; (*b*) change in vapor content of the atmosphere due to differences in world temperatures—also negligible in its effect on sea-level; (*c*) epochal changes in the amount of glaciation—effect on sea-level probably very important. It will be convenient to consider these factors separately:

a.—During northern winters snow accumulates to a greater or less extent over, roughly, one-tenth of the earth's surface, or over all land areas beyond latitude 40° N. Between this latitude and 60° N. the annual precipitation averages about 500 mm., the largest portion occurring during summer. At higher latitudes the precipitation appears to be less. A snow accumulation, therefore, equivalent to 50 mm. of water over all this area would seem to be a conservative estimate. If this estimate is approximately correct, it follows, allowing for the 5 to 12 ratio of land to water, that northern snows lower the sea-level some 7 mm., an amount which, geologically, is negligible. This assumes, though it is only approximately true, that the northern and southern hemispheres compensate each other in their temperature effects on the volume of the oceans and on the moisture content of the atmosphere.

b.—If we assume that the average surface temperature of the world is 5°C. warmer now than it was at the time of the last maximum glaciation, it follows that the atmosphere must now hold more water vapor than then to the extent of a layer of water about 7 mm. deep. This would imply that from this effect alone the ocean level is about 10 mm. lower than it otherwise would be. On the other hand, the corresponding temperature change of the oceans themselves has produced an opposite effect, probably several (10, perhaps) times as great.

c.—The fact that the average thickness of the ice-cap during the last glaciation can be only roughly estimated renders any calculation of its effect on ocean level correspondingly doubtful. It does not seem probable, however, that they could have averaged much if any thicker than the present caps of Greenland and of Antarctica, which a number of good observers have estimated to be about 1000 meters. Taking this value and assuming the deglaciated area to be equal to one-fifteenth the area of the ocean, or, roughly, twice the glaciated area of North America, we estimate the change in sea-level to have been about 67 meters. As already stated, this is only an estimated change, but perhaps it is a conservative estimate.

In this connection it is interesting to note that the complete deglaciation of Greenland and Antarctica, if their ice caps average 1000 meters thick, would raise the sea-level about 40 meters, of which Greenland would contribute about 6 and Antarctica 34. Presumably these changes in sea-level which must have occurred as a result of glaciation and deglaciation are best preserved in equatorial regions. The change of load was more evenly distributed here than in the higher latitudes, and therefore local warping was probably much less.

Discussion: President WOODWARD of the Carnegie Institution of Washington had been expected to lead the discussion of the papers which had been presented, but was unable to be present. President VAUGHAN called upon Dr. WILLIAM BOWIE of the Coast and Geodetic Survey for some remarks. Dr. BOWIE said that in his opinion the oscillations of the strand-line spoken of by Professor BARRELL, involving movements over large areas, could hardly be accounted for by the theory of isostatic adjustment. Deposition of sediment on ocean floors, continued over long periods of time, would be expected to cause eventually a sinking of the floor on which they rested, and islands which were surrounded by such areas of loading would naturally participate in the downward movement; but a subsequent rise or oscillation of level, such as had frequently been noted, could not be explained by isostasy, and other physical and chemical forces must be invoked. Likewise the unloading of land areas by erosion would be expected to result in upward movements, but oscillations could not be explained as effects of isostatic adjustment. He thought that as regards this question as a whole geodesists should not be expected to advance theories in explanation of the movements which geologists have recognized. The primary purpose of the geodetic work in making measurements of gravity is to determine the shape of the geoid. The results thus obtained give quantitative data which geologists may employ in explaining the phenomena observed.

J. W. SPENCER spoke of the great submergences which he had formerly believed were shown in the West Indian region. He was now somewhat doubtful about the evidence on this matter, but was more certain regarding the region of the Great Lakes. He had traced several low terraces around Lake Ontario, and their parallelism with the present water-surface showed that the region had undergone no deformation during the time taken by the St. Lawrence River to cut its channel 15–20 feet deeper. He spoke also of the work of D. W. JOHNSON as tending to establish the lack of recent deformation along the Atlantic Coast. At the same time various observers have found evidences of the presence of platforms submerged to a great depth along several of the continents—one at 3000 feet and the trace of another at 6000 feet. Spencer did not believe that the phenomena in Norway justified De Geer's estimate of 10,000 years for the period which had elapsed since the end of the ice-age. There has been too much subsequent erosion. · From the phenomena shown at Niagara 40,000 years seemed a probable estimate.

BAILEY WILLIS spoke of the delta plain of the Yellow River in China. He did not believe that the explanation which some had advanced, attributing its origin to submarine planation, was correct. He believed that it has been maintained as a very flat plain because of subsidence of its inner portion, and that therefore the low gradient is to be attributed to warping. The delta of the Amazon likewise has a very low gradient in spite of the great quantities of sediment which are being deposited upon it. Here also the phenomena must be explained by postulating a subsiding area. Along the Argentine coast there are evidences of warping on an extensive scale. Such phenomena cause a rise in one area and sinking in another, and complicate the strand-line problem.

ARTHUR KEITH expressed his agreement with Professor Barrell in considering that there are evidences of many successive terraces along the Atlantic Coast, but disagreed with the view that attributed to them a submarine origin. He asked for Barrell's criteria. BARRELL replied that the terraces along the broad river-valleys were, in his belief, subaerial, and were to be attributed to river erosion at the periods corresponding to stages of sea-level at which marine planation had formed the platforms whose inner margins were essentially parallel to the present coast-line. The evidence regarding the marine origin of the latter terraces was too extensive for presentation at the moment, but would appear later in published form.

SIDNEY PAIGE inquired as to Barrell's reasons for believing that along the Atlantic coast an oscillatory movement of the strand-line had occurred just previous to the development of each platform. Barrell replied that in every case the coast-line was very sinuous at the time of platform development. Analysis of the features showed that just prior to the long stand of the sea represented by each platform there had been an elevatory movement, resulting in the carving of stream-valleys, followed by a slight re-submergence, with drowning of the valleys; and a long stand, resulting in the development of a submarine plain. President Vaughan thought that all those who had been engaged on coastal plain work would be in essential accord with Barrell's views.

E. W. SHAW spoke of the evidence of movements in the southern coastal plain region during Quaternary time. The effects observed could not be explained by river-work, as Chamberlain and Salisbury had attempted to do. President Vaughan spoke of the great importance of the study of the nature and character of submarine profiles which Barrell had made.

C. N. FENNER, *Secretary.*

THE BIOLOGICAL SOCIETY OF WASHINGTON

The 542d meeting was held in the Assembly Hall of the Cosmos Club, Saturday, May 15, 1915, with President BARTSCH in the chair and 43 persons present.

On recommendation of the Council, FRANCIS N. BALCH, Boston, Massachusetts, and ERNEST P. WALKER, Wrangell, Alaska, were elected to active membership.

Under heading exhibition of specimens, L. O. HOWARD showed lantern slides from photographs of a moth, *Ceratomia amyntor*, bringing out its protective coloration while at rest on bark.

The first paper of the regular program was by C. H. T. TOWNSEND, *Two years' investigation in Peru of verruga and its insect transmission.*

The four stages of verruga are defined as *incubative, fever. quiescent* and *eruptive*. The most important symptom of the fever stage is the presence of the bacilliform bodies (*Bartonia bacilliformis* Strong et al.) in the erythrocytes. The histology of the eruptive papules is not yet sufficiently defined for positive diagnosis in the absence of the clinical history, but its chief feature is a marked proliferation of angioblasts.

Verrugas Canyon is the best known and probably one of the strongest endemic foci of the disease. Extended investigations were carried on there both day and night at all seasons of the year. The result was an ecological demonstration of *Phlebotomus verrucarum* Townsend as the vector of the disease. This demonstration is built on the unique etiological conditions already known. Verruga can be acquired only by direct inoculation into the blood, is only contracted at night, is confined to very restricted areas within which it is almost universally contracted at any time of year by non-immunes who remain from 7 to 10 consecutive nights. These conditions necessitate a blood-sucking vector which is abundant, active only at night but throughout the year, and whose distribution is coterminous with the infested areas. The above *Phlebotomus* is the only bloodsucker which meets these requirements.

Clinical verification of the vector was obtained from the history of numerous cases of verruga observed by Dr. Townsend. Transmissional demonstration in laboratory animals lacked completeness only by reason of the impossibility of positively diagnosing verruga eruptive tissue, papules having been produced in animals by injection of the crushed *Phlebotomus*.

A biting experiment was carried through, resulting in what appeared to be a light infection. This was the case of McGUIRE, who exhibited all the symptoms but with a paucity of the bacilliform bodies in the erythrocytes. Papules appeared sparingly after the subject had been discharged. Dr. Townsend's assistant, Mr. NICHOLSON, accidentally received many *Phlebotomus* bites, thereby furnishing a clean experiment with two checks. The checks were Dr. Townsend and his assistant, Mr. RUST, both of whom were subjected to exactly the same conditions as Mr. Nicholson except that they did not receive the bites. They did not contract the disease, while Mr. Nicholson showed a well marked case, with both the bacilliform bodies in the erythrocytes and the characteristic eruption.

Lizards were suggested as a possible reservoir of verruga, from the fact that were the only vertebrates aside from man, domestic or wild, at Verrugas Canyon, whose blood showed bacilliform bodies. The lizards inhabit the numerous loose rock walls which everywhere in the Andean region take the place of fences, and these are the favorite diurnal hiding places of the *Phlebotomus* swarms. Injection of the lizard blood into guinea-pigs resulted in similar bodies in the erythrocytes of the injected animal.

The unity of verruga was insisted on, in opposition to the thesis of Dr. R. P. STRONG and his associates. The entire Peruvian medical fraternity concur in this view. The facts given in support of it appear to be irreconcilable with the opposite view.

Prophylactic measures were outlined; and the remarkably perfect climatic conditions of the verruga zones, unequalled for sanatoria, were dwelt on. (*Author's abstract.*)

Dr. TOWNSEND's paper, which will be published in full in the *American Journal of Tropical Diseases and Preventive Medicine*, was illustrated by lantern slides made from photographs of *Bartonia bacilliformis*, of clinical cases, of the micro-pathology, of the *Phlebotomus*, and of Verrugas Canyon, etc. It was discussed by Admiral C. W. BAIRD and Medical Inspector H. E. AMES.

The second paper was by W. DWIGHT PIERCE, *The uses of weevils and weevil products in food and medicine.* Mr. Pierce described in particular the trehala manna of Syria which is the cocoon of the large weevil known as *Larinus nidificans*. These cocoons are used by the natives as a food similar to tapioca and are commonly sold in the drug stores for use in making a decoction said to be efficacious against bronchial catarrh. The cocoons are made by an abdominal excretion of the larvae and contain a large percentage of sugar known as trehalose, as well as a carbohydrate, a little gum, and a small amount of inorganic mineral matter. (*Author's abstract.*)

Specimens of the trehala manna and of the weevil were exhibited.

The third communication was by L. O. HOWARD, *Some observations on mosquitoes and house flies.* DR. HOWARD spoke of the work which is being done in New Jersey against mosquitoes, describing the organization of county inspectors which was effected at Atlantic City in February at an "antimosquito convention." He showed a series of lantern slides illustrating the very effective work done by the Essex County Commission in the vicinity of Newark, New Jersey. He then spoke of the work done by Mr. HUTCHINSON, of the Bureau of Entomology, in regard to trapping the maggots of the house-fly, illustrating his remarks with lantern slides showing a large out-door maggot trap in use during the summer of 1914 under Mr. Hutchinson's directions at College Park, Maryland. The illustrations in question appear in U. S. Department of Agriculture Bulletin No. 200. (*Author's abstract.*)

The last communication was by A. L. QUAINTANCE, *Remarks on some little known insect depredators.* Mr. QUAINTANCE called attention to certain species of insects which have but recently come into prominence as of economic importance and to other species which, although long known to entomologists as occasional pests, have recently attracted attention in view of local outbreaks. A species of Jassidae, *Typhlocyba obliqua*, is at the present time seriously destructive to apples in portions of the Ozark mountain region and in Kansas. These insects occurred in countless numbers in some orchards, infesting the lower surface of the leaves, causing the foliage to drop with subsequent injury to the fruit crop and the trees. A tineid insect of the genus *Marmara* was reported to have caused a good deal of injury to certain apple orchards in Albemarle County, Virginia. The caterpillar makes long serpentine mines under the skin of the apple, resulting in blemishes. The keeping quality of the fruit is also lessened. The common walking stick, *Diapheromera femorata*, while often the cause of more or less local defoliation in forests, occasionally becomes a serious pest in orchards, especially in orchards adjacent to woodlands. These walking sticks have recently been complained of on account of important injuries to apple and peach orchards in Virginia and West Virginia. *Rhabdopterus picipes*, a chrysomelid beetle, has recently been discovered as damaging cranberries. The insect is a near relative of the grape root worm, *Fidia viticida*, and the larvae work on the roots of the cranberry, feeding principally on the fibrous roots, but also stripping the bark from the older roots. Investigations of the insect by Mr. H. B. SCAMMELL indicate that it is restricted in cranberry bogs to the higher and sandier soils. *Nezara hilaris*, one of the stink bugs, and long known to feed on vegetation of various sorts, has recently become very abundant and destructive to peaches in the Marblehead district in northern Ohio. These plant bugs in feeding insert their beaks in the developing fruits, causing the peaches to become knotty and misshapen as they grow, and many of which fall from the trees. *Parandra brunnea*, better known as the chestnut telephone borer, following investigations by Mr. SNYDER has been determined by Mr. FRED E. BROOKS to be very generally present in the heartwood of old apple trees and as a result of its work the trees are often so weakened that they are easily broken or blown over by winds. Various species of Cecidomyidae are known to be serious crop pests, as the sorghum midge, the pear midge, etc. A new midge pest, *Contarina johnsoni*, has during recent years come into prominence on account of its injuries to grapes in the Chautauqua and Erie grape belts. The adults oviposit in the blossom buds, which may contain from 10 to 70 maggots, though the average number is much less. Many blossoms are thus destroyed, resulting in very ragged and imperfect bunches of grapes.

This paper was illustrated by lantern slides showing the insects and their work from photographs prepared mostly by Mr. J. H. PAINE.

At 10.15 the Society adjourned until October.

M. W. LYON, JR., *Recording Secretary.*

THE ANTHROPOLOGICAL SOCIETY OF WASHINGTON

At the 484th meeting of the Society, held March 2, 1915, in the Public Library, an address was given on *Confucianism, the State Religion of China*, by Mr. E. T. WILLIAMS, of the State Department, who spent 26 years in China and supplemented his personal observations by a study of the Institutes of the Manchu Dynasty and the Manual of the Ministry of Rites. The interpretation of the ritual he takes from the Chinese classics, particularly the Book of History and the Book of Rites. Confucianism for two thousand years has been the state religion of China. It existed long before Confucius was born, but is properly called by his name, since its sacred scriptures were in large part edited by him and he has become one of the chief objects of worship in the system. While the lofty character of its ethical teaching is characteristic, it is a mistake to say that Confucianism is merely a system of ethics. The teaching of the Book of Rites and the ceremonies observed in the offering of sacrifices to the Supreme Being and to lesser deities and saints, makes its religious character clear. By an edict in 1907 the Empress Dowager raised Confucius to equal rank with the Supreme Deity in the pantheon.

At the service in the temple of Confucius at the spring and autumn equinoxes, the worship of the sage does not consist merely in making obeisance before his tablet, as has sometimes been said, but in making offerings of incense and food, libations of wine (more properly, rice spirits), and sacrifices of oxen, sheep, and pigs, together with a burnt offering of silk. The worship is conducted by the chief official of the county. There are kneelings and prostrations and a chanting of hymns to the accompaniment of an orchestra consisting of a great variety of wind and stringed instruments, drums, bells, and musical stones. The services in the Temple of Heaven in Peking are held at the winter solstice. The Temple of Heaven is a large park situated in the southern suburb of the capital. It is enclosed by a strong wall and is divided into a number of courts. Even the Emperor could not enter the inner court except on foot. Within this court is a most holy place, the court of the altar. There has never been at any time in China more than one recognized altar to the Most High. The principal altar is of white marble and consists of three circular terraces. It is open to the sky, and the offerings made here are presented by the head of the state two hours before dawn on the longest night of the year. Three, and its multiple, nine, are the important numbers in the construction of the altar, while four and eight are those represented at the altar to the earth, north of the capital; for odd numbers belong to heaven and even ones to earth. Near the marble altar there is also an altar of burnt offerings constructed of green, glazed tiles. One young bullock, black and without blemish, was consumed on this altar as a sacrifice to Shangti. The Emperor, after donning his priestly robes, washed his hands and ascended the marble altar, facing the north. There he worshipped Shangti and his imperial ancestors. There are some striking analogies between this ritual and that of the ancient Hebrews.

Since the revolution of 1911 the state sacrifices have been quite generally suspended. Last September, however, President Yuan Shih-kai, participated in the worship of Confucius at the temple erected to him in Peking, and in December offered sacrifice to Shangti in the Temple of Heaven. The whole burnt offering heretofore sacrificed to Shangti was omitted and simple bows were substituted for the kotow. Sacrifices to ancestors are made by all classes in their homes at the winter solstice, and at eastertide all visit the family tombs and set out gifts of rice and wine.

The apparent failure of this religion to satisfy the longings of the human heart is shown by the popularity of Buddhism, particularly the modified form prevalent in China, which instead of Nirvana holds out the hope of immortality in the "Western Heaven." The restoration of the state religion by the President does not mean the abolition of religious liberty; for the Chinese government holds that, as Great Britain allows freedom of worship and yet supports one state church in England and another in Scotland, so China may have its official religion and yet grant toleration to other faiths.

DANIEL FOLKMAR, *Secretary.*

JOURNAL

OF THE

WASHINGTON ACADEMY OF SCIENCES

Vol. V · JULY 19, 1915 No. 13

PHYSICS.—*A direct-reading device for use in computing characteristics of vacuum tungsten lamps.*[1]   J. F. SKOGLAND, Bureau of Standards.

It has been shown in a previous paper[2] that the ordinary characteristic relations of vacuum tungsten lamps can be expressed with high precision by a set of characteristic equations, each involving two variables; or solutions can be made more quickly by employing tables computed from the equations.   For example, having given observed values of voltage, candle-power, and watts per candle, the values of Cp and wpc at any other voltage are obtained from the equations or tables as follows:

1. From the observed values of voltage and Cp their normal values, that is, their values at normal wpc (1.20), are computed.

2. The ratio of the desired voltage to the normal voltage just found is computed.

3. Substitution of this voltage ratio in the proper equations, or reference to the corresponding point in the tables, gives a Cp factor and the actual wpc.

4. The normal Cp is multiplied by the Cp factor to obtain the desired Cp.

[1] Communicated by the Bureau.   To appear in full as a Scientific Paper of the Bureau of Standards.

[2] Middlekauff and Skogland, Characteristic equations of tungsten filament lamps and their application in heterochromatic photometry, Journ. Wash. Acad. Sci. 5: 61.   1915; Bureau of Standards Scientific Paper No. 235.

This process though simple, requires considerable time before a solution is obtained. The direct reading device here described and presented ready for use solves directly and without preliminary reduction all problems introducing as variables the voltage, candlepower, and wpc of vacuum tungsten lamps. Its construction depends directly upon the characteristic equations mentioned above.

This device consists of volt, watts per candle, and per cent candlepower scales. The wpc and per cent Cp scales are fixed in their relation to each other. The volt scale is arranged to be detached from the plate, so that it may be applied to the fixed scales at the point corresponding to observed values of wpc and voltage. From a single setting of the volt scale to observed values within the range of from 0.70 to 2.05 wpc can be read values of any one of the variables at any other point within this range. The volt scale has a range of from 94 to 166 volts. The chosen limits of wpc and voltage are considered sufficient to include settings and solutions for 105–130 volt lamps in standardizing and life test-work.

A test of the device, illustrated in part by examples, indicates that, on an average, values of per cent Cp and of wpc read therefrom deviate from those obtained by use of Tables 20 and 22 of the paper just referred to by amounts not exceeding 0.10 per cent and 0.05 per cent respectively; also that values read from the scales agree with observed values nearly as closely as those computed by use of the tables. All of the points (referred to horizontal and vertical scales of equal parts) through which lines of the scales of this device were drawn have been tabulated, so that similar scales of the same or different range can be constructed directly from these values. Sufficient discussion of the derivation of these values and of the relative position of the scales has been given to direct the construction of scales not included within the wpc range here employed. By the general method of this paper any related functions of exponential form and of the same degree as the characteristic equations can be represented and used as scales of a similar device.

The chief merits of the device when compared with other methods of characteristic evaluation seem to be its simplicity and precision, and the saving of time resulting from its use. Solutions are made directly, without reference to normal wpc, voltage ratios, exponents, etc. These considerations should recommend it to testing and standardizing laboratories.

PHYSICS.—*The effective resistance and inductance of iron and bimetallic wires.*[1] JOHN M. MILLER, Bureau of Standards.

When a current of electricity flows through an iron wire, the lines of magnetic force and the resulting magnetization of the iron are circular. From measurements of the self-inductance of the wire with direct current an exact permeability curve for circular magnetization can be obtained. As ordinarily measured, the permeability for axial magnetization is obtained. A comparison of the two kinds of magnetization shows that for some wires the permeability curves are similar, but that for others the circular permeability may be considerably less than the axial. The differences are due probably to lack of homogeneity or isotropy of the iron caused by drawing and by heat treatment.

A method based upon Anderson's modification of the Maxwell bridge for measuring inductances is used to measure the effective resistance and inductance of six samples of iron telegraph and telephone wires and three samples of copper-clad steel, bimetallic wires. The measurements are made at frequencies up to 3000 cycles per second and with currents up to 10 amperes. The results are given by tables and curves. The so-called Steel telephone wires are considerably poorer conductors at low frequencies and low current strengths than the grade called "Extra Best Best," but at higher frequencies and current strength the Steel wires may be better conductors. At the higher frequencies the resistance and inductance of the copper-clad wires become practically independent of the current flowing through the wire.

[1] Detailed paper to appear in the Bulletin of the Bureau of Standards.

From considerations of bimetallic wires as two circuits in parallel, formulas are obtained which permit the computation of effective resistance and inductance of the wires. The core is treated as one circuit and the shell as another; the self inductance of each is computed, as well as the mutual inductance of one on the other. Assuming no skin effect in the shell and introducing the effective resistance and inductance of the core for a given frequency, the resistance and inductance of the whole wire can be computed for that frequency from the expressions for the equivalent resistance and inductance of two circuits in parallel. The measured values of the copper-clad wire for low current strengths are compared with the computed values, and the agreement is very satisfactory. The formulas are also used in computing wire tables for copper-clad steel wire. Values of effective resistance and inductance are tabulated for the even sizes from No. 0 to No. 12 A. W. G. for conductivities of 30, 40, and 50 per cent of hard drawn copper and for frequencies up to 1000 or 3000 cycles per second.

PHYSICS.—*The calculation of the maximum force between two parallel, coaxial, circular currents.*[1] FREDERICK W. GROVER, Bureau of Standards.

The force of attraction or repulsion between two currents flowing in parallel, coaxial, circular paths of unequal radii, increases as the distance between their planes is increased, until a maximum value of the force is reached, and then, as the distance is indefinitely increased, decreases toward zero as a limit.

It was shown by Maxwell that the distance for which the force is a maximum bears a ratio to either of the radii, which is a function of the *ratio of the radii alone*, and depends in no way on their absolute values. Further, the maximum value of the force, with unit current in each circuit, is also a function of the radii alone.

These facts have been utilized in the current balance, first used by Lord Rayleigh, in which is measured the force between

[1] Detailed paper to appear in the Bulletin of the Bureau of Standards

two parallel circular coaxial coils, one fixed, and the other attached to one end of the beam of a balance, the distance between the planes of the coils having been adjusted until the force exerted between the currents in the coils is a maximum. From the observed weights, which must be added to the other arm of the balance to restore equilibrium, the value of the current flowing through the two coils in series may be calculated, provided the ratio of the radii is known. The latter may be determined experimentally by an electrical method, without measuring the individual radii, and with an accuracy not attainable from direct measurements of the dimensions of the coils.

The calculation of the constant of the balance is based on the theory for two circular filaments to which the coils may be regarded as equivalent. The corrections necessary to be taken into account, because of the finite cross section of the coils, have been derived by Rayleigh, Lyle, and others, and reference may be made to the paper on the "Determination of the International Ampere in Absolute Measure," by Rosa, Dorsey, and Miller, for a treatment of this question and for other details concerning the theory and methods of manipulation of the balance.

The force between two parallel, circular coaxial currents of given radii, situated with any desired distance between their planes, may be calculated by the formula of Maxwell in elliptical integrals, or by the formulas of Nagaoka which involve q series.

Previously, the value of the maximum value possible of the force between any two such circular currents, of given radii, has been obtained by calculating the force directly (by means of the formulas just mentioned) for a number of chosen distances of the coils in the neighborhood of the critical distance, which was supposed to have been approximately determined beforehand. The final value of the maximum force was determined by interpolation from this series of calculated values. This process is indirect and laborious.

In the detailed paper to be published a formula is derived for calculating the value of the critical distance from the assumed ratio of the radii. By substituting the distance thus found in one of the above general formulas for the force, the maximum value of the force can at once be determined. In some cases the maximum force can be calculated directly from a formula given here in which this substitution has been made once for all.

The formula for the critical distance is, unfortunately, not simple enough to allow of the direct calculation of the critical distance from the given ratio of the radii. It is, however, not difficult to obtain the desired value with great accuracy by a method of successive approximation, provided a first approximation is at hand.

The latter part of the paper is devoted to the development of methods for facilitating this process. The formulas derived are fully illustrated by numerical examples, and tables are given of the critical distance and the value of the maximum force for such values of the ratio of the radii as are likely to occur in practice. It is further shown how the constants for coils, whose dimensions differ slightly from one of the exact ratios given in the table, may be derived from the latter values with little trouble and labor.

To test the new formulas the complete calculations of the constants of the coils of the Bureau of Standards current balance have been carried through, and the results were found to be in agreement with the values obtained by the interpolation method within less than a part in a million.   •

PHYSICS.—*On the construction of primary mercurial resistance standards.*[1] F. A. WOLFF, M. P. SHOEMAKER, and C. A. BRIGGS, Bureau of Standards.

This paper deals with the construction of four one-ohm mercury standards of resistance in accordance with specifications adopted by the International Conference on Electrical Units and Standards (London, 1908). The London Conference defined the international ohm as the resistance offered to an unvarying electric current by a column of mercury at the temperature of melting ice, 14.4521 grams in mass, of a constant cross-sectional area and of a length of 106.300 cm.

---

[1] To be presented in full as a Scientific Paper of the Bureau of Standards.

Because of the impossibility of exact realization of the above conditions, principally because of the impracticability of securing glass tubing of strictly uniform bore, certain specifications were essential. Those adopted specified that the tubes used must be made of a glass the dimensions of which change little with time; that they be well annealed and straight; that the bore be as nearly as possible uniform and circular; that the area of cross-section of the bore be approximately one square millimeter; and that the mercury have a resistance of approximately one ohm. It was also specified that each tube be accurately calibrated, and that no tube have a caliber correction greater than 5 parts in 10,000. The length of the tube, the mass of mercury the tube contains, and the electrical resistance of the mercury must all be determined at a temperature as near to 0°C. as possible, all measurements being corrected to 0°C.

The four tubes used at the Bureau were selected from a large number of tubes of Jena 59 III glass, specially drawn by Schott and Geñossen, and were straightened, annealed, and graduated by M. Baudin in Paris.

At the Bureau of Standards, they were very carefully calibrated, their caliber factors, ranging from 1.000047 to 1.000096, being determined to an accuracy of about one part in a million. The tubes were cut at points giving a resistance, including the end correction, of approximately one ohm, the cuts being located at points for which the cross-section could be most accurately calculated. The ends were ground and plane polished. The tubes were tapered at the ends to fit into the end bulbs, used in making electrical measurements, and into the glass cleaning and drying fittings.

The Reichsanstalt method was employed for the determination of M_o, the mass of mercury required to just fill a tube at 0°C. A tube was exhausted, filled with mercury and placed vertically within a double walled ice bath, the lower end of the tube being sealed by a plane polished plate, and the upper end, carrying a slight excess of mercury, being protected by a ground glass cap.

The excess of mercury was removed by stroking off with a plane polished glass plate in a gimbal mounting, the condensation of moisture being eliminated by a current of cooled and dried air directed at the end of the tube and at the stroking off plate. Weighings were made in a special balance room, on a Stückrath balance sensitive to a hundredth of a milligram. Six fillings of each tube were made, the mean of the average deviations of the individual fillings from their respective means being but ± 4 parts per million.

The problem of determining L_o, the length of the axis of a tube at 0°C., was reduced, through the use of suitably ruled end pieces of platinum-iridium, from one of comparing end standards to that of comparing line standards. Comparisons were made directly with corresponding known intervals on a nickel-steel meter. The length constant added, due to the end pieces, was determined by abutting the end clips and measuring the interval between the lines on them by comparison with a subdivided decimeter standard. The probable error in the lengths as determined, all things considered, did not exceed five ten-thousandths of a millimeter.

Electrical comparisons of the mercury units were made by the Thomson bridge method, the mercury units and five sealed manganin standards being substituted in turn in the same bridge arm. The ratio coils and the manganin standards were contained in a thermostatically controlled oil bath, while the mercury units were in the ice bath adjoining. Connections from the tubes to the bridge were made by inserting heavy copper conductors in the glass terminal protecting tubes of the end bulbs employed, the tubes being partly filled with mercury.

Seven fillings of each tube for electrical comparison were made in 1911. The international ohm as defined by the four mercury standards was found to be 25.5 millionths smaller than the international ohm as represented by the manganin coils at that time. The average deviation of the four tubes from their mean was but ± 5 parts per million.

A second and third series of electrical comparisons, made in June and December, 1912, showed the mercury standards to have changed with respect to the wire standards. Redeterminations of M_o, L_o and the calculated R_o were therefore made for each tube, the average change found being 1.1, 9.4 and 8.2 parts per million respectively.

On the basis of the above new determinations the international ohm, as represented by the four mercury standards in December, 1912, was 12.5 millionths smaller than the international ohm as represented by the manganin coils at the same time. England, Germany, Japan, Russia, France, and the United States now have mercury standards of resistance. Comparison of the units defined by the mercury standards of the above countries in 1913 (those of France excepted; dates not being available) indicate a very satisfactory agreement, the average deviation of the units of the several countries from the mean being about ± 7 parts per million.

PHYSICAL CHEMISTRY.—*An investigation of fusible tin boiler plugs.*[1] G. K. BURGESS and P. D. MERICA, Bureau of Standards.

An investigation of fusible tin boiler plugs has been conducted at the Bureau of Standards to determine what are the types of deterioration to which they are subject in service and to what these various types are due. The function of the fusible tin boiler plug is, as its name indicates, to give warning by the melting of the tin plug and blowing out of the boiler overheating. The attention of the Bureau has, however, been directed to several instances of the failure of such plugs so to operate, and examination showed that the tin in these plugs had become oxidized in service to SnO_2, melting above 1600°C.

About 1050 plugs—including used and new plugs—were obtained through the courtesy of the Steamboat-Inspection Service, and were examined as to design and construction, and condition and purity of the tin filling. Of the four classes or types of deterioration noticed in such used plugs, one could be pronounced dangerous, and that consisted in the formation of this

[1] To appear as a Technologic Paper of the Bureau of Standards.

oxide SnO_2, either as a solid mass at the fire end of the plug or as a network throughout the tin filling.   It was discovered that this latter form of oxidation in service depended on the presence of zinc in amounts as small as 0.3 per cent.   This zinc is insoluble (that is, it does not form a solid solution with tin) in solid tin, and upon long heating at about 180°C. the zinc in such a tin plug coalesces to form a network bounding the tin grains.   This zinc is easily corroded by many kinds of boiler water, for instance alkaline waters, and the oxide or corrosion products of this zinc and of the tin afterwards attacked, remain and form a solid, continuous oxide mass which in some cases has held the pressure of the boiler even after the tin remaining had melted. Tin plugs containing zinc were made up and heated in an autoclave with water at from 180° to 195°C. for 500 hours, after which this network structure was seen clearly developed.   Plugs of pure tin were unchanged under the same conditions of test.

Lead and zinc were found to be the principal impurities in tin plug fillings, and since all "failed" plugs contained these or other impurities the conclusion is reached that if these impurities are eliminated by strict specifications and inspection, which will allow only admittedly superior qualities of tin such as Banca and some others, the dangers of these plugs will no longer exist.

It was found that a determination of the freezing points of samples of tin by a cooling curve method afforded a very good criterion of the purity of such tin, as approximately 0.1 per cent of either lead or zinc could be detected.   This method was developed and is recommended as a quick and convenient method for the inspection of the purity of tin in tin plugs.

Various existing specifications for fusible tin boiler plugs are discussed in the complete paper and the conclusion is reached that tin equal to Banca tin 99.9 per cent pure should be used for such plugs where possible; where such tin can not be obtained it is likely that tin of 99.8 per cent purity including all high grade tin qualities would be satisfactory.

GEOLOGY.—*Nepheline basalt in the Fort Hall Indian Reservation, Idaho.*[1] GEORGE R. MANSFIELD and ESPER S. LARSEN, Geological Survey.

OCCURRENCE[2]

One of the igneous rock samples collected by the United States Geological Survey party in the Fort Hall Indian Reservation, Idaho, in the summer of 1913, proved upon examination in thin sections to be nepheline basalt. Because of the relative rarity of rocks of this type any new occurrence of them is of scientific interest and is worthy of note. Indeed, nepheline-bearing rocks and all the so-called alkali rocks are very rare on the Pacific slope of North America.

The Fort Hall Indian Reservation is in southeast Idaho and may be conveniently reached from either Pocatello or Blackfoot on the Oregon Short Line Railroad. Pocatello lies about 3 miles south of the central part of the reservation and Blackfoot is on the northern border. The locality of the nepheline basalt is in the northeast part of the reservation about 24 miles nearly due east of Blackfoot. The rock forms a little knoll on a ridge that descends northeast along the north side of Wood Creek in the SW.$\frac{1}{4}$ of the SE.$\frac{1}{4}$ sec. 18, T. 3 S., R. 38 W. Boise meridian. The area occupied by the basalt is small and the occurrence would be insignificant were it not for the unusual mineralogical composition of the rock.

The rocks in the immediate vicinity of the basalt are mainly sedimentary rocks of Triassic and possibly Jurassic age that outcrop in bands extending from northwest to southeast and apparently form the west limb of a syncline that is inclined northeast. The eastern limb of the syncline is more or less concealed by Tertiary sediments and volcanic rocks. The sedimentary rocks are somewhat faulted. The knoll on which the basalt occurs lies in the belt of Portneuf limestone, a massive and siliceous limestone that constitutes the upper formation of the Thaynes group (Lower Triassic). About one-third mile to the northeast are massive ledges of the Higham grit, the basal member of the Nug-

[1] Published by permission of the Director of the U. S. Geological Survey.
[2] By Mr. Mansfield.

get sandstone, of Jurassic or Triassic age. Associated with the nepheline basalt and apparently surrounding it is a rhyolitic rock that was not examined closely in the field but may underlie or be penetrated by the basalt. This rock resembled other fine-textured, siliceous, igneous rocks observed elsewhere in the reservation and no sample was collected. The unusual character of the accompanying basalt was not then recognized and the contact of the two rocks was not observed. No fragments of the rhyolitic rock were found in the basalt although some search for them was made. Inclusions, at first mistaken for pieces of the above-mentioned grit, proved to be fragments of a coarse-textured igneous rock.

Other igneous rocks occur in various parts of the reservation but these all, so far as studied, are normal rhyolites, basalts, andesites, and quartz-latites. In general the igneous rocks lie around the borders of the sediments on the north, northeast, and northwest, and compose larger or smaller portions of the lower hills. They occupy some of the valleys and are accompanied in places by large bodies of ash beds and tuffs.

The geology of the igneous rocks has not been worked out in detail and their geologic age has not yet been accurately determined. Present information points to at least four epochs of volcanic activity, extending from perhaps middle Tertiary into the Pleistocene. The order of succession appears to be an early intermediate or basic series of eruptions with andesites and perhaps basalt followed by outpourings of rhyolite. These were in turn followed by olivine basalts in a number of places, well exposed in the canyon of the Blackfoot River. The latest eruptions appear to have been latitic with both flows and clastics, the last forming an extensive sandy area which is in part dune-covered. The place of the nepheline basalt in this succession is not known, but it appears to be extrusive and is very fresh. It probably was not closely connected with the olivine basalts.

PETROGRAPHY[3]

Description. The nepheline basalt is dark greenish gray and is dense except for a few large, rough cavities. In the hand

[3] By Mr. Larsen.

specimen it shows abundant pale yellowish green grains of olivine up to 2 millimeters across and a few small grains of augite in an aphanitic groundmass. It contains a few small inclusions of shaly material and one large inclusion of a nearly white, granular rock made up almost entirely of striated feldspar and quartz.

Microscopic examination shows the rock to be made up largely of pyroxene and olivine with some nepheline, phlogopite, iron ore, and apatite. The texture is porphyritic and the phenocrysts, which average about a millimeter in cross section, and are chiefly forsterite with some diopside, make up about a third of the rock. They are imbedded in a holocrystalline groundmass made up chiefly of rods and grains of diopside which lie in a clear matrix or are poikilitically included in phlogopite. The clear matrix is probably in part nepheline but may contain some glass. The average cross section of the minerals of the groundmass is about 0.01 mm.

The forsterite is in clear grains of the usual form. In cross sections the grains range from over 2 millimeters to a small fraction of a millimeter, but the greater part are not far from a millimeter. They have the following optical properties: $\alpha = 1.641 \pm 0.003$; $\beta = 1.661 \pm 0.003$; $\gamma = 1.680 \pm 0.003$; $2V = 87°$ (computed from the refractive indices); optically $+$. In convergent light the bars of the interference figure are nearly straight and the dispersion of the optic axes is barely perceptible with $\rho < v$.

In addition to embayments filled with the groundmass the forsterite carries a few inclusions of the iron ore and chains of gas or liquid inclusions. The mineral shows no signs of alteration except for a narrow reddish border which probably represents incipient alteration to iddingsite. A Rosiwal determination on two thin sections showed 24.9 ± 1 per cent by volume or 26.4 per cent by weight of olivine.

The diopside is mostly in the groundmass, but the crystals vary greatly in size and some are a millimeter across. The diopside is nearly colorless but shows a faint greenish cast as compared with the water-clear olivine. A very few of the larger crystals show small cores or narrow zones which are rather deep green and pleochroic. It shows zonal growths with somewhat different extinction angles and a faint hour-glass structure. The extinction angles are very large; those for the green part are the larger, indicating a higher content in iron.

The nepheline is interstitial to the diopside. It is clear, has an index of refraction near that of Canada balsam, and is indistinctly polarizing. It is commonly without crystal outline but square sections are occasionally present. It is in too small grains for positive identification by optical means alone. Some glass may be present; no feldspar was found.

In elongated streaks or irregular patches the abundant diopside rods are embedded poikilitically in mica, the mica forming less than half of the area. This mica is pleochroic, rather light reddish brown parallel to the cleavage and nearly colorless normal thereto. It is probably phlogopite or a biotite rather poor in iron.

Chemical composition. An analysis of the nepheline basalt, made by W. C. Wheeler in the laboratory of the Geological Survey, is given in column 1 below and is accompanied by the analyses of similar rocks for comparison:

Analyses of nepheline basalt and related rocks.

	1	2	3	4	5
SiO_2	45.17	44.99	48.29	39.47	39.92
Al_2O_3	10.02	5.91	10.00	11.26	8.60
Fe_2O_3	3.55	3.42	2.93	8.74	4.40
FeO	5.03	8.30	5.46	4.98	8.00
MgO	19.84	21.02	17.22	14.33	20.17
CaO	8.57	7.89	11.80	12.08	10.68
Na_2O	3.11	0.91	2.78	5.04	1.91
K_2O	1.61	0.74	0.45	1.86	1.03
H_2O-	0.69	3.82	1.95	0.63	0.43
H_2O+	1.58				1.45
TiO_2	0.54	0.97		1.56	2.70
CO_2	none	trace			
P_2O_5	0.28	0.05		0.99	0.51
S	0.06				trace
Cr_2O_3	0.11	0.25			0.14
NiO		none			0.06
MnO	0.13	trace		trace	0.24
BaO	0.07				0.06
SrO	0.06				0.04
	100.42	99.17	100.88	100.94	100.42*

* Including V_2O_3 0.04, F 0.07, and deducting 0.030 for F.

1. Nepheline basalt (III) IV. 1 '(2).₃.2. (1) 2 Rossweinose. About 24 miles east of Blackfoot, Idaho.
2. Periodtite, IV.1.'.₃.'2.'2, Crystal Falls, Mich. H. N. Stokes, analyst. Described by J. Morgan Clement, Jour. Geol., 6: 386. 1898.
3. Gabbro, 'IV.1'.'₃.'2.'2, Etzdorf, Rosswein, Saxony. Sachsse and Becker, N. J., 1893, II, p. 503.
4. Nepheline basalt, 'IV.2.₃.2'.'2, Schafberg Plateau, Saxony, J. Stock, Tsch. Min. Pet. Mitt., 9: 466. 1888.
5. Nepheline basalt, IV.'2.₃.2.'2, Black Mt., Uvalde Co., Texas. W. F. Hillebrand, analyst. Described by Whitman Cross, U. S. Geological Survey, Bull. 419, p. 43.

Classification. The great abundance of augite, olivine, and biotite, and the presence of nepheline as the only feldspathic mineral, places the rock as a biotite-bearing nepheline basalt rather high in olivine.

In the Quantitative Classification the norm and the systematic position of the rock are as follows:

Norm and systematic positions of nepheline basalt from about 24 miles east of Blackfoot, Idaho

or	9.45	Class: Sal = 34.91 = 0.554 (III) IV	
		Fem 63.03	
ab	5.76	Order: PO = 55.96 = 8.74 1 (2)	
		M 6.40	
an	8.62	Section: P = 25.35 = 0.826 3	
		O 30.61	
ne	11.08	Rang: Mg + Fe + K₂O + "Na₂O 568 =	
		CaO =116	
		4.90 '2	
di (MgO: FeO = 12: 1)	25.35		
ol (MgO: FeO = 12: 1)	30.61	Subrang: MgO = 496 = 6.89 (1) 2	
		FeO 72	
il	1.06		
mt	5.34	(III) IV. 1 (2).₃.'2.ₓ (1) 2, Rossweinose.	
ap	0.67		
H₂O, etc.	2.18		
	100.12		

Comparison of the norm and mode. The presence of considerable phlogopite in the norm and the presence of feldspar in the mode and its absence in the norm are the most apparent differences between the two. The following calculation of the mode from the chemical composition and the known mineral composition is no doubt a close approximation to the actual mineral composition.   The composition of the norm is given for comparison.

Mode and norm of nepheline basalt from about 24 miles east of Blackfoot, Idaho

	Mode	Norm	Difference
Apatite	1	1	0
Ilmenite	1	1	0
Magnetite	3	5	2
Biotite	8		−8
Forsterite	26	31	5
Diopside	39	25	−14
Nepheline	20	11	.−9
Orthoclase		9	9
Albite		6	6
Anorthite		9	9
H₂O	2	2	0
Total	100	100	

The comparison of the norm and the mode thus indicates that the norm shows more magnetite, forsterite, and feldspar than the mode and less biotite, diopside, and nepheline.

BOTANY.—*Some new caesalpiniaceous trees of Panama.*   HENRY PITTIER, Bureau of Plant Industry.

The botanical exploration of the Isthmus of Panama begun under the auspices of the Smithsonian Institution in 1910, and since continued occasionally, has brought to light startling facts with reference to the occurrence of certain genera hitherto unknown within that region.   It has been known for a long time that Middle America is mainly a territory of transition between the floras of two continents, in which many genera have their northernmost or southernmost limit, the proportion of either South American or North American species respectively decreasing or increasing according to the distance from their centers of dispersion.   But there was no indication whatever of the very sudden change which takes place in Darien, the eastern part of Panama and the connecting link with South America.

This abrupt transition brings in as new elements of the flora several genera known heretofore as represented exclusively in the Amazonian Hylea or in the eastern part of South America. The presence of these species in a district separated from regions of identical climatic conditions both by imposing mountain ranges and the semixerophytic belt of Colombia and Venezuela constitutes a most interesting problem, the solution of which may not be reached until the interlocking slopes and valleys of Colombia and Venezuela have been thoroughly explored. Among such Panamanian representatives of Brazilian genera one species each of Stachyarrhena, Cassupa, Browneopsis, and Colignonia has already been detected, while many others are certain to appear during the further progress of the work of identifying and naming the extensive collections now at hand.   In the present paper, 3 more species, belonging to 2 genera, are described under the names *Peltogyne purpurea, Centrolobium yavizanum,* and *Centrolobium patinense.* Furthermore, an undescribed species of Dilodendron has been collected in the hilly region of the Chucunaque Valley, while the forests of Darien in general have furnished an unusually strong contingent of Lecythidaceae, among them 1 species of Couroupita, 4 of Lecythis, 3 of Eschweilera, and 2 of Gustavia.

Another interesting fact never brought out before is the considerable development, along the Pacific coast, of the mangrove formation, and the presence in the inner part of the tidal-belt of a characteristic tree allied to the *mora* of Guiana and never described. Besides being of importance as an ecologic element, this species enjoys the peculiarity of possessing the largest known dicotyledonous seed. It also is described below under the name *Dimorphandra megistosperma.*

Centrolobium yavizanum Pittier, sp. nov., ramulis juvenibus foliisque pube molli ferruginea evanescente dense vestitis, petiolis communibus teretibus, longitudinaliter striatis, stipulis ovatis, obtusis, extus dense villoso-lanatis, intus pubescentibus, foliolis membranaceis, breviter petiolulatis, ovatis vel elliptico-lanceolatis, argute acuminatis, basi rotundatis, leviter emarginatis, supra glabrescentibus, infra glabratis, ad costas venasque rufo-villosis; floribus . . . . . ; legumine primum glanduloso-tomentello dein glabrato, aculeis partis seminiferae densis, acicularibus, stili vestigio adscendente, apice recurvato, ala cultriformi, apice rotundata, venis a basi alae adscendentibus, demum a latere stilifero arcuatis.

Arbor decidua, 25–30 metralis, cortice griseo, coma elongata. Petiolus communis 30–50 cm. longus, e basi attenuatus; petioluli circa 3 mm. longi, folioli 13–17, 6.5–12 cm. longi, 4–5.5 cm. lati, jugis inferioribus latioribus brevioribusve, intermediis longioribus. Pedicelli floriferi 7–8 mm. longi, puberuli, bracteolis angustis, 3 mm. longis, persistentibus; calyx glandulosus, ferreo-puberulus, persistens, lobulis obtusis; ovarium stipitatum. Pedicellus fructifer 1 cm. longus, calycem incrassatum sustinens; legumen cum ala 12–14 cm. longum, 4–5 cm. latum, e stipite 2 cm. longo aculeato suffultum, aculeis circa 1.8 cm. longis.

Type in U. S. National Herbarium, no. 716,636.

PANAMA: In virgin forest between Pinogana and Yaviza, southern Darien, leaves and fruits only, April 22, 1914 (*Pittier 6572*, type).

Centrolobium patinense Pittier, sp. nov., ramulis juvenibus petiolisque pube molli fulva vel obscure purpurea dense vestitis, petiolis communibus teretibus, longitudinaliter striatis, stipulis late ovatis, subobtusis, lanatis, foliolis membranaceis, breviter petiolulatis, ovatis, abrupte acuminatis, basi rotundatis nunc emarginatis, ad costas venasque sparse rufo-villosulis, supra pubescentibus, infra glabratis, floribus . . . . .; legumine juveni glanduloso, rufo-tomentello, demum glabrato, aculeis partis seminiferae densis, acicularibus, stili vestigio adscendente, recto, ala flabelliformi, apice oblique truncata, venis a basi alae adscendentibus dein a latere stilifero arcuatis.

Arbor decidua, 30 m. et ultra alta, cortice griseo, ligno duro, rubro-spadiceo, coma elongata. Petiolus communis 30–35 cm. longus; folioli 11–15, 3–12 cm. longi, 2.5–7 cm. lati, jugis intermediis majoribus; petioluli 4 mm. longi. Pedicellus fructifer 1.5 cm. longus; calyx persistens, incrassatus; stipes dense rufo-hirsutus, aculeatus, 1.4 cm. longus; legumen cum ala 17–20 cm. longum, 6–8 cm. latum, aculeis usque ad 3 cm. longis.

Type in U. S. National Herbarium, no. 716,677.

PANAMA: Forest on dry hills at Punta Patiño, southern Darien, leaves and fruits only, June, 1914 (*Pittier 6611*, type).

These two species of a genus hitherto considered as exclusively Brazilian were one of the surprises of my last expedition to Darien. Besides having the characteristically shaped fruit of Centrolobium, they show minor details as to the numerous minute, resinous glands covering the leaves, young shoots, parts of the inflorescence, and the fruits in their first stage of maturity. In shape the fruit of *C. yavizanum* reminds one of that of *C. robustum* Mart., but in size it comes between the two varieties of this latter species and its veins are more strongly arcuate than in either of the two.

In size the fruit of *C. patinense* equals and even surpasses that of *C. robustum macrochaete*, but the form of the wing is quite distinct, its apex being cut in a distinct line almost parallel to the opposite margin. From the other Brazilian species the difference is greater still, so that there can be no doubt as to these Panamanian forms being specifically distinct.

Centrolobium yavizanum and *C. patinense* differ from each other in their leaflets, these more numerous on the average, more elongated, and emarginate at the base in the former, less numerous, shorter and broader, and simply rounded at the base in the latter. The petiolules also are sensibly shorter in the first species, which has comparatively smaller fruits, the wing rounded at the tip like a table knife, and not obliquely truncate as in the latter. The flowers of both species are unknown, the few details included in the description of *C. yavizanum* having been obtained from remnants collected along with the fruits.

Centrolobium patinense is known among the natives of Panama under the name of *amarillo de Guayaquil*, and is reputed as a cabinet wood on account of its hard, fine-grained wood, beautifully veined in several shades of red.

Peltogyne purpurea Pittier, sp. nov., ramis teretibus cortice grisea, ramulis gracilibus, violaceis; foliis deciduis, glaberrimis, stipulis semiovatis, acuminatis, membranaceis, caducissimis; foliolis unijugis, breve petiolulatis, falcatis, acuminatis, inaequilateralibus, basi oblique rotundatis, stipellis filiformibus, caducissimis; inflorescentia racemosa, pauciflora, floribus . . . . .; legumine 1-spermo, pedicellato, semiorbiculato, glaberrimo, suturis angustissimis, laevibus, superiore arcuata, apice mucronulata, inferiore recta, longitudinaliter 1-sulcata; semine oblique ovato, depresso, funiculo in arillum anguste cupuliformem dilatato.

Arbor magna, duramine durissimo, purpureo, cortice griseo, ramulis foliisque glaberrimis. Stipulae 10 mm. longae, 6 mm. latae, stipellae 6–8 mm. longae. Petiolus 1.2–1.7 cm. longus, petioluli 3–4 mm. longi, lamina 5.5–6.5 cm. longa, 2.5–3 cm. lata, eleganter reticulato-venosa. Legumen 3 cm. longum, 1.6 cm. latum, pedicello 7 mm. longo. Semen 1.9 cm. longum, 1.1 cm. latum, "e legumine aperto ejectum diu tamen ei adhaerens."

Type in U. S. National Herbarium, no. 716,675.

PANAMA: On rocky hills along the Chucunaque River beyond Yaviza, southern Darien, young leaves only, April 22, 1914 (*Pittier* 6586); Punta Patiño, southern Darien, on hills along the seashore, leaves and mature pods (*Pittier* 6610,); also noticed by me in the dry forests around La Palma del Darien, and reported from Coiba Island.

Peltogyne purpurea, called *nazareno* or *morado* by the natives of Panama, is one of the most remarkable trees of the forest in the districts with a well defined dry period. It grows preferably on ridges free of higher vegetation. The height of a full grown tree is seldom less than 25 meters and the trunk reaches up to 60 cm. in diameter. The tree is evidently deciduous, as only very young leaves, with the stipules still attached, were found near Yaviza. But at Punta Patiño, a few days later, there were individuals with the old leaves and pods still on, and others with young shoots and leaves only.

One of the peculiarities of the morado tree is that the seed remains hanging from the dehiscent pod by the hilum after maturity, probably until the rainy season sets in. This curious habit, which has been observed also in *Peltogyne congestiflora* Benth., of Brazil, may be considered as a means of protection against ants and other insects, or the extreme dryness of the soil. On the tree, however, the seeds are not immune from attacks, as I found many of them inhabited by a coleopterous insect.

The wood of Peltogyne is very hard, the sapwood white and little developed, and the heartwood of a beautiful purple color.

Dimorphandra megistosperma Pittier, sp. nov., ramis teretibus, verruculosis, brunneis, glabris; foliis exstipulatis, glaberrimis, petiolo communi infra foliola inferiora anguloso, superne plano, subtus tereti; foliolis bijugis, oppositis, coriaceis, breve petiolulatis, oblongo-acuminatis, basi plus minusve inaequilateralibus, apice obtusis, supra nitidis, infra glaucis; floribus sessilibus, densissime spicatis, spicis terminalibus vel subterminalibus; calyce glabro, lobulis rotundatis, ciliatis; petalis oblongis, calyce subduplo longioribus, basi attenuatis, apice rotundatis plus minusve irregulariter emarginatis, margine scarioso ciliato; staminibus fertilibus corolla longioribus, filamentis crassis, leviter attenuatis, antheris apicem antice lanoso-barbatis, demum glabrescentibus; pistillo staminibus subaequante, stipitato, ovario 3-ovulato, dense lanoso, stylo glabro; legumine 1-spermo, glabro, coriaceo, dehiscente; semine maximo, extus brunneo, nitido.

Arbor excelsa, 15–45 m. alta, trunco erecto 10–15 m. longo, usque ad 1 m. diametro, cortice nigrescente, coma elongata. Rhachis foliorum 5–9.5 cm. longa, parte infra foliola inferiora 2.5–5 cm.; petioluli 3–4 mm. longi, incrassati; foliola 10–18 cm. longa, 4.5–7 cm. lata, reticulato-venosa. Spicae floriferae 8–10 cm. longae; calycis lobi inaequales, 3.5–4 mm. longi; petala alba, 6 mm. longa, 2.5–3 mm. lata; stamina et staminodia 7–8 mm. longa. Legumen usque ad 25 cm. longum, 13 cm. latum, leviter depressum. Semen phaseoliforme, usque ad 18 cm. longum, 12 cm. latum.

Type in U. S. National Herbarium, no. 716,658.

PANAMA: In groves, in the tidal forest along the Mamoní River, near its confluence with the Bayano River, Province of Panama, pods and leaves, October 23, 1911 (*Pittier* 4582); below Sumacate, along the Tuyra River, southern Darien, flowers, April 25, 1914 (*Pittier* 6593, type). This species was observed also along the Sta. Lucia River in eastern Chiriquí; around La Palma del Darien, on the margin of the mangrove forest; and along the lower course of the Sambú River, also in southern Darien.[1]

In the course of my exploration of Panama I had repeated opportunities to collect on the beaches of the Pacific and its tributary tidal rivers stray specimens of the enormous seed of the above described tree. Dr. M. A. Howe, of the New York Botanical Garden, had also gathered specimens of the same in the course of his explorations in 1910. The unusual size of this seed made me very anxious to know more about it from my own experience, especially since all queries among European and American botanists failed to procure further enlightenment about it. Finally, the tree producing these beans was discovered, on October 23, 1911, on a point of land at the meeting of the Mamoní and Bayano rivers, below Chepo, in the Province of Panama. Later on it was found again in Chiriquí and Darien, always playing an important rôle as a constituent of the forest of the tidal belt. But my discovery was only partial at that time, because I left the Isthmus without having been able to collect flowering specimens. It was not until April, 1914, that I had the privilege of seeing the *alcornoque*, as it is called by the natives, in full bloom in mile-long stretches along the lower course of the Tuyra River in southern Darien.

The alcornoque is a gregarious tree, seldom found as isolated individuals. With reference to the root system, there seems to be a great variety in the size of the buttresses and the way they part from the base of the trunk. At times they form large wings, generally three in number, reaching up the latter to a distance of 1.5 meters and over; at other times they are low and hardly noticeable. The main roots run horizontally on the surface of the ground and can often be followed

---

[1] In the Kew Herbarium there are specimens of a Panamanian tree, cited as *Dimorphandra oleifera* Triana in Hemsley's botanical part of the Biologia Centrali-Americana (**1**: 342). This species, collected by Sutton Hayes in the swamps of the Río Grande near Panama, has never been described. Through the courtesy of the Director of the Kew Gardens, I am informed that the species is "quite distinct from any species of Dimorphandra (Mora) represented here." In the absence of further data, however, and in order to avoid a possible confusion, I deem it preferable to describe under a new name the material collected by myself.

to a distance of some 15 meters from the trunk; they are flattened laterally and end in several secondary branches, each of which lies on the flat bottom, forming a succession of bow-like arches, with numerous rootlets growing downward at the lowest points.   Around the base of the tree, in parts temporarily submerged, there appear sometimes bunches of thin roots, which are supposed to be pneumatophores.

The trunk is usually straight with a smooth, dark brownish, peeling bark.   It will give logs of 6 to 8 meters, of any diameter up to 1 meter, of a pale brown, tough, close grained wood.   The sap once excluded, this wood is, it is claimed, incorruptible and adapted as a substitute for oak or other hard timbers in their various industrial uses.   According to another statement the wood of the alcornoque is better than any other for structures kept permanently under sea water.

The crown of the tree is elongated and the main limbs are rather short.   The middle-sized specimen which was felled to procure herbarium material was 31 meters high; the trunk measured 10 meters in length and 75 cm. in diameter; the white sapwood had a thickness of 5 to 7 cm.; and the heart was dark reddish.

Botanically speaking the affinities of *Dimorphandra megistosperma* are with *D. excelsa* (Schaub.) Baillon, of British Guiana.   Its leaves, however, are pinnate, with only 2 pairs of leaflets, instead of the 3 or 4 pairs of the latter.   The floral spikelets are not paniculate but solitary at the end or in the upper axils of the branchlets.   In the several ovaries which were dissected a constant number of ovules was found, 3, of which only one reaches maturity.   The enormous pods, once ripe, open with a twist of the valves without parting from the branchlets, and the seed slips to the muddy ground, where germination starts almost immediately.   From the cotyledons the natives extract by infusion a dark red dye.

The dimensions of the pods and seeds are variable.   As reported in the description, the largest specimen found measured 18 cm. in length with a breadth of 12 cm. and a thickness of 8 cm.

REFERENCES

Under this heading it is proposed to include, by author, title, and citation, references to all scientific papers published in or emanating from Washington. It is requested that authors coöperate with the editors by submitting titles promptly, following the style used below. These references are not intended to replace the more extended abstracts published elsewhere in this JOURNAL.

PHYSICS

ABBOT, C. G. *The solar constant of radiation.* J. Wash. Acad. Sci., **4**: 89–110. 1914.

ADAMS, L. H. *Calibration table for copper constantan and platinum-platinrhodium thermo-elements.* J. Am. Chem. Soc., **36**: 65–72. 1914.

AGNEW, P. G. *A watthour meter method of testing instrument transformers.* J. Wash. Acad. Sci., **4**: 509–511. 1914.

AGNEW, P. G., and SILSBEE, F. B. *Accuracy of formulas for ratio, regulation, and phase angle of transformers.* Bureau of Standards Sci. Paper No. 211. 1914.

ALLEN, IRVING C., JACOBS, WALTER A., CROSSFIELD, A. S., and MATHEWS, R. R. *Physical and chemical properties of petroleums of California.* Bureau of Mines Tech. Paper No. 74. 1914.

AUSTIN, L. W. *Quantitative experiments in radiotelegraphic transmission.* J. Wash. Acad. Sci., **4**: 570–572. 1914. Bureau of Standards Sci. Paper No. 226, 17 pp. 1914.

BATES, FREDERICK, and PHELPS, FRANCES P. *Influence of atmospheric conditions in testing of sugars.* J. Wash. Acad. Sci., **4**: 317–318. 1914. Bureau of Standards Sci. Paper No. 221, 18 pp. 1914.

BATES, S. J., and VINAL, G. W. *Comparison of the silver and iodine voltameters and the determination of the value of the faraday.* J. Am. Chem. Soc., **36**: 916. 1914.

BEARCE, H. W. *Supplementary report on the density and thermal expansion of turpentines.* Rep. Committee D1 on Preservative Coating for Structural Materials, pp. 108–112. Proc. Am. Soc. Testing Materials. 1914.

BEARCE, H. W. *Studies in the expansion of milk and cream.* J. Agricultural Research, **3**: 251–268. 1914.

BLEININGER, A. V., and TEETER, PAUL. *Viscosity of porcelain bodies.* Bureau Standards Tech. Paper No. 30, 11 pp. 1914.

BROOKS, H. B. *Testing potential transformers.* Bureau of Standards Sci. Paper No. 217, 5 pp. 1914.

BUCKINGHAM, E. *On physically similar systems. Illustrations of the use of dimensional equations.* Phys. Review, **4**: 345. 1914.

BUCKINGHAM, E. *Physically similar systems.* J. Wash. Acad. Sci., **4**: 347–353. 1914.

BUREAU OF STANDARDS. *Units of weight and measure, definitions, and tables of equivalents,* 1st ed. Circular No. 47, 68 pp. 1914.

BUREAU OF STANDARDS. *Pyrometer testing and heat measurements.* 5th ed. Circular No. 7, 19 pp. 1913.

BUREAU OF STANDARDS. *Polarimetry and polarimetric analyses of raw and other sugars.* Circular No. 44, 140 pp. 1914.

BURGESS, G. K., and FOOTE, P. D. *The emissivity of metals and oxides. I. Nickel oxide (NiO) in the range 600 to 1300°C.* J. Wash. Acad. Sci., **4**: 279–280. 1914. Phys. Zeits. **15**: 721–723. 1914. Bureau of Standards Sci. Paper No. 224, 23 pp. 1914.

BURGESS, G. K., and SALE, P. D. *Thermoelektrische Verfahren zur Bestimmung der Reinheit von Platingeräten.* Zeitsch. Anorg. Chem., **88**: 349–354. 1914.

BURGESS, G. K., and KELLBERG, D. N. *Electrical resistance and critical ranges of pure iron.* J. Wash. Acad. Sci., **4**: 436–440. 1914. Bureau of Standards Sci. Paper No. 236, 13 pp. 1914.

BURGESS, G. K., and WALTENBERG, R. G. *The emissivity of metals and oxides. II. Measurements with the micropyrometer.* J. Wash. Acad. Sci., **4**: 566–567. 1914.

BURGESS, G. K., and CROWE, J. J. *Critical ranges A2 and A3 of pure iron.* Bureau of Standards Sci. Paper No. 213, 55 pp. 1914.

BURROWS, CHARLES W. *Experimental study of the Koepsel permeameter.* J. Wash. Acad. Sci., **4**: 491–492. 1914. Bureau of Standards Sci. Paper No. 228, 29 pp. 1914.

COBLENTZ, W. W. *Measurements on standards of radiation in absolute value.* J. Wash. Acad. Sci., **4**: 565–566. 1914. Bureau of Standards Sci. Paper No. 227, 13 pp. 1914.

COBLENTZ, W. W. *A comparison of stellar radiometers and radiometric measurements on 110 stars.* Phys. Review, **4**: 545. 1914.

COBLENTZ, W. W. *Absorption, reflection, and dispersion constants of quartz.* Bureau of Standards Sci. Paper No. 237, 10 pp. 1913.

COBLENTZ, W. W. *Diffuse reflecting power of various substances.* Bureau of Standards Sci. Paper No. 196, 42 pp. 1913.

COBLENTZ, W. W. *Constants of spectral radiation of uniformly heated inclosure or so-called black body.* Bureau of Standards Scientific Paper No. 204, 77 pp. 1913.

COBLENTZ, W. W. *Note on the radiation from stars.* Astronomical Soc. Pacific, **26**: 169. 1914.

COBLENTZ, W. W. *Die Empfindlichkeit von Thermosaülen.* Phys. Zeits., **15**: 453. 1914.

COBLENTZ, W. W. *Bemerkung über die Konstante der Gesamtstrahlung eines schwarzen Körpers.* Phys. Zeits., **15**: 762. 1914.

COBLENTZ, W. W. *Radiation constants of a nitrogen-filled tungsten lamp.* Lighting Journal, 1914, p. 35.

COBLENTZ, W. W. *Radiation from straight and helical filaments.* Elect. World, **64**: 1048. 1914.

COBLENTZ, W. W. *Various modifications of bismuth-silver thermopiles having continuous absorbing surface.* J. Wash. Acad. Sci., **4**: 511–514. 1914. Bureau of Standards Sci. Paper No. 229, 56 pp. 1914.

CURTIS, HARVEY L. *A vibration electrometer.* J. Wash. Acad. Sci., **4**: 567–569. 1914.

CURTIS, HARVEY L. *The insulating properties of solid dielectrics.* J. Wash. Acad. Sci., **4**: 492–494. 1914.

DELLINGER, J. H. *Resistivity on trial.* Elect. World, **64**: 35–36. 1914.

DICKINSON, H. C. *Combustion calorimetry and heats of combustion of cane sugar, benzoic acid, and naphthalene.* J. Wash. Acad. Sci., **4**: 434–435. 1914. Bureau of Standards Sci. Paper No. 230, 68 pp. 1914.

DICKINSON, H. C., and MUELLER, E. F. *New calorimetric resistance thermometers.* Bureau of Standards Sci. Paper No. 200, 9 pp. 1913.

DICKINSON, H. C., HARPER, 3RD, D. R., and OSBORNE, N. S. *Latent heat of fusion of ice.* Bureau of Standards Sci. Paper No. 209, 31 pp. 1913.

FOOTE, PAUL D. *Note on cold junction corrections for thermocouples.* Bureau of Standards Sci. Paper No. 202, 13 pp. 1914.

FOWLE, F. E. *Avogadro's constant and atmospheric transparency.* J. Wash. Acad. Sci., **4**: 529–530. 1914.

FOWLE, F. E. *Smithsonian Physical Tables.* Sixth Revised Ed. 1914. 355 pp. Smithsonian Misc. Coll. **63**, No. 6. 1914.

GRAY, A. W. *Production of temperature uniformity in electric furnace.* J. Wash. Acad. Sci., **4**: 134–138. 1914. Bureau of Standards Sci. Paper No. 219, 22 pp. 1914.

GRAY, A. W. *Micrometer microscopes.* J. Wash. Acad. Sci., **4**: 45–52. 1914. Bureau of Standards Sci. Paper No. 215, 15 pp. 1914.

GROVER, FREDERICK W. *Analysis of alternating-current waves by method of Fourier, with special reference to methods of facilitating computations.* Bureau of Standards Sci. Paper No. 203, 79 pp. 1913.

HARPER, D. R., 3rd. *Specific heat of copper in the interval 0° to 50°C with note on vacuum-jacketed calorimeters.* J. Wash. Acad. Sci., **4**: 489–490. 1914. Bureau of Standards Sci. Paper No. 231, 70 pp. 1914.

HERSEY, M. D. *The laws of lubrication of horizontal journal bearings.* J. Wash. Acad. Sci., **4**: 542–552. 1914.

HEWLETT, C. W. *The atmospheric-electric observations made on the second cruise of the Carnegie.* J. Ter. Mag., **19**: 127–171. 1914.

HEWLETT, C. W. *Investigation of certain causes responsible for uncertainty in the measurement of atmospheric conductivity by the Gerdien conductivity apparatus.* J. Ter. Mag., **19**: 219–233. 1914.

HEWLETT, G. A., and VINAL, G. W. *Studies on the silver voltameter.* J. Wash. Acad. Sci., **4**: 593–594. 1914.

KANOLT, C. W. *Melting points of some refractory oxides.* Bureau of Standards Sci. Paper No. 212, 19 pp. 1914. Zeits. anorg. Chem., **85**: 1–19. 1914.

KIMBALL, H. H. *A return to normal atmospheric transparency.* J. Wash. Acad. Sci., **4**: 17–25. 1914.

KOLSTER, FREDERICK A. *A direct reading instrument for measuring the logarithmic decrement and wave length of electromagnetic waves.* J. Wash. Acad. Sci., **4**: 569–570. 1914.

MELCHER, A. F. *Note on the change of density of sulphur with rupture.* J. Wash. Acad. Sci., **4**: 431–434. 1914.

NUTTING, P. G. *The brightness of optical images.* J. Wash. Acad. Sci., **4**: 129–134. 1914.

NUTTING, P. G., and JONES, L. A. *A transmission and reflection photometer for small areas.* J. Wash. Acad. Sci., 4: 313-317. 1914.

NUTTING, P. G. *The axial chromatic aberration of the human eye.* J. Wash. Acad. Sci., 4: 385-388. 1914.

OSBORNE, N. S., McKELVY, E. C., and BEARCE, H. W. *Density and thermal expansion of ethyl alcohol and of its mixtures with water* (with bibliography of literature on alcohol and alcoholometry). Bureau of Standards Scientific Paper No. 197, 47 pp. 1913.

REID, H. F. *The free and forced vibrations of a suspended magnet.* J. Ter. Mag., 19: 57-72, 189-203. 1914.

ROSA, E. B., VINAL, G. W., and McDANIEL, A. S. *Silver voltameter. Pt.4. Third series of quantitative experiments and special investigations.* J. Wash. Acad. Sci., 4: 52-58. 1914. Bureau of Standards Sci. Paper No. 220, 56 pp. 1914. Elect. World, 63: 373. 1914. Elecktrotech. Zeits., 35: 789. 1914.

ROSA, E. B., and CRITTENDEN, E. C. *Flame standards in photometry.* J. Wash. Acad. Sci., 4: 280-282. 1914. Bureau of Standards Sci. Paper No. 222, 38 pp. 1914.

STILLMAN, M. H. *Note on setting of mercury surface to required height.* Bureau of Standards Sci. Paper No. 214, 6 pp. 1914.

STRATTON, S. W. *Annual report of directors Bureau of Standards for the fiscal year 1913,* 38 pp. *Report for 1914,* 99 pp.

SWANN, W. F. G. *On the electrical resistance of thin metallic films.* Phil. Mag., (6) 28: 467-496. 1914.

SWANN, W. F. G. *On the expression for the electrical conductivity of metals as deduced from the electron theory.* Phil. Mag., (6) 27: 441-455. 1914.

SWANN, W. F. G. *On certain new atmospheric-electric instruments and methods* J. Ter. Mag., 19: 171-185. 1914.

SWANN, W. F. G. *The measurement of atmospheric conductivity, together with certain remarks on the theory of atmospheric radioactive measurement.* J. Ter. Mag., 19: 23-38. 1914.

SWANN, W. F. G. *The theory of electrical dispersion into the free atmosphere, with a discussion of the theory of the Gerdien conductivity apparatus and of the theory of a collection of radioactive deposit by a charged conductor.* J. Ter. Mag., 19: 81-93. 1914.

SWANN, W. F. G. *On certain matters relating to the theory of atmospheric-electric measurements.* J. Ter. Mag., 19: 205-218. 1914.

SWANN, W. F. G. *Some points with regard to the variation of the specific magnetization of a substance with temperature.* Phys. Review, (2) 3: 485. 1914.

TILLYER, E. D. *Supplementary report on refractive indices of turpentines.* Rep. Committee D 1 on Preservative Coatings for Structural Materials, pp. 113-114, Proc. Am. Soc. Testing Materials.

VINAL, G. W., and BATES, S. J. *Comparison of silver and iodine voltameters and determinations of value of faraday.* J. Wash. Acad. Sci., 4: 69-70. 1914. Bureau of Standards Sci. Paper No. 218, 25 pp. 1914.

WENNER, F., and WEIBEL, E. *Adjustments of Thomson bridge in measurement of very low resistances.* J. Wash. Acad. Sci., 4: 471-473. 1914. Bureau of Standards Sci. Paper No. 225, 3 pp. 1914.

WENNER, F., and WEIBEL, E. *Testing of potentiometers.* J. Wash. Acad. Sci., 4: 469-471. 1914. Bureau of Standards Sci. Paper No. 223, 40 pp. 1914

WHITE, WALTER P. *A significant instance of galvanometer instability.* Phys. Review, (2) **3**: 491–492. 1914.

WHITE, WALTER P. *Thermoelements of precision, especially for calorimetry.* J. Am. Chem. Soc., **36**: 2292–2313. 1914.

WHITE, WALTER P. *Easy calorimetric methods of high precision.* J. Am. Chem. Soc., **36**: 2313–2333. 1914.

WHITE, WALTER P. *Einige neue Doppelkompensatoren.* Zeits. Instrumentenkunde, **34**: 71–82; 107–113; 142–151. 1914.

WHITE, WALTER P. *Thermoelements installations, especially for calorimetry.* J. Am. Chem. Soc., **36**: 1856–1868. 1914.

WHITE, WALTER P. *Potentiometers for thermoelectric measurements, especially in calorimetry.* J. Am. Chem. Soc., **36**: 1868–1885. 1914.

WIGAND, ALBERT. *Measurement of the electrical conductivity in the free atmosphere up to 9000 meters in height.* J. Ter. Mag., **19**: 93–102. 1914.

WRIGHT, FRED. E. *A simple method for the accurate measurement of relative strain in glass.* J. Wash. Acad. Sci., **4**: 294–298. 1914.

WRIGHT, FRED. E. *The optical properties of roscoelite.* Am. Jour. Sci., (4) **38**: 355–359. 1914.

WRIGHT, FRED. E. *The measurement of the refractive index of a drop of liquid.* J. Wash. Acad. Sci., **4**: 269–279. 1914.

WRIGHT, FRED. E. *The optical character of the faint interference figure observed in high power objectives between crossed nicols.* J. Wash. Acad. Sci., **4**: 301–309. 1914.

WRIGHT, FRED. E. *A new half shade apparatus with variable sensibility.* J. Wash. Acad. Sci., **4**: 309–313. 1914.

WRIGHT, FRED. E. *The determination of the relative refringence of mineral grains under the petrographic microscope.* J. Wash. Acad. Sci., **4**: 389–392. 1914.

WRIGHT, FRED. E. *Measurements of refractive indices on the principal optical sections of birefracting minerals in convergent polarized light.* J. Wash. Acad. Sci., **4**: 534–542. 1914.

ENTOMOLOGY

CRAWFORD, J. C. *The species of Perilampidae of America north of Mexico.* Proceedings of the Entomological Society of Washington, **16**: 69–76. June 12, 1914. (Gives tables for the genus Perilampus, describing nine new species, and Chrysolampus, describing three new species.—J. C. C.)

CRAWFORD, J. C. *New parasitic Hymenoptera from British Guiana.* Proceedings of the Entomological Society of Washington, **16**: 85–88. June 12, 1914. (Describes three new Serphidoidea and three new Chalcidoidea.—J. C. C.)

CRAWFORD, J. C. *Some species of the bee genus Coelioxys.* Annals of the Entomological Society of America, **7**: 148–159, figs. 1-6. June, 1914. (Contains a key to the females of the species found north of the Mexican boundary and describes eight new species and one new variety.—J. C. C.)

CUSHMAN, R. A. *A new species of the braconid genus* Phanerotoma *Wesmael.* Proceedings of the Entomological Society of Washington, **16**: 78-79. June 12, 1914.

DYAR, H. G., and KNAB, F. *New mosquitoes from Peru.* Insecutor Inscitiae Menstruus, **2**: 58-62. April 24, 1914. (Describes *Phalangomyia debilis,* new genus and species, and *Aedes epinolus,* n. sp.—J. C. C.)

DYAR, H. G. *The pericopid larvae in the National Museum.* Insecutor Inscitiae Menstruus, **2**: 62-64. April 24, 1914. (Describes the larvae of some species and gives references to the descriptions of larvae which had been published previously.—J. C. C.)

DYAR, H. G. *The noctuid moths of the genera Palindia and Dyomyx.* Proceedings of the U. S. National Museum, **47**: 95-116. May 7, 1914. (Sixteen new species in Eulepidotis (Palinda) and one new species in Dyomyx.—J. C. C.)

HEIDEMANN, O., *O. M. Reuter.* Proceedings of the Entomological Society of Washington, **16**: 76-78. June 12, 1914. (A short biography giving a list of the papers by Dr. Reuter on American Hemiptera.—J. C. C.)

HEINRICH, C. *Notes on some forest Coleophora, with descriptions of two new species.* Proceedings of the Entomological Society of Washington, **16**: 66-69. June 12, 1914. (Describes three new species in this genus.—J. C. C.)

HOOD, J. D. *Two new Thysanoptera from Panama.* Insecutor Inscitiae Menstruus, **2**: 49-53. April 24, 1914. (Describes the new genus Holopothrips, based on two new species.—J. C.C.)

HOWARD, L. O. *Concerning some Aphelininae.* Proceedings of the Entomological Society of Washington, **16**: 79-85, *fig. 1.* June 12, 1914. (Describes Dirphys, new genus, and seven new species; gives a table of the species of Physcus.—J. C. C.)

KNAB, F. *Ceratopogoninae sucking the blood of caterpillars.* Proceedings of the Entomological Society of Washington, **16**: 63-66. June 12, 1914. (Gives records of these flies sucking the blood of caterpillars and describes *Forcipomyia erucicida* and *F. crudelis,* new species.—J. C. C.)

KNAB, F. *Supplementary notes on Peruvian Simuliidae.* Proceedings of the Biological Society of Washington, **27**: 123-124. July 10, 1914. (Describes one new species and gives notes on others.—J. C. C.)

McATEE, W. L. *Key to the nearctic genera and species of Geocorinae.* (*Heteroptera; Lygaeidae.*) Proceedings of the Biological Society of Washington, **27**: 125-136. July 10, 1914. (In addition to key to the genera of Geocorinae of the world, describes the new genus Isthmocoris together with *Geocoris carinatus,* sp. nov., and *G. punctipes* var. *paulus,* var. nov.—J. C. C.)

MALLOCH, J. R. *American black flies or buffalo gnats.* U. S. Department of Agriculture, Bureau of Entomology, Technical Series, No. 26. Pp. 1-70, pls. 1-6. April 6, 1914. (Includes tables for the known larvae and pupae, as well as for the adults; describes the new genus Parasimulium and thirteen new species, and proposes the new name *lutzi* for *minutum* Surcouf & Gonzales-Rincones, not Lugger.—J. C. C.)

MALLOCH, J. R. *Description of a new species of Agromyza from Porto Rico.* Proceedings of the Entomological Society of Washington, **16**: 89-90, *fig. 1.* June 12, 1914.

PROCEEDINGS OF THE ACADEMY AND AFFILIATED SOCIETIES

THE CHEMICAL SOCIETY OF WASHINGTON

The 246th meeting was held at the Cosmos Club, March 11, 1915. W. D. BIGELOW, Director of the Research Laboratory of the National Canners' Association, gave an illustrated lecture on *Some of the problems and difficulties of the canning industry.* Motion pictures were presented showing the work of the Bureau of Chemistry with the various canning industries, especially along the line of the betterment of sanitary conditions in the sardine packing industry, and the solution of the difficulties encountered by corn-packing establishments. The scope of the work of the Canners' Laboratory was given and many of the specific problems were outlined, such as the causes of the darkening of corn and other packed materials, the effect of the nature of the tin plate used in can manufacture on the finished pack, etc. The latter point is being made the object of an extensive investigation by the makers and users of tin plate in coöperation with the government.

Under the head of informal communications H. C. GORE, of the Bureau of Chemistry, discussed the *Preparation and uses of calcium acid malate.* This material is readily prepared from what is ordinarily apple refuse and offers possibilities as a substitute for the acid constituent used in baking powders. Samples of the materials were shown.

The 247th meeting (special) was held at the Cosmos Club, March 17, 1915. Mr. W. S. LANDIS, Chief Technologist of the American Cyanamid Company, presented an illustrated lecture on *The fixation of atmospheric nitrogen.* A review of the methods for the fixation of nitrogen in commercial use was presented, giving particular attention to the manufacture of cyanamid which according to the speaker occupies a preëminent place and has been making steady progress since its introduction by Frank and Caro. Many of the uses of cyanamid in the chemical industries and agriculture and as an intermediate product in the production of ammonia were described. Motion pictures showing the plant of the American Cyanamid Company at Niagara Falls, Canada, in operation presented an interesting feature of the lecture. This lecture is published in full in the *Journal of Industrial and Engineering Chemistry,* **7**: 433–8 (1915).

The 248th meeting was held at the Cosmos Club, April 8, 1915. H. D. GIBBS, of the Bureau of Chemistry, presented a paper entitled, *A study of some palm trees, with special reference to the sugar and alcohol industries.* Practically all the alcohol used in the Philippines is obtained

481

from the sap of palm trees; 97 per cent of this is used for beverages and 3 per cent for industrial purposes or export. While several varieties of palm trees are the source of alcohol in the tropics, the Nipa palm overshadows all for this purpose in the Philippines and may be regarded as the cheapest source of alcohol in the world, the cost of raw materials being about two cents per liter. The sap has at present no value as a source of sugar, as it rapidly becomes impure. When fresh it contains 15 per cent sucrose. Inversion may be prevented by the addition of milk of lime, and enzyme action inhibited by means of SO_2. Sugar obtained in this way on a small experimental scale showed this source to be cheaper than the use of beets or cane; 150 kg. were obtained from 1000 l of sap. The lecture was illustrated by slides showing the various palm trees and the mills used in the experimental work.

There was some discussion as to the nature of the changes in the sap and their cause.

C. S. HUDSON, of the Bureau of Chemistry, spoke on *The acetyl derivatives of the sugars*. A brief review was given showing the various new sugars and types of sugars obtained by acetylation. This reaction is easily carried out except where the sugar is easily hydrolysed. In general the new compounds were crystalline with sharp physical properties. Oxyacetate were also prepared. The preparation of these compounds is important from the standpoint of the constitution of cellulose. More detailed information regarding these compounds and the latest developments are given in papers published in the *Journal of the American Chemical Society*, **37**: 1264, 1270, 1276, 1280, 1283, 1589, 1591 (1915).

Under the head of informal communications, Mr. J. B. TUTTLE, of the Bureau of Standards, spoke on *The requirements and purchase of rubber tubing for laboratory purposes*. The difficulties incurred at the Bureau of Standards in obtaining rubber tubing with a reasonable life and satisfactory rubber content were outlined. Former sources of supply have been cut off by the war and an effort is being made to have American manufacturers take up the manufacture of a good grade of laboratory tubing at a reasonable price. Such samples are now being tried out at the Bureau of Standards.

The 249th meeting (special) was held at the Cosmos Club, April 21, 1915. Prof. A. A. NOYES, of the Massachusetts Institute of Technology, gave a lecture on *A system of qualitative analysis including nearly all the elements*. The speaker reviewed briefly and gave the present status of the work on this subject that has been under way at the Institute for some twenty years. This lecture was also delivered on the occasion of the acceptance by the author of the Fifth Willard Gibbs Medal at Chicago, April 16, 1915; a brief abstract of it will be found in the *Journal of Industrial and Engineering Chemistry*, **7**: 450 (1915).

While the work is not finished in all its details, the fundamentals have been well established and we may expect soon a system of qualitative analysis that has its quantitative aspects also from the stand-point of adequacy and limits of the separation process.

The 250th meeting was held at the Cosmos Club, May 13, 1915. Members of the American Chemical Society resident in Virginia with the exception of Alexandria county have withdrawn, with the permission of the council, from the Washington section, forming a Virginian section with headquarters at Richmond. This withdrawal reduces the membership of the local section from 371 to 318 members, of whom 14 reside in Maryland.

Mr. R. R. WILLIAMS, of the Bureau of Chemistry, formerly of the Bureau of Science, Manila, P. I., presented a paper entitled *Vitamines and beriberi*. The proof of the existence of substances now called vitamines was an outgrowth of the study of beriberi. This is still a disease of primary importance in Oriental countries, though the etiology is now fairly established. Extensive studies and observations throughout the world have shown that the beriberi is produced by the exclusive consumption of a specifically deficient diet such as rice. The deficiency which produces the pathological condition is solely one of so called vitamines. These are ashfree nitrogenous substances which occur in minute quantities in some foodstuffs and are absent in others. Their existence and nature was first demonstrated by Funk in 1911, who was able promptly to cure polyneuritis in fowls by administration of relative minute amounts of a product separated from rice polishings or yeast. As yet, however, no vitamine has been isolated in a pure condition and we have little knowledge of their chemical nature. Twenty-seven cases of human beriberi were treated with vitamine preparations from rice polishings. The result of this treatment proved no less prompt and radical in the case of human beriberi than it had already been shown to be in polyneuritis gallinarum, thus demonstrating more conclusively the essential identity of the two. A temperature reaction was observed following the administration of vitamines to human patients.

The suggestion was offered that beriberi is due to a metabolic tox-aemia which is inhibited or corrected by administration of vitamines. The chemical and pathological evidence in favor of this theory was reviewed and some experimental evidence presented that polyneuritis may be produced by the ingestion of the internal organs of birds dying from the disease resulting from white rice feeding. This view of the function of the vitamines appears to account rationally for the observed facts regarding beriberi. The conception of the vitamines as foods necessary for tissue construction must be subjected to further critical investigation (author's abstract).

Discussion: Dr. VOEGTLIN in the discussion remarked that the modern method of milling corn does not appear to account for pellagra. A similar deficiency is however believed to be important in this disease as well as beriberi.

Dr. SALANT said he had found carrot-fed rabbits more resistant to the toxic effects of tartrates and certain heavy metals than were animals fed on other diets, such as oats. E. C. McKELVY, *Secretary.*

THE GEOLOGICAL SOCIETY OF WASHINGTON

The 295th meeting was held in the lecture room of the Cosmos Club on April 14, 1915.

INFORMAL COMMUNICATIONS

E. W. SHAW: *Sulphur in rocks and in river waters.* Sulphur is indicated by analyses to be about 36 times as abundant in rivers as in rocks and yet the mineral matter of rivers must come directly or indirectly from the rocks. Several questions arise. Is the sulphur being brought back from the sea to the land so that it makes two or more trips while other elements make one? Evidently not. Are there other agents which carry loads in which sulphur is scant or wanting? The dust carried by the wind probably contains very little sulphur, but the quantity reaching the sea is small compared with the rock waste carried by streams. The clay, silt, sand, and gravel carried by streams contain, no doubt, less sulphur than the rocks do, and assist considerably in explaining the discrepancy, but it is known that the amount of material carried in suspension by streams is not more than about twice that carried in solution, and hence if the suspended matter contains no sulphur at all the discrepancy would still be about 1200 per cent. The bottom load of streams is an unknown quantity, but it is probably considerably less than the suspended load. Is sulphur more abundant in rivers because sulphur compounds are in general more soluble than others? The long periods of geologic time and great amount of erosion which the lands as a whole have suffered would seem to nullify this possibility, for in the lowering of a land surface hundreds or thousands of feet, both soluble and insoluble materials, must be removed. But the removal may not proceed at a uniform rate and hence arises the question as to whether or not present conditions are unusual. Apparently they are, first, because of the activities of man in bringing sulphur-containing minerals—pyrite, gypsum, etc.—within reach of streams; and second, because of a generally lower position of ground water surface and thicker zone of active oxidation at present due to the unusual height of the continents and to the withdrawal of water from wells. Coal mining alone is apparently responsible for a considerable part of the discrepancy, especially since most of the waters analyzed come from well settled regions. However, a part of the sulphur sent into the atmosphere is carried out over the ocean and there brought down by rain. Finally, it appears that the amount of sulphur in the earth's crust has been underestimated because, first, the specimens of sedimentary rocks analyzed were taken from at or near the surface where much of the sulphur has been leached out and carried away, and second, because sedimentary rocks are weighted at only 5 per cent, whereas most of the waters have access only to such rocks. The moral is that composite samples of strata lying below the surface of ground water should be made up and analyzed.

F. C. SCHRADER: *A sulphide-bearing monzonite from Arizona.* A description of a monzonite was given, in which pyrite, chalcopyrite, and molybdenite are disseminated throughout the entire rock, apparently as original constituents. Green copper stains are quite common on the rock, and a few mining prospects have been started.

Discussion: A. C. SPENCER said that in his study of the disseminated copper ores of Ely, Nevada, the microscopic examination had led him to infer at first that the copper minerals in these bodies had been deposited as original constituents. He had later come to the conclusion that his first impressions were wrong. SCHRADER said that in his specimens the copper ores occupied an interstitial position as regards the quartz and feldspar. In similar California occurrences described by Turner the same relations had been found. From such relations the original nature of these constituents had been inferred.

REGULAR PROGRAM

J. B. MERTIE: *Copper and gold deposits of the Kotsina-Kuskulana District, Alaska.* The Kotsina-Kuskulana District lies on the south flank of the Wrangell Mountains. The geologic column in this area is as follows: At the base there is a formation composed essentially of tuffs, interbedded lavas, and basic intrusives, with which are associated minor amounts of argillite and limestone. Fossils from the sedimentary members have been determined to be of Carboniferous age. Overlying this conformably is a series of altered basaltic lava flows, about 6,500 feet thick, which are designated as the Nikolai greenstone. Lying upon the Nikolai greenstone without apparent disconformity is the Chitistone limestone, a formation of upper Triassic age about 700 feet thick. This grades upward into thin-bedded limestone and shale, likewise of upper Triassic age, which comprise probably about 5,000 feet of sediments. The youngest hard-rock formations of the area include massive conglomerates, sandstone, and limestone of upper Jurassic age, which lie unconformably on all the underlying formations. Glacial and recent stream gravels occur along the drainage channels. Dioritic rocks intrude all the formations up to and including the upper Triassic sediments.

The copper deposits occur in the basal formation, in the Nikolai greenstone, and to a minor extent in the Chitistone limestone. The copper minerals commonly found are bornite, chalcocite, chalcopyrite, malachite, azurite and native copper, but not all of these are found in any one deposit. The gangue minerals are quartz, epidote, and calcite. The loci of the copper deposits are shear zones. The ore-bodies are irregular in shape and of doubtful persistence. Five types of ore deposits are recognized. All of these types, with the exception of the native copper deposits, are thought to be primary. The presence of a quartz-epidote gangue in much of the ore, considered in relation to numerous quartz-epidote veinlets which have their maximum development in the vicinity of the dioritic intrusives, leads to the belief that the ore deposits are connected genetically with the intrusive rocks. The

486   PROCEEDINGS: GEOLOGICAL SOCIETY

gold deposits are confined to the basal member of the geologic column.
The gold occurs both in the native state, and intergrown with pyrite.
The gangue is dominantly siliceous, with calcite occasionally present.
The gold ores are more often in well-defined veins than are the copper
deposits.

Discussion: SIDNEY PAIGE inquired whether acid solutions might
be capable of depositing the calcite of the ore-bodies, as might be
inferred under the supposition that the deposits were due to atmospheric waters. MERTIE thought it unlikely. SCHRADER inquired
regarding the thickness of the basal formation. MERTIE explained
that folding made it difficult to compute this, but thought that it was
probably about equal in thickness to the Nikolai greenstone, or 6,500
feet.

CHASE PALMER: *The silver precipitating capacity of certain arsenides
as an index of their constitution.* The speaker described a number of
experiments he had made on certain metallic arsenides, in which they
had been subjected to the action of silver solutions. Their silver-
precipitating capacity was believed to afford an indication of the valence
of the iron present.

Discussed by SIDNEY PAIGE.

G. W. STOSE: *The mechanics of a cross fault in the Northern Appalachians.* Cross faults in the Appalachians are generally of two kinds:
(1) Faults in which the thrust plane is so flat that, when slightly folded,
erosion produces deep reëntrants across the strike; (2) shear faults
accompanying thrust faults, resulting from differential displacement.
The fault here described is of the latter class.

South Mountain is broken by a cross fault in southern Pennsylvania.
The rocks affected are pre-Cambrian lavas, Cambrian sandstones,
quartzites, conglomerates, and shales, and Cambro-Ordovician limestones. The fault passes under cover of the Triassic sediments east of
the mountain. Adjacent to the cross fault the formations have been
offset a mile or more. Drag of the beds along the fault is conspicuously
shown on both sides. A transverse depression across the mountain
eroded along the crushed zone of faulting conceals the exposures, so
·that fault brecciation was not observed, but the adjacent metarhyolite
is crushed and intensely jointed. Two major anticlines and the enclosing syncline are the chief structures in the area. Overturned folds
and a prevailing southeastward-dipping schistosity show that the
direction of thrust and pressure at the level here studied is from the
southeast. Therefore the eastern of the two anticlines was the first
to rise, and the oldest pre-Cambrian rocks are brought up along its
axis. The western anticline did not rise so high and is still capped by
the massive Cambrian sandstones which plunge south and pass under
the limestone at the cross fault. North of the cross fault this western
massive anticline of sandstone blocked the way to further westward
movement and the rocks in the syncline between the two anticlines were
intensely folded and faulted. South of the cross fault, however, the
Cambrian sandstone lay so low that westward movement was not

obstructed, but found relief in an overthrust fault in the limestone to the west. The differential horizontal movement resulted in shearing along the plane of the cross fault, which is nearly vertical, and passes into the thrust fault to the west.

Discussion: A. C. Spencer remarked that it was to be regretted that the later Triassic sediments concealed the relations so that the extension of the fault to the eastward could not be traced.

Sidney Paige asked whether the cross-cutting portion of the fault was necessarily vertical. Might it not have a rather shallow dip? Stose explained the evidence which pointed to a steep dip. D. F. Hewett inquired whether there was any indication of thickening of strata on the limbs of the folds which had been described. Stose replied that there was no evidence of this. Sidney Paige asked regarding the evidence of faulting and as to the presence of igneous masses to whose intrusion the compression and folding could be ascribed. Stose cited a number of features which gave evidence of the fault. Regarding intrusions, he said that there was nothing of the kind near enough to attribute the compression to this cause. R. B. Sosman inquired whether the injections of Triassic basalts showed any connection with the fault. Stose replied that none was shown.

C. N. Fenner, *Secretary.*

The 296th meeting was held in the lecture room of the Cosmos Club on April 28, 1915.

INFORMAL COMMUNICATIONS

Sidney Paige: *A model illustrating character of faulting at the Homestake ore-body.* At a previous meeting of the Society the speaker had suggested an hypothesis to explain the origin of the Homestake Ore-Body of Lead, South Dakota. At that time it was pointed out that stratigraphic work on the pre-Cambrian had shown the presence of a fault, on the two sides of which the schist series had divergent strikes, and that the series on the eastern side terminated at this fault line. It was also shown that dolomitic limestones and their impure schistose equivalents formed an important member of the series and occupied precisely the outcrops of the Homestake Ore-Body along the fault line. The folded character of these beds was pointed out and the significance of these folds in determining the shape of the ore-body at various levels within the mine was emphasized. To portray this relationship a plaster model has been constructed and a wooden copy made. Very simple structural assumptions (based on field observations) were made in constructing this model. An anticlinal fold was modeled in wax; on the main fold minor folds were imposed much after the fashion of innumerable instances observed in the field. This fold was given a pitch, was cut at an oblique angle by a fault, and was penetrated by horizontal mine levels. The results are shown in the model. Considering that the solutions which formed the ore-body rose along the fault-plane and permeated the calcareous series for a certain distance only, it is not difficult to see the resemblance between the artificial mine levels and the actual shape of the ore-body as shown on the maps of the 300, 400, and 500-foot mine levels published in U. S. Geological Survey Professional Paper No. 26.

F. C. SCHRADER gave abstracts of the following papers: *Magmatic copper sulphide deposits in Plumas County, Cal.*, by H. W. TURNER and A. F. ROGERS. *Iron ore deposits of Kiruna, Sweden*, by R. A. DALY.

Discussed by LA FORGE and A. C. SPENCER.

REGULAR PROGRAM

C. W. GILMORE: *Some new dinosaurs* (illustrated). The speaker discussed briefly some of the more important discoveries of dinosaurian fossils made in North America during the past two or three years, referring especially to the explorations conducted by the American Museum of Natural History and by the Canadian Geological Survey in the Edmonton and Belly River formations in the Province of Alberta, Canada. He stated that the recent finding of several specimens, with which were preserved impressions of considerable parts of the epidermal covering, leads us to hope that the time is not far distant when the external appearance of these animals will be as well known as is the internal skeleton. Lantern slides of many of the more striking specimens were shown, the speaker confining himself to brief explanatory remarks regarding their systematic position and their more striking characteristics. The following forms were discussed, *Saurolophus*, and *Corthyosaurus* of the trachodont dinosaurs; *Ankylosaurus*, an armored reptile; *Monoclonius*, *Anchiceratops*, *Ceratops*, *Styracosaurus*, and *Brachyceratops*, all of the Ceratopsia or horned dinosaurs. In conclusion life restorations of *Brachyceratops*, *Thescelosaurus*, and *Stegosaurus* modeled by the speaker were exhibited for the first time.

Discussion: SIDNEY PAIGE asked by what means it was possible to distinguish in dinosaurs between adult and young individuals. GILMORE said that the principal distinguishing feature was that in the young the sutures of the skull were open, and in the adult they became closed. R. S. BASSLER spoke in appreciation of GILMORE's work and referred to the scientific attainments and artistic skill required to make the restorations.

C. N. FENNER: *A geological reconnaissance of Porto Rico* (illustrated). The New York Academy of Sciences, with the coöperation of the Insular Government of Porto Rico, has undertaken a natural history survey of the island. A number of expeditions have already been sent out and have made preliminary studies in the botany, zoology, anthropology, geology, etc. The geological expedition consisted of Prof. Berkey, of Columbia University, and the speaker. They spent four weeks on the island during the past summer. A description was given of the principal geologic and topographic features, most of which were illustrated by lantern slides. (The chief results of the expedition have been published by C. P. Berkey in *Annals N. Y. Acad. Sci.*, **26**: 1–70. 1915.

Discussion: T. WAYLAND VAUGHAN stated the results of his expedition to Antigua, St. Bartholomew, and Anguilla in 1914, and gave a résumé of the present status of the geologic correlation of the Cretaceous and Tertiary formations of the Antilles.

Cretaceous: The peculiar Upper Cretaceous fauna of Jamacia has also been found in Cuba and St. Thomas. HILL has noted in Porto Rico "volcanic tuffs and conglomerates with interbedded Cretaceous rudistean limestone similar to that of Jamacia," thereby confirming a previous inference of Cleve that the same horizon which he found in St. Thomas also occurred in Porto Rico. Quin figures a specimen of *Barrettia* from the "Blue-beach" formation of St. Croix and a similar fauna occurs in Mexico. This fauna is closely related to that of Gosau, Austria. Gabb reports Cretaceous in Santo Domingo.

Eocene: Miss MAURY has described from the lower beds of Soldado rock, Trinidad, a fauna which corresponds to that of the Midway group in Alabama, and she correlates the fauna of the uppermost bed of Soldado rock with that of the Wilcox group. VAUGHAN's studies of the fossil corals of Jamaica and St. Bartholomew resulted in the correlation of the Richmond and Catadupa beds of Jamacia with the coraliferous limestone in St. Bartholomew. These deposits appear to correspond to the Ocala limestone of Florida and Georgia. The same or a closely related horizon is represented in Oriente Province, Cuba, in Panama, and in the island of Trinidad. HUSSAKOF has described an Eocene marine fish from Antigua.

Oligocene: VAUGHAN in 1900 correlated the fossil coral reef beds of Antigua with the base of the Chattahoochee formation of Bainbridge, Georgia. DALL identified *Orthaulax* in collections from Antigua, showing that the deposits correspond to the upper group of Oligocene deposits in the southern United States. This horizon or a closely related one has been recognized by VAUGHAN through collections from the following localities: 4 miles west of Lares, Porto Rico; in Oriente Province, Cuba; in Province of Pinar del Rio, Cuba; in eastern Mexico; and in the island of Arube, Netherlandic West Indies. The lower part of the fossiliferous marls and limestones of Anguilla are slightly younger. They may be correlated with the upper portion of the Chattahoochee formation of Georgia and Florida, with the Tampa formation of Florida, and with the Emperador limestone of Panama. DALL has shown that this, or a closely related horizon, is found in Santo Domingo. DALL has indicated parallelism between the Bowden beds of Jamaica and the Chipola horizon in Florida. The Bowden horizon, as is shown by fossil corals, is present at several places in eastern Costa Rica. Perhaps the upper part of the Anguilla limestone and marls may be of this age. Upper Oligocene deposits are wide-spread in Cuba, Costa Rica, and Panama.

Miocene: As no undoubted Miocene has been identified in the West Indies, this is supposed to have been a period of high uplift.

Pliocene: Pliocene has not been positively identified in the West Indies, but some of the fossil corals from Santo Domingo are suggestively similar to species found in the Caloosahatchee marl of Florida.

R. T. HILL spoke of work which he had done years before in the West Indies, and expressed gratification that the New York Academy of Sciences had taken up the Porto Rican field. He mentioned some of the structures which had been exhibited in the views and advanced the opinion that the islands of Porto Rico, Santo Domingo, and Cuba, with the connecting banks, represented horsts left at a high relative elevation by the down-sinking of faulted blocks at the sides. SIDNEY PAIGE inquired about the structures shown in the San Juan formation, whose origin FENNER had ascribed to the consolidation of old sand-dunes. He thought that for such an origin the cross-bedding should be of a somewhat different type than that shown. FENNER replied that the reference to such an origin had been made because of the areal distribution of these hills along the north coast and because of the internal structures, which were difficult to account for otherwise. A. C. SPENCER inquired as to whether any mineral deposits had been seen and as to the mineral resources of the island. FENNER replied that indications of mineral were known at various places and several of these had been visited. The only active work being done was a little gold-washing by natives along streams, but prospects had been opened up in gold, copper, lead, and iron.

R. B. SOSMAN: *Types of columnar structure in igneous rocks* (illustrated). From the physical standpoint two principal types of columnar structure may be distinguished. The first and most common is that due to contraction of the crystallized rock during cooling, whereby strains and stresses are produced which yield different sizes and kinds of prisms according to the magnitude of the temperature gradient, the rate of cooling, and other factors. The second type arises from convectional circulation of the still liquid rock. Experiments on low-melting materials have demonstrated that the vertical transfer of heat by convection is capable of dividing a liquid into hexagonal cells which leave their record in the crystallized mass and control its further division by contraction into hexagonal columns. The two methods produce prisms which differ in attitude, in the relation of diameter to length, in the frequency of 4, 5, 6 and 7-sided polygons, in the frequency of certain angles, and in the type of their cross-jointing. Attention was especially called to the usefulness of quantitative data on prismatic structures in igneous rocks as an index to the original conditions of occurrence of the rocks containing these structures.

C. N. FENNER,
C. H. WEGEMANN, *Secretaries.*

The 297th meeting was held in the lecture room of the Cosmos Club on May 12, 1915.

INFORMAL COMMUNICATIONS

R. B. SOSMAN: *Two subordinate types of prismatic structure.* In addition to the two principal types discussed at the meeting of April 28, two subordinate types should be distinguished. The first of these is due to contraction in a physically heterogeneous material (mixture of solid and liquid) and is fundamentally different from the type produced by prismatic division in a cooling solid; a common example is mud cracks produced by drying. The second type is due to internal expansion, whereby the surface is stretched and broken; a prismatic structure produced in a cement briquet by internal expansion was shown as an example. It was suggested that the "weather cracks" on the surface of diabase boulders are of this type, and that they are due to sub-surface hydration and expansion, which produces a tension in the surface of the block.

REGULAR PROGRAM

R. C. WELLS: *The solubility of magnesium carbonate in natural waters.* Under atmospheric conditions at 20°C. magnesite was found to dissolve in pure water to the extent of 0.018 gram magnesium and 0.065 gram total carbon dioxide per liter, and somewhat more in solutions of other salts. But some natural waters freely exposed to the air contain much more magnesium and carbon dioxide than this. A true equilibrium was obtained at 20° only with $MgCO_3.3HO_2$ as solid phase, the final solubility being 0.37 gram magnesium and about 1.00 gram CO_2 per liter.

Discussion: T. WAYLAND VAUGHAN said he had been greatly interested in a closely related subject—that of the solubility of calcium carbonate in sea-water. He had come to the conclusion that the sea-water was very nearly saturated with calcium carbonate and that anything which disturbed the equilibrium would be apt to precipitate the carbonate. He had experiments in mind to ascertain whether $MgCO_3$ might not be thrown down with $CaCO_3$ under natural conditions.

W. H. FRY: *The weathering stability of minerals as illustrated in soils and soil-like materials.* Soils from various climatic, physiographic, and geologic regions of the United States were examined petrographically. The minerals identified are as follows: quartz, orthoclase, plagioclase, muscovite, biotite, hornblende, augite, calcite, dolomite, chlorite, serpentine, olivine, kaolin, sericite, limonite, hematite, magnetite, and a great variety of less common minerals. As to mineralogical composition, the various soils resemble each other qualitatively; but quantitatively they differ widely. Orthoclase occurs both fresh and altered. Microcline always occurs as fresh fragments. Acid plagioclases generally appear as fresh grains, while the more basic ones are at times deeply altered. Hornblende sometimes shows a tendency to alter to chlorite. Epidote shows practically no signs of chemical alteration. The micas are apparently very stable. Tourmaline, rutile, and zircon usually occur as fresh crystals, although occasionally the edges are rounded. Garnet appears to be fairly resistant. Magnetite appears to alter to the hydrated sesquioxide of iron. Quartz is the most abundant of the soil minerals, and occurs both as primary and secondary grains. Judging from the mineralogical composition, the processes of soil-weathering tend to leach out the alkalies and alkaline earths, to separate iron as the oxide, leaving silica and insoluble Mg and Al silicates. In general, the percentage of quartz increases with increase of exposure of the soil to the weathering agencies.

Discussion: R. B. Sosman inquired whether any distinction is made between the effects of purely mechanical processes of destruction and those due to chemical alteration. Fry replied that in soils there was usually no means of finding out which process had been most effective. D. F. MacDonald inquired whether sizing had been used in the analysis of soils. Fry said that it had. F. E. Wright asked as to percentage of quartz grains in soils, and also as to whether the mineral composition gave any indication of fertility. Fry answered that in the Norfolk soil the silica formed 97 per cent. As to fertility, the mineral composition formed at least as good a basis for judgment as chemical analysis. E. T. Wherry asked whether the secondary enlargement of quartz grains took place after the grains had left the parent rock. Fry said he had no means of deciding this. La Forge asked regarding limestone soils—whether the variety of minerals found could be attributed to contributions by wash from foreign sources. Fry said that limestone soils showing no such contributions possessed a great variety of minerals.

G. R. Mansfield: *Geology of the Fort Hall Indian Reservation, Idaho.* The physiographic history is complex, involving at least three cycles of erosion. Numerous physiographic features are due to vulcanism. The sedimentary rocks include a long sequence of formations ranging in age from early Cambrian to Quaternary, but with no representatives of the Cretaceous. The geologic section corresponds with that of the Montpelier district in southeastern Idaho. The revision of certain Triassic formations in the reservation is found advisable. The Nugget sandstone is divisible into four members: (4) main sandstone member 1500± feet thick, (3) Wood shale 220–250 feet, (2) Deadman limestone 150 feet, (1) Higham grit 500 feet, at the base of the formation. The Thaynes limestone becomes the Thaynes group with three members: (3) Portneuf limestone at the top 1500± feet, (2) Fort Hall formation 800 feet, (1) Ross limestone 1350 feet. Igneous rocks occur in considerable variety and abundance, with much fragmental material. An interesting single occurrence of nepheline basalt is reported. The general sequence of igneous rocks seems to have been (1) an earlier basic or intermediate lava, (2) acid eruptives, (3) basalt, (4) latite, the last being perhaps as late as middle or late Pleistocene. The structure is very complex in detail and is marked by both faulting and folding. There seem to have been at least three epochs of deformation. The Putnam Overthrust, a fault comparable with the Bannock Overthrust and with other great faults in the Rocky Mountain region, is particularly noteworthy. Phosphate deposits occur in the eastern part of the reservation. The main bed appears to average about 6 feet in thickness and to be of 70 per cent or better quality. The tonnage estimate for the reservation is 738,526,700 long tons. Other mineral deposits of the reservation are negligible except the great deposits of volcanic ash, which may later have some value as abrasives.

Discussion: J. B. UMPLEBY spoke of several points which had interested him because of his work in the Mackay district. The general sequence of formations in the two districts was quite similar, and the sequence noted by LINDGREN in the Boise district was also similar, but the thickness of members of the Paleozoic rocks and certain other characteristics were quite unlike, and in the Hailey district there is little in common. R. B. SOSMAN spoke of the vanadium content of the phosphate rock and asked if this was deleterious in using as a fertilizer. There seemed to be no information on this point.

C. N. FENNER, Secretary.

ANTHROPOLOGICAL SOCIETY OF WASHINGTON

The 485th meeting of the Society was held in the Public Library, March 16, 1915, the program consisting of a paper by Dr. MANUEL V. ARGUELLES, University of the Philippines, Manila, P. I., entitled, *The Filipino racial complex.* The lecturer defined the present Filipino race as a mixture of Malay stock from the South, with an infusion of Chinese and Hindu, their early culture being largely of Chinese origin. The aboriginal occupants of the islands were represented by the surviving Negrito remnant, a black dwarfish race of lowest culture status.

At the 486th meeting of the Society, held April 6, 1915, in the Public Library, Dr. GUDMUND HATT, of the University of Copenhagen, read a paper entitled *At home with Lapps and reindeer,* which was illustrated with lantern slides. The Lapps, or Samoyed (Samid), live in the northern part of Norway, Sweden, and Finland, and on the Kola peninsula in Russia. Of the total number of 30,000, about 6000 are reindeer nomads. The nomadic Lapps are a factor of economic value, for by means of their large reindeer herds they utilize vast stretches of mountain land which otherwise would be of no value. Although the Lapps have for centuries been under strong influences from the surrounding peoples, they retain much of their old culture. This is due to the fact that old thoughts and habits are closely and necessarily connected with their nomadic life as reindeer herders. They cannot further their business by imitating sedentary populations. The inner life of the mountain people, therefore, although they are thoroughly Christianized, still retains important old traits, which, however, are not easily noticed by foreign observers. The younger generation does not retain much of the old thought, but among the middle-aged and the old are still found beliefs, customs, and tales that supplement and interpret their early mythology.

According to Lappish beliefs, the world is full of supernatural powers, which are not clearly defined or classified. These seem to have been recruited from the ghosts of the dead. A belief in an underground people is prominent. These are called by some Lapps "saivo," and are generally invisible and haunt certain saivo places. These saivo people are believed to be reindeer breeders. Several facts make it appear that the saivo world originally was the world of the dead; thus, in some shamanistic tales the shaman goes to the saivo world to fight for the recovery of a sick person, and until recent years offerings have been made to the saivo world, in order to prolong the life of a person. A belief is also common in certain vagrant spirits, "muones," who bring sickness to people; their traits disclose their original nature as spirits of the dead, although they are not now always conceived as such. The Lappish shaman, or noaide, still uses the ghosts of dead persons as helping spirits. There is, however, also among the Lapps a belief in local spirits, which probably have nothing to do with the spirits of the dead. According to the beliefs of the northern Lapps, every thing and every locality may be inhabited by local spirits, "haldek," who in some way are the owners of these localities. In Pithe he heard a Lapp woman sing a song to the locality when the tent was set up in a new place, and a song of parting when the camp was moved again. Important supernatural powers are connected with the lodge, in which every place has some occult significance. The place behind the fire is still sacred; the fire itself or the powers of the fireplace have some intimate connection with the renewal of life, as can be seen from certain old customs.

The Lapps have always been considered great magicians. The magic drum, which was still in use in some parts of Lapland 50 years ago, has now disappeared, and magic is much less prominent than in earlier times. As magic knowledge is a personal possession which loses part of its power by being given to others, information is hard to obtain. The main purposes of Lappish magic are, to bring sickness and death to men and reindeer and to cure sickness. Sickness is always due to some sort of spiritual contagion, which may come from the dead but also may come from the earth, stagnant water, whirlwinds, or certain rocks. The evil influences are driven back to the place whence they came, by terrifying the hostile power. The magician, therefore, in his magic formulas, talks in a superior and commanding way to the sickness-bringing power. In order to remove the evil influence, the sick part may be touched by the same object from which the evil came— very much as electricity is unloaded by means of a conductor. The two concepts, individual spirits and supernatural power, are in Lappish magic and religion usually connected; but in some cases the idea of power itself is so highly emphasized that it seems devoid of personality.

The idea of reindeer luck is characteristic of the Lapps. Reindeer luck is the standard form of happiness, for which our modern idea of wealth can not be substituted. In order to insure reindeer luck, sacrifices until lately have been in vogue. The main feature in sacrifice of reindeer is that not a single bone must be broken, for in the bones resides the vital principle, and in the saivo world the bones will again be clothed with flesh. In ordinary slaughtering no bone is hurt; the slaughtering of reindeer must be done in accordance with old rules.

Reindeer bones were in former days sometimes placed in a spring; this was believed to restore life. According to Lappish ideas the relations between reindeer and man are rather intimate. In former days the same deity took care of the birth of children and of reindeer calves. A reindeer's life can buy life for man, and the life of a human being can buy reindeer luck.

At the 487th regular and 36th annual meeting of the Society, held April 20, 1915, Dr. HENRY R. EVANS, of the Bureau of Education, read a paper on *The old and new magic*. In addition to explanations given in his book under this title, the speaker held, in common with others taking part in the discussion, that thought transference and even hypnotism might be the real explanation of peculiar phenomena exhibited by so-called mediums and clairvoyants. At any rate, this would throw light upon some of the spiritualistic seances in which he had taken part. In interviews with "psychics" in different parts of the country, a knowledge was shown by these exhibitors of the occult that could not possibly have been obtained through any ordinary channels of information. Although "orthodox" science sneers at so-called telepathy, many eminent psychologists have little doubt that there is a basis of fact underlying clairvoyance and thought transference which has not as yet been fully worked out in a scientific manner.

Mr. J. N. B. HEWITT said that shamans among the Iroquois were all jugglers and had annual meetings at which they showed their skill. They believed that each trick came from a "dangerous dream." Each juggler was obliged at these meetings to show a new trick or he forfeited his life, and a simple trick answered the purpose if it deceived the other jugglers. Jugglers could swallow pebbles, knives, and the like, by the use of a tube inserted in the throat, made of a piece of *Angelica*. They also caused "appearances" in the smoke after putting tobacco and perfumes upon the fire. A juggler that could not tell the meaning of a dream also forfeited his life.

Mr. FRANCIS LA FLESCHE related some tricks played by the Pawnee jugglers. One feat, the swallowing of a deer's head, he could not explain. "Arrows" were swallowed which were made of a vine soaked and greased so as to render them pliable. Pawnee tricks were more remarkable than those described by the speaker of the evening, in that the jugglers were nearly nude, remained in the midst of the audience, and did not use any of the aids employed by professional prestidigitators. Medicine men sometimes avenged themselves by playing tricks that seemed simple enough when explained. One secretly tied a horse's hair tightly around the exposed tip of the tail of the offender's horse, causing the animal to walk backward in circles until restored to its normal condition by the medicine man on payment of a fee.

Mr. MOONEY spoke of remarkable hypnotic phenomena which he had observed among the Indians. He believed in the possibility of hypnotizing an entire audience of Indians, especially during the ghost dance, when subjects become hysterical. After a Wichita dance he saw a subject who offered unusual resistance finally hypnotized. First, a black handkerchief was waved by the shaman before the eyes of the woman as she circled in the dance, then an eagle's feather. After a half hour's struggle, during which time she trembled as if in agony and at times braced herself to avoid falling, she finally fell rigid, as others had done. The speaker had seen ten or twenty persons stretched upon the ground in a hypnotic trance in the remarkable dramatic performance of the Hopi Indians.

Dr. E. L. MORGAN reported having seen an Indian shaman manipulate a man who had been shot in the chest, and produce by sleight-of-hand the bullet from his back. It is said that American Indians also perform a trick similar to the famous mango trick of India, making a bush grow in a few moments under a buffalo robe. Most spiritualistic phenomena are to be explained, he thought, as mind reading.

Dr. GUDMUND HATT, of the University of Copenhagen, said that much of Lapp magic also is explainable by hypnotism. Very susceptible persons can not only be strongly influenced, but cured from sickness, or made sick, or even killed, by the hypnotic influence exercised by Lapps. Many Scandinavians believe this, and there are well authenticated instances of it. Lapps also understand "second sight;" instead of a crystal, they use a glass of liquor. In one such instance a Lapp saw a favorite deer of his which was being treacherously killed in a distant place; the fact was afterwards confirmed.

Dr. JOHN R. SWANTON was elected President of the Society for the ensuing year; Dr. I. M. CASANOWICZ, Vice-President; and WILLIAM A. BABCOCK a member of the Board of Managers. The following officers were reëlected: Secretary, Dr. DANIEL FOLKMAR; Treasurer, Mr. J. N. B. HEWITT; Councilors: Mr. FRANCIS LA FLESCHE, Mr. GEORGE C. MAYNARD, Dr. EDWIN L. MORGAN, and Mr. FELIX NEUMANN.

DANIEL FOLKMAR, Secretary.

JOURNAL

OF THE

WASHINGTON ACADEMY OF SCIENCES

Vol. V AUGUST 19, 1915 No. 14

GEOLOGY.—*Plumbojarosite and other basic lead-ferric sulphates from the Yellow Pine district, Nevada.*[1] ADOLPH KNOPF, Geological Survey.

Plumbojarosite and beaverite. The gold, platinum, and palladium in the quartz lode at the Boss mine, Clark County, Nevada, are especially associated with plumbojarosite, a basic lead-ferric sulphate.[2] The mineral occurs as small masses of comparatively pure ocher enclosed in a fine-grained quartz mass, which forms a replacement of a Carboniferous dolomite, the country rock at the mine. It is a greenish-yellow mineral whose most obvious physical feature is its smooth talc-like feel. Under the highest power of the microscope the ocher is seen to consist of perfect hexagonal tablets averaging 0.01 mm. in diameter. Very rarely triangular plates can be found. Dr. F. E. Wright has kindly determined certain of the optical properties of the mineral and for comparison has also determined the refractive indices of the analyzed plumbojarosite from American Fork, Utah,[3] and from

---

[1] Published with the permission of the Director of the U. S. Geological Survey.

[2] Knopf, Adolph, A gold-platinum-palladium lode in southern Nevada. U. S. Geol. Survey Bull. 620-a, 1–18. 1915.

[3] Hillebrand, W. F., and Wright, F. E., A new occurrence of plumbojarosite. Am. Jour. Sci., 4th Ser., 30: 191–192. 1910. In this paper the refractive index ω is given as greater than 1.83; at that time it could not be determined more closely, as index-solutions of higher indices than 1.83 had not then been prepared.

the Red Warrior mine, Beaver County, Utah.[4]   The results of the
measurements for sodium light are:

Refractive indices of plumbojarosite

SOURCE OF MATERIAL	ω	ϵ
Boss mine, Nev..............	1.876 ± 0.005	1.784 ± 0.005
American Fork, Utah........	1.878 ± 0.005	1.784 ± 0.005
Red Warrior mine, Utah......	1.872 ± 0.005	1.783 ± 0.005
Cook's Peak, N. Mex.*.......	1.872	1.786

* This unpublished determination, made by E. S. Larsen (on the type
material originally analyzed by Hillebrand), has been added for the sake of
completeness.

In regard to this material Wright states that "The differences
in refractive indices between the different samples are not great
and within the limits of error, which I have put purposely large
because of the character of the material.   Of the three samples
that from the Red Warrior mine seemed to contain the most
impurity in the form of opaque inclusions scattered through the
crystals.   The sample from Nevada is much finer grained than
the other two."

Chemical composition.   An analysis of the plumbojarosite from
the Boss mine has been made by Dr. R. C. Wells.   This is given
in the following table together with the analysis of the Utah
material   whose   indices   were   determined   by   Wright.   For
comparison   the   composition   calculated   from   the   formula
$PbO3Fe_2O_34SO_36H_2O$ is also given.

The silica and titania shown by the analysis represent a mechanical admixture of quartz and octahedrite crystals, which
remain as a residue after dissolving the mineral in hydrochloric
acid; the precious metals are present in minute metallic particles.   In spite of the apparent homogeneity of the analyzed
material and its optical identity with the very pure mineral
from American Fork and Beaver County, the material from the
Boss mine shows a divergence in chemical composition from the
other analyzed specimens, the most important being the lower

[4] Butler, B. S., and Schaller, W. T., Some minerals from Beaver County,
Utah. Am. Jour. Sci., 4th Ser., **32**: 422. 1911.

ferric iron, the high content of bismuth, and the noteworthy amount of copper, an element not present in considerable quantities in the previously published analyses of plumbojarosite.

Analyses of plumbojarosite

	BOSS MINE NEV.	AMERICAN FORK UTAH	BEAVER CO. UTAH	CALCULATED
Fe₂O₃...........	32.24	42.87	42.11	42.38
Al₂O₃..........	0.14			
PbO..........	16.75	18.46	18.32	19.74
K₂O..........	0.22	0.15	} 0.13	
Na₂O..........	0.52	0.52		
SO₃............	24.08	27.67	27.59	28.33
H₂O−..........	0.02			
H₂O+..........	8.55	10.14	9.16	9.55
CuO..........	1.97	0.10		
CaO..........	0.06	0.06		
MgO..........	0.14			
Insol..........		0.40	2.64	
ZnO..........			0.30	
SiO₂..........	6.90			
TiO₂..........	0.37			
Bi₂O₃..........	6.34			
CO₂............	0.43			
As₂O₅..........	0.09			
P₂O₅..........	Trace			
Au.............	0.79			
Pt.............	0.05			
Pd.............	0.22			
Ag.............	Trace			
	99.88	100.37	100.25	100.00

The presence of this copper suggested the possibility that the analyzed material contains an admixture of beaverite ($CuOPbOFe_2O_3 2SO_3 4H_2O$), a mineral recently discovered by Butler, and shown by him to occur in some abundance in the oxidized ores of Utah.[5] Under the microscope the optical prop-

[5] Butler, B. S., and Schaller, W. T., Some minerals from Beaver County, Utah. Am. Jour. Sci., 4th ser., **32**: 418. 1911. Butler, B. S., Occurrence of complex and little known sulphates and sulpharsenates as ore minerals in Utah. Econ. Geology, **8**: 316–318. 1913.

erties of beaverite are nearly identical with those of plumbojarosite. It is seen to be crystallized in minute hexagonal
plates of yellow color. According to Mr. E. S. Larsen[6] the
optical properties of the type material are: Optically negative,
probably uniaxial; $\omega = 1.83$; $\epsilon = 1.79$. From these data it is
obvious that under the microscope the only way of distinguishing plumbojarosite from beaverite lies in determining the refractive index ω of the hexagonal plates.

Computation of analysis

	ORIGINAL ANALYSIS	RECALCULATED ANALYSIS	MOLECULAR RATIOS	REQUIRED FOR BEAVERITE	REQUIRED FOR PLUMBOJARO- SITE
Fe_2O_3	32.24	38.18	0.239	0.027	0.219
Al_2O_3	0.14	0.17	0.002	0.002	
SO_3	24.08	28.50	0.356	0.058	0.292
PbO	16.75	19.82	0.089	0.029	0.060
H_2O	8.55	10.12	0.562	0.116	0.043
CuO	1.97	2.33	0.029	0.029	
K_2O	0.22	0.26	0.003		0.003
Na_2O	0.52	0.62	0.010		0.010
	84.47	100.00			

$$\left. \begin{array}{l} 0.027 \times 694 = 18.74 \\ 0.002 \times 636 = 1.27 \end{array} \right\} = 20.01 \text{ per cent beaverite.}$$

$$\left. \begin{array}{l} 0.060 \times 1131 = 67.86 \\ 0.003 \times 1002 = 3.00 \\ 0.010 \times 972 = 9.72 \end{array} \right\} = 80.58 \text{ per cent plumbojarosite.}$$

100.59

On careful re-examination of the material from the Boss mine by
immersion in a liquid of index of approximately 1.84 certain of the
hexagonal plates were found to have indices that were below this
value, and the remainder were found to .exceed considerably
this value. Those of the lower index were then determined by
F. E. Wright to have an index whose value is 1.84 ± 0.01, suggesting strongly, therefore, the presence of beaverite. The
chemical analysis was then computed as follows: The bismuth,
which is possibly present in the native state, since no compound

[6] Personal communication.

to which it can be referred was recognized under the microscope, the silica, titania, the minor constituents, and the precious metals are regarded as impurities; the analysis was recalculated to 100 per cent. The molecular ratios were then obtained, the CuO was used to determine the amount of beaverite, and the other constituents were allotted in accordance with the formula $CuOPbOFe_2O_32SO_34H_2O$; the remaining PbO together with the alkalis, was used to determine the amount of plumbojarosite according to the formula $PbO3Fe_2O_34SO_36H_2O$.

This summation of the calculated mineral composition to 100.59 strongly confirms the microscopic diagnosis that the analyzed material is a mixture of plumbojarosite and beaverite.

Vegasite, a newly recognized basic lead-ferric sulphate. A straw colored ocherous mineral, forming relatively pure lumps up to several inches in size, occurs at the Rosella prospect, which is situated several hundred feet north of the Boss mine. Qualitatively it gives the reactions of plumbojarosite, but quantitative data show apparently that it is a new mineral. It differs from plumbojarosite in specific gravity, refractive indices, and molecular ratios.

Under the highest power of the microscope the mineral is found to be exceedingly fine grained. It is well crystallized, however, showing principally minute fibers; but scattered among these are also a considerable number of six-sided plates, apparently belonging to the hexagonal system. The plates are all under 0.01 mm. in diameter and range down to 0.002 mm. By causing the fibers to move with a rotatory motion through the liquid in which they are immersed, it can be seen that the fibers represent the edges of the hexagonal plates.

The plates are isotropic; the fibers are strongly birefringent and give parallel extinction. The mineral is therefore probably uniaxial. The fibrous sections are markedly pleochroic, ranging from brownish yellow to pale yellow, the absorption being $\epsilon > \omega$. The indices as determined by the immersion method are: $\epsilon = 1.82 \pm 0.01$ and $\omega = 1.755 \pm 0.002$; the mineral is therefore optically positive.

An analysis of this mineral was made by Dr. R. C. Wells in the laboratory of the U. S. Geological Survey.

Analysis of basic lead-ferric sulphate, Yellow Pine district, Nevada

		MOL. RATIOS	
SiO₂	1.14		
Fe₂O₃	38.90	0.243 ⎫	0.276 or 2.88
Al₂O₃	3.33	0.033 ⎭	
H₂O−	0.94		
H₂O+	10.77	0.598	0.598 or 6.23
SO₃	24.60	0.308	0.308 or 3.21
PbO	18.44	0.083 ⎫	
Na₂O	0.76	0.012 ⎬	0.096 or 1
K₂O	0.10	0.001 ⎭	
CaO	0.45	0.008	
MgO	0.49	0.012	
	99.92		

Specific gravity: 3.458.

The interpretation of this analysis presents some difficulty. If the small amounts of silica, lime, and magnesia are neglected as belonging to impurities, the ratios suggest the formula $PbO3Fe_2O_3.3SO_3.6H_2O$, in which the lead has been isomorphously replaced to a minor extent by sodium and potassium, and the ferric iron partly by aluminum. This formula, however, cannot be interpreted rationally; moreover, the considerable amount of hygroscopic water suggests the possibility that colloidal hydrates of aluminum and iron are present. Under the microscope the material appears to be of high purity; nevertheless in such minutely crystallized material, a gram of which would probably contain more than 6,000,000 crystals, it is quite possible that a considerable amount of impurity might be included and escape detection; nor would such an admixture be surprising, as was pointed out by Hillebrand and Penfield in the original paper on plumbojarosite, where a similar computation was made.[7] Possibly the material analyzed represents a mixture consisting of a basic sulphate of the composition $Pb [Fe (OH)_2]_4(SO_4)_3$

[7] Am. Jour. Sci., 4th ser., **14**: 215–216. 1902.

and aluminum and iron hydroxides amounting to about 10 per cent.

The name vegasite[8] is suggested for the mineral from Las Vegas, the principal town of the county in which it occurs. Briefly, vegasite may be characterized as a mineral giving chemical reactions similar to those of plumbojarosite, but distinguishable by widely different optical constants.

BOTANY.—*Eysenhardtia polystachya, the source of the true Lignum nephriticum mexicanum.*[1] WILLIAM EDWIN SAFFORD, Bureau of Plant Industry.

INTRODUCTION AND HISTORY

Among the wonderful products of the New World brought to Europe shortly after the discovery of America was a Mexican wood supposed to be efficacious as a diuretic and therefore called lignum nephriticum. Water kept in cups of this wood and an infusion of its chips in spring water had the remarkable property of reflecting a blue color, though apparently colorless or yellow when held up to the light in a glass receptacle. This led to the experiments of Athanasius Kircher,[2] in 1646, and afterwards to the more systematic study by the Hon. Robert Boyle, in 1663, which may be regarded as the first serious investigation of the phenomenon now known as fluorescence.[3] One result of Boyle's work was to make lignum nephriticum a classic wood. Strange to say, however, the botanical identity of the plant from which this wood was derived has remained uncertain until the present day. Though celebrated throughout Europe in the 16th, 17th, and the early part of the 18th centuries, sacrcely a fragment of

---

[8] The "e" in the first syllable should be given the Spanish pronunciation: like "a" in late.

[1] Based upon a paper entitled "The rediscovery of Lignum nephriticum," read by the author February 2, 1915, at a meeting of the Botanical Society of Washington. Published with the permission of the Secretary of Agriculture.

[2] "Of a certain wonderful wood coloring water all kinds of colors," in Ars Magna Lucis et Umbræ, pp. 77 and 78. 1646.

[3] Boyle, Robert, Experiments and considerations touching colours, p. 203. 1664.

it is now to be found in drug collections, and its very name has disappeared from encyclopedias.

Monardes (1565) was the first to call attention to the wood, but he knew nothing of its origin except that it came from Mexico. Hernández, writing about the year 1576, described the plant producing it under the name *coatl*, or *coatli*, as follows: A shrub or tree with leaves like those of a chick-pea (*Cicer arietinum*) but smaller, and with spikes of small longish flowers. The color of the flowers he described as yellow and faded; but he evidently drew his description from dried material, as was the case with the majority of plants described by him, which were gathered and brought to him by Indian herb doctors. Hernández was a physician rather than a naturalist, and many of his descriptions and illustrations of both plants and animals are so crude as to be unrecognizable. Of lignum nephriticum he gave no illustration. He was even uncertain regarding the plant producing it, stating that they had described it to him as a shrub, but that he had seen specimens of it exceeding very large trees in size. Hernández's work on the products of Mexico remained in manuscript for almost two centuries and never appeared as a whole. The portions of it relating to medicine were grouped together and prepared for publication by Nardo Antonio Recchi; but owing to lack of funds or for some other reason Recchi's compilation did not appear until 1751, seventy-three years after Hernández's death, though a Spanish translation from Recchi's Latin manuscript by Fray Francisco Ximénez appeared in 1615, in the city of Mexico.

In the meantime the plant itself remained unidentified botanically. Caesalpinius (1583) and Caspar Bauhin (1623) supposed it to be a species of Fraxinus. Terrentius, in Recchi's epitome of Hernández (1651), referred it to the Leguminosae but did not attempt to identify it. Johan Boeclerus (1745), believing it to be a Laburnum, called it *Cytissus mexicanus*. Linnaeus, in his Materia Medica (1749), added to the confusion by referring it to *Moringa pterygosperma*, an East Indian tree, in spite of the fact that it was originally declared to be of Mexican origin; and Gui-

bourt, in his Histoire abrégée des drogues (1820), identified it
with the West Indian cat's-claw (*Mimosa unguis-cati* L.).

The first to indicate its true botanical classification was Dr.
Leonardo Oliva, Professor of Pharmacology in the University of
Guadalajara. In his Lecciones de Farmacología[4] he identified
it with *Varennea polystachya* DC. (*Viborquia polystachya* Ortega;
Eysenhardtia amorphoides H.B.K.). Subséquent authorities,
however, did not accept his identification. Dr. Fernando
Altamirano (1878), while recognizing the identity of the *coatli*
of Hernández with the tree called by the modern Mexicans *palo
dulce* and referring it to *Viborquia polystachya* Ortega, was not
aware that the latter was the same as *Eysenhardtia amorphoides*
H.B.K., and he followed Alfonso Herrero in referring lignum
nephriticum to *Guilandina moringa*, a mistake which may be
traced at once to Linnaeus. In describing the uses of *coatli*
wood by the modern Mexicans, he states that the country people
make drinking-troughs of it for their fowls, to guard against
certain epidemics to which the latter are subject; or, if the vessel
from which they drink is of some other substance, they put a
piece of the wood in the water and allow it to remain there. The
water assumes a blue color, he says; but Mariano Barcena, who
experimented with it, observed that the blue color was the result
of the refraction of light, and the water, instead of yielding a blue
coloring matter like indigo, yielded a yellowish brown dye-stuff.[5]

Sargent, in his Silva of North America, gave an amended
description of the genus Eysenhardtia, in which he for the first
time established the combination *Eysenhardtia polystachya*, but
it is evident that he was unaware that this species had anything
to do with lignum nephriticum, or that its wood yielded a fluorescent infusion. Concerning it he simply says: "The wood of
some species is hard and close-grained and affords valuable fuel.
The genus is not known to possess other useful properties.[6]

The third edition of the Nueva Farmacopéa Mexicana (1898)

[4] 2: 429. 1854.
[5] Altamirano, Fernando, "Leguminosas indígenas medicinales," in La Natural-
eza, 4: 97–98. 1879.
[6] Sargent, C. S. The Silva of North America, 3: 30. 1892.

506   SAFFORD: LIGNUM NEPHRITICUM

repeats Oliva's observations under the heading "Taray de Mexico," but in a footnote states that *leño nefrítico* had been erroneously attributed to *Varennea polystachya*, or *Eysenhardtia amorphoides* H.B.K., and that its classification was not known.[7] In a subsequent edition of this work the name *palo dulce* is omitted, except as applied to the European licorice. Flückinger and Hanbury, in their well known Pharmacographia (1879), are silent about lignum nephriticum, although for years before the publication of this work Hanbury had been seeking to identify it.[8] Dragendorf refers to it as a species of Guajacum.[9] Otto Stapf, however, guided by Ramírez and Alcocer's Sinonimía vulgar y científica de las plantas Mexicanas (1902), referred a piece of wood labeled *"cuatl"* in the Paris Exposition to *Eysenhardtia amorphoides;* but the wood was unaccompanied by botanical material by which it might be identified with certainty.[10] He gives a history of the wood known as lignum nephriticum in early literature, and also quotes several Mexican authorities but not Oliva, cited above. He accounts for the fact that the flowers were described by Hernández as yellow by the supposition that there are varieties of Eysenhardtia yielding lignum nephriticum which have yellow flowers, although, as a matter of fact, no such forms occur in the localities cited by writers on the subject; and the only species in which the flowers are yellow are low scrubby plants which never attain the size even of a small tree or have a stem with a diameter approaching the dimensions of the pieces of lignum nephriticum hitherto described. The last author to investigate the origin of lignum nephriticum is Dr. Hans-Jacob Möller, of Copenhagen, who after an exhaustive study of the subject referred it to a Mexican tree belonging to the

[7] Nueva Farm. Mex. 153. 1896.

[8] See Oliver and Hanbury, in Admiralty Manual of Scientific Inquiry, p. 391. 1871. "Lignum nephriticum.—This rare wood, noticed by some of the earliest explorers of America, is a production of Mexico. To what tree is it to be referred? Its infusion is remarkable for having the blue tint seen in a solution of quinine."

[9] Das Lignum nephriticum der älteren Medicin wird wohl von einer Guajacum-Art stammen." Dragend. Heilpfl. 345. 1898.

[10] See Stapf, Otto. Kew Bull. Misc. Information, 1909, pp. 293–305. 1909.

genus Pterocarpus. Dr. Möller made a careful examination of the various woods hitherto supposed to be the true lignum nephriticum mexicanum, among them specimens of the wood of *Eysenhardtia amorphoides*, sent to him by C. A. Purpus, the latter described as "das Kernholz von einen recht dicken Ast," but with negative results ("keine Fluoreszenz)." On examining the heartwood of a Philippine species of Pterocarpus, however, he found that in water containing lime it yielded an infusion having the characteristic sky-blue fluorescence of lignum nephriticum mexicanum as described by early investigators. He therefore assumes that the mother-plant of lignum nephriticum mexicanum, "sought in vain for 300 years by so many investigators, is a Mexican species of Pterocarpus," in all probability *Pterocarpus amphymenium* DC. (*Amphymenium pubescens* H.B.K., *Pterocarpus pubescens* Sprengel); and he refers a second kind mentioned by Hernández, endemic in Quauchinango, to *Pterocarpus orbiculatus* DC.[11]

There can be no doubt that the heartwood of some species of Pterocarpus does yield a fluorescent infusion; but the "lignum nephriticum mexicanum," or "*coatl*," of Hernández, the leaves of which are described as "resembling those of *Cicer arietinum* but smaller," and which are also compared with the finely divided leaves of the common wild rue, cannot possibly be identified with any known Mexican species of Pterocarpus. The leaflets of the species of Pterocarpus figured by Möller himself exceed 6 cm. in length by 3.5 cm. in breadth.

IDENTIFICATION OF LIGNUM NEPHRITICUM

In connection with his work on the economic botany of Mexico the writer has for years been seeking the source of lignum nephriticum. Among other woods examined for the blue fluorescence characterizing this wood were specimens of branches of *Eysenhardtia polystachya*, collected by the writer in 1907 in the vicinity of Aguascalientes, the infusion of which gave no evidence of fluorescence in ordinary sunlight. From this fact and from the

[11] Möller, Hans-Jacob. Lignum nephriticum. Berichte der Deutschen Pharmaz. Gesellsch. **23**: 88–154. 1913.

fact that all specimens seen by the writer were either shrubs or trees too small to yield wood for the manufacture of bowls and cups, the writer was inclined to agree with Möller in discarding Eysenhardtia as a source of the famous wood. In July, 1914, however, specimens of a medicinal wood from Mexico were brought to the writer accompanied by herbarium material from the same tree sufficient to identify it. It proved to be *Eysenhardtia polystachya*, commonly known by the modern Mexicans in many localities as *palo dulce*, or "sweet wood." Its collector had not noticed anything peculiar about the color of its infusion, but dwelt upon its efficacy as a cure for certain diseases to which fowls are subject in Mexico. The wood was a section of a tree trunk, which deprived of its bark was 7 cm. in diameter, and which, unlike all specimens of Eysenhardtia wood hitherto seen by the writer, consisted chiefly of dark brown, dense, fine-grained heartwood very much like *Guaiacum officinale* in appearance, surrounded by a ring of brownish-white sapwood 5 to 8 mm. thick. A few small chips of the heartwood in ordinary tap-water tinged the latter a golden yellow, which soon deepened to orange, and looked like amber when held between the eye and the window. When the glass vial containing the liquid was held against a dark background the liquid glowed with a beautiful peacock blue fluorescence, very much like that seen in quinine. Placed partly in a sunbeam, half of the liquid appeared yellow and the other half blue; and when the sunlight was focused upon it by the lens of a common reading glass, the vial appeared to be filled with radiant gold penetrated by a shaft of pure cobalt. There was no longer any doubt as to the identity of the wood. It could only be the true lignum nephriticum of Robert Boyle's experiments; and it was undoubtedly the wood of *Eysenhardtia polystachya*, a tree with small pinnately compound leavs which might well suggest those of a chick-pea or of the common wild rue of Spain, and with spikes of small flowers which had turned yellowish in drying, corresponding with Hernández's description of the *coatl* of the Aztecs.

Chips of the sapwood tinged tap-water only slightly at first, but when left over-night the infusion deepened to a greenish yellow and glowed with a decided fluorescence. With distilled water neither the sapwood nor the heartwood produced fluorescence, as seen by ordinary sunlight; but this phenomenon was distinctly visible when, at the suggestion of Dr. Arno Viehoever, U. S. Department of Agriculture, these infusions were held in the ultraviolet rays of a fluorescence lamp, and it was also displayed in ordinary daylight when a small amount of sodium carbonate or other alkali was added to the infusions of the wood in distilled water. On boiling chips of the wood in tap-water for several hours a deep amber-colored extract was obtained not unlike Madeira wine in color. When placed on the table the surface of this extract appeared to be outlined by a deep blue marginal ring, and when held away from the light the fluorescence of the liquid gave it the appearance of certain mineral oils. A drop of the extract in a glass of water caused the whole glass to glow with fluorescence when held in the rays of the sun admitted through a hole in a screen.

At a conversazione at the house of Dr. Alexander Graham Bell, on the evening of January 6, 1915, at which the wood and accompanying herbarium material were shown by the writer, specimens of the infusion when exhibited by ordinary electric light failed to show fluorescence; but afterwards, when held in the rays of an arc light the liquid glowed with an intense blue which illuminated the faces of those standing near by.

Experiments were made by Dr. Lyman J. Briggs, Biophysicist of the Bureau of Plant Industry, with a view to determine the possible value of lignum nephriticum as an indicator in titrimetric determinations. The result of Dr. Briggs' observations have not been published, but he recognized at once the advantage which this, like other fluorescent substances, must have over those indicators which show color changes only by transmitted light, especially in testing dark liquids, in which the color of the liquid masks the color changes of the indicator. Eysenhardtia wood has one great advantage over fluorescein itself, from the fact that its extract is readily soluble in cold water. With most acids it does not fluoresce, but in the presence of acetic acid its fluorescence is not destroyed. It cannot, therefore, be used as an indication of alkalinity in all cases. As compared with phenolphthalein it has a neutral point nearer the acid end of the scale; that is to say, it will fluoresce in a solution in which phenolphthalein develops no color whatever.

FURTHER BOTANICAL HISTORY

As already stated, the first description of the plant yielding lignum nephriticum is that of Hernández, written about the year 1575, but first published in the form of a Spanish translation, in the city of Mexico, by Ximénez, in 1615. It is as follows:

They call *coatl* a plant which they describe as a shrub; but I have seen it larger than very large trees; and some call it *tlapalezpatli*, or "blood-red medicine." It is a large shrub which has a thick trunk devoid of knots, like that of a pear tree. The leaves are like those of the garvanzo [*Cicer arietinum*], but smaller and almost like those of rue [*Ruta chalepensis* L.] and somewhat larger, a mean between these two extremes; the flowers yellow and faded, small and longish, are arranged in spikes. . . . It grows in moderately warm regions like the valley of Mexico, and in still warmer situations like Guachinango [state of Puebla], Chimalhuacan [district of Texcoco], Chalco, and Tepuztlan [near Cuernavaca, state of Morelos] and almost throughout ·the entire extent of the *malpais* [pedregal or lava-beds] of Coyohuacan; and in many other places.

· Following Monardes, whose description of the wood he quotes, the author tells of the blue color of the infusion of the wood and of its virtues as a diuretic; and he adds: "There is another kind of plant of this nature, but it does not color the water;" and on his return trip to Spain he says: "In this fleet there is a Viscayan merchant who is taking more than fifty large logs of this wood to Spain."

From the above description it is evident that Hernández refers to two distinct species, the first of which, with leaves resembling those of *Cicer arietinum* and *Ruta chalepensis* and with spikes of small longish flowers, is undoubtedly *Eysenhardtia polystachya*, which never exceeds the size of a small tree. It was undoubtedly the wood of this species which Robert Boyle used in making his experiments on fluorescence. The second is in all probability one of the trees called by the Aztecs *tlapalezpatli*, or *tlapaliz-patli* (from *tlapalli*, tincture; *eztli*, blood; and *patli*, medicine), and by the Spaniards *sangre de drago*, or dragon's blood. Among the latter are species of Pterocarpus, which grow to much larger dimensions than the Eysenhardtia, and one of these was in all probability the source of the large logs carried to Spain by the Viscayan merchant mentioned by Hernández. Hernández never described a Pterocarpus botanically, and in all probability he never saw specimens of their leaves or flowers. As already indicated, none of them has leaves with small leaflets in any way comparable to those of *Cicer arietinum* or of *Ruta chalepensis*.

THE GENUS EYSENHARDTIA

Following is the original description of the genus Viborquia of Ortega,[12] with a reproduction of Ortega's original illustration (fig. 1). The name itself, on account of its prior use for another genus by Konrad Moench of Marburg, in 1794, under the form Viborgia, had to be abandoned in favor of the much later name Eysenhardtia of Humboldt, Bonpland and Kunth, proposed in 1823.[13]

GENERIC CHARACTER

CALYX tubular-campanulate, five-toothed at the mouth; teeth equal, obtuse, very small, the two upper ones more remote, broader, and a little deeper.
COROLLA papilionaceous. *Vexillum* cuneiform, emarginate, carinate, with the margins involute. *Wings* longer than the keel, spathulate, falcate, within concave above. *Keel* two-petaled, spathulate, falcate, within concave above.
STAMENS ten. *Filaments* shorter than the corolla, united into a cylinder cleft above. *Anthers* subrotund, incumbent, bifid at the base.
PISTIL with the *ovary* oblong compressed. *Style* subulate, ascending, a little longer than the stamens. *Stigma* capitate.
LEGUME oblong, compressed flat, subfalcate, containing the seed at the apex.
SEED oblong-reniform, affixed to the apex of the legume.

DIFFERENTIAL CHARACTER

CALYX 5-toothed, the two upper teeth the broader. *Corolla* composed of 5 petals: vexillum cuneiform, the remaining petals spathulate. *Legume* sessile, foliaceous, 1-seeded, containing the seed at its apex.

[12] Hort. Matr. Dec. **5**: 66. 1798.
[13] Nov. Gen. et Sp. **6**: 489. 1823.

Fig. 1. *Eysenhardtia polystachya* (Ortega) Sargent. A copy of Ortega's original illustration, with details of flower and fruit.

DESCRIPTION OF EYSENHARDTIA POLYSTACHYA

The plant positively identified as yielding the lignum nephriticum of Hernández may be described briefly as follows:

Eysenhardtia polystachya (Ortega) Sargent, Silv. N. Am. **3**: 29. 1892 (excl. Texas references).
Viborquia polystachya Ortega, Hort. Matr. Dec. **5**: 66, *pl. 9.* 1798.
Eysenhardtia amorphoides H.B.K. Nov. Gen. et Sp. **6**: 491, *pl. 592.* 1823.
Varennea polystachya DC. Prodr. **2**: 522. 1825; Oliva, Lecc. Farm. **2**: 429. 1854.

An erect, sweetly aromatic shrub or small tree, glandular-punctate, with spreading, recurved branches. Leaves even-pinnate or odd-pinnate, with numerous small opposite or alternate stipellate leaflets, these oval or oblong-elliptical, entire, usually decreasing in size toward the extremity of the rachis, the terminal one of odd-pinate leaves usually obcordate, the others rounded or slightly retuse at the apex and often terminating in a short acumen, pubescent when young, often becoming glabrate, usually punctate with glandular dots on the lower surface; rachis grooved above, irregularly glandular-dotted, often retaining the persistent minute subulate stipels after the leaflets have fallen. Flowers fragrant, small, white, turning yellow in drying, borne in terminal densely spicate racemes; pedicels subtended by a lanceolate deciduous bracteole, short and slender, often reflexed at length, but sometimes ascending or widely spreading; calyx glandular-punctate, 5-toothed, persistent; corolla scarcely at all papilionaceous, composed of 5 nearly equal unguiculate petals, the standard slightly broader than the wings and keel, emarginate, carinate, with involute margins; stamens 10, diadelphous, the superior one free, the filaments of the others united into a tube; ovary subsessile, oblong, compressed, terminating in a long slender style, somewhat longer than the stamens, geniculate and glandular below the apex; stigmas introrse. Legume small, oblong, compressed flat, subfalcate or almost straight, subtended by the persistent companulate calyx and tipped by the persistent base of the style, usually glandular-punctate, indehiscent, pendent or abruptly reflexed, sometimes widely spreading or ascending but never erect and appressed, purplish at the apex when fresh, usually containing a single seed near the apex.

This species was first described by Gómez Ortega, under the name *Viborquia polystachya* in 1798, as shown in the synonymy given above, from specimens grown in the Royal Garden of Madrid from seeds sent by Sessé from Mexico. Ortega named the genus in honor of "Viborq, most distinguished professor of the botanical garden of Copenhagen, who, when a short time ago he journeyed through Spain and visited Madrid, left in us deep appreciation of his kindliness and his conversation." The generic name Viborquia had to be aban-

Fig. 2. *Eysenhardtia polystachya* (Ortega) Sargent. A Tamaulipas specimen, showing reflexed legumes and cross-section of the trunk (lignum nephriticum). Natural size.

doned for the reason given above, and that of Eysenhardtia H.B.K. substituted for it.

The general range of the genus Eysenhardtia is from Guatemala to Texas and Arizona. On account of their great variability it is difficult to delimit the species. It is quite certain, however, that the low shrubby *Eysenhardtia texana* Scheele, with erect appressed falcate seed-pods, the type of which was collected by Lindheimer in the vicinity of New Braunfels, Texas, is a valid species quite distinct from *E. polystachya* of central and southern Mexico, which often attains the size of a tree; and it is quite probable that the more robust *E. adenostylis* Baillon, of Guatemala, is also a valid species. On the other hand *E. orthocarpa* Watson, of western Texas and southern Arizona, approaches so closely to forms of *E. polystachya* collected in the Valley of Mexico, Jalisco, and Michoacán, that it may prove to be specifically identical with them. A critical study of the genus Eysenhardtia is greatly to be desired. The group of low scrubby plants including *Eysenhardtia spinosa* Engelm., *E. parvifolia* Brandeg., and *E. peninsularis* Brandeg., is so distinct from typical Eysenhardtia that it is quite possible it may have to be removed from this genus.

Eysenhardtia polystachya, as understood by the author, is remarkably variable in size and form of leaves, density of pubescence, and appearance of seed pods. It sometimes occurs as a stunted bush with very small leaflets, sometimes as a spreading shrub with straight stems, and sometimes as a slender tree 5 to 7 meters high, the wood of which is prized by cabinet makers on account of its hardness, durability, and fine, dense, straight grain. In the vicinity of Mexico City on the pedregales, or lava beds, sometimes called the *malpais*, a form with small pubescent leaves is the most prevalent. In the northern Mexican states it occurs on elevated dry plateaus in the form of shrubs about 2 meters high with relatively small leaflets. A distinction has been made between the forms having reflexed pedicels and those with ascending or spreading pedicels; but in the barrancas of Jalisco forms very closely allied are found almost side by side, some with mature pods reflexed, and others with them ascending but never closely appressed as in *E. texana*. In this region also there are subglabrous forms with seed pods at least twice as large as those of the type.

In addition to the localities mentioned, specimens of *Eysenhardtia polystachya*, or of forms so closely allied to it as to be scarcely distinguishable, have been collected on the volcanoes of Colima, near the Pacific coast of Mexico, and Orizaba, near the Gulf coast; on the high water-shed between Chilapa and Tixtla, in the State of Guerrero; in the State of Oaxaca at elevations of 1500 to 1800 meters, especially on the slopes of barrancas or canyons; and in northeastern Michoacán, where the trees are large enough to yield valuable cabinet wood. A specimen in the U. S. National Herbarium collected at the station of La Junta, Michoacán, by Langlassé (no. 226) is described by the collector as "arbre au tronc élancé; bois, recherché pour ébénisterie, prouduit une teinture bleue." The specimens in the Economic Herbarium of the U. S. Department of Agriculture, including the wood with fluorescent properties, described in the present paper, were collected in north-central Tamaulipas, not far from the village of San Nicolás. They are shown in figure 2.

DENDROLOGICAL NOTES

Microscopic sections of the wood of *Eysenhardtia polystachya* were made at the writer's request, by Dr. Albert Mann, Plant Morphologist of the Bureau of Plant Industry, and by Mr. C. D. Mell, Assistant Dendrologist of the Forest Service. Dr. Mann found the heartwood to be extremely compact, heavily lignified, and impregnated with a gum, or resinoid substance, which did not break down in xylol. This gum is contained in tracheae, which in cross sections appear like pores, either solitary or in groups of two or three. Radial and tangential sections show the tubes, with pitted walls, to be partly or entirely filled with this gum, and they also show the medullary or pith rays, which in the cross-sections are inconspicuous. The annular lines of growth, however, are well marked in the cross sections.

Specimens of Philippine lignum nephriticum (*Pterocarpus indicus*) commercially known as *narra*, from Baggao, province of Cagayan, Island of Luzon, were obtained by the writer from the newly installed wood-collection in the U. S. National Museum. This wood bears little resemblance to that of Eysenhardtia. In the specimens obtained the color was a beautiful deep flesh tint variegated with light red; the grain coarse and somewhat twisted; and the annular lines of growth, as seen in the cross-section, very distinct, with conspicuous large pores between them. Chips of this wood in tap water yielded a yellow infusion of a lighter shade than that of *Eysenhardtia polystachya* but reflecting a very similar blue fluorescence.

SUMMARY

Lignum nephriticum mexicanum, a wood remarkable for the blue fluorescence of its infusion in spring water, was celebrated throughout Europe in the 16th century as a diuretic. Its botanical identity has remained uncertain until the present time.

It proves to be the wood of a leguminous tree, *Eysenhardtia polystachya* occupying an exensive range in the interior of Mexico. The botanical description of the tree corresponds well with that of Hernández written in the 16th century. Its pinnately compound leaves bear a general resemblance to those of *Cicer arietinum* and also suggest the divided leaves of *Ruta chalepensis*. Its small flowers, arranged in spicate clusters, though white when fresh, soon turn yellow in dried specimens. Its wood, straight-grained and dense and free from knots, yields a tincture in spring-water (containing a slight percentage of lime) which shows a remarkable blue fluorescence and in an opaque vessel appears quite blue.

Its botanical identity remained uncertain for so long a time owing to the following causes; (1) Commercial specimens of the wood were unaccompanied by botanical material; (2) botanical material in herbaria was lacking in wood; (3) the phenomenon of fluorescence as seen in ordinary daylight is produced by an infusion of the dark-colored heartwood, while the light-colored sapwood of stems and of moderate-sized branches, though yielding a fluorescent infusion as seen in ultra-violet rays, does not yield a fluorescence perceptible in daylight; (4) the plant was first described from a shrub in all probability too young to possess heartwood, and the author of the species was unaware of its identity with lignum nephriticum or even of its power to produce the phenomenon of fluorescence.

For the first time the botanical identity of the true lignum nephriticum mexicanum has been established beyond a doubt, by the study and exhibition of specimens of wood corresponding accurately with the descriptions of Robert Boyle, yielding the characteristic fluorescence obtained by him in his experiments, and accompanied by botanical specimens from the tree producing the wood, these agreeing in all respects with the original description by Hernández of the plant yielding lignum nephriticum.

ABSTRACTS

Authors of scientific papers are requested to see that abstracts, preferably prepared and signed by themselves, are forwarded promptly to the editors. Each of the scientific bureaus in Washington has a representative authorized to forward such material to this journal and abstracts of official publications should be transmitted through the representative of the bureau in which they originate. The abstracts should conform in length and general style to those appearing in this issue.

GEOLOGY.—*The calcite marble and dolomite of eastern Vermont.* T. NELSON DALE. U. S. Geological Survey Bulletin No. 589. Pp. 67, with maps and sections.

Some of the rocks discussed are of pre-Cambrian age and associated with granite-gneiss. Some are of Cambro-Ordovician age and appear to be sporadic in a great schist mass. A few are probably of Ordovician age and are parts of narrow impure calcareous belts. Twenty varieties of marble and dolomite are described.

Of special interest is the occurrence of finely interbedded coarse pink calcite marble, colored by manganese, with a white fine-grained twinned dolomite. Attention is called to some recent French determinations of the presence of manganese both in the calcareous and soft parts of marine mollusks, and hence to the probability that the pink marbles are of organic origin and to the possibility that the interbedded dolomite was formed by chemical precipitation.

The presence of actinolite and diopside schist along the contact of marble and granite-gneiss, and of felty asbestos along the joint and bedding planes of marble and dolomite are regarded as reaction products under regional metamorphism.

A marble synclinal outlier is described, illustrating in miniature principles governing mountain masses in a region of folding. This has been transversely folded in the direction of the pitch, while the underlying schist has acquired slip-cleavage with a strike parallel to the pitch.

Attention is called to the frequent occurrence in the Cambro-Ordovician schist of Vermont of the interesting secondary twinned albites first described by Wolff and Whittle. These enclose plicated beds

518

beyond the edges and ends of which the feldspar has grown and, therefore, cannot have been pebbles of another feldspar.   T. N. D.

GEOLOGY.—*Geology and underground waters of the southeastern part of the Texas Coastal Plain.* ALEXANDER DEUSSEN. U. S. Geological Survey Water-Supply Paper No. 335. Pp. 365, with 9 plates and 17 figures. 1914.

The report treats of the physiography, geology, and underground water resources of the Texas Coastal Plain between Brazos River and the eastern boundary of the State. Under physiography are described an interesting succession of wolds, with the gentle gulfward-sloping Cuestas and steep inland sloping bajadas, parallelling the Gulf Coast. The wolds are produced by differential erosion, and they have had an appreciable influence on parts of the stream courses.

The geologic formations indicated or described include Carboniferous rocks which form the basement on which the deposits of the Coastal Plain rest, undifferentiated Cretaceous deposits, the water recourses of which are not treated at length, and differentiated deposits of Eocene, Oligocene, Miocene, Pliocene, Pleistocene, and Recent age. The general structure of the region is monoclinal, the formations dipping gulfward, and the successively younger ones outcropping nearer and nearer the coast. Flexures, domes, and faults of relatively minor importance, are recognized. The general artesian conditions of the area are indicated.   L. W. STEPHENS.

GEOLOGY.—*Mineral deposits of the Santa Rita and Patagonia Mountains, Arizona.* FRANK C. SCHRADER and JAMES M. HILL. U. S. Geological Survey Bulletin No. 582. Pp. 373, with maps, sections, and illustrations. 1915.

The Santa Rita and Patagonia Mountains, located in Pima and Santa Cruz counties in southern Arizona, form an irregular range of the Great Basin type. Longitudinal faulting has played an important part in its orogeny, and later faulting has given to many of the surface features, as well as the rock outcrop belts and fissure veins, a northwesterly trend. The range consists fundamentally of a granitic axis of pre-Cambrian (?) rocks which is flanked by overlapping and locally highly tilted sediments which are from Cambrian (?) to Cretaceous in age. All the formations, except the Cretaceous, have been freely invaded by Mesozoic intrusives and all flooded later by Tertiary volcanics. The structure in general is monoclinal with dip gently to the east. Areally, the igneous rocks are dominant. On the piedmont slopes the hard rock formations are mantled by a sheet of gravels, sand, and stream alluvium 150 feet in maximum thickness and ranging in age from early Quarternary to Recent.

The principal sedimentary rocks in descending order are about 6000 feet in thickness of Mesozoic, red shales, sandstones, and conglomerates, which are chiefly Cretaceous, and mostly Comanche series, resting uncomformably on 4000 feet of Carboniferous and Devonian limestone which in turn rest unconformably on 4000 feet of Cambrian (?) conglomerate, quartzite, shale, and schist. The most important of these rocks with reference to the mineral deposits are the Paleozoic limestones, which locally are highly altered by contact metamorphism.

The principal igneous rocks are (1) Tertiary effusives, consisting of beds of tuffs and agglomerates, and flows of rhyolite, andesite, and quartzlatite porphyry, aggregating 2500 feet in thickness; (2) Mesozoic intrusives, consisting of rhyolite porphyry, aplite, quartz monzonite, and granite, and diabase, gabbro, syenite, and lamprophyric rocks; (3) pre-Cambrian (?) granite (basal). The most abundant and important of the igneous rocks with reference to the ore deposits are the Mesozoic acidic intrusives.

Mineralogically the range is a part of the northwestern continuation in Arizona of the celebrated mining region of Mexico. Seventy-five per cent of the metalliferous deposits occur in the igneous rocks, and 25 per cent in the sedimentary rocks, and 54 per cent of the deposits are genetically connected with later intrusives.

The lower limit of the oxidized zone is irregular and ranges from less than 100 to 300 feet in depth, but sulphides generally begin to appear near the surface. The surface deposits, worked mostly in early days, yielded chiefly rich silver ores; but in depth the deposits change to ores of copper, lead, and zinc, and the metals now produced are gold, silver, copper, lead, zinc, iron, tungsten, and molybdenum.

The deposits occur chiefly as fissure veins, but also as contact metamorphic, replacement, and shear zone deposits. These were formed chiefly by ascending thermal solutions that circulated as a close after-effect of the intrusion of the igneous rocks in which they occur or with which they are genetically connected.

The deposits occur in two large and contrasting groups that differ considerably in age and represent two distinct periods of mineralization. The older and more important group, which besides veins includes important contact metamorphic and later replacement deposits, occurs in association with the Mesozoic granular acidic intrusives and in part with the Paleozoic sedimentary rocks. It is probably of early Cretaceous age, is referred to the late Mesozoic epoch of metallization, and was formed at considerable depth.

The younger group of deposits occurs in or associated with the Tertiary effusive volcanic rocks, notably the rhyolite and andesite. It is regarded as of late Miocene age and belonging to the late Tertiary epoch of metallization. This great group in general consists of gold-silver-bearing quartz veins. F. C. S.

MINERALOGY.—*The microspectroscope in mineralogy.* EDGAR T. WHERRY. Smithsonian Miscellaneous Collections, **65**[5]: 1–16. 1915.

Previous work with the microspectroscope having been limited to a very few minerals, observations have been made on a number of additional ones. The most convenient apparatus is a binocular microscope with an Abbe-Zeiss Spectral-Ocular. Light is best obtained from a Welsbach burner or Nernst lamp, and is concentrated laterally on the specimens, the wave lengths of the absorption bands being read off on a scale. The method is of considerable practical value in the identification of certain colored minerals, and in particular of cut gems.

Most of the rare-earth minerals show two or more bands, which are useful in distinguishing these minerals from all others, and to some extent in differentiating individual species. Violet calcite from Joplin, Missouri, shows bands which indicate that its color is due to the presence, in mix-crystal form, of a carbonate of neodymium. Some minerals containing uranic uranium show characteristic bands, while zircon, containing this element in the uranous form, exhibits a different set of bands. The colors of the various members of the garnet group have been ascribed to several elements, but it is shown by tabulating the colors, spectra, and percentages of chromium, vanadium, and manganese for six different specimens that the colors are due chiefly to the first two of these elements.

Tables are given of the spectra of rare-earth minerals, uranium minerals, and minerals with red, yellow, green, blue, and violet colors; a determinative table for minerals showing bands of sufficient intensity for diagnostic purposes; and finally a table of the elements producing absorption spectra, with their forms and the limits to the amounts present. E. T. W.

BOTANY.—*Flora of New Mexico.* E. O. WOOTON and PAUL C. STANDLEY. Contributions from the U. S. National Herbarium, Vol. 19. Pp. 1–794. 1915.

This volume consists of a systematic account of the phanerogams and vascular cryptogams native and adventive in New Mexico. There are provided keys to the orders, families, genera, and species, and brief diagnostic descriptions of the genera are given. Under each species are included the place of publication of the specific name, the principal synonyms, type locality, general range, and distribution in New Mexico, and any notes of particular interest concerning the peculiarities of the plant. Definite collections are cited in the case of some of the rare species.

There are listed for the state 2903 species, distributed among 848 genera. Of these 42 species are pteridophytes and 25 gymosperms. The largest family is naturally the Asteraceae, including 511 species. The other large groups are the grasses (270 species), Brassicaceae (101), Fabaceae (189), and Scrophulariaceae (100). The Cactaceae are represented by no less than 67 species. The largest genus is Astragalus, with 54 species; but some of the others are notable, for example, Carex (41 species), Quercus (24), Eriogonum (40), Opuntia (32), Gilia (20), Pentstemon (35), Castilleja (20), Erigeron (46), Artemisia (23), and Senecio (41).

The work includes also a geographic index of all the localities in the state at which plants are known to have been collected, and the altitude for each is given when it could be definitely ascertained. P. C. S.

ZOOLOGY.—*Echinoderma II: Crinoidea.* A. H. CLARK. Beiträge zur Kenntnis der Meeresfauna Westafrikas, herausgegeben von W. Michaelsen (Hamburg) S. 307–318. 1914.

The relationships of the crinoid fauna of west Africa to that of the other regions of the Atlantic basin are discussed in detail, as well as the relation between the Atlantic and the Indo-Pacific basins.

A revision of the genus *Antedon*, with a key to the species and the range of each, is included. A. H. C.

REFERENCES

Under this heading it is proposed to include, by author, title, and citation, references to all scientific papers published in or emanating from Washington. It is requested that authors coöperate with the editors by submitting titles promptly, following the style used below. These references are not intended to replace the more extended abstracts published elsewhere in this JOURNAL.

ENTOMOLOGY

MARTINI, E. *Some new American mosquitoes.* Insecutor Inscitiae Menstruus **2**: 65-76, pl. 2. June 8, 1914. (Describes two new species from Panama and one from Cuba.—J. C. C.)

MILLER, J. M. *Insect damage to the cones and seeds of Pacific Coast conifers.* Bulletin of the U. S. Department of Agriculture, No. 95. Pp. 1-7, pls. 1-3. July 9, 1914. (Gives an account of the various insects attacking cones and seeds, together with methods of preventing loss.—J. C. C.)

PHILLIPS, E. F. *The temperature of the honeybee cluster in winter.* Bulletin of the U. S. Department of Agriculture, No. 93. Pp. 1-16. April 30, 1914. (This paper records a series of experiments to ascertain the optimum temperature for the bee cluster in winter.—J. C. C.)

QUAINTANCE, A. L. *The control of the codling moth in the Pecos Valley in New Mexico.* Bulletin of the U. S. Department of Agriculture, No. 88. Pp. 1-8. April 30, 1914. (This economic paper advocates the application of three sprays in the region under discussion.—J. C. C.)

ROHWER, S. A. *Descriptions of two new genera of parasitic Hymenoptera.* Psyche, **21**: 79-81, *figs. 1 and 2.* April, 1914. (Describes *Anomopterus fasciipennis* and *Centistidea ectoedemiae,* new genera and new species of Braconidae, from Virginia.—J. C. C.)

WALTON, W. R. *Four new species of Tachinidae from North America.* Proceedings of the Entomological Society of Washington **16**: 90-95. June 12, 1914. (Describes the new genus Polychaetoneura.—J. C. C.)

TECHNOLOGY

ABBOTT, FREDERICK V. *Concrete in sea water on New England coast.* Prof. Mem. U. S. Army, **6**: 111-118. 1914.

BLEININGER, A. V., and MONTGOMERY, E. T. *Effect of overfiring upon structure of clays.* Bureau of Standards Tech. Paper No. 22, 23 pp.

BLEININGER, A. V., and BROWN, G. H. *Veritas firing rings.* J. Wash. Acad. Sci., **4**: 446. 1914. Bureau of Standards Tech. Paper No. 40, 10 pp. 1914.

BROWN, G. H., and MURRAY, G. A. *Function of time in vitrification of clays.* Bureau of Standards Tech. Paper No. 17, 26 pp. 1914.

BROWN, G. H., and MONTGOMERY, E. T. *Dehydration of clays.* Bureau of Standards Tech. Paper No. 21, 23 pp. 1914.

BUCKINGHAM, EDGAR. *Windage resistance of steam turbine wheels.* Bureau of Standards Sci. Paper No. 208, 43 pp. 1914.

BUREAU OF STANDARDS. *Relation of horsepower to kilowatt.* Circular No. 34, 2nd ed., 16 pp. 1915.

BUREAU OF STANDARDS. *Safety rules to be observed in operation and maintenance of electrical equipment and lines.* Circular No. 49, 2nd ed., 50 pp. 1915.

BUREAU OF STANDARDS. *Testing of barometers.* Circular No. 46, 2nd ed., 12 pp. 1914.

BUREAU OF STANDARDS. *Standard specifications for incandescent electric lamps.* Circular No. 13, 6th ed., 20 pp. 1914.

BUREAU OF STANDARDS. · *Testing of barometer.* Circular No. 46, 12 pp. 1914.

BUREAU OF STANDARDS. *Testing of hydrometers.* Circular No. 16, 3rd ed., 16 pp. 1914.

BUREAU OF STANDARDS. *Testing of materials.* Circular No. 45, 89 pp. 1913.

BURGESS, G. K., CROWE, J. J., RAWDON, H. S., and WALTENBERG, R. G. *Observations on finishing temperatures and properties of rails.* J. Wash. Acad. Sci., 4: 353–354. 1914. Bureau of Standards Tech. Paper No. 38. 1914.

CAIN, J. R. *Determination of carbon in steel and iron by barium carbonate titration method.* Bureau of Standards Tech. Paper No. 33, 12 pp. 1914.

CAIN, J. R., and CLEAVES, H. E. *The determination of carbon in steels and irons by direct combustion in oxygen at high temperatures.* J. Wash. Acad. Sci., 4: 393–397. 1914.

FITCH, T. T., and HUBER, C. J. *Comparative study of American direct current watthour meters.* Bureau of Standards Sci. Paper No. 207, 29 pp. 1913.

GILLETT, H. W., and NORTON, A. B. *Approximate melting points of some commercial copper alloys.* Bureau of Mines Tech. Paper No. 40, 10 pp.

KLEIN, A. A., and PHILLIPS, A. J. *The hydration of Portland cement.* J. Wash. Acad. Sci., 4: 573–576. 1914.

LEWIS, WALTER S. *Physical testing of cotton yarns.* Bureau of Standards Tech. Paper No. 19, 31 pp. 1913.

LYON, DORSEY A., KEENEY, ROBERT M., and CULLEN, JOSEPH F. *Electric furnace in metallurgical work.* Bureau of Mines Bull. 77, 216 pp.

McCOLLUM, BURTON, and PETERS, O. S. *Surface insulation of pipes as a means of preventing electrolysis.* Bureau of Standards Tech. Paper No. 15, 44 pp. 1914.

MONTGOMERY, E. T. *Some leadless borosilicate glazes maturing at about 1100°C.* Bureau of Standards Tech. Paper No. 31, 22 pp. 1913.

PRIEST, I. G. *Supplementary report on color of turpentines.* Rep. Committee D 1 on Preservative Coatings for Structural Materials, pp. 115–116, 1914, Am. Soc. Testing Materials.

ROSA, E. B., and McCOLLUM, BURTON. *Special studies in electrolysis mitigation. 1. Preliminary study of conditions in Springfield, Ohio with recommendations for mitigation.* Bureau of Standards Tech. Paper No. 27, 55 pp. 1913.

ROSA, E. B., McCOLLUM, BURTON, and LOGAN, K. H. *Special studies in electrolysis mitigation. 2. Electrolysis from electric railway currents and its prevention; experimental test of insulated negative feeders in St. Louis.* Bureau of Standards Tech. Paper No. 32, 34 pp. 1913.

ROSA, E. B., McCOLLUM, BURTON, and PETERS, O. S. *Electrolysis in concrete (with bibliography).* Bureau of Standards Tech. Paper No. 18, 137 pp. 1911.

WAIDNER, C. W., and MUELLER, E. F. *Industrial gas calorimetry.* Bureau of Standards Tech. Paper No. 36, 150 pp. 1914.

WRIGHT, C. L. *Fuel-briquetting investigation.* Bureau of Mines Bull. 58, 277 pp.

JOURNAL

OF THE

WASHINGTON ACADEMY OF SCIENCES

VOL. V   SEPTEMBER 19, 1915   No. 15

RADIOTELEGRAPHY.—*Resistance of radiotelegraphic antennas.*
L. W. AUSTIN, Naval Radiotelegraphic Laboratory.

The resistance of a radiotelegraphic antenna may be divided into three parts: first, the ohmic resistance of the wires; second, the so-called radiation resistance; and third, the so-called earth resistances. The first is generally negligible where a sufficient number of wires in parallel is used. The second is derived from the expression for the radiated energy of an antenna, which is

$$E = 160\pi^2 \frac{h^2}{\lambda^2} I_s^2$$

where h represents the height to the center of capacity of the antenna, λ the wave length, and I_s the current measured at the base of the antenna. The expression $160\pi^2\frac{h^2}{\lambda^2}$ is called the radiation resistance, as it takes the same position in the energy equation as that occupied by R in the case of ohmic losses. The expression shows that the radiation resistance falls rapidly as the wave length is increased.

Up to the present no satisfactory theory of ground resistance has been developed. The experimental curves of antenna resistance, on account of the decreasing radiation resistance, fall rapidly at first, as the wave length is increased, and then, as the wave length is further increased, remain nearly constant if the ground conditions are good as in the case of a ship's antenna, or again rise nearly in a straight line if the ground conditions are poor. This rise may be very rapid in the case of peculiarly poor grounds. For instance, the resistance of the Bureau of Standards antenna rises from 13 ohms at 800 meters wave length to 28 ohms at 2000 meters. Great difficulty has been found in explaining this increase of resistance with increasing wave length, but it is believed that the following explanation is the true one:

The antenna system must be looked upon as a condenser, the antenna itself being the upper plate and the ground water the lower plate. Between the ground water and the surface there is usually a layer of semi-conducting material which would correspond to a poor dielectric in the case of an ordinary condenser. It is well known that the dielectric losses in imperfect condensers generally increase in proportion to the wave length of the current employed in the measurement. It is found that by covering the surface of the ground under and around the antenna with a wire net, thus making the net the lower plate of the condenser, the ground losses nearly disappear.

PHYSICS.—*The "center of gravity" and "effective wave length" of transmission of pyrometer color screens.* PAUL D. FOOTE, Bureau of Standards.

Some ten years ago Waidner and Burgess[1] called attention to the shift in effective wave length of the color screens used with optical pyrometers, when the temperature of the source sighted upon changes. Pirani[2] has contributed two papers upon this subject and in the past month a paper by Hyde, Cady, and Forsythe[3] has appeared.

Heretofore it has been assumed that the effective wave length is the so-called "center of gravity" of the luminosity curve. Hyde, Cady, and Forsythe have given a new definition of the mean effective wave length between any two temperatures,

[1] Waidner and Burgess. Bureau of Standards Scientific Paper, No. 55, p. 175
[2] M. v. Pirani. Verh. d. Phys. Ges., **15**: 826-838. 1913; **17**: 47-62. 1915.
[3] Hyde, Cady, and Forsythe. Phys. Review, **6**: 70-74. 1915.

which has a real physical basis. They have defined the effective
wave length of the glass used between these two temperatures
as that wave length for which the ratio of the two radiation
intensities corresponding to the two temperatures exactly equals
the ratio of the integral luminosities through the screen for the
same two temperatures.

In the following discussion the difference between the "center
of gravity" and the true effective wave length is discussed and
a simple and accurate method is derived for obtaining the true
effective wave length.

Let $J_\lambda = c_1 \lambda^{-5} e^{-\frac{c_2}{\lambda\theta}}$ = Wien's law.

$T = f(\lambda)$ = transmission of color screen.

$V = \varphi(\lambda)$ = visibility.

T and V are functions of λ only but the analytical forms of the
functions are unknown. Consider two temperatures θ_1 and θ_2.

(1)
$$\begin{cases} \text{for } \theta_1, \quad J_1 = c_1 \lambda^{-5} e^{-\frac{c_2}{\lambda\theta_1}} \\ \text{for } \theta_2, \quad J_2 = c_1 \lambda^{-5} e^{-\frac{c_2}{\lambda\theta}} \end{cases}$$

(2)
$$J_1/J_2 = e^{\frac{c_2}{\lambda}\left(\frac{1}{\theta_2} - \frac{1}{\theta_1}\right)}$$

Since λ may have any arbitrary value from 0 to ∞ the ratio
J_1/J_2 may have any chosen value by properly choosing λ. Let
L_1 = luminosity at temperature θ_1 and L_2 = luminosity at
temperature θ_2.

$$L_1 = \int_0^\infty JVTd\lambda = \int_0^\infty J(\lambda\theta_1) T(\lambda) V(\lambda) d\lambda$$

$$L_2 = \int_0^\infty J(\lambda\theta_2) T(\lambda) V(\lambda) d\lambda$$

(3)
$$L_1/L_2 = \frac{\int_0^\infty J(\lambda\theta_1) TVd\lambda}{\int_0^\infty J(\lambda\theta_2) TVd\lambda}$$

L_1 and L_2, and hence the ratio L_1/L_2, can be determined by graphical integration. Let the ratio be any definite number. It

is possible to choose λ in (2) such that $J_1/J_2 = L_1/L_2$. Call this value of $\lambda = \lambda_L$. Substituting in (2):

$$(4) \qquad \text{mean } \lambda_L = \frac{c_2\left(\dfrac{1}{\theta_2} - \dfrac{1}{\theta_1}\right)}{\log L_1 - \log L_2} \quad \text{(natural logarithms)}$$

This is the definition, expressed analytically, of the mean effective wave length over a given temperature range, proposed by Hyde, Cady, and Forsythe. Instead of referring the effective wave length to a given temperature range it may be referred to a definite temperature by letting the two temperatures approach one another. Let θ_1 and θ_2 approach θ as a limit. The right term of (4) is indeterminate but can be evaluated by the ordinary rule of L'Hospital, observing in the differentiation of the denominator that $L = \int_0^\infty TVJd\lambda$ where only J is a function of θ. Then for the limit $\theta_1 = \theta_2 = \theta$, the following value of λ_L is obtained.

$$(5) \qquad \lambda_L = \frac{\int_0^\infty TVJd\lambda}{\int_0^\infty \dfrac{TVJ}{\lambda}d\lambda}$$

This is the true effective wave length of the glass for a temperature θ. Define the wave length corresponding to the line which bisects the area of $\int_0^\infty TVJd\lambda$ as λ_g, that is, the axis of the center of gravity of the luminosity curve, so chosen that $\int_0^\infty TVJd\lambda = 2\int_0^{\lambda_g} TVJd\lambda$. Then by definition of the center of gravity:

$$(6) \qquad \lambda_g = \frac{\int_0^\infty TVJ\lambda d\lambda}{\int_0^\infty TVJd\lambda}$$

Having drawn the luminosity curve on any arbitrary scale whatever, paying no attention to actual values of the scale of ordinates (L), only relative values of L needing consideration, λ_g can be determined with a planimeter having two indicating dials, one of area and the other of moments, such as the Amsler integrator No. 1. Surprising accuracy is obtainable in measuring λ_g. This is evident when one considers that the luminosity curve for a good red glass extends only from about $\lambda = 0.600$ to $0.750\ \mu$. Since all errors are actually based on the difference of these two wave lengths, a low precision in the determination of the center of gravity as far as the curve is concerned still means a very high precision in the determination of the absolute value of λ_g. Four or five significant figures are obtainable.

The method of determining λ_L suggested by Hyde involves the log ratio of the areas of two luminosity curves, and when λ_L is expressed by equation (5) its determination requires the ratio of the areas of two curves. In general the area of luminosity curves can not be measured by a planimeter with an accuracy much better than 0.5 per cent; and since a direct mathematical integration is impossible, because $T = f(\lambda)$ and $V = f(\lambda)$ are not expressible by any usable equations, it is evident that great precision is not readily possible in the determination of λ_L by such a method—probably not better than three significant figures when great care is taken.

Inspection of equation (5) however shows a very curious relation. Suppose that instead of plotting λ versus JTV as ordinates, the ordinary luminosity curve, we plot JVT/λ as ordinates. The line of the center of gravity of this curve is given by the following expression:

$$(7) \qquad \lambda \text{ (center gravity)} = \frac{\int_0^\infty JVTd\lambda}{\int^\infty \frac{JVT}{\lambda} d\lambda}$$

which is identical with (5)

Therefore the true effective wave length of the pyrometer glass is the wave length corresponding to the center of gravity of the curve $f(\lambda) = JVT/\lambda$, i.e., the luminosity at any wave length divided by the wave length. The true value of λ_L is slightly different from the value of λ_g. The center of gravity of the curve JVT/λ versus λ can be determined with great accuracy, so that a curve of $\lambda_L = f(\theta)$ may be easily obtained by this method. Whether such high mathematical accuracy is of value is a point open to question since the transmission of the glass can not be measured extremely accurately and visibility curves appear very different for different observers. But in the case of the transmission, absolute values are not required, merely the form of the curve needs to be known. And in the case of the visibility, only a short range of the curve is important, and over this range the slope of the visibility curves of various observers is in good agreement.

In a more complete paper which will be published at an early date several specific pyrometer glasses are considered. One of these glasses is a black absorption glass used with optical pyrometers for extrapolating the temperature scale to say 2500°C. The calibration of such a glass by the usual method necessarily tacitly involves the visibility or scope of the visibility curve over a small range of color. Different observers obtain practically the same calibration of the glass which would indicate that the effective wave length of the system could be determined with greater accuracy than one would ordinarily expect. Also the values of the effective wave length of a red glass obtained by Hyde, Cady, and Forsythe by different methods show such excellent agreement that a more accurate method of computing the data is warranted.

In conclusion the writer desires to thank Dr. Waidner, Dr. Kanolt, and Mr. Crittenden for suggestions given him in this work.

BOTANY.—*On the application of the generic name Nauclea of Linnaeus.* E. D. MERRILL, Bureau of Science, Manila, P. I. (Communicated by WILLIAM R. MAXON).

It sometimes happens that the current and universally accepted concept of a genus is quite different from that of the genus as originally described. This is due to misconception or to misinterpretation of the group on the part of later authors; sometimes because the original genus is subdivided, the various species being referred to other genera until all or most of them are dissociated from the original generic name; and sometimes because certain species have been added after the original description of the genus, by the original author or by others, which later botanists have interpreted as representing the genus, even when these are generically distinct from the original type. The case presented by *Nauclea* is of especial interest as illustrating this latter type of interpretation, for the genus was originally based on a single species, a plant thoroughly well known, and one generically distinct from *Nauclea* as this genus has been interpreted by all modern botanists. Use of the generic name *Nauclea* for the genus sò called by all botanists during the past century is logically incorrect and is not permissible under any rules of botanical nomenclature; but *Nauclea* in the original Linnaean sense is entirely valid. It is, however, decidedly unfortunate that, in revising the nomenclature of the group, *Nauclea* must be used for those species now placed by all botanists in *Sarcocephalus*, while those species now placed under *Nauclea* must receive a new generic name.

Haviland[1] has given us a very careful and critical revision of this group and in connection with his work has examined most of the types of the species considered and determined the types of most of the genera. His position as to nomenclature can best be indicated by the following quotation from the introduction to his paper:

> I have also assumed that rules of priority were made to help and not to hinder; if they were exactly followed, *Uncaria* would be *Ourouparia*, *Sarcocephalus* would be *Nauclea*, *Nauclea* would have to be renamed, and probably *Mitragyna* would be *Mamboga*. ˙

From my knowledge of the Philippine flora and of the genera and species described by Blanco, I can definitely state that *Mamboga* of Blanco is identical with *Mitragyna* of Korthals and antedates Korthals' name by two years. The status of *Uncaria* and *Mitragyna*, however, is determined by the list of *nomina conservanda* adopted by the Vienna Botanical Congress, these two generic names being retained in preference to *Ourouparia* and *Mamboga*. The case presented by *Nauclea* and *Sarcocephalus* is entirely different, and it is really unfortunate that Haviland

[1] A revision of the Tribe Naucleeae (Nat. Ord. Rubiaceae). Journ. Linn. Soc. Bot. **33**: 1-94, *pl. 1-4*. 1897.

did not solve this problem of nomenclature in his revision of the group. Britten,[2] in his appreciative review of Haviland's paper, states:

The retention of *Nauclea* necessitates the statement "typus nullus" after the name; then, after a definition of the genus as now understood, comes a reference to "*Nauclea* Linn. Sp. Pl. ed. 2, 243," followed by the remark, "none of the plants called *Nauclea* by Linnaeus are now in this genus, although there is no doubt he would have called those in it *Nauclea* if he had seen them." But as Mr. Haviland tells us elsewhere that "Linnaeus founded his *Nauclea orientalis* on two species of *Sarcocephalus*" it is difficult to see how the retention of his name for the plants he described could be regarded as a hindrance.

To be strictly accurate, *Nauclea orientalis* Linn. involves three different species of *Sarcocephalus*, rather than two. Haviland's stand on this simple question had led him illogically to retain *Sarcocephalus* as the valid name for what should be *Nauclea;* he has quoted the type of genus *Nauclea* as a synonym of *Sarcocephalus cordatus* Miq.; and as to *Nauclea* itself, while still crediting Linnaeus as authority for the genus, he retains nothing in the genus placed there by Linnaeus himself, and is obliged to admit that *Nauclea* as interpreted by him, following modern usage, has no type. Others[3] have solved the dilemma by illogically and incorrectly crediting the authorship of *Nauclea* to Korthals.

The history of this nomenclatural anomaly begins with the publication of the genus *Cephalanthus* by Linnaeus;[4] but the type of the genus *Cephalanthus* is perfectly clear, · although Linnaeus included in the first edition of his Species Plantarum two generically distinct species, *Cephalanthus occidentalis* Linn. and *C. orientalis* Linn. The type of the genus is clearly indicated as the former by Linnaeus: "Character desumtus est a specie occidentali, quum orientalis fructus nobis non dum sufficienter innotuit."

In the second edition of the Species Plantarum Linnaeus separated *Cephalanthus orientalis* from the genus *Cephalanthus*,

---

[2] Notes on the Naucleeae. Journ. Bot. **35:** 336–340. 1897.

[3] Dalla Torre and Harms, Genera Siphonogamarum, 495. 1905.

[4] Genera Plantarum, 61. 1737; ed. 5, 42. 1754.

making it the type and only species of the genus *Nauclea*. The genus *Nauclea*, then, must be interpreted solely by a consideration of the original publication of the name.[5] Unfortunately *Nauclea orientalis* Linn. is *Sarcocephalus* of all modern authors, but the mere fact that a genus has been consistently misinterpreted is no logical reason for ignoring the original application of the name. Although *Nauclea orientalis* Linn. is in itself a mixture of three species, the five references given by Linnaeus are congeneric.

The first reference is "Cephalanthus foliis oppositis Fl. zeyl. 53. Sp. pl. I. p. 95," and this is *Sarcocephalus cordatus* Miq. (= *Nauclea orientalis* Linn.), and this number of the Flora Zeylanica is represented in Hermann's herbarium by a drawing, according to Trimen.[6] This reference I consider typifies the species. The second reference is to "Platanocephalus citri foliis bijugis, capite majore. Vaill. act. 1722, p. 259," which in turn is based on "Katou Tsjaca, Rheede, Hortus Malabaricus 3: 29, t. 33," and is *Nauclea missionis* W. & A. (*Sarcocephalus missionis* Havil.).[7] The third reference is to "Arbor indica, fructu aggregato globoso. Raj. hist. 1441," which is also based on the same figure and description of Rheede as the above reference. The fourth reference is directly to "Katu Tsiacca Rheed. Mal. 3, p. 29, t. 33," which, as noted above, is *Nauclea missionis* W. & A. (*Sarcocephalus missionis* Havil.). The fifth reference is a doubtful one to "Bancalus Rumph. amb. 3, p. 84, t. 55?" and Kuntze has adopted *Bancalus* for the generic name in place of *Nauclea*. *Bancalus* of Rumphius, however, is a *Sarcocephalus* (= *Nauclea* of Linnaeus, not of other authors), a species closely allied to *Sarcocephalus junghuhnii* Miq., *S. mitragynus* Miq., and *S. tenuiflorus* Havil. *Cephalanthus orientalis* Linn.,[8] on which *Nauclea orientalis* Linn.[9] is based, presents the first, second, and fourth of these citations.

The generic nomenclature of *Nauclea* is as follows:

[5] Linnaeus, Species Plantarum, ed. 2, 243. 1762.

[6] Hermann's Ceylon Herbarium and Linnaeus's "Flora Zeylanica." Journ. Linn. Soc. Bot. **24**: 129–155. 1887.

[7] See Haviland, Journ. Linn. Soc. Bot. **33**: 32. 1897.

[8] Species Plantarum, 95. 1753.

[9] Species Plantarum, ed. 2, 243. 1762.

NAUCLEA Linn. Sp. Pl. ed. 2, 243. 1762.
  Sarcocephalus Afzel. ex R. Br. in Tukey's Congo App. 267.
    1818.
  Cephalina Thonn. in Schumm. Beskr. Guin. Pl. 125. 1827.
  Platanocarpum Endl. Gen. 557. 1838; Korth. Obs. Naucl.
    Ind. 18. 1839.
  Bancalus O. Ktze. Rev. Gen. Pl. **1**: 276. 1891.

  The type of the genus *Nauclea*, and the sole species cited under
this name in the original publication, is *Nauclea orientalis* Linn.
(*Sarcocephalus cordatus* Miq.).

  The type of the genus *Cephalina* Thonn. is *Cephalina esculenta*
Thonn., the only species cited (= *Sarcocephalus esculentus* Afzel.).

  The type of the genus *Platanocarpum* Endl. is not indicated
by that author; but he cites "*Naucleae*, sectio *Nauclearia*, §. 1.
DC. Prodr. IV. 343," the description applies to *Nauclea* of
Linnaeus (*Sarcocephalus* Afzel.), and the first three of the four
species placed by DeCandolle in the first section of *Nauclearia*
are *Nauclea* of Linnaeus (*Sarcocephalus* Afzel.). Interpreting
the genus upon the first species cited by DeCandolle, the type
would be *Nauclea undulata* Roxb. (*Sarcocephalus undulatus*
Miq.). Korthals' interpretation of *Platanocarpum* a year later
is based on two species: the first, *Platanocarpum subditum* Korth.
(= *Sarcocephalus subditus* Miq.); the second, *Platanocarpum
cordatum* Korth. (=*Sarcocephalus cordatus* Miq. = *Nauclea
orientalis* Linn.).

  Bancalus of O. Kuntze was based on "*Bancalus* Rumph.
Herb. Amb. 3: 84, *t. 55.* 1743," ostensibly because *Bancalus*
is an older name than *Nauclea*. Kuntze included in *Bancalus*
species of *Sarcocephalus* and of *Nauclea* as currently understood
by modern botanists; but whether *Bancalus* be typified by
the Rumphian plant or by the type of the Linnaean genus *Nauclea*,
it is a synonym of *Sarcocephalus* Afzel. (= *Nauclea* Linn.). Dalla
Torre and Harms are wrong in referring *Bancalus* O. Ktze. to
Nauclea Korth. as a synonym; it is a synonym of *Nauclea* Linn.
If *Bancalus* is to be interpreted as an exact equivalent of *Nauclea* of Linnaeus, the type is *N. orientalis* Linn., cited by O.
Kuntze as *Bancalus orientalis* (Linn.) O. Kuntze. If typified
by the plant Rumphius actually described and figured under

Bancalus, the type is also a true *Nauclea* (*Sarcocephalus*), for Rumphius' description refers unmistakably to *Sarcocephalus:* "fructus . . . non facile manibus confringendus, lentus enim ac tenax est, interna substantia similis est, sed siccior praecedente" [*Arbor noctis* = *Sarcocephalus*!]. ·Most of the species transferred by Kuntze to *Bancalus*, however, belong in *Nauclea* as currently interpreted, but not in *Nauclea* (*Sarcocephalus*) as defined by Linnaeus.

Nauclea as here interpreted in the original Linnaean sense consists of the following species, extending from tropical Africa through tropical Asia and Malaya to tropical Australia and Polynesia, nearly 25 being known.

NAUCLEA Linnaeus.

Nauclea annamensis (Dubard & Eberh.)
Sarcocephalus annamensis Dubard & Eberh. Bull. Mus. Hist. Nat. Paris **15**: 493. 1909.
Indo-China.

Nauclea dasyphylla (Miq.)
Sarcocephalus dasyphyllus Miq. Fl. Ind. Bat. **2**: 133. 1856.
Sumatra.

Nauclea diderrichii (Wildem.)
Sarcocephalus ·diderrichii Wildem. in Masui État Indep. Congo Expos. Brux. 439. 1897 (*nomen*); Rev. Cult. Colon. **9**: 7. 1901.
Tropical Africa.

Nauclea elmeri nom. nov.
Sarcocephalus ovatus Elm. Leafl. Philip. Bot. **1**: 33. 1906; non *Nauclea ovata* Merr. 1913.
Philippines.

Nauclea esculenta (Afzel.)
Sarcocephalus esculentus Afzel. ex R. Br. in Tukey, Congo App. 467. 1818.
Nauclea sambucina Winterb. Acc. Sierra Leone 45. 1803 (*nomen*).
Tropical Africa.

Nauclea gilleti (Wildem.)
Sarcocephalus gilletii Wildem. in Rev. Cult. Colon. **9**: 8. 1901.
Tropical Africa.

Nauclea glaberrima Bartl. ex DC. Prodr. **4**: 28. 1830.
Sarcocephalus glaberrimus Miq. Fl. Ind. Bat. **2**: 133. 1856.
Philippines and Celebes.

Nauclea hirsuta (Havil.)

Sarcocephalus hirsutus Havil. Journ. Linn. Soc. Bot. **33**: 32.   1897.
Borneo.

Nauclea junghuhnii (Miq.)

Sarcocephalus junghuhnii Miq. Fl. Ind. Bat. **2**: 133.   1856.
Malay Peninsula and Cambodia to Sumatra, Borneo, and the Philippines.

Nauclea maingayi Hook. f. Fl. Brit. Ind. **3**: 27.   1880.

Sarcocephalus maingayi Havil. Journ. Linn. Soc.·Bot. **33**: 33.   1897.
Bancalus maingayii O. Ktze. Rev. Gen. Pl. **1**: 277.   1891.
Malay Peninsula and Borneo.

Nauclea missionis W. & A. Prodr. 392.   1834.

Sarcocephalus missionis Havil. Journ. Linn. Soc. Bot. **33**: 32.   1897.
Bancalus missionis O. Ktze. Rev. Gen. Pl. **1**: 277.   1891.
India.

Nauclea mitragyna (Miq.)

Sarcocephalus mitragynus Miq. Ann. Mus. Bot. Lugd.-Bat. **4**: 180.
   1868–69.
Ceram.

Nauclea multicephala (Elm.)

Sarcocephalus multicephalus Elm. Leafl. Philip. Bot. **5**: 1896.   1913.
Philippines.

Nauclea orientalis Linn. Sp. Pl. ed. 2, 243.   1762.

Cephalanthus orientalis Linn. Sp. Pl. 95.   1753.
Nauclea cordata Roxb. Fl. Ind. ed. Carey **1**: 509.   1832.
Sarcocephalus cordatus Miq. Fl. Ind. Bat. **2**: 133.   1856.
Platanocarpum cordatum Korth. Obs. Naucl. Ind. 16.   1839.
Bancalus orientalis O. Ktze. Rev. Gen. Pl. **1**: 277.   1891.
Sarcocephalus orientalis Merr. Philip. Journ. Sci. Bot. **3**: 436.   1908.
India through Malaya to tropical Australia.   The type of the genus.

Nauclea pacifica (Reinecke)

Sarcocephalus pacificus Reinecke, Bot. Jahrb. Engler **25**: 684. *pl.
13, f.C.*   1898.
Samoa.

Nauclea parva (Havil.)

Sarcocephalus parvus Havil. Journ. Linn. Soc. Bot. **33**: 31.   1897.
Borneo.

Nauclea pobequini (Pobéquin)

Sarcocephalus pobequini Pobéquin, Ess. Fl. Guin. Fr. 313.   1906.
Tropical Africa.

Nauclea pubescens (Valet.)
Sarcocephalus pubescens Valet. Bot. Jahrb. Engler **44:** 550. 1910.
Borneo.

Nauclea ramosa (Lauterb.)
Sarcocephalus ramosus Lauterb. Bot. Jahrb. Engler **41:** 235. 1908.
Samoa.

Nauclea robinsonii nom. nov.
Sarcocephalus pubescens C. B. Rob. Philip. Journ. Sci. Bot. **6:** 225.
1911; non Valet. 1910.
Philippines.

Nauclea subdita (Korth.)
Platanocarpum subditum Korth. Obs. Naucl. Ind. 19. 1839 (*nomen*);
Verh. Nat. Gesch. Bot. 133, *pl. 32.* 1840.
Sarcocephalus subditus Miq. Fl. Ind. Bat. **2:** 133. 1856.
Malay Peninsula, Borneo, Sumatra, and Java.

Nauclea tenuiflora (Havil.)
Sarcocephalus tenuiflorus Havil. Journ. Linn. Soc. Bot. **33:** 32. 1897.
New Guinea.

Nauclea trillesii (Pierre)
Sarcocephalus trillesii Pierre ex Wildem. Not. Pl. Util. Congo 37. 1903.
Tropical Africa.

Nauclea undulata Roxb. Fl. Ind. ed Carey, **1:** 508. 1832.
Sarcocephalus undulatus Miq. Fl. Ind. Bat. **2:** 133. 1856.
Malay Archipelago and New Guinea.

Having demonstrated that logically, historically, and under
all rules of botanical nomenclature those species which have been
described under *Sarcocephalus* must be transferred to *Nauclea,*
it becomes necessary to establish a new generic name for the
more numerous species that have been described by many
authors since Linnaeus under the latter generic name. In my
quest for a published name I have even looked up the original
publications of the various synonyms placed under *Cephalanthus*
Linn., but none of them are available for the species that have
up to this time been placed under *Nauclea. Acrodryon* Spreng.
(Syst. **1:** 386. 1825) is based on *Cephalanthus orientalis* Lour.[10]

[10] Loureiro, Flora Cochinchinensis, 67. 1790, under *Cephalanthus occidentalis:*
"Si cum Ceph. Americano (mihi non obvio) non conveniat, vocetur Ceph.
orientalis."

and *C. angustifolius* Lour. From Loureiro's description the former is a true *Nauclea* (*Sarcocephalus*), for the fruits are described as edible and baccate, while the latter is a true *Cephalanthus*, the type of which Haviland has examined in the herbarium of the British Museum. *Axolus* Rafinesque (Sylv. Tellur. 61. 1838) is based on *Cephalanthus angustifolius* Lour., and is a proper synonym of *Cephalanthus*. *Eresimus* Rafinesque (loc. cit.) is based on *Cephalanthus stellatus* Lour., which is cited by Haviland as a synonym of *Cephalanthus angustifolius* Lour. *Gilipus* Rafinesque (loc. cit.) is based on *Cephalanthus montanus* Lour., which Loureiro has described as having alternate leaves. If Loureiro's description is correct, *Gilipus* does not even belong to the *Rubiaceae*, and from other characters given, such as leaves crenate, rough, and flowers dioecious, the plant even·if rubiaceous can scarcely belong to the *Naucleeae*. *Silimanus* Rafinesque (op. cit. 60) is based on *Cephalanthus procumbens* Lour., which like *Gilipus* cannot be a rubiaceous plant, if Loureiro's description is correct, as the leaves are described as alternate; the description otherwise as to habit, flowers dioecious, and other characters, at once removes the plant from the *Naucleeae*.

The list of synonyms of *Sarcocephalus*, *Nauclea*, and *Cephalanthus* being exhausted, and none of them being applicable to the numerous species that have erroneously been placed in *Nauclea*, I propose for these species the new generic name **Neonauclea** as a substitute for *Nauclea* as described by Korthals,[11] by Bentham and Hooker,[12] by K. Schumann,[13] and by Haviland.[14]

Neonauclea as now constituted contains nearly 50 species, and extends from India to New Guinea. Unlike *Nauclea* proper (*Sarcocephalus* Afzel.) no species have been reported from tropical Africa, from tropical Australia, or from Polynesia. I transfer to *Neonauclea* the following species.

[11] Observationes de Naucleis Indicis, 17. 1839.
[12] Genera Plantarum, **2**: 31. 1873.
[13] In Engler and Prantl, Natürlichen Pflanzenfam. **4**⁴: 57. 1891.
[14] Revision of the Tribe Naucleeae. Journ. Linn. Soc. Bot. **33**: 48. 1897.

NEONAUCLEA Merrill.

Neonauclea angustifolia (Havil.)
Nauclea angustifolia Havil. Journ. Linn. Soc. Bot. **33**: 55, *pl. 3*. 1897.
Borneo.

Neonauclea ategii (Elm.)
Nauclea ategii Elm. Leafl, Philip. Bot. **5**: 1877. 1913.
Philippines.

Neonauclea bartlingii (DC.)
Nauclea bartlingii DC. Prodr. **4**: 344. 1830.
Bancalus bartlingii O. Ktze. Rev. Gen. Pl. **1**: 276. 1891.
Philippines.

Neonauclea bernardoi (Merr.)
Nauclea bernardoi Merr. Philip. Journ. Sci. Bot. **10**: 101. 1915.
Philippines.

Neonauclea calycina (Bartl.)
Nauclea calycina Bartl. in DC. Prodr. **4**: 346. 1830.
Nauclea purpurascens Korth. Verh. Nat. Gesch. Bot. 158. 1840.
Philippines and Borneo.

Neonauclea celebica (Havil.)
Nauclea celebica Havil. Journ. Linn. Soc. Bot. **33**: 54. 1897.
Celebes.

Neonauclea chalmersii (F. Muell.)
Nauclea chalmersii F. Muell. Notes Papuan Pl. **8**: 44. 1886.
New Guinea.

Neonauclea cordatula (Merr.)
Nauclea cordatula Merr. Philip. Journ. Sci. Bot. **8**: 40. 1913.
Philippines.

Neonauclea cyclophylla (Miq.)
Nauclea cyclophylla Miq. Ann. Mus. Bot. Lugd.-Bat. **4**: 181. 1868-69.
Moluccas.

Neonauclea cyrtopoda (Miq.)
Nauclea cyrtopoda Miq. Fl. Ind. Bat. **2**: 342. 1856.
Borneo and Sumatra.

Neonauclea excelsa (Blume)
Nauclea excelsa Blume, Bijdr. 1009. 1826.
Java.

Neonauclea fagifolia (Teysm. & Binn.)
Nauclea fagifolia Teysm. & Binn. Cat. Hort. Bogor. 117. 1866
(*nomen*); Hàvil. in Journ. Linn. Soc. Bot. **33**: 63. 1897.
Amboina.

Neonauclea formosana (Matsum.)

Nauclea formosana Matsum. Bot. Mag. Tokyo **14**: 127. 1900.
Formosa.

Neonauclea forsteri (Seem.)

Nauclea forsteri Seem. Fl. Vit. 121. 1865–73.
Bancalus forsteri O. Ktze. Rev. Gen. Pl. **1**: 277. 1891.
Philippine, Society, Tonga, Samoa, and Fiji Islands.

Neonauclea gageana (King)

Nauclea gageana King, Journ. As. Soc. Beng. **72**^{2}: 123. 1903.
Andaman Islands.

Neonauclea gigantea (Valet.)

Nauclea gigantea Valet. Bot. Jahrb. Engler **44**: 549. 1910.
Borneo.

Neonauclea gracilis (Vidal)

Nauclea gracilis Vidal, Phan. Cuming. Philip. 176. 1885.
Bancalus gracilis O. Ktze. Rev. Gen. Pl. **1**: 277. 1891.
Philippines.

Neonauclea griffithii (Hook. f.)

Adina griffithii Hook. f. Fl. Brit. Ind. **3**: 24. 1880.
Nauclea griffithii Havil. Journ. Linn. Soc. Bot. **33**: 51. 1897.
India.

Neonauclea hagenii (K. Schum. & Lauterb.)

Nauclea hagenii K. Schum. & Lauterb. Fl. Deutsch. Schutzgeb.
Südsee 557. 1901.
New Guinea.

Neonauclea havilandii (Koord.)

Nauclea havilandii Koord. Meded. Lands Plant. Buitenz. **19**: 498.
1898.
Celebes.

Neonauclea jagori (Merr.)

Nauclea jagori Merr. Philip. Journ. Sci. Bot. **4**: 326. 1910.
Philippines.

Neonauclea kentii (Merr.)

Nauclea kentii Merr. Philip. Journ. Sci. Bot. **8**: 43. 1913.
Philippines.

Neonauclea lanceolata (Blume)

Nauclea lanceolata Blume, Bijdr. 1010. 1826.
Bancalus affinis O. Ktze. Rev. Gen. Pl. **1**: 276. 1891.
Java.

Neonauclea media (Havil.)
Nauclea media Havil. Journ. Linn. Soc. Bot. **33**: 56. 1897.
Philippines.

Neonauclea mindanaensis (Merr.)
Nauclea mindanaensis Merr. Philip. Journ. Sci. Bot. **8**: 44. 1913.
Philippines.

Neonauclea mollis (Blume)
Nauclea mollis Blume, Bijdr. 1010. 1826.
Bancalus mollis O. Ktze. Rev. Gen. Pl. **1**: 277. 1891.
Java.

Neonauclea moluccana (Miq.)
Nauclea moluccana Miq. Ann. Mus. Bot. Lugd.-Bat. **4**: 183. 1868–69.
Buru.

Neonauclea monocephala (Merr.)
Nauclea monocephala Merr. Philip. Journ. Sci. Bot. **8**: 44. 1913.
Philippines.

Neonauclea morindaefolia (Blume)
Nauclea morindaefolia Blume, Bijdr. 1011. 1826.
Java.

Neonauclea nicobarica (Havil.)
Nauclea nicobarica Havil. Journ. Linn. Soc. Bot. **33**: 59. 1897.
Nicobar Islands.

Neonauclea nitida (Havil.)
Nauclea nitida Havil. Journ. Linn. Soc. Bot. **33**: 53. 1897.
Philippines.

Neonauclea obtusa (Blume)
Nauclea obtusa Blume, Bijdr. 1009. 1826.
Bancalus obtusus O. Ktze. Rev. Gen. Pl. **1**: 277. 1891.
Bancalus cordatus O. Ktze. op. cit. 276. 1891.
Java and Sumatra.

Neonauclea ovata (Merr.)
Nauclea ovata Merr. Philip. Journ. Sci. Bot. **8**: 42. 1913.
Philippines.

Neonauclea pallida (Reinw.)
Nauclea pallida Reinw. ex Blume Cat. Gew. Buitenzorg 38. 1823.
Sumatra and Java.

Neonauclea peduncularis (G. Don)
Nauclea peduncularis G. Don, Gen. Syst. **3**: 469. 1834.
Bancalus peduncularis O. Ktze. Rev. Gen. Pl. **1**: 277. 1891.
Malay Peninsula and Borneo.

Neonauclea philippinensis (Vidal)

Adina philippinensis Vidal, Rev. Pl. Vasc. Filip. 148. 1886.
Nauclea philippinensis Havil. Journ. Linn. Soc. Bot. **33**: 52. 1897.
Philippines.

Neonauclea puberula (Merr.)

Nauclea puberula Merr. Philip. Journ. Sci. Bot. **8**: 41. 1913.
Philippines.

Neonauclea reticulata (Havil.)

Nauclea reticulata Havil. Journ. Linn. Soc. Bot. **33**: 62. 1897.
? *Nauclea formicaria* Elm. Leafl. Philip. Bot. **3**: 989. 1911.
Philippines.

Neonauclea sessilifolia (Roxb.)

Nauclea sessilifolia Roxb. Fl. Ind. ed. Carey **1**: 515. 1832.
India and Cochin China.

Neonauclea strigosa (Korth.)

Nauclea strigosa Korth. Verh. Nat. Gesch. Bot. 157. 1840.
Bancalus strigosus O. Ktze. Rev. Gen. Pl. **1**: 277. 1891.
Borneo and the Philippines.

Neonauclea synkorynes (Korth.)

Nauclea synkorynes Korth. Verh. Nat. Gesch. Bot. 160. 1840.
Bancalus synkorynes O. Ktze. Rev. Gen. Pl. **1**: 277. 1891.
Borneo, Celebes, and Cambodia.

Neonauclea tenuis (Havil.)

Nauclea tenuis Havil. Journ. Linn. Soc. Bot. **33**: 55. 1897.
New Guinea.

Neonauclea venosa (Merr.)

Nauclea venosa Merr. Philip. Journ. Sci. Bot. **8**: 45. 1913.
Philippines.

Neonauclea vidalii (Elm.)

Nauclea vidalii Elm. Leafl. Philip. Bot. **1**: 16. 1906.
Philippines.

Neonauclea wenzelii (Merr.)

Nauclea wenzelii Merr. Philip. Journ. Sci. Bot. **9**: 386. 1914.
Philippines.

Neonauclea zeylanica (Hook. f.)

Nauclea zeylanica Hook. f. Fl. Brit. Ind. **3**: 26. 1880.
Bancalus zeylanicus O. Ktze. Rev. Gen. Pl. **1**: 277. 1891.
Ceylon.

ANTHROPOLOGY.—*The origin of the unit type of Pueblo architecture.*[1]   J. WALTER FEWKES, Bureau of American Ethnology.

An important step in the study of the origin of the pueblos of our Southwest was the recognition, by Dr. T. Mitchell Prudden, of the "unit type," from which more complex architectural forms may have been evolved.   This "unit type," so well defined by him,[2] consists of a row of rooms with consolidated walls and extensions at right angles from each end, directly in front of which is a circular subterranean ceremonial chamber, or kiva, and near by a cemetery with other features.   Another important advance in the study of pueblos was the recognition of the existence of an architectural type known as the pre-puebloan, preceding the "unit type."   The object of the present paper is to consider a cause that may have developed the "unit type" of habitation from the pre-puebloan.

The accepted classification of our Southwestern sedentary Indians inhabiting terraced houses is based on differences in their languages, and includes the following stocks: Tanoan (Tewa, Tigua, Piros), Keresan, Zuñi, and Hopi, to which list may be added others now extinct.

It is evident that in ancient times each of these linguistic stocks inhabited a much larger area than its descendants, or those speaking the above-mentioned languages, now occupy. We know of a diminution in the number of villages, not only from legendary accounts, supplemented by archaeological data, but also from historical evidences.   The number of inhabited villages in the Rio Grande region recorded in 1540 was larger than that existing at the present day.   The rate of decrease of certain Pueblo stocks in historical times may even be determined, and the probability is that the number of inhabited pueblos in prehistoric times was considerably larger than when they were first visited by white men, although many were in ruins even at that time.   We are hardly justified in supposing that the people

---

[1] Published by permission of the Secretary of the Smithsonian Institution.

[2] American Anthropologist, n. s., **5**: 224.   1903; *ibid.*, **16**: 33.   1914.

who lived in all buildings now ruins spoke one of the surviving languages; or at all events we have not sufficient data to decide to what linguistic stock many of them should be assigned. The existing classification of Pueblos, according to Major Powell, is one of languages, not cultures; for linguistic data are not comprehensive enough to include culture areas of Pueblos of the past.

The first archaeological feature to be considered in a classification based on the culture of people whose language is unknown is architecture, the character of the houses. Sufficient evidence is accumulating to show that a greater uniformity existed in buildings in the earliest times than later in their history. The most ancient people of our Southwest inhabited a type of dwelling which differed greatly from a Gila compound, like Casa Grande, and from a terraced pueblo, like Laguna. We find evidences of the existence of prehistoric dwellings, subterranean rooms of circular or rectangular forms, and of simple buildings above ground whose walls were constructed of stones or of logs with entwined twigs plastered with clay. Evidences may be adduced to show that there formerly existed in what is now called the pueblo area an antecedent more or less uniform culture, called the pre-puebloan, in which habitations were solitary, the rooms unconnected and one story high. This pre-puebloan type of habitation is widespread; it has been reported even from localities where the true pueblo style of building was later evolved, while on the periphery of the pueblo area the single one-house type survived into historic times and was never submerged by more complex forms. This early simple style, recognized by Mr. C. Mindeleff, Baron Nordenskiöld, Cushing and others, is here regarded as the nucleus from which later types have sprung.

When we examine the present distribution of ruins in our Southwest it is found that they fall geographically into northern and southern groups, separated by a line extending from Fort Craig on the Rio Grande, along the rim of the Mogollons to Oak Creek, Arizona, and thence north to the mouth of the Little Colorado. One of these areas may be called the northern, the other the southern. They differ in climatic, biologic, and other environmental conditions, to which may be traced in part marked cultural differences. The most ancient habitations of both these areas have architectural features in common, as simple houses, and natural and artificial cave-dwellings. There exist also marked architectural differences; in the south the dwellings are large and isolated, grouped into rancherias, or, when communal, contracted into compact blocks of rooms. The inhabitants of these buildings looked for protection to the latter or to fortifications called trincheras, situated on the neighboring hillsides. They had no specialized ceremonial rooms, called kivas, and few if any of the ruins were terraced or had more than one story. The dwelling of the southern group closely resembles those of an early epoch, of which they may be a survival or of a time when there were slight differences in the buildings in the several geographical regions of the Southwest. A close similarity exists between these earliest habitations and those of southern California or of the plains east of the pueblo region. In course of development, differentiation, however, soon came about by reason of climatic influences and the pressure of hostile tribes, the nature of which in the southern area does not concern us in this discussion.

Did the terraced compact form of architecture in the north and the isolated type of dwellings with communal houses in the south arise independently in these two regions, or was one evolved from the other? ᐧ My answer would be that there is no relation of sequence, but that each originated independently and developed from a common type. The pueblo form was not due to extraterritorial influences from the southern area, as suggested by some archeologists, but is the result of local growth through a stage when defence was necessary. We need not follow those who regard the "unit type" as a cultural phase, but may look upon it as a cultural stage from which the pueblo evolved. But here we must discriminate, for there are cliff-habitations on the Upper Gila and in the Sierra Madre in Mexico that are morphologically different from those of the Mesa Verde, Colorado, and those along the San Juan. These latter cliff-dwellings are stages in the development of terraced pueblos; the former may have been phases of architecture adapted to use in caves.

An important contribution to our knowledge of prehistoric culture evolution in the Southwest is the recognition that form and symbolic designs on prehistoric pottery are more important than color, in a determination of chronology. When we study the geographical distribution of designs on food bowls and vases, we find it possible to identify roughly the pre-puebloan, partially by color and form, but mainly by the character of ceramic symbolism, which gives a cultural classification corresponding with that built on architectural features. The various complicated types of designs appearing in the several regions are comparatively late in evolution; with this diversity there exist certain common geometrical designs almost identical throughout the whole Southwest. There are localities in which these simple geometrical forms make up the majority of decorative motives;[3] there are others in which they are subordinate to, or more or less replaced by, a specialized symbolism characteristic of different regions. It is a significant fact that while geometrical decoration reached a high development in cliff-houses, what is most important is that such designs as life figures rarely occur there, although abundant in pueblos which are believed to be of later development. The designs on cliff-dwellers' pottery are practically pre-puebloan survivals.

Objections may be made to the statement that the pre-puebloan culture is characterized by the geometrical nature of pottery designs and a poverty of life figures, since the inhabitants of the Mimbres valley decorated their bowls with a wealth of human and animal designs unsurpassed in the Southwest; especially as it has been held elsewhere that the prehistoric inhabitants of the Mimbres were not Pueblos, but belonged to an earlier culture. The Mimbres people were not in the evolutionary series above considered; their geometrical designs on pottery are radically different from the so-called pre-puebloan of the north.

---

[3] As a rule, black and white ware is archaic and older than red, or polychrome, and the prevailing decorations on it are geometric designs. It is essentially cliff-dwelling pottery, but not confined to caves.

The conclusion arrived at by a comparative study of the simple or complicated designs on cliff-dwellers' pottery is that they represent a past stage of culture, and that the presence of the same in pueblo ruins accompanied by more complicated designs, realistic or symbolic, is a survival.

Bearing in mind what is said above, let us pass to the consideration of the causes that have led to the formation of the "unit type" from the pre-puebloan. The main cause is a desire for protection from enemies, which led to the choice of sites for habitations on inaccessible mesa tops or in caves. In some instances the "unit type" was formed in the open, directly from the pre-puebloan, but in certain localities it was developed in caves.

Nordenskiöld seems to the author to have expressed better than any other archeologist the cause which developed the pueblo form of architecture. He writes: "The manner in which the villages are built, the numerous small rooms huddled together in one large structure, and the several stories rising in terraces one above another can be explained only on the assumption that this architecture was developed during the construction of houses in the caves, where the crowded grouping of the apartments and the erection of several stories were necessitated by the confined space. This circumstance has already been pointed out by Cushing with respect to the Zuñi villages."[4] The author regrets that this writer has not discussed more at length the evidences which led him to state so confidently that there was a secondary occupation of some of the cliff-houses of the Mesa Verde. He writes "We are forced to conclude that they [cliff-houses] were abandoned later than the villages on the mesa," and, later, "they [cliff-houses] were first abandoned, and had partly fallen into ruin, but were subsequently repeopled, new walls being now erected on the ruins of the old." The reason for this belief he briefly states to be the "superposition of walls constructed with the greatest proficiency on others built in a more primitive fashion." This difference in masonry might

---

[4] The Cliff Dwellers of the Mesa Verde. Stockholm, 1893.

account for a later rebuilding of a room, rather than abandonment and secondary occupation of a cliff-house, but even that is a doubtful interpretation, for foundation walls were often more roughly constructed than those built upon them, at the same epoch. It is still an open question whether such a ruin as Community House, on the Mesa Verde, was abandoned earlier than the neighboring Cliff Palace. The author has seen no adequate evidence to prove that the Mesa Verde cliff-houses were deserted later than the villages on the Mesa.[5]

In southern Colorado and northern Arizona, where caves are especially commodious and abundant, pre-puebloan man moved into them for protection from foes, building his single-roomed isolated dwelling in one of the most convenient.[6] Later his clan or family was joined by others or increased naturally in numbers. Rooms to accommodate the increase multiplied until the floor space of the cave, which at first was ample for foundations of habitations, became too small, and the houses were crowded together; later the people were so hard pushed for space upon which to build their habitations that they were obliged, when cave floors failed, to erect rooms on the roofs of houses already occupied, thus imparting a terraced form to the structure.

---

[5] This of course does not mean that now and then there has not been a secondary occupation of certain well known cliff-houses; thus the Asa clans of the Hopi inhabited caves in Chelly canyon well into the historic epoch. The pre-puebloan houses were of course abandoned when their inhabitants moved into the cliffs.

[6] The cliff-pueblos of the Navajo National Park, in northern Arizona, have several architectural features different from those of the Mesa Verde, but show the transition from a pre-puebloan habitation to the "unit type." The construction of rooms and kivas in this region is much ruder, the walls as a rule being made of undressed stones, or of clay or adobe laid on wattles, supported by upright logs. A circular ceremonial opening corresponding to a Hopi or Mesa Verde sipapu has not yet been described or figured from this region, although there are depressions in the floors of some of the rooms which have been given that name. The feature in a kiva which the author identifies as the same as the sipapu of the Hopi kiva is a small circular hole having a diameter of a few inches, situated in the floor about midway between the fireplace and the kiva wall, on the side opposite the deflector. Other holes or depressions are also found in kiva floors. Some of these, as fire-holes, may be ceremonially known as sipapus. These are not the same, however, as the sipapus of the Hopi kivas, nor have they the same symbolic interpretation.

Thus the restricted area of the cave led to modification of the pre-puebloan type of dwellings and developed them into terraced communal houses since called the "unit type." Security dependent on life in caves having become less necessary on account of the increase of numbers, the cliff-dwellers later moved out of the caves to sites on the mesa tops, and afterwards into the valleys, carrying with them this type of architecture, born in caves. Through conservatism they still retained this "unit type," which was partially preserved by the matriarchal system of house holding and clan descent, even after several "unit types" had united to form a complex modern pueblo.

The question naturally arises: Which of the surviving linguistic stocks above mentioned may be regarded as nearest related to that of the early culture when the "unit type" originated?

Studies of the migration stories, myths, and ceremonies still surviving among the Hopi and the Zuñi point to the so-called Keres as the most ancient linguistic stock. This stock is now shrunken in its distribution, surviving in the pueblos of Laguna, Cochiti, Acoma, Sia, Santo Domingo, and a few smaller villages. The cultural center of the area in which the "unit type" originated was the San Juan, the Chaco, and Chelly canyons, and the valley of the Puerco. The Keres pueblos are situated approximately on its southern boundary, while on the east side their influence extended as far as the Rio Grande or crossed to the left bank. Survivals of this stock are still represented in many pueblos, speaking other Pueblo languages, showing that Keresan clans were widely distributed in prehistoric times. It is probable that colonies from its cultural center migrated into northern Arizona, and that some of its clans followed down the San Juan river to the region now occupied by the Hopi villages. Keresan colonies were planted near Zuñi and contributed originally to the modification of this pueblo, the nucleus of which, as shown by Cushing, was a group of clans from the Gila basin migrating by way of the Little Colorado.

The cause of the origin of the several minor forms in pueblo architecture is secondary to that which led to the evolution of the "unit type;" for instance, in the ancient Keres culture area there are rectangular ruins, round ruins, and circular kivas of subterranean character, as well as the terraced houses which distinguish the consolidated community dwellings. Archaic pueblo cults, as those of the Snake dances (Acoma, Sia, Laguna, and Hopi), some of which are extinct, and others (as of the Hopi) still celebrated, distinguish in a measure the ancient pre-puebloan, and were transmitted into Keres culture.[7]

There are not enough data at hand to show that the Keresan language was once spoken on the San Juan or throughout northern New Mexico or southern Colorado; legends declare that Keresan colonists have introduced Keresan rites, songs, and prayers in the distant pueblos Zuñi and Hopi, and elsewhere. While we may never know the speech of the ancient pre-puebloan inhabitants or of the cliff-dwellers, there are legends among Pueblos that their ancestors inhabited caves, and strangely enough the Navajo Indians have a like legend for their oldest clan.

The area above identified shows evidences of long occupation by man, and in it occur some of the finest terraced-house ruins in the Southwest. Although it is commonly believed that the particular form of buildings that characterize the pueblos was derived from Mexico, there is little in comparative data to support this conclusion. Aboriginal terraced buildings are not found in Mexico or in California.[8]   It is more probable that this

[7] The known association of Snake dances and Snake clans and their presence in the Keresan pueblos Sia, Acoma, and old Laguna, as well as at Hopi, may play an important rôle, when enough data are collected to permit an intelligent discussion of the theory of a close kinship between the inhabitants of the San Juan pueblos and the Keres and Shoshoneans (as Paiute and others). The Hopi claim that their Snake clan and its festival, the Snake dance, came from Tókonabi on the San Juan, and that the Acoma Snake dance, now extinct, came from the same region.

[8] The observation that "casas grandes a la manera de los de la Nueva Espana," and "pueblo-like" settlements are found on the California coast, as stated by Cabrillo (Doc. Ined. de Indias, 3: 401, 412–13; 5: 491; 14: 177, 181.) is believed to be too indefinite to support the theory that terraced pueblos were intended. The ruins Quiarra and Abojo in Lower California, mentioned by Johann Xantus (Globus, 1861, p. 143), and referred to pueblos by Fritz Krause, in his excellent monograph on pueblos, are not terraced, and do not belong to the true pueblo type as limited by the author of the present article.

unique culture was autochthonous, being largely due to environment. Judging from the characteristics of the ruins and the evidences of their antiquity, it is much more likely that the terraced-house architecture in our Southwest arose in a region of caves like those of the San Juan, and reached its highest development in the Chaco canyon, or in the Rio Grande valley. Whereever we find this peculiar form outside this area it can be traced either to the influence of colonists that had migrated from this center of distribution or to transmission of cultural ideas.

But the Keresan were not the only group of ancient sedentary people with community dwellings, in the Southwest. Compact buildings existed along the Gila river, in early times, and dwellings ascribed to another stock are found in the Rio Grande valley. Prominent among the latter may be mentioned ancestors of a Tanoan people who inhabited northern New Mexico; valleys peopled by them extend along the upper Rio Grande valley, from Taos to Isleta, and as far west as Jemez. In the early days the Tanoans also probably did not build terraced houses or pueblos; they may have become acquainted with this specialized architecture, and circular ceremonial rooms, or kivas, through association with other peoples, or even have acquired it independently. There are at the present time evidences of variation in the composition of this people, which is believed to have originated from a mixture of Tanoans with Keresan clans and wilder nomads from the Great Plains or elsewhere. So great was the mixture that the various members of the Tanoan stock speak widely divergent dialects of the Tewa language, as evidenced by the Taos and Isleta.

The third of the great prehistoric culture areas of the Southwest, the inhabitants of which were linguistically allied to the Tanoan, especially Jemez, once extended from the pueblo Pecos, a few miles east of Santa Fe, to the border of Texas,[9] following down the Pecos river, which practically formed its eastern border, and extending through the salt regions (Salinas) near Alamagordo, on the eastern side. The pre-puebloan habitations of

[9] A ruin is marked on the "Engineer's Map" (1877) on the Pecos in Texas, but this site has not been verified.

this area were clusters of houses, generally isolated, which in some places, however, had been built closer together, either for protection or because of the influx of Pueblos. This was practically a region of agricultural tribes and buffalo hunters.[10]

Bordering the prehistoric Keres on the south and the west we find evidences of the existence of an extensive population along the headwaters of the Gila and the Little Colorado, including the inhabitants of several fertile valleys along numerous tributaries. The language spoken in this region is unknown, and the culture has not been connected with any special pueblo area, but this culture was greatly modified by admixture with incoming Keres and Tewa clans. Zuñi, on a tributary of the Little Colorado, was modified, as shown by Mr. Cushing, by clans of Keres stock that inhabited the "round" ruined pueblos,[11] and later by Tanoan elements, which joined it not long before 1540, the beginning of the historic epoch.

A word should be said, in closing this brief discussion, on the relation of the Casa Grande or "compound type,"[12] characteristic of the Gila and Salt River valleys, and the pueblo proper. This architectural type, like the true pueblo, originated independently in the valley in which it is now found. The interpretation of its relation to the true pueblo is that both were evolved from a common pre-existing type, the so-called pre-puebloan.

The same explanation of independent origin holds also in regard to Sierra Madre plateau, or "Casas Grandes" type, and that found among the prehistoric inhabitants of the Mimbres valley, southern New Mexico. This latter culture, like terraced pueblos, was evolved independently in the valley in which its remains are now found. It likewise was preceded by a culture comparable, in architectural features, with the pre-puebloan, a type represented by great buildings, Casa Grandes, in the south, and highly developed pottery symbols in the north.

[10] The Pecos language survived to within a few years in a small, extra-territorial village on the Rio Grande near El Paso, but is now extinct.

[11] Matyata ("Archeotekopa"), Jour. Amer. Arch. Eth., 1: 2. 1891.

[12] The "compound" type is so clearly defined in the author's report on Casa Grande (28th Ann. Rept. Bureau of American Ethnology) that only confusion will result if true pueblos are designated "compounds."

PROCEEDINGS OF THE ACADEMY AND AFFILIATED SOCIETIES

THE WASHINGTON ACADEMY OF SCIENCES

The 98th meeting of the Washington Academy of Sciences, a joint meeting with the Biological Society, was held on Thursday, March 11, 1915, at 8.30 p.m. in the Auditorium of the New National Museum. Mr. WILFRED H. OSGOOD, of the Field Museum of Natural History, gave a lecture on *Fur seals and other animals on the Priblof Islands.*

Mr. Osgood was engaged in a special investigation of the fur seal question for the Department of Commerce during the summer of 1914, and therefore had had unusual opportunities to become well informed on this subject, which he discussed from both the biological and economic standpoints. The life history of the seal and other animals that inhabit or frequent the Priblofs was explained and made especially vivid by numerous lantern slides and by motion pictures.

The 99th meeting of the Academy was held Thursday, March 18, 1915, at 4.45 p.m., in the Auditorium of the New National Museum. Dr. ARTHUR L. DAY, Director of the Geophysical Laboratory of the Carnegie Institution, gave an illustrated lecture on *The volcano Kilauea in action.* Dr. Day explained that the somewhat hazardous and uncomfortable trip into the crater was made for the purpose of studying the processes, chemical and physical, that take place in active volcanoes. By the accidental formation of a lava dome over active molten lava a rare opportunity was offered, and fully utilized, for collecting a considerable quantity of volcanic gases before there had been any opportunity for contamination with the atmosphere. These had been studied in detail and, among other important results, the presence of considerable quantities of water vapor definitely confirmed.

The 100th meeting of the Academy was held Thursday, March 25, 1915, at 4.45 p.m. in the Auditorium of the New National Museum. Dr. N. A. COBB, of the Bureau of Plant Industry, gave an illustrated lecture on *Nematodes, their relations to mankind and to agriculture.* It was explained that nematodes are amost universal in distribution; that they abound in every soil, swarm in the depths of the ocean, prey on all vegetation, infest animals of every species and man of every race. If forests and cities should disappear, leaving behind only their nematodes, it would be quite possible for the scientist, judging by the numbers and the species involved, accurately to locate not only every one of the lost cities and every vanished forest, but even in great measure, the streets, the kinds of trees and other details. As abundantly demonstrated, the subject of nematodes, in addition to its unusual scientific interest, is also of great economic importance.

The 101st meeting of the Academy was held Thursday, April 1, 1915, at 4.45 p.m., in the Auditorium of the New National Museum. Dr. CHARLES E. MUNROE, Dean of Graduate Studies, George Washington University, gave an illustrated lecture on *High explosives and their effects*. The nature of an explosion was made clear by reference to combustion, and the way in which it is facilitated by subdivision of the combustible. The history of each of the more important explosives was given. Its chemical structure, the process of its manufacture, and its uses, both in civil operations and in warfare, were all fully explained. In several cases the original ingredients and the final compound were all shown. Many surprising results produced by high explosives were illustrated by lantern slides, and a remarkable series of iron plates was exhibited on which high explosives had left impressions of leaves, laces, and other relatively soft and delicate objects.

The 102d meeting of the Academy was held Thursday, April 8, 1915, at 4.45 p.m., in the Auditorium of the New National Museum. Mr. W. D. HUNTER, of the Bureau of Entomology, gave a lecture on *Insects and their relation to disease*. It was shown that with the discovery of Pasteur the empirical age of medicine began gradually to be replaced by an exact knowledge of the cause of disease and an understanding, in many cases, of how to prevent it. A further great advance was made when it was clearly recognized that of several of the more formidable diseases, such as malaria, yellow fever, bubonic plague, sleeping sickness, and typhus fever, each depends not only for its transmission but even for its existence upon one or another species of insects; while still others, of which diphtheria and typhoid fever are typical examples, are similarly spread from place to place. Hence the relation of insects to disease is of the greatest importance. Sanitation, the prevention of epidemics, and the reduction of disease to a minimum is, therefore, a biological rather than a medical problem.

The 103d meeting of the Academy was held Thursday, April 15, 1915, at 8.30 p.m., in the Auditorium of the New National Museum. Dr. R. S. WOODWARD, President of the Carnegie Institution, gave a lecture on *The Earth*. The dimensions and mass of the Earth were given in terms of ordinary familiar units and, therefore, for the most part in exceedingly large numbers. The Earth was conveniently divided into four distinct but very unequal parts, namely: The atmosphere, concerning whose upper or outer portion but little is known; the hydrosphere, essentially the oceans, which in many respects is well known; the lithosphere, or rocky crust, also comparatively well known; and the centrosphere, or all that part of the earth below its rocky shell. In comparison with the other parts almost nothing is known of the centrosphere.

W. J. HUMPHREYS, *Recording Secretary*.

THE PHILOSOPHICAL SOCIETY OF WASHINGTON

The 754th meeting was held on March 13, 1915, at the Cosmos Club, President Eichelberger in the chair; 50 persons present.

Mr. G. K. BURGESS gave an illustrated account of *Some researches in metals at the Bureau of Standards*, describing investigations now being carried out on the preparation, properties, and failure of metals and alloys. The methods developed for determining critical ranges with the thermoelectric and resistance pyrometers and their application to pure iron in which the characteristics of the A_2 and A_3 transformations were brought out, were described. The application of the micropyrometer to the determination of monochromatic emissivities of metals and oxides in the solid and liquid states were demonstrated in the range 900° to 1700°C. Coöperative work with some of the technical societies in the preparation of alloys and the determination of suitable specifications for typical bronzes and brasses was described. A study of the volatilization of various grades of platinum ware with the object of forming a basis for defining the quality of such ware for exact chemical analysis has been made. Investigations are being made on the causes of failure of railway rails, the deterioration of fusible tin boiler plugs, and failures of wrought bronzes and brasses used in engineering construction. The paper was discussed by Messrs. WHITE and C. A. BRIGGS with references to improved method for casting steel ingots and the precise character of stresses in bronze bolts and bars.

Mr. W. BOWIE then gave an illustrated account of *The errors of precise leveling*. Very accurate determinations of elevations from some adopted datum have been made possible by the great improvements of the wye level during the past half century. In 1912 the International Geodetic Association defined leveling of high precision as that which must have a probable accidental error not greater than 1 mm. per kilometer and a probable systematic error not greater than 0.2 mm. per kilometer. The effect of most of the errors of precise leveling can be eliminated by the method employed. There are, however, errors of refraction in leveling on steep slopes which depend upon the time of day and the weather conditions. It is concluded from an investigation carried on at the Coast and Geodetic Survey that, on an average, the afternoon running gives a greater difference in elevation between two points than a morning running. The difference is greater in cloudy than in sunshiny or clear weather. It is also greater during wind than in calm. The speaker is of the opinion that the runnings in the afternoon in wind and in cloudy weather give results nearer the truth than in the forenoon in calm and in sunshiny weather. In the discussion Mr. WINSTON gave some details of leveling across Florida; Mr. BURGESS referred to possible lines across Mexico and the Isthmus of Panama for determining possible difference in the ocean levels; Mr. SOSMAN raised question as to difference of results with time particularly on the Atlantic Coast; Mr. BURGESS referred to possible effect of expansion coefficients of materials in ground on values. Mr. BOWIE stated that some redeterminations of elevations for old Coast and Geodetic Survey marks by the New York City survey indicated no differences with time for stations set on solid rock; for one at Sandy Hook a subsidence of 0.35 foot is indicated; there is probably no error on account temperature changes because of constant conditions at slight depth and rapidity with which work is done.

The 755th meeting was held at the Cosmos Club, March 27, 1915, President Eichelberger in the chair; 62 persons present.

Mr. C. G. ABBOT spoke on *Recent progress in astronomy*. The speaker summarized briefly results of recent discussion placing total number of stars between 1 and 2 million, and determinations of proper motions and stellar drifts, reviewing particularly the work of Boss. Attention was called to work on star spectra by Pickering and the types of spectra; the excellent agreement for position of apex of solar motion by measurements from displacement of spectrum lines by Pickering and from Boss' discussion of star groups was pointed out. A brief review of our knowledge of star distances and the methods for determining them was given.

Mr. L. J. BRIGGS then presented an illustrated paper on *A new method for measuring gravity at sea*. The necessity of measuring the boiling point of water in connection with barometer readings in determining gravity at sea can be eliminated by the use of an apparatus in principle similar to a closed barometer, maintained at constant temperature. This was the method employed, the apparatus in addition being so designed that the enclosed mass of gas supporting the mercury column always occupied the same volume at the time of making the observations. This avoids the necessity of measuring volume changes, and doubles the sensitiveness of the apparatus. The apparatus was constructed of glass and consisted of a capillary mercurial column to reduce pumping, which expanded at the top into an evacuated spherical bulb, while the lower end of the column opened below a mercury surface in the pressure chamber. The evacuated bulb contained at its center a fixed reference point. Above the air chamber the capillary was bent into a zigzag spring which allowed a small vertical adjustment of the observing bulb, controlled by a micrometer screw. In making an observation the bulb was so adjusted that the mercury surface was barely in contact with the fixed point. This confined the gas always to the same volume. The height of column was then read from the micrometer head. This arrangement avoids the necessity of any measurement of the position of the lower mercury surface. The whole apparatus can thus be kept surrounded by melting ice, which was used to maintain constant temperature. On board ship, the apparatus was swung on gimbals to secure verticality, and suspended from spiral springs to reduce vibration. Observations were made daily between Tahiti and San Francisco. The results indicate a slight excess of mass in this part of the ocean, particularly in latitude 16° to 24° north, and longitude 130° to 135° west. The paper was discussed by Messrs. ABBOT, MARvin, Paul, Wenner, Swann, and C. A. Briggs, particularly with reference to correction on account of velocity of ship, pumping effects and damping by decreasing diameter of capillary tube, correction due to mean variation of instrument from vertical, and effect of non-uniformity in ice packing.

The 756th meeting was held on April 10, 1915, at the Cosmos Club, President Eichelberger in the chair; 43 persons present.

Mr. W. Bowie spoke on *Geodetic work of the Coast and Geodetic Survey*. Reference was made to the measurement of arcs in Europe in the 17th and 18th centuries, but for lack of time the history during the ages before the 19th century was not dwelt upon. The problems before the geodesist today were presented. Some of the earlier problems have been solved, the measurement of base lines being one of them. The nickel-steel (invar) tapes and wires now in general use give results which are entirely satisfactory. The illustrations showed the instruments used in the several branches of geodetic surveying and the field methods were described. Every effort is made by the Survey to reduce the unit costs of the work without decreasing the accuracy of the results. The motor truck has been used successfully as the means of transportation for several seasons. Three of them will be used by the primary triangulation party this year on the Utah-Idaho line. Aside from the scientific value of the geodetic surveys they have great practical value, for they furnish the fundamental control for maps and surveys made by government and private organizations. The paper was discussed by Messrs. Winston, Curtis, Priestly, and L. A. Fischer.

Mr. R. B. Sosman then presented a paper by himself and Mr. J. C. Hostetter entitled *Note on the magnetic properties of iron dissolved in platinum*. This paper is printed in the Journal of the Washington Academy of Sciences, **5:** 293. 1915. The communication was discussed by Messrs. Burgess and Swann.

Mr. H. E. Merwin then spoke on *Chromatic reflection of covellite*. (Published in the Journal of the Washington Academy of Sciences, **5:** 341–344. 1915.) The paper was discussed by Messrs. Humphreys, Priestly, and C. A. Briggs.

Mr. G. W. Vinal then spoke on *The solubility of metallic silver in distilled water*. The practice of nearly all observers with the silver voltameter has been to continue the washing of the deposit until the presence of silver nitrate can no longer be detected in the wash waters by chemical tests, but many have taken the further precaution of allowing distilled water to stand on the deposit for a considerable period of time. As a test on the completeness of the washing, Prof. G. A. Hulett and the speaker compared the conductivity of the water before being put in the cup with its conductivity after it had stood in the cup for various periods of time. In every case the conductivity increased with time. It was at first supposed that this increase was due to entrapped silver nitrate gradually soaking out, as the silver in the water could be detected after allowing the water to stand over night. All subsequent experiments showed that this is not the case, but rather that an electrolytic process was taking place by which the silver was passing into solution at the rate of about 0.006 mg. per hour from a 4 gram deposit of silver on platinum. Confirming this it was shown by a galvanometer that a current actually passed from the silver through the water to the platinum. In washing the deposits over night this effect becomes appreciable. The paper was discussed by Messrs. BURGESS and C. A. BRIGGS.

Mr. M. JAMES then spoke on *A conducting paint.* An electrically conducting paint has been obtained through the action of hydrochloric acid on bronze powder. The resistance of a paint film depends largely upon the surface to be painted. The resistance increases with time; the rate of change, however, decreasing. For such surfaces as glass, wood, and paper, the resistance increases about 30 per cent in two months, and then is fairly constant. The resistivity of a painted surface is about 1000 times that of copper. The paper was discussed by Messrs. SWANN, PRIESTLY, and BESSACHES.

The 757th meeting was held on May 8, 1915, at the Bureau of Standards, President Eichelberger in the chair; about 90 persons present. President Eichelberger called upon Vice-President Humphreys to take the chair for the meeting. Mr. HUMPHREYS introduced the speaker of the evening, Prof. E. NORTHRUP, of Princeton University, who gave an experimental lecture on *Some physical properties of matter at high temperatures.* Temperature was defined as a condition of matter which results from the disorganized motion of its molecules or atoms, as contrasted with any organized motion which is impressed upon a mass as a whole. It was pointed out that any body tends to acquire a disorganized motion of its ultimate parts, called its temperature, because this kind of motion is the most probable of all motions. A "visible molecules apparatus" was exhibited which illustrated the above conception of temperature as well as some of the fundamental principles belonging to the kinetic theory of gases. With this apparatus, in which 16,000 one-sixteenth-inch steel balls were caused to move in the manner of gas molecules, experiments were shown to illustrate change of pressure with temperature, the volume being constant, and change of volume with temperature the pressure being constant. With the aid of accessories attached to this apparatus the viscosity of a gas was illustrated and an imitation was given of the Brownian movements. Other experiments which could be performed with this apparatus were described. It was stated that temperature was a unique condition of matter and that it affects its manifested properties more than any other single condition to which matter may be subjected.

The problem of the electrical conduction of matter throughout the producible temperature range of some 4000°C. was discussed. Methods and apparatus were described and shown for experimentally studying the electrical conduction of matter in its solid, liquid, and vapor phases. Two types of furnaces were operated, to show the production of very high temperatures. The advantage of using the cascade principle of heating was explained and a tungsten wire 1 mm. in diameter was melted in the cascade attachment to the larger model furnace exhibited. It was pointed out that temperatures up to 1680°C. may be accurately measured by means of the speaker's new type tin pyrometer which makes use of the property possessed by molten tin of increasing in resistance linearly with the temperature.

The characteristic facts of metallic conduction over a wide range of temperature were explained and several curves were thrown on the screen. The peculiarities of the electrical conduction of hot gases were described and it was explained how the unstable character of gas conduction at very high temperature may be used to make a small furnace act in the capacity of a telephone receiver and talk. The commonly accepted "free electron theory" of metallic conduction was explained and reasons given why the theory appears quite inadequate to account for experimental facts. A new hypothesis, which the speaker called the "electric transport theory" of conduction, was briefly explained. The lecture concluded with a plea for employing experimental methods of investigation in acquiring new knowledge of the properties of matter under all temperature conditions. As a final experiment an electromagnetic piece of apparatus which the speaker called "an electric Jack-in-the-box," was shown.

The Chair expressed to Professor NORTHRUP the appreciation and thanks of the members of the Society and guests present for his interesting and instructive lecture and experiments.

The 758th meeting was held on May 22, 1915, at the Cosmos Club, President Eichelberger in the chair; 30 persons present.

Mr. C. E. VAN ORSTRAND presented a paper by himself and Mr. F. P. DEWEY entitled *Preliminary report on the diffusion of solids.* The coefficients of diffusion of gold into lead at temperatures of 100°, 150°, and 197°C. were found to be in close agreement with values obtained by Roberts-Austen. Preliminary tests on the variation with pressure of the coefficients of diffusion of gold into lead were not conclusive, but point to the possibility that the coefficient is increased. Various methods of determining the constants of the Fourier integral which represents the diffusion of heat and of substances in solution were discussed for the case of constant initial quality. The exceptional agreement between the observed and theoretical curves was emphasized. The paper was discussed by Messrs. HUMPHREYS and SWANN.

Mr. H. C. DICKINSON then spoke on *The specific heat of ice at temperatures near the melting point,* presenting results obtained in cooperation with Mr. N. S. OSBORNE. (Published in the Journal of the Washington Academy of Sciences, **5:** 338–340. 1915.)

Mr. W. D. LAMBERT then spoke on *An exact formula for theoretical gravity at the earth's surface.* The mathematical expressions usually given for the force of gravity at the earth's surface constitute only 2 or 3 terms of an infinite series. An expression in closed form may be derived, if it is assumed that the surface of the earth is an equipotential surface having the form of an ellipsoid of revolution. The expression for the surface gravity g is:

$$g = g_0 \left(\sqrt{1 - e^2 \sin^2 \varphi} + m\, e f\,(e) \frac{\sqrt{1 - e^2}}{\sqrt{1 - e^2 \sin^2 \varphi}} \sin^2 \varphi \right).$$

In this equation g_0 is the force of gravity at the equator, e is the eccentricity of a meridian ellipse, φ is the geographic latitude, m is ratio of the centrifugal force at the equator to gravity there, and

$$f\,(e) = \frac{i\, Q_1 \left(i \dfrac{\sqrt{1 - e^2}}{e} \right)}{Q_2 \left(i \dfrac{\sqrt{1 - e^2}}{e} \right)},$$

the Q's being zonal harmonics of the second kind. An expression was also derived for $\dfrac{\partial g}{\partial h}$, the rate of decrease of gravity with elevation above the earth's surface, the results agreeing with those derived from a formula given by Helmert. Attention was drawn to the fact that Helmert's formula is really a geometrical interpretation of Laplace's equation and hence is more general than might appear from Helmert's proof of it. The paper was discussed by Messrs. SWANN and L. J. BRIGGS.

J. A. FLEMING,
Secretary.

JOURNAL

OF THE

WASHINGTON ACADEMY OF SCIENCES

Vol. V   OCTOBER 4, 1915   No. 16

PHYSICS.—*A method for measuring Earth resistivity.* FRANK WENNER, Bureau of Standards.

A knowledge of earth resistivity may be of value in determining something of its composition, such for example as moisture content, whether or not it contains oil or ore of high conductivity, etc., or in the calculation of damages to pipe systems by the return current of street railway systems. For some of these or other reasons we may wish to determine the resistivity of limited portions of the earth.

For those cases in which we desire the resistivity of a fairly large portion of earth, extending to a considerable depth, or where there are reasons why the measurement should be made without disturbing the portion to be measured, the following method is suggested.

Four holes are made in the earth approximately uniformly spaced in a straight line. The diameter of the holes is not more than 10 per cent of the distance between them and all extend to approximately the same depth, which is usually that at which we are most concerned with the resistivity. In each hole is placed an electrode which makes electrical contact with the earth only near the bottom. Two of these electrodes serve as current terminals and two as potential terminals in the measurement of the resistance.

Knowing the resistance, the depth of the holes and the distance between them we have data from which the effective resistivity in the vicinity can be calculated.

In case a is the distance between the holes, b is the depth of the holes, ρ is the resistivity, and R the measured resistance, then

$$\rho = \frac{4\pi aR}{1 + \dfrac{2a}{\sqrt{a^2 + 4b^2}} - \dfrac{2a}{\sqrt{4a^2 + 4b^2}}} = \frac{4\pi aR}{n} \qquad (1)$$

where n varies between 1 and 2 according to the ratio of the depth of the electrodes to their distance apart. If the holes are not in a straight line or are not of a uniform depth or spacing the resistivity is easily calculated from the depth of each of the holes and the distance of each from each of the other three.

Concerning the resistance measurements there is in general no need for a high accuracy. There is therefore no reason why we may not use an ammeter for measuring the current and a voltmeter for measuring the resulting difference in potential between the potential terminals, providing no current is drawn from these terminals. As the voltage to be measured is low and the resistance between electrodes and earth high, errors would be introduced if the ammeter-voltmeter method were used in the ordinary way.

The following potentiometer arrangement, using alternating current to obviate the more serious difficulties which might arise on account of polarization with direct current, seems to answer the purpose fairly well. The current terminals or electrodes are connected to a source of alternating voltage of suitable value, and across the line is connected a step-down transformer, the low voltage side of which is connected to the ends of a slide wire. One of the potential terminals is connected to one end of the slide wire and the other through a vibration galvanometer to the adjustable contact on the slide wire. An ammeter is connected into a lead to one of the current terminals and a voltmeter across the ends of the slide wire. On account of the polarization at the current electrodes a variable inductance is connected into one end of the leads, for the purpose of bringing the test current in phase with the voltage of the low side of the transformer.

If then adjustments are made so that no current flows through the galvanometer, the position of the sliding contact, the value of the test current, and the voltage across the slide wire are read, we have data from which the resistance R is readily calculated.

From the measured resistance, and the depth and distance between electrodes a value may be obtained for the effective resistivity as explained above. The value depends mainly upon the resistivity in the neighborhood of and between the potential electrodes and very little upon the resistivity at distances from either of these electrodes equal to half the distance between the current electrodes.

So far the method has been used only for determining resistivities in a region very close to the surface, a few meters or less in radius. To measure the effective resistance of a much larger portion of earth extending to a considerable depth, the electrodes would be placed much farther apart. Such a measurement might be of assistance in locating deposits of ore of high conductivity.

CHEMISTRY.—*The dissociation of calcium carbonate below 500° C.* R. B. SOSMAN, J. C. HOSTETTER, and H. E. MERWIN, Geophysical Laboratory.

In connection with investigations in progress in this Laboratory it appeared possible to apply a vacuum furnace, developed by the authors for the measurement of low dissociation pressures of oxides,[1] to the measurement of the carbon dioxide pressures of calcite and aragonite. If aragonite is a metastable form at all temperatures, its dissociation pressure should be measurably higher than that of calcite at temperatures below that at which aragonite is rapidly transformed into calcite.

This transformation takes place in a few minutes in air at 470°, although in contact with solutions it will go on as low as 350°, according to results obtained by Williamson in this Laboratory. The problem was therefore to measure the dissociation pressures at several temperatures below 470°.

[1] This Journal, 5: 277–285. 1915.

The downward extrapolation of Johnston's curve,[2] obtained from measurements between the temperatures 587° and 894° and the pressures 1 mm. and 716 mm., indicates the following carbon dioxide pressures at lower temperatures: 450°, 0.017 mm. mercury; 400°, 0.0020 mm. A "blank" run in the furnace up to 400° showed that the expected pressure from calcite at 400° could be measured definitely and without ambiguity; the equilibrium pressure decreases so rapidly with temperature, however, that at 350°, or even 375°, it would be obscured by the evolution of gases from the walls of the furnace and the glass connections, if measurements were necessary over a period of an hour or more.

Measurements were accordingly begun at 425° on aragonite. The material used consisted of clear crystals (U. S. National Museum No. 17692) ground to pass 65 mesh. 350 mg. of this powder was mixed with 150 mg. CaO made by heating the aragonite powder in platinum over a Meker burner. The measurements at 425° lasted 90 minutes. When cold, the aragonite was found to have been completely converted into calcite.

At 400°, on the other hand, 68 minutes heating converted none of the mixture into calcite. The few calcite grains visible were not more numerous than the calcite grains in the original aragonite. It is evident, therefore, that 400° is practically the only temperature at which calcite and aragonite can be compared as regards their dissociation pressures.

Measurements were therefore made on aragonite and calcite at 400°. Two varieties of calcite were used: (1) clear crystals of Iceland spar (Kahlbaum, 1913);[3] (2) artificial precipitated $CaCO_3$ (J. T. Baker, lot No. 8212).[4] The latter is in small well-formed rhombs, each with an inclusion at its center. Mixtures were made containing 350 mg. calcite, and 150 mg. CaO made from the calcite by ignition. Experiments were also made on the combination of CaO with CO_2.

[2] Jour. Am. Chem. Soc., **32**: 938–946. 1910.

[3] Containing 0.098 per cent $MgCO_3$ (Hostetter, J. Ind. and Eng. Chem., **6**:392. 1914).

[4] Containing 0.081 per cent $MgCO_3$.

The result of the dissociation pressure measurements, so far as their original purpose is concerned, was disappointing. The cause lies probably in the slow rate of dissociation of the dry materials at 400°. A number of interesting facts were obtained, however, which have been thought worth present publication, as we have had to discontinue the work for the present.

Forms of lime. CaO is obtainable in two distinct physical states. That made by heating Iceland spar at 700° in the vacuum furnace, and pumping out the last traces of CO_2, is very fine grained and porous, with a faint double-refraction. The refractive index seems to be quite variable, but on account of the porosity of the material accurate measurements of the index could not be made. The oxide is very reactive, absorbing water from the air even when confined in a desiccator in the presence of calcium chloride. After being reheated to 1200°, the index rose, and gave values varying from 1.725 to 1.77; the oxide was then much more stable in air, and did not take up moisture while the microscopic examination was being made, as did the first sample. As in the first case, however, the porosity interferes with accurate measurement. Again reheated, to 1400°, the oxide showed a prevailing refractive index of 1.81, with some grains as low as 1.79. It still showed double-refraction.

On account of its fineness, it is impossible to say conclusively whether this variety is crystalline or amorphous. The double-refraction may be the result simply of strains within an amorphous solid.

The reactivity of this porous lime was shown by another experiment. 452.5 mg. of 200 mesh Kahlbaum calcite was heated and evacuated at 750° in the vacuum furnace, in presence of P_2O_5, for about 30 minutes. When it had cooled to 110°, 15 mg. dry CO_2 was admitted. (The gas had been drawn from a cylinder of liquid CO_2, passed over hot copper and copper oxide, dried over P_2O_5 and stored over mercury.) The reaction began immediately with a rise of temperature; as the charge cooled to room temperature the absorption still continued, but at a decreasing rate. Even at room temperature the absorption continued slowly, 0.48 mg. being taken up in $21\frac{1}{2}$ hours. About

4 mg. remained unabsorbed.   Practically all of this was absorbed on reheating to 460°, the small residue being probably nitrogen. An interesting feature of this reheating was the *increase* of pressure observed between 400° and 460°, in which interval the pressure nearly doubled, although already at least 10 times the calculated dissociation pressure of $CaCO_3$ at these temperatures. On continued heating the pressure again continued to fall.   The phenomenon suggests a condensation or absorption of the gas in the porous solid before true chemical union occurs.

A second variety of lime is obtained by carefully dehydrating calcium nitrate, melting it, and gradually raising the temperature until all nitric oxide is driven off.[5]   The resulting crystals are isotropic cubes and octahedra, of refractive index 1.83.   They are identical with the CaO found in the lime-alumina-silica melts of Rankin and Wright.[6]   The porous lime obtained from calcium carbonate seems to gradually go over to the cubical form on heating; calcite heated in platinum over the blast lamp for 1 hour gave cubic lime of index 1.83, and impure commercial building-lime also had the same properties.

Some lime which had been fused in a graphite vacuum furnace in 1913 by C. W. Kanolt of the Bureau of Standards was also examined.   The greater part of it consisted of rounded grains of isometric lime of index 1.83, being similar to the rounded lime grains formed in silicate melts.

The much lower reactivity of the cubical crystalline lime is shown by the following experiment: 501 mg. of 100-mesh crystalline CaO from calcium nitrate was heated in the vacuum furnace with quantities of from 5.0 to 12.5 mg. CO_2, and at temperatures between 400° and 600°.   The pressures were from 1.65 to 4.10 mm.   Although the dissociation pressure at 600° is only 2.35 mm. according to Johnston, the total amount of CO_2 absorbed in all these heatings was not over 0.86 mg.   The porous lime referred to above, on the other hand, absorbed 11 mg. in a few minutes at 110° and lower.

[5] By special precautions clear crystals of CaO up to 10 mm. in length can be obtained by this method.   Brügelmann, Zs. anorg. Chem., **10**: 415–433.   1895; **59**: 248–270.   1908.

[6] Am. Jour. Sci., **39**: 1–79.   1915.

Transition point in CaO. Lastchenko[7] has shown by specific heat measurements that a transition point probably exists in crystalline lime at about 400–415°, having a heat effect of 280 calories per molecular weight, or 5 calories per gram. This heat effect is just about on the border of recognizability by a direct time-temperature heating curve. Nevertheless we tried heating curves on a sample of the crystalline lime from calcium nitrate, using the vacuum furnace in order to avoid any heat effect due to hydration or carbonation. At 11° per minute no break was detected. At 5° per minute there was a distinct absorption of heat at about 425–430°, but the corresponding evolution was not distinguishable on the cooling curve. From the forms of the crystals obtained from melts at higher temperatures it is evident that both the high- and low-temperature forms must be cubic; the transformation is probably a crystallographic change similar to the inversion of quartz at 575°.

Dissociation pressures of calcite and aragonite. Although not sufficiently definite to decide the question as to which is the more stable form, the CO_2 pressures measured were not without certain regularities. All of the pressures measured at 400° lie between the limits 0.0019 mm. and 0.0168 mm.[8] The greater part lie between 0.0030 and 0.0090 mm. The dissociation pressure of calcite at 400° calculated from Johnston's curve is 0.0020 mm.; the pressures found are of this order of magnitude, which is all that might reasonably be expected of an extrapolation to a pressure only about $\frac{1}{1000}$ of the lowest accurately measured pressure on the curve referred to.

Both calcite and aragonite, when heated alone at 400°, were found to dissociate so slowly that it seemed hopeless to wait for the pressure to reach an equilibrium, since the vacuum furnace could be operated only during the working hours of the day. Even at 600° calcite dissociated quite slowly. The addition of 5 per cent Fe_2O_3 to calcite did not seem to affect its dissociation

[7] J. Russ. Phys.-Chem. Soc., **42**: 1604–1614. 1911. Bull. Inst. Polyt. Don. 1913, II, 9–46.

[8] The relatively high pressure of 0.0168 mm. was obtained from the inclusion-bearing artificial calcite.

rate appreciably. At 400° this mixture gave a pressure of 0.0026 mm. in 18 minutes, and 0.0039 in 35 minutes; aragonite gave 0.0019 mm. in 18 minutes.

The carbonate formed by absorption of CO_2 by porous lime dissociates readily. After the initial pumping out of residual gas it gave at 400° a falling pressure of 0.0129 in 25 minutes, and after a second pumping, a constant pressure of 0.0117 mm. in 42 minutes.

Mixtures were made containing 30 per cent CaO and 70 per cent calcite or aragonite, in the expectation that the presence of the second phase would hasten the establishment of equilibrium. This seemed at first to be the case, as pressures were quickly attained which then rose only slowly. But repeated pumping out of the gas caused a progressive lowering of the pressures attained and of the rates of increase, until the condition of pure slow-dissociating calcite or aragonite was approached. It seems probable, therefore, that the gases came chiefly from the $CaCO_3$ formed by absorption of small amounts of CO_2 from the air by the CaO. This $CaCO_3$ dissociates readily, as just shown, and, after the exhaustion of the CO_2, the CaO remains simply as a neutral substance in the presence of the slowly dissociating crystals of original calcite or aragonite.

Whether the compound formed by the combination of the porous CaO with CO_2 is calcite, aragonite, or amorphous $CaCO_3$ we are unable to say. The high dissociation pressure suggests that it is amorphous.

Summary. Pure lime, CaO, is obtainable in two forms. The first, which is probably amorphous, results from the dissociation of $CaCO_3$ at low red temperatures. On heating for a considerable time at higher temperatures, it changes gradually into the cubic crystalline lime of refractive index 1.83. The latter forms directly from silicate melts or from fused calcium nitrate, and is the stable form at high temperatures. There are indications that it has an inversion point (perhaps similar to the inversion between high- and low-temperature quartz) between 400° and 430°.

The porous lime unites very readily with dry carbon dioxide, and the compound dissociates readily with rising temperature. The crystalline lime unites very slowly with dry carbon dioxide. The crystalline forms of calcium carbonate dissociate very slowly at low temperatures, and the rate does not seem to be hastened by the presence of Fe_2O_3 or of CaO. Aragonite is transformed into calcite within an hour at 425° in the vacuum furnace. The dissociation pressures of crystalline calcium carbonate at 400° are of the order of magnitude of 0.003 to 0.009 mm.

BOTANY.—*Microcitrus, a new genus of Australian citrous fruits.* WALTER T. SWINGLE, Bureau of Plant Industry.

In the first quarter of the nineteenth century Allan Cunningham collected in Australia and sent to Europe scanty specimens of a plant which at first was referred by botanists to Limonia and later to Citrus. Four species of Citrus in all have been described from Australia: *C. australis* Planchon, *C. australasica* F. Muell., *C. inodora* Bail., and *C. Garrowayi* Bail.

In the course of a systematic study of the species of Citrus and related plants the writer has been able to examine these Australian citrous fruits both as dried specimens in the principal European and American herbaria and as live plants in Italy and in the greenhouses of the Department of Agriculture at Washington, D. C. It soon became apparent that they differed from the other species of Citrus in a number of characters of importance in this group. The dimorphic foliage showing marked contrast between the juvenile and mature forms, the minute flowers with free stamens and very short pistils, the parallel venation of the leaves and their very short wingless petioles, and the few-celled fruits, with subglobose stalked pulp-vesicles and small rounded seeds, give these plants a very different aspect from the commonly cultivated species of Citrus. Furthermore, in greenhouse cultures the young seedlings show cataphylls like Eremocitrus and Poncirus, instead of a pair of subsessile broadly oval or ovate leaves as in Citrus. In view of these important differences from Citrus it seems proper to create a new genus, Microcitrus,[1] to include these plants.

MICROCITRUS Swingle.[2] Small trees or shrubs; young branches angular, minutely puberulent, the older ones rounded, glabrous; spines borne singly at one side of the bud in the axil of the leaf. Leaves unifoliolate, rather thick, dimorphic, the juvenile ones often very small, oval-elliptical or linear, the mature ones subrhombic or obovate, sometimes broadly cuneiform or lanceolate, blunt-pointed, rounded, or emarginate; veins nearly parallel, extending from the midrib to the margin; lower surface with few oil glands; petiole very short, slender, subcylindric, apterous, puberulent when young, articulated with the blade in some species. Flowers very small, borne singly or rarely in pairs in the axils of the leaves, with very short pedicels, 5-merous (rarely 4- or even 3-merous). Flower buds small, circular in cross-section. Petals 5 (rarely 4, or even 3), white, blunt, often concave. Stamens free, divergent, 12-20 or even 30; filaments slender; anthers small. Pistil very short, seated on a small disk; style blunt, short, ending in a slightly furrowed stigma not much thicker than the style; ovary subglobose, 5-6- (rarely 7-8-) celled; ovules in 2 rows, numerous, 8-20 in each cell. Fruits finger-shaped to ovoid or subglobose, 3-10 cm. long, 1.5-5 cm. in diameter. Peel rather thin, with large oil glands; segments 5-7 or 8; pulp vesicles subglobose, stalked, small (2-3 mm. in diameter), pale greenish in mass, separating easily and containing a sharply acid juice. Seeds small, 6-7 mm. long, ovate in outline, usually flattened on one side, smooth, pale yellowish; embryo whitish. Germination with hypogeous cotyledons; first leaves slender cataphylls, merging gradually into the juvenile foliage.

Type species, **M. australasica** (*Citrus australasica* F. Muell.), a native of Queensland and New South Wales.

[1] **Microcitrus** Swingle, gen. nov., *Citro* affinis, foliis dimorphis, in plantis juvenilibus minutis, staminibus liberis, stylo brevissimo, ovario 4-8-loculari, loculis polyspermis.

Folia unifoliolata, petiolis brevissimis apteris puberulis, laminae venis subparallelis; rami novelli virentes plus minusve angulosi, minute puberulenti; spinae ut in *Citro*. Flores parvae, in axillis foliorum singulae vel binae brevissime pedicellatae, 4-5- (rarius 3-) meris; petala ovalia vel ovata plus minusve cucullata; stamina libera numero petalorum quadrupla; ovarium 4-8-loculare, ovulis numerosis; stylus crassus, brevissimus; stigma diametro stylo paulo major. Fructus cylindrico-fusiformis vel ovoideus vel globosus, cortice ut in *Citro* carnosa, glandulis oleiferis instructa, pulpa vesiculari acida, vesiculis subglobosis vel ovoideis, pedicellatis. Semina parva, ovata, 6-7 mm. longa, glabra; cotyledones albidae in germinatione hypogeae; folia prima cataphylla minuta alterna.

Arbusculae vel frutices, juventute spinosissimae. Species typica, **Microcitrus** **australasica** (*Citrus australasica* F. Muell.) Habitat in Australia.

[2] So called because the very small juvenile leaves, the slender twigs, and the minute flowers with the very short styles and small stigmas are in each case the smallest occurring among the plants previously included in the genus Citrus.

The genus Microcitrus differs from Citrus in its dimorphic foliage and especially in its very small juvenile leaves, in the shape and venation of the adult foliage, in its very small flowers, these with free stamens and a very short pistil (the thick style merging into the only slightly thicker stigma), in the few-celled (4–6, rarely 7–8) ovary with numerous ovules in each cell, in the subglobose stalked pulp vesicles, in the presence of cataphylls in the seedling, and in the succeeding microphyllous juvenile foliage. Its nearest affinities in, Citrus are with the aberrant *C. hystrix* and related species. It has little affinity with Fortunella (the kumquat oranges), although both genera have few-celled ovaries. It is, however, closely allied to the Australian genus Eremocitrus, but differs in having unifacial glabrous leaves of mesophytic rather than xerophytic structure, as well as in having more cells in the fruits and many more ovules in each cell, and in having larger seeds, these not wrinkled. The leaves show on the upper face two layers of palisade cells but no stomata, and on the lower face only chlorenchyma with stomata, thus agreeing in general with Citrus, and differing widely from Eremocitrus. Doubtless both Eremocitrus and Microcitrus are descended from a common ancestral type.

There is no evidence of any close relationship between Microcitrus and the New Caledonian *Oxanthera fragrans* Montr. (*Citrus oxanthera* Beauv.) and the recently discovered *Citrus neo-caledonica*. It is very doubtful whether these plants are at all closely related to Citrus; it is clear that they are not congeneric with Microcitrus.

THE SPECIES OF MICROCITRUS

Altogether four species, one of them with a well marked variety or subspecies, all described under Citrus and all from eastern Australia, are to be placed in this genus. Three of them are very distinct; but the fourth, the last to be discovered, *Citrus Garrowayi* of northern Queensland, is very close to the common finger lime.

The species of Microcitrus may be distinguished by means of the following key:

Leaves very large, 7.5–18 cm. long, 4–6.5 cm. broad, lanceolate, not
    articulated with the very short petiole; flowers inodorous;
    fruits 5–6.5 cm. × 3.2 cm., oval or oblong in outline, 8-celled,
    ribbed.......................................4. **M. inodora**

Leaves medium-sized or small; fruits 4–7-celled, not ribbed.
    Fruits round, rough-skinned, 2.5–6.5 cm. in diameter, 5- (rarely
    6- or 7-) celled; juvenile leaves linear, borne on flexuose
    branches.......................................3. **M. australis**
    Fruits long and slender; juvenile leaves very small, oval or ovate,
    on ·stiff spreading branchlets.
        Fruits oval, 5–6.5 cm. × 2.5–3.3 cm., rough-skinned, 5-celled;
        mature leaves broadly rhombic, medium-sized, 2.5–4.5
        cm. long, 1.2–2.5 cm. broad.............2. **M. Garrowayi**
        Fruits cylindric-fusiform, 5–10 cm. × 1.5–2.5 cm., smooth-
        skinned; mature leaves small, obovate, cuneiform or rhombic,
        2–4 cm. long, 1.2–2 cm. broad..........1. **M. australasica**

THE FINGER LIME

The finger lime, native to the mountain scrubs of the coastal region
of northern New South Wales and Queensland, has been named *Citrus
australasica* by F. Mueller. It is the type of the genus Microcitrus.

1. **Microcitrus australasica** (F. Muell.) Swingle.
    Citrus australasica F. Muell. Fragm. Phytogr. Austr. **1**: 26. 1858;
    2: 178. 1861.

TYPE LOCALITY: "In nemoribus circum sinum Moretoñ Bay," Queensland, Australia.

Mueller's description was based on flowering specimens, but apparently none of this particular collection has as yet been sent to Europe or America; consequently it has not been possible to examine it. Two or three years later Mueller referred to this species fruits of the finger lime collected by Beckler on the Clarence River. The original description is not sufficiently detailed to make it certain that it applies to the finger lime rather than to the Australian round lime, which also occurs at Moreton Bay; and when Mueller referred the fruits of the finger lime to this species he was apparently unaware of the fact that there were two species occurring in the same region. As it has not been possible for the writer to examine the type specimen it is necessary for the present to accept Mueller's determination which, it should be said, is concurred in by F. M. Bailey,[3] J. H.

Fig. 1. *M. australasica.* Seedling showing hypogeous cotyledons and alternate cataphylls merging into juvenile foliage leaves. Natural size.

[3] Bailey, F. M. Queensl. Flora, **1**: 215. 1899.

Maiden, and other Australian botanists.   No reliance can be placed in the identifications of Bentham and Mueller in the Flora Australiensis (1863) which are based confessedly on imperfect material and on the false assumption that the round-fruited species had flowers with only 10 stamens.

Fig. 2.   *M. australasica*.   Horizontal spiny twigs of a young plant showing juvenile foliage.   Natural size.

The finger lime is one of the most curious and interesting of the citrous fruits. The young plants have more or less horizontally arranged branchlets, with very short internodes, and small oval or ovate juvenile leaves, these much shorter than the stiff, erect spines (fig. 2); the mature leaves are small, 1.5–4 cm. long, 1.2–2.5 cm. broad, ovate, cuneiform or subrhombic, usually very blunt or emarginate at the apex (fig. 3).   The flowers are small, sub-sessile, usually 5-merous but sometimes 3–4-merous, with erect, concave, broadly rounded petals (fig. 3); the pistil is very short and thick-set, the ovary 5–7-celled, with numerous ovules in each cell (8–16 or even 20).   The fruits are long and slender, cylindric-fusiform, 6.5–10 cm. × 1.5–2.5 cm., often slightly curved, frequently showing a short blunt protuberance at both the base and tip (fig. 4, A).   The pulp is composed of loosely cohering, subglobose, long-stalked pulp vesicles (fig. 4, B, C) filled with a sour, rather strongly pungent juice.   The seeds are small, 6–7 mm. long, ovate, usually flattened on one side and often showing small depres-

. Fig. 3.   *M. australasica*.   Flowering twig of a young plant showing mature leaves and 3-merous flowers.   Natural size.

sions on the other faces, probably due to the pressure of the pulp vesicles during the development of the seed; no wrinkling of the testa such as occurs in Eremocitrus is to be seen (fig. 4, D). On germination the cotyledons remain buried in the ground; the first leaves are reduced to cataphylls, alternately arranged, which merge gradually into the juvenile foliage (fig. 1).

A variety, the red-fruited finger lime, is indigenous to north-eastern New South Wales:

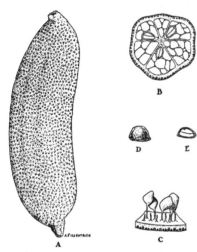

1a. **Microcitrus australasica sanguinea** (Bail.) Swingle.
Citrus australasica var. *sanguinea* Bail. Contr. Queensl. Flora, Dept. Agric. Queensl., Bull. 18 (Botany 5), 8. 1892.
TYPE LOCALITY: "Tambourine Mountain," southern Queensland, Australia.
ILLUSTRATION: Penzig, Studi bot. sugli Agrumi, in Annali di Agric. No. 116, 214, *pl. 21, fig. 13.* 1887.

Fig. 4. *M. australasica.* A, fruit; B, cross-section of fruit; C, pulp vesicles; D, seed; E, seed in cross-section. A, B, D, E, natural size; C, scale 2.

This seems to differ from the typical form of the species only in having a blood-red fruit, with pink pulp. The fruit has been described rather fully by Penzig. This variety has been introduced into America and is being grown in the greenhouses of the U. S. Department of Agriculture at Washington, D. C.

GARROWAY'S FINGER LIME

Another finger lime from northern Queensland is considered by F. M. Bailey to be a distinct species.

2. **Microcitrus Garrowayi** (Bail.) Swingle.
Citrus Garrowayi Bail. Queensl. Agric. Journ. **15**: 49. 1904.
TYPE LOCALITY: "Summit of Mount White, Cape York Peninsula, altitude about 1300 ft.," northern Queensland, Australia.

Specimens from the type locality, kindly sent to the writer by Prof. F. M. Bailey, show this plant to have larger, broader leaves and shorter, thicker fruits than the typical finger lime. The fruits are said by Bailey to be 4- or 5-celled, while the finger lime has 5-7 cells; the oil glands also are said to be larger; and the fruit is broader and has a rougher skin than the ordinary finger lime. Seedlings grown in the greenhouse of the Department of Agriculture at Washington, D. C., from seed collected in the type locality in Queensland, show the same peculiar juvenile growth as the ordinary finger lime; that is, several tiers of very spiny small-leaved branches spread out horizontally before a few upright branches at length arise. The twigs are more slender and the upright branches more flexuose than in the typical *M. australasica.*

It is a still a matter of doubt to the writer whether this is a valid species or merely a geographical form of the finger lime.

THE DOOJA OR AUSTRALIAN ROUND LIME

The round-fruited Australian lime, native to the subtropical coast forests of New South Wales and Queensland, is generally referred to *Citrus australis* Planchon.

3. **Microcitrus australis** (Planchon) Swingle.
   Limonia australis A. Cunn. in Sweet, Hort. Brit. ed. 3, 91. 1839 (*nomen subnudum*).
   Citrus australis Planchon, Hort. Donatensis, 18. 1854–58.
   Citrus Planchoni F. Muell. Australian Vegetation Indigenous or Introduced, etc., in Intercolonial Exhibition Essays 1866, 5 and 23. 1867 (*nomen subnudum*); Proc. Zool. Acclim. Soc. Victoria, **1**: 282. 1872.
   TYPE LOCALITY: "Nouv. Holl.," Moreton Bay Region, Queensland, Australia.
   ILLUSTRATION: Penzig, Studi bot. sugli Agrumi, in Annali di Agric. No. 116, 210–214, *pl. 21, figs. 8–12.* 1887.

The round fruited Australian lime or *dooja*, as it is called by the aborigines, is one of the most interesting but at the same time one of the least known of the Australian citrous fruits. As early as 1827 Allan Cunningham collected a fruiting branch of this species on the Brisbane River. This specimen is preserved under his number 163 in the British Museum. Another of Cunningham's specimens, preserved in the herbarium at Kew, has the following label:

"The *Limonia australis* (C). The "lime" of Moreton Bay. A solitary flower alone found after felling many of these trees on the banks of the Brisbane proves the genus to be *Limonia* and not *Citrus*, the 10 stam. being all distinct."

This sheet shows two twigs, one with a young fruit, the other with leaves only, though possibly it originally bore the single flower reported. There can be no reasonable doubt that this material is the round-fruited Australian lime, though the flower must have been abnormal, as the number of stamens usually runs about 16–20 or sometimes a few less by reduction. Unfortunately no adequate description of Cunningham's *Limonia australis* seems ever to have been published, so his name cannot be used.

Between 1854 and 1858 Planchon described *Citrus australis*, stating expressly that it was based on "an imperfect specimen of Leichardt's preserved in the Muséum d'histoire naturelle at Paris."

In June, 1911, the writer found two sheets of Leichardt's material, collected at Moreton Bay in 1845, in the herbarium of the Paris Muséum, one a small twig with a flower, the other a branched leafy twig with no flowers or fruits but having pasted on the sheet a note by the collector and an analysis by Baillon,[4] reading "Calyx 5-dent. petala 5, stamina plura, filam. liberis." A pencil drawing of the pistil in profile and in section by A. G. [A. Guillaumin] shows the ovary to have 7 cells. No flower is now found on this sheet. Planchon speaks of the "flore unico effoeto," so he must have seen only an imperfect specimen. Possibly the flower has been lost or is the one preserved on the second sheet. The leaves of this specimen are cuneate-obovate, 2.5–5 cm. long by 1.5–3.2 cm. broad, and rounded or blunt-pointed at the apex.

It is difficult to place this material, as it is somewhat intermediate in appearance between the two species common in the Moreton Bay region. For this reason the application of the name must for the present remain somewhat doubtful, though possibly a careful study of the Paris material would decide to which species it belongs.

A later name, *Citrus Planchoni* F. Muell., published in 1872, undoubtedly applies to the round-fruited species.

The *dooja* reaches a height of 9–18 meters (30–60 ft.) and bears fruits 2.5–6.5 cm. or even 7.5 cm. in diameter; the juvenile leaves are often very narrow, even linear in shape, not oval or ovate as in the finger lime, and are borne on slender, rather flexuose branches. The growing shoots and immature leaves on vigorous plants grown in the open are deep wine-red in color. The spines, at least in greenhouse specimens, are often minutely puberulent toward the base. Unlike the finger lime, which flowers and fruits when only a few years old, the *dooja* rarely ever flowers and fruits in greenhouse culture.

---

[4] Fide Beauvisage, G. Genera Montrouzierana Plant. Nouv. Caled., in Ann. Soc. Bot. Lyons, **26**: 12. 1901.

THE RUSSELL RIVER LIME

The largest and most striking member of the genus is the Russell River lime, discovered only a few decades ago by Archibald Meston.[5] It is native to the Bellenden-Ker region of North Queensland.

4. **Microcitrus inodora** (Bail.) Swingle.

> *Citrus inodorus* Bail. Bot. Bellenden-Ker Exped., in Report of the Government Scientific Expedition to Bellenden-Ker Range, 34. 1889.
>
> *Citrus inodora* Bail. Third Suppl. Syn. Queensl. Fl., 12. 1890.
>
> TYPE LOCALITY: "Harvey's Creek, Russell River," Nares County, Queensland, Australia.
>
> ILLUSTRATION: Bail. Queensl. Fl. **1**: *pl. 10.* 1899.

This species is remarkable for having very large leaves, while its congeners are small-leaved. Its leaves are lanceolate or ovate-lanceolate, 7.5–18 cm. long and 4–6.5 cm. wide. In spite of the large size of the leaves the petioles are very short, only 3–5 mm. long, wingless, and, to judge by an excellent specimen collected by Meston in the type locality and sent to the writer by Prof. F. M. Bailey, not articulated with the blade of the leaf. Nothing is known as to the character of the juvenile foliage. The flowers are said to be odorless. They are small, like those of the other species of Microcitrus, but have more numerous stamens (over 30). The fruits are unique among true citrous fruits, being ribbed; they are oval or oblong in outline, 5—6.5 × 3.2 cm., and have a pulp of a sharp agreeable acid flavor.

Although undoubtedly related to the other species of Microcitrus, *M. inodora* nevertheless departs widely in several important characters. It is greatly to be desired that additional and more complete material be secured in order to determine the exact relationship of this aberrant species.

UTILIZATION OF MICROCITRUS

Young plants of the finger lime, showing the juvenile foliage arranged in several successive tiers somewhat like a young Auracaria plant, are very ornamental and should become better known for decorative purposes. Both the finger lime and the *dooja* are of promise for hedge plants, as they are very spiny and can be grown from cuttings. The *dooja* grows vigorously enough to deserve trial as a stock upon which to graft the common citrous fruits.

[5] Meston, Archibald. Expedition to the Bellenden-Ker Range. Report to the Minister for Lands, Queensland, A. C. 36–1904, 3. 1904.

The fruits of all of the species of Microcitrus have an acid pulp which is rather disagreeably pungent except in the case of the Russell River lime. However, as the two commonly cultivated species, the *dooja* and the finger lime, are decidedly more hardy than the lime or lemon, they may prove of use in breeding new types of hardy citrous fruits. A number of hybrids have recently been made by the writer between the finger lime and the common lime (*Citrus aurantifolia*).

The Russell River lime is the only species in the genus that yields fruits of sufficiently good quality to be of promise for culture even without any improvement by cross-breeding or selection. Speaking of this plant F. M. Bailey says, "This new species of Citrus is well worthy of cultivation for its fruit, which is juicy and of equal flavour with the West Indian Lime."[6]

So far all attempts to introduce the Russell River lime into culture have failed and the rapid clearing up of land along the Russell River threatens to exterminate the species altogether. It is to be hoped that Australian botanists and fruit growers will not permit this to happen.

The species of Microcitrus are closely related to the desert kumquat, *Eremocitrus glauca*,[7] a hardy drouth-resistant shrub native to the semi-arid scrubs of the interior of Australia, and could doubtless be hybridized with it. As the desert kumquat is edible in the wild state and is the hardiest known evergreen citrous fruit, such a hybrid would be of great interest in the breeding of new types of hardy substitutes for the lime and lemon.

[6] Bailey, F. M.   Queensl. Flora, **1**: 216.   1899.

[7] Swingle, Walter T.   Eremocitrus, a new genus of hardy drouth-resistant citrous fruits from Australia, in Journ. Agric. Research, **2**: 85–100, *figs. 1–7, pl. 8. May, 1914.*

ABSTRACTS

Authors of scientific papers are requested to see that abstracts, preferably prepared and signed by themselves, are forwarded promptly to the editors. Each of the scientific bureaus in Washington has a representative authorized to forward such material to this journal and abstracts of official publications should be transmitted through the representative of the bureau in which they originate. The abstracts should conform in length and general style to those appearing in this issue.

GEOLOGY.—*Guidebook of the Western United States, Part A, the Northern Pacific route, with a side trip to Yellowstone Park.* M. R. CAMPBELL and others. U. S. Geol. Survey Bull. 611. Pp. 212, with maps and illustrations. 1915. (For sale by Superintendent of Documents, Washington, D. C.; price $1.)

The first of a series of handbooks for railway travelers in the Western States, describing the geography, geology, history, and natural resources of the region traversed by the principal transcontinental routes. The present volume deals with the country along the Northern Pacific Railway from St. Paul to Seattle and along the branch line to Yellowstone Park.

He is a very unobservant traveler who can cross the Great Plains, the Rocky Mountains, the lava plateau of the Columbia, and the Cascade Range, without noting some of the diversities in the color and character of the rocks and the striking differences in the landscape. It is the purpose of this volume to answer some of the questions which these views from the car windows evoke, to tell what the rocks are and how they got there, to explain the effects of earth movements upon them, to show how that conspicuous element in scenery which we call topography is the result of a long succession of geologic events—in brief, to tell the story of the mountains, valleys, and plains. It does not stop there, however. It connects this record of the prehistoric past with the present march of western progress and development by showing the relation of geologic processes to natural resources of various kinds; it describes the utilization of these resources and tells how man has turned them to account since Lewis and Clark toiled over the route that is now so quickly traversed in luxurious comfort.

Every effort has been made to make the volume interesting as well as accurate. Matter slightly more detailed or technical than that in the body of the text has been separated as footnotes, and a glossary has been provided for such geologic terms as it was necessary to use. The more important sources of geologic information on the region are listed in the back of the book, and a table showing the principal divisions of geologic time appears on the back of the title-page. Each map unfolds so that it can be consulted conveniently without turning the page which the traveler may be reading. The halftone views and text figures have been chosen with care to convey definite information.

F. L. R.

GEOLOGY.—*Guidebook of the Western United States, Part B, the overland route, with a side trip to Yellowstone Park.* W. T. LEE, R. W. STONE, H. S. GALE, and others. U. S. Geol. Survey Bull. 612. Pp. 244, with maps and illustrations. 1915. (For sale by Superintendent of Documents, Washington, D. C.; price $1.)

A handbook for the traveler which deals not only with the geology but with the natural resources, history, and development of the country between Omaha and San Francisco. It shows how differences in scenery and climate depend upon past geologic events and dispels the monotony of the great plains by taking the traveler back to times when these regions supported vegetation very different from their present scanty covering and were inhabited by animals of strange forms and huge size. The scenery of the mountains acquires additional interest from the explanation of the earth movements and the resulting rock structures to which fundamentally the mountains forms are due. Even the desert becomes attractive when the traveler is told of its vanished lakes and is shown the old beach lines which their waves cut on the now arid hillsides.

The book is intended to educate by being interesting, to win hearing for the story of geology by telling it in a clear and simple way, with abundant illustration from the car windows not only of the story itself but of its intimate connection with human life. F. L. R.

GEOLOGY.—*Geology and mineral deposits of the National mining district, Nevada.* WALDEMAR LINDGREN. U. S. Geol. Survey Bull. 601. Pp. 58. 1915.

The National mining district is in Humboldt County, Nevada, near the Oregon line. No large production of precious metals had been recorded from this region up to 1908, but in that year a bonanza shoot of gold quartz was discovered in the National mine, which within four years yielded about $4,000,000. This shoot is, in fact, one of the most remarkable and interesting bodies of high-grade ore discovered in the West.

The district is located in the Santa Rosa Mountains, a narrow range rising abruptly out of the desert. The northern part of this range in which the camp of National is located consists of flows of basalt, latite, rhyolite, and trachyte and some rhyolite dikes. These are of Tertiary, probably Miocene, age. The flows dip at gentle angles to the east or northeast.

The mineral deposits are steeply-dipping, narrow fissure veins which are distinctly later than any rock in the district. The National vein is the only one that has been extensively developed. Most of the veins are essentially silver veins of very moderate tenor and contain in a drusy, fine-grained quartz gangue, small amounts of pyrite, sphalerite, galena, chalcopyrite, arsenopyrite, and stibnite, the latter being the most characteristic mineral of the deposits. At least one deposit carries cinnabar. Native gold is abundant only in the unique rich shoot of the National vein, where it occurs as electrum carrying about 50 per cent of silver. The National ore shoot was encountered 40 feet below the surface and has been followed for about 800 feet down the dip of the vein; the stope reaches 250 feet in length. It appears to be of the same age as the leaner parts of the same vein and the other veins of the region. Much of the ore was remarkably rich, the first-class ore during one period averaging about $25 a pound, and the second-class ore $4000 a ton.

The National and other veins of the district are believed to have been deposited at slight depths by ascending waters during an epoch of hot-spring action following the eruption of the rhyolitic rocks. The fine-grained quartz, scarcity of pyrite, constant presence of stibnite, and occasional occurrences of cinnabar, point decidedly to deposition near the surface. The propylitic alteration of the country rocks points to the same conclusion.

Subsequent to the principal mineralization there has been in the National mine a deposition of secondary marcasite, pyrargyrite and stibnite along joints and fissures below the water level. This deposition was accompanied by solution of quartz and the development of irregular cavities. There are no placers in the region.   E. S. B.

GEOLOGY.—*Guidebook of the Western United States, Part D, the Shasta route and coast line.* J. S. DILLER and others. U. S. Geol. Survey Bull. 614. Pp. 142, with maps and illustrations. 1915. (For sale by Superintendent of Documents, Washington, D. C.; price $1.)

A manual for the traveler between Seattle or Los Angeles and San Francisco, which describes in clear, simple language the geography, geology, history, and natural resources of the region visible from the car window. Geology is made interesting to the reader by an avoidance of details and by the selection for treatment of the features that are likely to attract the eye. Care is taken also to point out the connection between the story of the earth and the present human activity in the region.

The book is divided into two parts, one dealing with the route from Seattle to San Francisco and one with the route from Los Angeles to San Francisco. Both routes go through regions that present great diversity in geology, scenery, climate, and resources. For the northern route the history of civilized settlement goes back to the early fur traders and trappers, and for the southern route to the Spanish padres and their Indian converts.

As in the other guidebooks in this series the route is completely covered by convenient maps and the text is well illustrated by views and diagrams.   F. L. R.

PALEONTOLOGY.—*Contributions to the knowledge of the mammals of the Pleistocene of North America.* OLIVER P. HAY. Proceedings of the U. S. National Museum, **48**: 515–575, pls. 30–37. April 8, 1915.

The results detailed in the present paper include descriptions of two extinct horses, one new extinct bison, one new and one previously described musk-ox, and measurements of certain limb bones of fossil horses, with discussion of variations observed. There are given also measurements from many skulls of various equids, as Przevalsky's horse, a number of fossil horses, domestic horses, three species of zebras, the chigetai (*Equus hemionus*), and the kiang (*E. Kiang*); from which certain indices in equine craniometry have been computed.

From these measurements and indices an attempt has been made to determine to what extent the various unmixed and wild species which are considered deviate from an average condition; to ascertain the value of some of the measurements and indices which have been employed in the study of domestic horses; and to throw some light on the elements which have contributed to the formation of that assemblage of horses which bears the name *Equus caballus*.

O. P. H.

ZOOLOGY.—*The relation between the maximum and the average bathymetric range, and the mean and the average depth of habitat, in the subfamilies and higher groups of recent crinoids.* AUSTIN H. CLARK. American Journal of Science, **40**: 67–74. July, 1915.

In general the more specialized families possess small, and the more generalized large, bathymetric ranges; the thermal adaptability of the groups increases with specialization. The average range of the families of recent crinoids is very nearly the same as, but slightly more than, the average depth of habitat.

A. H. C.

ZOOLOGY.—*A study of the recent crinoids which are congeneric with fossil species.* AUSTIN H. CLARK. American Journal of Science, **40**: 60–66. July, 1915.

The eight genera of recent crinoids which include fossil species fall into the following three groups: (1) Genera confined to the western Pacific; *Eudiocrinus, Catoptometra, Proisocrinus* and *Carpenterocrinus;* (2) genera confined to the western, or western and northern, Atlantic, but occurring as fossils in the Indo-Pacific basin; *Isocrinus, Rhizocrinus* and *Holopus;* (3) genus common to the Indo-Pacific and Atlantic; *Democrinus.*

All but one of these genera are chiefly developed in shallow water; this single exception is also the only one which, so far as we know, does not occur within 100 fathoms of the surface, three of the others being entirely confined to water of less than 155 fathoms in depth.

In the total range, average range, and mean depth of habitat these genera show a close approximation to the genera peculiar to the Atlantic, in contrast to those peculiar to the Indo-Pacific, which have a much greater total range but lesser average range and mean depth of habitat, and to those common to both oceans, which have a much greater average range and mean depth of habitat, as well as total range. In depth the maximum representation is between 0 and 200 fathoms, especially between 50 and 150 fathoms. As, taking the ocean as a whole, we find at a depth of 200 fathoms a temperature of 50°.1, and at 100 fathoms 60°.7, it is evident that these genera are most strongly represented within the optimum temperature for crinoid life, which is between 50° and 65°.

A. H. C.

ZOOLOGY.—*A phylogenetic study of the recent crinoids, with special reference to the question of specilization through the partial or complete suppression of structural characters.* AUSTIN H. CLARK. Smithsonian Miscellaneous Collections, 65^{10}: 1-67. August 19, 1915.

A detailed analysis of the structure of the recent crinoids and a comparison with fossil types indicates that phylogenetical advance has been through a progressive simplification of the organism, evidenced by a reduction in the number of the component parts. The pairs of contrasted characters employed in differentiating the recent crinoids are given, the more generalized of each pair being numbered 1 and the more specialized 2, and the types falling under each are listed. By simple addition this gives a numerical basis for the determination of the phylogenetical status of all the recent types. Taking the most primitive family (Plicatocrinidæ) as 1 we find the families to be specialized, in terms of this family, as follows:

Holopodidæ	3.12	or	2.59
Pentacrinitidæ	2.79	or	2.19
Bourgueticrinidæ	2.48	or	2.13
Apiocrinidæ	1.87	or	1.67
Phrynocrinidæ	1.74	or	1.55
Plicatocrinidæ	1.00	or	1.00

Thus the families according to their specilization fall into three groups: (1) Holopodidæ, Pentacrinitidæ and Bourgueticrinidæ; (2) Apiocrinidæ and Phrynocrinidæ; and (3) Plicatocrinidæ.

Of the individual structures which collectively make up the crinoid whole the sequence in specialization is: (1) The skeleton as a whole (most specialized); (2) calyx; (3) disk; (4) arms; (5) column; (6) pinnules.

On the basis of a broad average the more specialized characters occur in shallower and warmer water than the more primitive.

A. H. C.

ZOOLOGY.—*The distribution of the recent crinoids on the coasts of Australia.* AUSTIN H. CLARK. Internationale Revue der gesamten Hydrobiologie und Hydrographie, 1915, pp. 222–234. 1915.

Australian crinoids fall into three groups, (1) Tropical Australian types, (2) South Australian types, and (3) East Indian types. The distribution of each of these groups on the Australian coasts is treated in great detail.

A. H. C.

REFERENCES

Under this heading it is proposed to include, by author, title, and citation, references to all scientific papers published in or emanating from Washington. It is requested that authors coöperate with the editors by submitting titles promptly, following the style used below. These references are not intended to replace the more extended abstracts published elsewhere in this JOURNAL.

CHEMISTRY

CURRIE, J. N. *Composition of roquefort-cheese fat.* Journal of Agricultural Research, **2**: 429–434. September, 1914.

GORE, H. C. *Changes in composition of peel and pulp of ripening bananas.* Journal of Agricultural Research, **3**: 187–203, fig. 1. December, 1914.

HOAGLAND, D. R. *Organic constituents of Pacific coast kelps.* Journal of Agricultural Research, **4**: 39–58. April, 1915.

HOAGLAND, RALPH. *Coloring matter of raw and cooked salted meats.* Journal of Agricultural Research, **3**: 211–226, fig. 1, pls. 32–33. December, 1914.

MacINTIRE, W. H. *Decomposition of soil carbonates.* Journal of Agricultural Research, **3**: 79–80. October, 1914.

SHOREY, E. C., and WALTERS, E. H. *A nitrogenous soil constituent: tetracarbonimid.* Journal of Agricultural Research, **3**: 175–178. November, 1914.

THOMPSON, ALICE R. *Organic phosphoric acid of rice.* Journal of Agricultural Research, **3**: 425–430. February, 1915.

WILLAMAN, J. J., and WEST, R. M. *Notes on the hydrocyanic-acid content of sorghum.* Journal of Agricultural Research, **4**: 179–185, figs. 1–2. May, 1915.

BOTANY

DAHLBERG, R. C. *Identification of the seeds of species of Agropyron.* Journal of Agricultural Research, **3**: 275–282, figs. 1–4, pls. 34–37. December, 1914.

EDSON, H. A. Rheosporangium aphanidermatus, *a new genus and species of fungus parasitic on sugar beets and radishes.* Journal of Agricultural Research, **4**: 279–292, pls. 44–48. July, 1915.

GRIFFITHS, D., BIDWELL, G. L., and GOODRICH, C. E. *Native pasture grasses of the United States.* Bulletin of the U. S. Department of Agriculture, No. 201. Pp. 1–52. May 26, 1915.

HEDGCOCK, G. G., and LONG, W. H. *Identity of* Peridermium fusiforme *with* Peridermium cerebrum. Journal of Agricultural Research, **2**: 247–250, pl. 11. June, 1914.

MANN, ALBERT, and HARLAN, H. V. *Morphology of the barley grain with reference to its enzym-secreting areas.* Bulletin of the U. S. Department of Agriculture, No. 183. Pp. 1–32. April 13, 1915.

MASON, S. C. *Botanical characters of the leaves of the date palm used in distinguishing cultivated varieties.* Bulletin of the U. S. Department of Agriculture, No. 223. Pp. 1–28. June 23, 1915.

PIPER, C. V., and MORSE, W. J. *Five oriental species of beans.* Bulletin of the U. S. Department of Agriculture, No. 119. Pp. 1–32. September 2, 1914.

SWINGLE, W. T. *Eremocitrus, a new genus of hardy, drouth-resistant citrous fruits from Australia.* Journal of Agricultural Research 2: 85–100, figs. 1–7, pl. 8. May 25, 1914.

WIGHT, W. F. *The varieties of plums derived from native American species.* Bulletin of the U. S. Department of Agriculture, No. 172. Pp. 1–44. March 13, 1915.

WOLLENWEBER, H. W. *Identification of species of Fusarium occurring on the sweet potato,* Ipomoea batatas. Journal of Agricultural Research, 2: 251–286, pls. 12–16. July, 1914.

FORESTRY

HAWLEY, L. F., and PALMER, R. C. *Yields from the destructive distillation of certain hardwoods.* Bulletin of the U. S. Department of Agriculture, No. 129. Pp. 1–16. September 10, 1914.

SURFACE, H. E. *Suitability of longleaf pine for paper pulp.* Bulletin of the U. S. Department of Agriculture, No. 72. Pp. 1–26. May 29, 1914.

AGRONOMY

CHILCOTT, E. C., COLE, J. S., and BURR, W. W. *Spring wheat in the great plains area; relation of cultural methods to production.* Bulletin of the U. S. Department of Agriculture, No. 214. Pp. 1–43. May 1, 1915.

HANSEN, D. *Experiments in the production of crops on alkali land on the Huntley Reclamation Project, Montana.* Bulletin of the U. S. Department of Agriculture, No. 135. Pp. 1–19. September 10, 1914.

HARTLEY, CARL. *Injury by disinfectants to seeds and roots in sandy soils.* Bulletin of the U. S. Department of Agriculture, No. 169. Pp. 1–35. February 20, 1915.

KNORR, F. *Experiments with crops under fall irrigation at the Scottsbluff Reclamation Project experiment farm.* Bulletin of the U. S. Department of Agriculture, No. 133. Pp. 1–17. September 16, 1914.

LETTEER, C. R. *Experiment in crop production on fallow land at San Antonio.* Bulletin of the U. S. Department of Agriculture, No. 151. Pp. 1–10. September 19, 1914.

STUART, WILLIAM. *Group classification and varietal descriptions of some American potatoes.* Bulletin of the U. S. Department of Agriculture, No. 176. Pp. 1–56. March 27, 1915.

BACTERIOLOGY

AYERS, S. H., and JOHNSON, W. T., JR. *Ability of streptococci to survive pasteurization.* Journal of Agricultural Research, 2: 321–330, figs. 1–3. July, 1914.

AYERS, H., and JOHNSON, W. T., JR. *Ability of colon bacilli to survive pasteurization.* Journal of Agricultural Research, 3: 401–410, fig. 1. February 1915.

BONAZZI, A. *Cytological studies of* Azotobacter chroococcum. Journal of Agricultural Research, 4: 225–240, pls. 31–33. June, 1915.

EVANS, ALICE C., HASTINGS, E. G., and HART, E. B. *Bacteria concerned in the production of the characteristic flavor in cheese of the cheddar type.* Journal of Agricultural Research, **2**: 167–192. June, 1914.

HART, E. B. *Relation of the action of certain bacteria to the ripening of cheese of the cheddar type.* Journal of Agricultural Research, **2**: 193–216. June, 1914.

PHYTOPATHOLOGY

CHARLES, VERA K., and JENKINS, ANNA E. *A fungous disease of hemp.* Journal of Agricultural Research, **3**: 81–84, fig. 1, pl. 11. October, 1914.

COBB, N. A. *Citrus-root nematode.* Journal of Agricultural Research, **2**: 217–230, figs. 1–13. June, 1914.

EDSON, H. A. *Seedling diseases of sugar beets and their relation to root-rot and crown-rot.* Journal of Agricultural Research, **4**: 135–168, pls. 16–26. May, 1915.

FAWCETT, G. L. Pellicularia koleroga *on coffee in Porto Rico.* Journal of Agricultural Research, **2**: 231–233, figs. 1–3. June, 1914.

GLOYER, W. O. Ascochyta clematidina, *the cause of stem-rot and leaf-spot of Clematis.* Journal of Agricultural Research, **4**: 331–342, pls. 50–54. July, 1915.

HARTER, L. L. *Fruit-rot, leaf-spot, and stem-blight of the eggplant caused by* Phomopsis vexans. Journal of Agricultural Research, **2**: 331–338, fig. 1, pls. 26–30. August, 1914.

HASSE, CLARA H. Pseudomonas citri, *the cause of Citrus canker.* Journal of Agricultural Research, **4**: 97–100, pls. 9–10. April, 1915.

HEALD, F. D., GARDNER, M. W., and STUDHALTER, R. A. *Air and wind dissemination of ascospores of the chestnut-blight fungus.* Journal of Agricultural Research, **3**: 493–526, figs. 1–3, pls. 63–65. March, 1915.

HEDGCOCK, G. G., and LOND, W. H. *Heart-rot of oaks and poplars caused by* Polyporus dryophilus. Journal of Agricultural Research, **3**: 65–78, pls. 8–10. October, 1914.

JAMIESON, CLARA O. Phoma destructiva, *the cause of a fruit-rot of the tomato.* Journal of Agricultural Research, **4**: 1–20, pls. A–B, pls. 1–6. April, 1915.

LONG, W. H. *The death of chestnuts and oaks due to* Armillaria mellea. Bulletin of the U. S. Department of Agriculture, No. 89. Pp. 1–9. May 22, 1914.

LONG, W. H. *Influence of the host on the morphological characters of* Puccinia ellisiana *and* Puccinia andropogonis. Journal of Agricultural Research, **2**: 303–319. July, 1914.

ORTON, W. A., and RAND, F. V. *Pecan rosette.* Journal of Agricultural Research, **3**: 149–174, fig. 1, pls. 24–28. November, 1914.

POOL, VENUS W., and MCKAY, M. B. Phoma betae *on the leaves of the sugar beat.* Journal of Agricultural Research, **4**: 169–177, pl. 27. May, 1915.

POTTER, A. A. *Head smut of sorghum and maize.* Journal of Agricultural Research, **2**: 339–372, figs. 1–7, pls. 31–37. August, 1914.

ROBERTS, J. W. *Sources of the early infections of apple bitter-rot.* Journal of Agricultural Research, **4**: 59–64, pl. 7. April, 1915.

SHAPOVALOV, M. *Effect of temperature on germination and growth of the common potato-scab organism.* Journal of Agricultural Research, **4**: 129–133, fig. 1, pl. 15. May, 1915.

588 REFERENCES: TECHNOLOGY

STAKMAN, E. C. *Relation between* Puccinia graminis *and plants highly resistant to its attack.* Journal of Agricultural Research, 4: 193–199, pl. 28. June, 1915.

WEIR, J. R. *Two new wood-destroying fungi.* Journal of Agricultural Research, 2: 163–166, pls. 9–10. May 25, 1914.

WEIR, J. R. *A new leaf and twig disease of* Picea engelmanni. Journal of Agricultural Research, 4: 251–254, pl. 34. June, 1915.

PLANT PHYSIOLOGY

BRIGGS, L. J., and SHANTZ, H. L. *Relative water requirement of plants.* Journal of Agricultural Research, 3: 1–64, fig. 1, pls. 1–7. October, 1914.

BRIGGS, L. J. *Effect of frequent cuttings on the water requirement of alfalfa and its bearing on pasturage.* Bulletin of the U. S. Department of Agriculture, No. 228. Pp. 1–6. May 22, 1915.

BUNZEL, H. H. *Oxidases in healthy and in curly-dwarf potatoes.* Journal of Agricultural Research, 2: 373–404, figs. 1–21. August, 1914.

GARNER, W. W., ALLARD, H. A., and FOUBERT, C. L. *Oil content of seeds as affected by the nutrition of the plant.* Journal of Agricultural Research, 3: 227–249. December, 1914.

HASSELBRING, H., and HAWKINS, L. A. *Physiological changes in sweet potatoes during storage.* Journal of Agricultural Research, 3: 331–342. January, 1915.

KELLERMAN, K. F., and WRIGHT, R. C. *Relation of bacterial transformations of soil nitrogen to nutrition of citrous plants.* Journal of Agricultural Research, 2: 101–114, figs. 1–7. May 25, 1914.

EVOLUTION

COLLINS, G. N. *A more accurate method of comparing first-generation maize hybrids with their parents.* Journal of Agricultural Research, 3: 85–91. October, 1914.

COOK, O. F. *Brachysm, a hereditary deformity of cotton and other plants.* Journal of Agricultural Research, 3: 387–400, pls. 53–62. February, 1915.

GILBERT, A. W. *Heredity of color in* Phlox drummondii. Journal of Agricultural Research, 4: 293–302, pls. C–E. July, 1915.

HEDRICK, U. P., and ANTHONY, R. D. *Inheritance of certain characters of grapes.* Journal of Agricultural Research, 4: 315–330. July, 1915.

KEARNEY, T. H. *Mutation in Egyptian cotton.* Journal of Agricultural Research, 2: 287–302, pls. 17–25. July, 1914.

TECHNOLOGY

KREMERS, EDWARD. *Agricultural alcohol; studies of its manufacture in Germany.* Bulletin of the U. S. Department of Agriculture, No. 182. Pp. 1–35. February 2, 1915.

RUEHLE, G. L. A. *Methods of bacterial analyses of air.* Journal of Agricultural Research, 4: 343–368, figs. 1–3. July, 1915.

SCOBEY, F. C. *Behavior of cup-current meters under conditions not covered by standard ratings.* Journal of Agricultural Research, 2: 77–83, figs. 1–4. May, 1914.

JOURNAL

OF THE

WASHINGTON ACADEMY OF SCIENCES

VOL. V   OCTOBER 19, 1915   No. 17

PHYSICAL CHEMISTRY.—*Microstructural changes accompanying the annealing of bronze.* HENRY S. RAWDON, Bureau of Standards.[1]

A study of the structural changes in bronze induced by annealing was made to supplement the investigation of the standard zinc-bronze (88 Cu, 10 Sn, 2 Zn) recently carried out at the Bureau of Standards. The various changes together with the temperatures at which such changes are completed were determined.

After casting, the alloy exhibits a complex structure comprising a dendritic matrix consisting of a solid solution of tin (and zinc) in copper, in which are embedded numerous particles of a hard and brittle eutectoid similar in structure and formation to pearlite in steel. Upon annealing, the alloy is first rendered homogeneous by the absorption of the eutectoid by the matrix and the disappearance of the dendritic structure of the same matrix by diffusion. If the alloy has received no deformation previous to annealing, no other changes are observed, the crystal or "grain" size remains unchanged. The characteristic polyhedral twinned crystals seen in annealed brass and bronze rich in copper are obtained only after the structure has been distorted. Samples which had been cooled in a very drastic manner, thus inducing severe internal stresses, behaved similarly upon annealing to those which had been mechanically deformed before annealing.

[1] To appear in full as a Scientific paper of the Bureau of Standards.

BECAUSE OF SURFACE OXIDATION THE MEASURED THICKNESSES DO NOT REPRESENT THE TRUE DEPTH TO WHICH THE METAL WAS WORKED. AVERAGE WEIGHT OF SAMPLE, 20 GRAMS

SPECI-MEN NO.	MECHANICAL TREATMENT	THERMAL TREATMENT	THICKNESS OF "RECRYS-TALLIZED" LAYER[3]	AMOUNT OF EUTECTOID[1]	DENDRITIC STRUCTURE	REMARKS
			mm.			
B 1		1 hr. 400°C	0.056	85.0		Eutectoid was found shattered to a depth of {0.10 mm
B 2		2 hr. 400°C	0.076	82.0	Very evident.	0.113
B 3		4 hr. 400°C	0.088	85.5		0.15
B 4		Unheated	none	0.83		Aver. 0.135
B 6	These were turned down	8 hr. 400°C	0.07	76.5	The outlines of the cores are indistinct, diffusion has begun.	
			Av. 0.072			
B 7		1 hr. 600°C	0.161	41.5	Very evident.	
B 8		2 hr. 600°C	0.181	19.0		
B 9	Two hexagonal bars 1 in. on a face were cast in green sand.	4 hr. 600°C	0.163	12 0	Cores are quite faint and not continuous.	
B 10		8 hr. 600°C	0.183	6 5		
			Av. 0.172			
B 11		1 hr. 800°C	0.34	4.0	Dentrites are found in some grains, and are quite plainly seen in oblique illumination.[2]	
B 12	to ¾ in. diameter and cut into sections ¾ in. long.	2 hr. 800°C	0.33	0.4	Very faint trace of cores under obliqueillumination.	
B 13		4 hr. 800°C	0.34	0.0	All dendritic structure is erased.	
B 14		8 hr. 800°C	0.37	0.0		
			Av. 0.345			

[1] To obtain an approximate quantitative expression of the rate of absorption of the eutectoid, the number of inclusions in the successive microscope fields taken contiguously along a diameter of the sample (magnification 100×) was counted. On account of the difference in size of the particles, this method is a rough approximation only.

[2] When the dendritic structure appears to have disappeared entirely, upon examination under vertical illumination, with oblique illumination it is still to be seen.

[3] The thickness of the recrystallized layer was in all cases measured directly by means of a micrometer ocular.

The samples used were small cylinders, the surface layer of which had been distorted by machining in the lathe. These were annealed for periods of: 1, 2, 4, and 8 hours at 400°, 600°, and 800°C. The data tabulated below for one series indicate the general nature of the observations made and the results obtained.

The constancy of the thick ess of the recrystallized layer (different for different temperatures) is very striking. Though the crystals in this layer of recrystallized metal increase in size upon annealing, there appears to be no appreciable increase in thickness of the layer itself. The process is not a progressive one from exterior inward, but begins simultaneously throughout the layer which is capable of being affected at that temperature. The results obtained are in support of, and in accordance with, Tammann's theory of the recrystallization of "cold-worked" metals upon heating.

GEOLOGY.—*The geologic significance of the growth-rate of the Floridian and Bahaman shoal-water corals.*[1] THOMAS WAYLAND VAUGHAN, Geological Survey.

Except to allude to the continuation of the experiments and observations, no specific report on the results of the study of the growth rate of corals has been published since the one in Year Book No. 10 of the Carnegie Institution of Washington, pages 148–156, Plates 4–6, where all data then available on the size of year-old corals were presented. The technique for rearing and planting corals and that for measuring corals growing under natural conditions are described in the Year Book referred to and in Year Book No. 9, pages 136–144, Plate 1. The descriptions there given need not be repeated.

As the object of the investigation should be made clear, it should here be stated that stony corals are not suitable subjects

[1] Published by permission of the President of the Carnegie Institution of Washington and of the Director of the U. S. Geological Survey. The field studies were made under the auspices of the Department of Marine Biology of the Carnegie Institution of Washington while the office facilities were furnished by the U. S. Geological Survey. A fuller account of these investigations will appear in the Year Book of the Carnegie Institution of Washington for 1915.

for a critical study of the laws of growth rate. The proportion of living tissue to the stony skeleton is relatively small and as the skeleton after very young stages usually is not entirely covered by the living soft parts, organisms may attach themselves to it and increase its weight, or boring organisms may enter it, begin its destruction, and decrease its weight. As many boring organisms have calcareous tests, they destroy a part of the original skeleton and add the weight of their own. Minute algae, as Duerden has shown, bore into the skeleton and ramify through it almost or quite to the boundary of the living soft parts. Weights obtained from specimens cemented to discs are subject to all the sources of inaccuracy enumerated above and also to the practical inability of restoring the disc to its initial condition after affixing and planting a specimen, because of organisms attaching themselves to its surface. These remarks make it clear that the object of the investigation is not to make a contribution to the laws governing growth-rate, although some of the principles of growth-rate of some species have been ascertained. The actual object of the investigation has been to aid in understanding the relative amount of work stony corals may do as constructional geologic agents, and especially in the formation of those calcium carbonate structures designated "coral reefs."

In order properly to evaluate corals as constructional agents, the subject needs to be studied from at least five different viewpoints, viz.: (1) In dealing with sediments uplifted above the sea, the quantity of material contributed by corals and that contributed by other agents must be estimated and the respective proportions determined; (2) in coral reef areas, the ratio of the area covered by corals to that not covered by them should be estimated; (3) the relations of coral reefs to continuity and discontinuity of marginal submarine platforms must be ascertained; (4) marine bottom deposits must be analyzed according to the source of the material, and the percentage of the calcium carbonate contributed by the different agents estimated; (5) the rate of growth of corals needs to be known, especially for the light it may throw on the rate of reef formation.

That corals have been tremendously over-evaluated is established. In this connection, reference may be made to Murray and Renard's[2] description of their coral sand and coral mud and to some analyses Quin[3] has made of the calcareous sand on the shores of St. Croix Island, Danish West Indies.

From the table on page 596 it will be seen that there is no single formula for the growth-rate of corals, as the rate of growth is different for different species, and in each species it varies in accord with differences in local ecologic conditions. In order to understand the factors controlling growth-rate, the ecologic factors common to the entire reef-tract should be ascertained, and each species should be studied to discover the subordinate ecologic conditions of its more restricted habitat. Investigations of the Florida reef-tract along both these lines have been made, and some of the results have been presented in my previous papers.

Observations and experiments were conducted on the growth-rate of Tortugas corals as follows:

(1) Colonies obtained from planulae whose history was known. They were planted (a) off the northwest face of Fort Jefferson moat-wall and (b) on the reef off the northwest side of Loggerhead Key.

(2) Colonies cemented to tiles. These were planted (a) off the northwest face of Fort Jefferson moat-wall and (b) on the reef off Loggerhead Key.

(3) Colonies naturally attached: (a) in Fort Jefferson moat; (b) on piers of the Fort Jefferson wharf; (c) on the outside of the northwest face of the Jefferson moat-wall; (d) on the reef off the northwest face of Loggerhead Key.

The observations and experiments in the Bahamas were made on the leeward side of the north end of a small island, known as Golding Cay, which is on the east side of Andros Island at the mouth of South Bight. The specimens included, (a) those cemented to tiles and planted, (b) those living naturally attached.

---

[2] Challenger Repts., Deep-sea deposits, p. 246. 1891.
[3] Quin, John T. The building of an island, p. 15. 1907.

The size of the colonies of all species of corals seems limited, but some attain large dimensions, 2 to 3 meters or even more in diameter, and nearly as much in height, while other species are adult when a diameter of 35 to 50 mm. has been reached. Records of two species, *Favia fragum* and *Maeandra areolata* illustrate relatively rapid growth for the first 2 to 4 years, after which it decreases. Other species, for instance *Orbicella annularis* and *Maeandra strigosa* are not so limited in size. Ramose corals increase in dimensions more rapidly than massive species: while of the former, the growth rate of species with perforate, loose-textured skeletons is more rapid than that of species with dense skeletons. In general the more massive and the denser the corallum, the slower the growth; while the more ramose and the more porous the skeleton, the more rapid the growth.

TABLE OF INDICATED AVERAGE ANNUAL GROWTH-RATE

When practicable two diameters at right angles to each other were measured in successive years, and the increments were ascertained by subtracting the next earlier from the later measurements. All increments for each species at each station were added together and divided by the number of the annual increments entering into the computation. The averages for height were similarly determined. As the records are for annual growth-rate, each of the Bahama records is counted as 2, as each of those represents a period of 2 years.

It should be said regarding the nomenclature of the species that the specimens designated *Mussa* (*Isophyllia*) *dipsacea* Dana may include colonies of *M.* (*Isophyllia*) *fragilis* Dana. The specimens referred to *Porites clavaria* Lamarck may include more than one species of similar growth facies.

As has been stated, the primary object of this investigation was to get an approximate measure of the rate at which corals might build reefs. In order to make this estimate, the true reef corals must be considered separately from those which live in other habitats. The reef species *par excellence* in the Recent and Pleistocene reefs of Florida and the ·West Indies is *Orbicella annularis;* after it in importance are *Maeandra strigosa, M.*

labyrinthiformis, and *Siderastrea siderea*. Other corals, the most important of which is *Porites astreoides*, with *Agaricia* and *Favia fragum* of secondary importance, occur in the area intermediate between the prominent heads. In some areas *Acropora palmata* is the dominant species. The massive heads form the strong frame work of the reef, with infilling by other corals and other organisms. Therefore the upward growth rate of *Orbicella annularis* on the reef is critical. The data on it will be repeated:

Upward growth-rate of Orbicella annularis

Location	Annual average mm.
Ft. Jefferson, tiles outside moat wall	6.57
Loggerhead Reef, tiles	5.28
Loggerhead Reef, nat. att.	6.80
Golding Cay, tiles	5.67
Golding Cay, nat. att.	5.00

The highest figure is for naturally attached specimens on Loggerhead Reef, but the average is based on only 5 measurements which are not so accurate as those of specimens on tiles. The specimens attached to tiles all thrived and gave an annual average of 5.28 mm. for 14 measurements; while the Golding Cay specimens, which also thrived, gave an annual average of 5.67 mm. for 6 specimens, 2 years growth each. An estimate of 6 mm. for upward growth per year is probably somewhat liberal. This would indicate for an upward growth of a foot, $\dfrac{25.4 \times 12}{6} =$ 50.8 years. Should 7 mm. be taken as the average the rate would be 1 foot in 43.54 years. Using these figures as the basis of a further computation, a reef by the continuous upward growth of corals might attain at a rate of 6 mm. per year a thickness of 25 fathoms = 150 feet in 7620 years; and at a rate of 7 mm. per year it might attain the same thickness in 6531 years.

Should the growth rate of *Acropora palmata* be taken as a measure, the time to accumulate such a thickness would be considerably less. This species forms spreading, palmate fronds, rising from stout bases. As age advances the fronds thicken and can withstand the pounding of surf and breakers. The average upward growth is between 25 and 40 mm. per year,

Indicated average annual growth-rate of Floridian and Bahaman shoal-water corals

(NOTE.—Nat. att. = naturally attached. Note[1] in table, accuracy or record doubtful; note[2] tape-line measurements, accuracy somewhat doubtful)

NAME	STATION	INCREASE IN DIAMETER		INCREASE IN HEIGHT	
		Amount	No. of records as basis for estimate	Amount	No. of records as basis for estimate
		mm.		*mm.*	
Oculina diffusa Lam.	Ft. Jefferson, tiles outside moat wall	19.28	7	7.5	2
Oculina diffusa Lam.	Ft. Jefferson moat, nat. att.	19.25	4	12.70	5
Oculina diffusa Lam.	Ft. Jefferson wharf, nat. att.	29.57	28	22.61	13
Eusmilia fastigiata (Pallas)	Ft. Jefferson, tiles outside moat wall	9.61	22	4.5	10
Eusmilia fastigiata (Pallas)	Ft. Jefferson wharf, nat. att.	10.62	19	7	4
Eusmilia fastigiata (Pallas)	Loggerhead Key, reef, nat. att.	21	1	—	—
Dichocoenia stokesi M. Edw. & H.	Ft. Jefferson moat, nat. att.	6.67	12	5.2[1]	—
Dichocoenia stokesi M. Edw. & H.	Golding Cay, tiles	6.29	24	2.2	10
Dichocoenia stokesi M. Edw. & H.	Golding Cay, nat. att.	2	4	2	2
Dendrogyra cylindrus Ehr.	Golding Cay, tiles	7	16	10.375	8
Orbicella annularis (Ell. & Sol.)	Ft. Jefferson, tiles outside moat wall	7.43	29	6.57	14
Orbicella annularis (Ell. & Sol.)	Loggerhead Key, reef, tiles	6.89	29	5.28	14
Orbicella annularis (Ell. & Sol.)	Loggerhead Key, reef, nat. att.	9.02	36	6.80	5
Orbicella annularis (Ell. & Sol.)	Golding Cay, tiles	6.45	24	5.67	12
Orbicella annularis (Ell. & Sol.)	Golding Cay, nat. att.	0	2	5	2
Orbicella cavernosa (Linn.)	Ft. Jefferson, tiles outside moat wall	14.50	19	3.22	9
Orbicella cavernosa (Linn.)	Loggerhead Key, reef, tile	4.83	6	5.67	3
Orbicella cavernosa (Linn.)	Golding Cay, tile	9.5	4	3.5	2
Favia fragum (Esper)	Ft. Jefferson, tiles, outside moat wall	4.42	27	2.92	14
Favia fragum (Esper)	Ft. Jefferson, moat	4.2	27	3.77	11
Favia fragum (Esper)	Ft. Jefferson, outside moat wall, nat. att.	6.417	6	—	—
Favia fragum (Esper)	Loggerhead Key, reef, nat. att.	4.5	8	5.00	1
Favia fragum (Esper)	Golding Cay, tiles	3.62	24	3.83	12
Manicina gyrosa (Ell. & Sol.)	Ft. Jefferson, tiles, outside moat wall	9.75	4	2.5	2
Manicina gyrosa (Ell. & Sol.)	Loggerhead Key, reef, tiles	7.87	12	4.67	6
Manicina gyrosa (Ell. & Sol.)	Ft. Jefferson, moat (transplanted)	21.50	6	8.67	3
Manicina gyrosa (Ell. & Sol.)	Ft. Jefferson, wharf	16.77	22	7.00	4
Maeandra areolata (Linn.)	Ft. Jefferson, tiles outside moat wall	10.74	66	6.71	28
Maeandra areolata (Linn.)	Ft. Jefferson, moat (transplanted)	15.25	12	9.60	5
Maeandra areolata (Linn.)	Ft. Jefferson, outside moat wall, nat. att.	12.00	4	—	—
Maeandra areolata (Linn.)	Golding Cay, tiles	7.34	26	3.64	14
Maeandra labyrinthiformis (Linn.)	Golding Cay, tiles	9.17	24	4.92	12
Maeandra labyrinthiformis (Linn.)	Golding Cay, nat. att.	6.375	8	7.50	2
Maeandra strigosa (Dana)	Loggerhead Key, reef, tile	7.70	5	5.33	3
Maeandra strigosa (Dana)	Ft. Jefferson, moat, nat. att.	19.80	5	10.00	3
Maeandra strigosa (Dana)	Ft. Jefferson, wharf	11.17	6	3.50	2
Maeandra strigosa (Dana)	Loggerhead Key, reef, nat. att.	9.75	8	8.75	2
Maeandra strigosa (Dana)	Golding Cay, tiles	8.14	24	4.60	12
Maeandra strigosa (Dana)	Golding Cay, nat. att.	5.92	14	7.50	6
Maeandra clivosa (Ell. & Sol.)	Ft. Jefferson, tile, outside moat wall	20.90	10	8.83	6

NAME	STATION	INCREASE IN DIAMETER		INCREASE IN HEIGHT	
		Amount	No. of records as basis for estimate	Amount	No. of records as basis for estimate
		mm.		*mm.*	
Maeandra clivosa (Ell. & Sol.)	Loggerhead Key, reef, tiles	9.41	18	4.72	9
Maeandra clivosa (Ell. & Sol.)	Ft. Jefferson, moat, nat. att.	24.14	35	5.57	7
Maeandra clivosa (Ell. & Sol.)	Ft. Jefferson, wharf, nat. att.	14.91	12	4.00	1
Maeandra clivosa (Ell. & Sol.)	Golding Cay, tiles	5.25	4	2.50	2
Maeandra clivosa (Ell. & Sol.)	Golding Cay, nat. att.	7.67	12	—	—
Mussa (*Isophyllia*) *dipsacea* Dana	Golding Cay, tiles	6.04	24	3.33	12
Mussa (*Isophyllia*) *dipsacea* Dana	Golding Cay, nat. att.	0	2	5	2
Mussa (*Isophyllia*) *rigida* Dana	Golding Cay, tiles	2.56	16	1.13	8
Mussa (*Isophyllia*) *rigida* Dana	Golding Cay, nat. att.	6.75	12	2.75	4
Siderastrea radians (Pallas)	Ft. Jefferson, tiles outside moat	3.31	29	2.37	15
Siderastrea radians (Pallas)	Loggerhead Key, reef, tiles	2.13	4	1.5	4
Siderastrea radians (Pallas)	Ft. Jefferson, moat, nat. att.	7.59	24	—	—
Siderastrea radians (Pallas)	Golding Cay, tiles	2.50	8	2.13	4
Siderastrea radians (Pallas)	Golding Cay, nat. att.	0	8	0	4
Siderastrea siderea (Ell. & Sol.)	Ft. Jefferson, tile, outside moat wall	7.71	7	2.67	3
Siderastrea siderea (Ell. & Sol.)	Loggerhead Key, reef, tiles	3.75	4	4.16	3
Siderastrea siderea (Ell. & Sol.)	Loggerhead Key, reef, nat att.	7.41	12	5.00	1
Siderastrea siderea (Ell. & Sol.)	Golding Cay, tiles	5.05	20	2.70	10
Siderastrea siderea (Ell. & Sol.)	Golding Cay, nat. att.	4.38	8	2.50	2
Agaricia agaricites (Linn.)	Golding Cay, tiles	6.94	18	5.50	10
Agaricia purpurea LeS.	Ft. Jefferson, tiles, outside moat wall	5.67	37	3.76	17
Agaricia purpurea LeS.	Ft. Jefferson, from planulae nat. att. to tiles	8.33	6	—	—
Agaricia purpurea LeS.	Ft. Jefferson, wharf, nat. att.	17.25	8	—	—
Agaricia purpurea LeS.	Loggerhead Key, reef, nat. att.	4.84	16	—	—
Agaricia crassa Verrill	Golding Cay, tiles	2.25	8	6.50	4
Acropora cervicornis (Lam.)	Ft. Jefferson, tiles, outside moat wall	51.72	27	40.00	12
Acropora cervicornis (Lam.)	Golding Cay, tiles	—	—	45.33	6
Acropora prolifera (Lam.)	Golding Cay, tiles	44.50	18	37.17	6
Acropora palmata (Lam.)	Golding Cay, tiles	49.87	24	25.00	16
Acropora palmata (Lam.)	Golding Cay, nat. att.	95.36[2]	8	39.50	2
Porites clavaria Lam.	Ft. Jefferson, tiles, outside moat wall	20.19	50	20.45	21
Porites clavaria Lam.	Ft. Jefferson, moat, nat. att.	39.40	10	20.20	5
Porites clavaria Lam.	Ft. Jefferson, wharf, nat. att.	18.50	4	15.50	2
Porites clavaria Lam.	Loggerhead Key, reef, nat. att.	35.00	4	22.00	1
Porites clavaria Lam.	Golding Cay, tiles	18.06	42	20.25	32
Porites clavaria Lam.	Golding Cay, nat. att.	6.93	16	8.33	6
Porites furcata Lam.	Ft. Jefferson, tiles, outside moat wall	32.13	33	17.00	18
Porites furcata Lam.	Ft. Jefferson, moat, nat. att.	39.27	42	22.80	18
Porites furcata Lam.	Ft. Jefferson, wharf, nat. att.	44.75	4	16.00	2
Porites furcata Lam.	Ft. Jefferson, outside moat nat. att.	31.50	2	9.00	1
Porites astreoides Lam.	Ft. Jefferson, tiles, outside moat wall	16.19	34	5.70	15
Porites astreoides Lam.	Ft. Jefferson, moat, nat. att.	23.05	18	6.22	9
Porites astreoides Lam.	Ft. Jefferson, wharf, nat. att.	14.00	2	14.00	1
Porites astreoides Lam.	Ft. Jefferson, outside moat wall, nat. att.	13.11	9	—	—
Porites astreoides Lam.	Loggerhead Key, reef, nat. att.	10.60	25	13.28	7
Porites astreoides Lam.	Golding Cay, tiles	3.50	16	3.50	8
Porites astreoides Lam.	Golding Cay, nat. att.	7.56	16	8.75	4

but as the interspaces between the fronds are considerable in volume, comparisons with *Orbicella annularis* must be based upon relative increases in weight for a known period. The total of the weights[4] of 5 specimens of *Orbicella annularis* in 1912 was 1886 grams; the total increase in weight of the 5 specimens in 2 years was 1114 grams, or $\dfrac{1114}{1886}$ = 59.1 per cent. The average annual increase in height of these specimens was 5.7 mm.

The total of the weights of 5 specimens of *Acropora palmata* in 1912 was 745 grams; the total increase in the weight of the same 5 specimens in 2 years was 1727 grams, or $\dfrac{1727}{745}$ = 231.8 per cent. The average annual increase in height of these specimens was 24.4 mm.

According to weight, the specimens of *Acropora palmata* have grown 3.91 times as fast as those of *Orbicella annularis;* this may be stated in round numbers as 4 times as rapidly, while the increase in height is 4.28 times as rapid. Therefore a reef composed of *Acropora palmata* might grow upward at the rate of about an inch per year, a growth which would produce a thickness of 150 feet in 150 × 12 = 1800 years, but it is not probable that conditions so favorable have ever been realized in any area for a protracted period.

These two estimates give a measure of the limits of reef formation under continuously favorable conditions for upward growth. Such corals as *Orbicella annularis* might form a reef 150 feet thick in between 6500 and 7600 years; while such corals as *Acropora palmata* might form a similar thickness in 1800 years.

A few references to previous literature will indicate the rate of growth of Pacific and Indian ocean corals.

H. B. Guppy[5] has furnished interesting data on the rate of growth of corals around Keeling Atoll, including in his account the results of some experiments by G. C. Ross. According to Guppy, arborescent Acropores "grow at the average rate of four to five inches in a year, and will attain their full height in about

---

[4] The weights are of the wet living corals.
[5] Scottish Geog. Mag., 5: 573-376. 1889.

fifteen years." He estimates that branching species of *Porites* grow upward at the rate of 1½ inches per year, while the annual upward growth of massive species of *Porites* is from ½ to ¾ inch per year. *Montipora*, of the facies of *M. digitata*, is said to have an upward growth of not less than five inches per year.

Stanley Gardiner and F. Wood-Jones have made valuable contributions to the knowledge of the growth rate of Indo-Pacific corals. Wood-Jones has summarized the data in a privately published paper entitled, *The rate of growth of reef building corals*. His observations in Cocos-Keeling Islands corroborate the estimates of Guppy. According to his recomputation of the data supplied by Gardiner, based on a collection of presumably 3-year old corals from Hulule, North Male Atoll, a general average of the upward growth for branching forms is about 44 mm. per year, while that of massive forms is about 29 mm. Gardiner's estimates for the upward growth of massive forms would be as follows:

Massive "*Astreidae*"..............................22 mm. per year
Massive *Fungidae*................................29 mm. per year
Massive *Perforata*................................20.3 mm. per year

As it is probable that these corals, especially the massive ones, are more than three years old, I am inclined to the opinion that the estimates for the massive species are too high. Guppy's estimate of the upward growth of massive *Porites*, 12.7 to 19.05 mm. per year, seems better founded, and falls within the range of a number of the measurements on *Porites astreoides*. However, recent remeasurements by Mayer of some of the corals measured and marked by Saville-Kent indicate an annual increase in diameter of 1.9 inches (48.26 mm.) per year. As in massive corals the increase in height is usually one-half to two-third that in diameter, the increase in height would probably be between 24 and 32 mm. per year, or very nearly the figures given by Gardiner for massive species of corals.

The data available for the Pacific corals are not so abundant as those for the Atlantic, nor have the records, with few exceptions, the same degree of precision. However, they are sufficient for some general comparisons. The general growth rate of branching corals is nearly the same for both regions, but the growth of the massive forms in the Pacific appears to be appreciably more rapid than that of similar forms in the Atlantic. Therefore it seems probable that in the coral reef regions of the Pacific and Indian oceans a reef 150 feet thick may form under favorable conditions in less than 6000 years. According to Gardiner such a reef might form in 1000 years.

As the disappearance of the Wisconsin ice sheet is estimated to have been between 10,000 years ago in Scandinavia and Alaska and 40,000 years ago at Niagara, the data presented show that there has been ample time for the development of any known living reef since deglaciation. That Recent off-shore reefs have been formed either during or immediately subsequent to Recent submergence may be accounted established. That deglaciation was an important factor in this submergence can scarcely be doubted, but there are other factors which have not yet been evaluated.

BOTANY.—*A remarkable new Geranium from Venezuela.* PAUL C. STANDLEY, U. S. National Museum.[1]

The Geranium here described as new is of unusual interest as affording an additional evidence of the relationship which exists between the flora of the Hawaiian Islands and that of tropical North and South America. This relationship has long been known to botanists, being mentioned by Hillebrand in his Flora of the Hawaiian Islands,[2] and discussed in some detail by Alfred Russel Wallace in his "Island Life."[3] The affinities between the floras of these widely separated regions are best shown, perhaps, in the family Asteraceae: several of the genera occurring in Hawaii are represented also in tropical and subtropical North and South America, and most of the species of other genera are closely related to American plants. In other groups, also, the relationship is well shown. Hawaii possesses species of Gunnera, Phyllostegia, Fragaria, Sisyrinchium, Rubus, Dau-

[1] Published by permission of the Secretary of the Smithsonian Institution.
[2] Page XXIX.
[3] Pages 300–306.

cus, Sanicula, Portulaca, Vaccinium, Ranunculus, Osteomeles, Silene, Cleome, Nertera, Gnaphalium, Sida, Viola, Hibiscus, Drosera, Acaena, Colubrina, and Dioclea, as well as of many other genera, all of these more or less closely related to American representatives of the same groups.

Among the most interesting Hawaiian plants is a peculiar assemblage of species of Geranium, designated by Dr. Gray as the Neurophyllodea, well distinguished by their habit and by the peculiar form of their leaves. The new Geranium here described, while possibly deserving rank as a separate section of the genus, is most closely related to the Neurophyllodea, and if included in that section it is the first extra-Hawaiian species thus far discovered.

Geranium jahnii Standley, sp. nov.

A low shrub, 10 cm. high, from an elongate woody root; stems very stout, 2–3 cm. in diameter, branched, the branches ascending, the older ones nearly black, the others densely covered with the persistent stipules and petioles, the leaves present only at the apices of the branches; stipules 3–4 mm. long, lanceolate, attenuate to rigid setaceous tips; leaves densely crowded, the blades jointed with the petioles, these 1.5–2 mm. long, appressed, persistent; leaf blades cuneate, 6–8 mm. long, coriaceous, yellowish green, more or less tinged with red, glabrous, shallowly 3-lobed at the apex, the lobes triangular, acutish, the middle one longer than the others; peduncles 1-flowered, 9 mm. long, densely pilose with short spreading whitish hairs, the flowers apparently cernuous; sepals 6 mm. long, elliptic-oblong, acutish, short-mucronate, villous-ciliate, pilose, especially near the base; petals 9 mm. long, spatulate-obovate, purplish, broadly rounded or truncate at the apex, glabrous; filaments dilated at the base, the outer shorter than the inner ones; fruit not seen, the ovary densely white-pilose at the base, the beak glabrous.

Type in the U. S. National Herbarium, no. 602229, collected on the Páramo del Jabón, State of Trujillo, Venezuela, altitude 3000 to 3200 meters, October 2, 1910, by Dr. Alfredo Jahn (no. 34). The branches of the plant are covered with lichens, an indication of the humidity of the region in which it grows.

Although the material at hand is not so ample as might be desired, it is sufficient to show the proper position of this remarkable plant. Using Knuth's key to the sections of the genus,[4] which is based largely on habit, the present plant will run at once to the section Neurophyll-

[4] In Engl. Pflanzenreich, **53**: 44–47. 1912.

odea A. Gray, a group confined, so far as known heretofore, to the Hawaiian Islands. Not only in habit but in the form of the leaf blades does *Geranium jahnii* bear a strong resemblance to members of this group. Most of the species of the section have densely silvery-pubescent leaves, but in *G. cuneatum menziesii* A. Gray the leaves are glabrous and in general form much like those of the species here described, except that the blades are relatively broader and larger. Most of the species of the Neurophyllodea have a more ample inflorescence than the Venezuelan plant, but not infrequently one-flowered peduncles are found.

Knuth remarks[5] that this section is perhaps related to the group Andina, and the recent discovery of this new species tends to confirm that view. *Geranium jahnii*, however, is unlike the Andina in habit, and none of the species of that section have similar leaves. The most striking peculiarity of *G. jahnii* is the apparent articulation of the petiole with the leaf blade, a character not possessed by any other species, so far as the writer can learn, although in some of the densely cespitose species the leaf blade often does break from the petiole, which then persists upon the caudex.

[5] Op. cit., p. 216.

ABSTRACTS

Authors of scientific papers are requested to see that abstracts, preferably prepared and signed by themselves, are forwarded promptly to the editors. Each of the scientific bureaus in Washington has a representative authorized to forward such material to this journal and abstracts of official publications should be transmitted through the representative of the bureau in which they originate. The abstracts should conform in length and general style to those appearing in this issue.

GEOLOGY.—*The fauna of the Batesville sandstone of northern Arkansas.* G. H. GIRTY. U. S. Geol. Survey Bull. 593. Pp. 170, with 11 plates. 1915.

This bulletin is one of a series designed to describe and illustrate the succession of upper Mississippian faunas in the rocks of northern Arkansas, which differs surprisingly from the faunal succession of the typical Mississippian series in areas not far removed. The differences are so great that an exact correlation of the two series can not yet be made either faunally, lithologically, or stratigraphically. The Batesville sandstone overlies the Moorefield shale, whose fauna has been described in a previous bulletin. Sandstone fossils are rarely well preserved and rarely yield satisfactory results in the way of accurate generic and specific discrimination. It was therefore the fact of its occurrence in this series of formations rather than any intrinsic interest that led to the investigation of the fauna of the Batesville sandstone. The Batesville fauna had already been described by Professor Weller, whose report was based on collections from Batesville alone. The fossils described in Bulletin 593 include collections not only from the Batesville region but from Marshall as well. Weller's report recognized only about 30 species, whereas this one describes about 128, most of which are therefore new to the Batesville fauna as previously known, and some of which are new to science.

The fauna of the Batesville sandstone was found to differ widely from that of the underlying Moorefield shale and to be of upper Mississippian age, to which, indeed, it had been generally assigned. Its correlation is discussed at some length, but for the reason set down above no definite conclusion is reached as to its exact position in the typical upper Mississippian sections of Missouri and Illinois.   G. H. G.

GEOLOGY.—*Fauna of the so-called Boone chert near Batesville, Ark.* G. H. GIRTY. U. S. Geol. Survey Bull. 595. Pp. 45 with 2 plates. 1915.

The Moorefield shale which is typically exposed in the Batesville quadrangle of northern Arkansas has generally been regarded as of upper Mississippian age. Its fauna comprises a unique assemblage of species remarkably different from the typical upper Mississippian faunas of Missouri and Illinois, and in some ways reminiscent of the Devonian rather than of the Carboniferous types of life. In the Batesville region the Moorefield shale rests on a series of impure limestones and cherts that have heretofore been identified as Boone limestone because of their lithologic character. The Boone limestone is commonly regarded as of Osage age and its fauna differs as widely from that of the Moorefield shale as the Moorefield fauna differs from the faunas of the typical Mississippian. Recent studies, described in this report, have shown that the cherty beds underlying the Moorefield shale near Batesville differ in lithology from the typical Boone farther west. Aside from other less striking differences they contain an intercalated bed or beds of black shale quite alien to the Boone. Moreover they contain a fauna thoroughly unlike that of the typical Boone. Fossils are hard to find in this series of cherty beds, but several small collections were obtained, aggregating about 35 species. The noteworthy feature of this fauna is that practically all the species occur also in the Moorefield shale above, some of them being characteristic Moorefield types, while practically none of them occurs in the typical Boone. This fact bears in two directions. The Moorefield shale, as defined, contains at its base a few beds of dark gray, earthy limestone; most of the formation, however, consisting of black and green shale. The basal beds, for which at one time the name "Spring Creek" limestone was proposed, furnish nearly all of what is known as the Moorefield fauna. Only a few forms have been obtained from the shaly part of the formation and these make up a fauna considerably different from that found in the "Spring Creek" limestone. It is the "Spring Creek" limestone fauna which is represented in the cherts and impure limestone below, and in view of these facts it is proposed, to restrict the name Moorefield to the shale beds of which the formation mainly consists and to unite the "Spring Creek" limestone with the underlying formation which it resembles faunally and lithologically.

The second question considered is whether the cherty beds containing the "Spring Creek" limestone fauna are really Boone or some younger formation. It is true that their fauna and lithology are distinctly different from the typical Boone fauna and lithology, but these cherty beds appear to occupy the same place in the section as the Boone which farther west, as at Marshall, immediately underlies the Moorefield shale; furthermore, in western Tennessee, there are dark shales which must be of about the same geologic age as the Boone but which contain a fauna having many features in common with the "Spring Creek" limestone fauna. This broad and very interesting problem is as yet unsettled. A conclusion so far as the cherty beds at Batesville are concerned rests partly on the thickness and faunal content of some light gray crystalline limestones that underlie the cherts in question. They are almost certainly of Carboniferous age, but are as yet uninvestigated. G. H. G.

GEOLOGY.—*The faunas of the Boone limestone at St. Joe, Ark.* G. H. GIRTY. U. S. Geol. Survey Bull. 598. Pp. 50, with 3 plates. 1915.

This short bulletin consists of two parts, one describing the fauna of the St. Joe limestone member of the Boone limestone, the other describing a small fauna obtained in the Boone not far above the St. Joe. The collections described in both papers were obtained near St. Joe in northern Arkansas.

The St. Joe limestone comprises about 30 feet at the base of the Boone limestone and though composed of much the same materials, it is faunally and lithologically a rather distinct and widely recognizable unit. Except for some shaly beds of inconsiderable thickness below, these limestones of the St. Joe are the earliest deposits of Carboniferous age in this region. The fossils described in this report, which obviously represent the typical St. Joe fauna, comprise 30 species, some of which are new. The fauna, though differing in certain respects, strongly resembles the Fern Glen fauna of northeastern Missouri, thus corroborating a correlation suggested by Professor Weller on rather incomplete evidence. Weller's correlation of the Fern Glen and Chouteau is also agreed to in this report, but it is suggested, though not stated as a conclusion, that the Chouteau may really correlate with the lower part of the Burlington limestone instead of being entirely older, as commonly held.

The small but interesting fauna from the Boone, just above the St. Joe member, comprises 32 species, many of which are new. It is noteworthy that this fauna indicates a great change in the organic sequence following St. Joe time. The succeeding fauna does not possess either a distinctive Burlington or a distinctive Keokuk facies but differs markedly from both. G. H. G.

GEOLOGY.—*The fauna of the Wewoka formation of Oklahoma.* G. H. GIRTY. U. S. Geol. Survey Bull. 544. Pp. 353, with 35 plates. 1915.

This report is purely paleontologic in treatment and had its inspiration partly in the character and fine preservation of the fossils that occur in the Wewoka formation. These circumstances have permitted the recognition of a number of new genera and species. The Wewoka formation is one of the Pennsylvanian formations of Oklahoma and is exposed in the Wewoka and Coalgate quadrangles. It consists of alternating banks of shale and sandstone, about 700 feet in all. The fossils occur in the shale beds from which they weather free. In preservation they are unusual, the lime carbonate of which they were originally composed being replaced by a compound of lime, magnesia, and iron. As at present known, the Wewoka fauna contains about 150 species, all of which are described and figured in this report. Brachiopod types are relatively few, on the other hand, pelecypods and gastropods are relatively numerous, and the cephalopods are represented by an unusually large and interesting group of species. A tentative assignment is made of the Wewoka formation to about the position of the Fort Scott limestone of the Kansas section.

G. H. G.

GEOLOGY.—*Reasons for regarding the Morrison as an introductory Cretaceous formation.* WILLIS T. LEE. Bull. Geol. Soc. Amer. **26**: 303–314. 1915.

The Morrison formation contains bones of dinosaurs which correlate it with dinosaur beds in the Potomac group of the Atlantic Coast, with the Wealden of Europe, and with certain dinosaur beds in east Africa. Marsh, who described the Morrison dinosaurs, believed that they indicated Jurassic age. Later the Potomac and Wealden beds were classed as Lower Cretaceous; the dinosaur beds of east Africa are interstratified with sedimentary rocks containing marine invertebrates, which, on preliminary examination, seem to indicate Lower Cretaceous age. There is therefore a paleontologic basis for referring the Morrison formation to the Lower Cretaceous. The present paper deals, however, mainly with physical features, which also support the reference of the formation to the Lower Cretaceous.

The problem of classification is considered from the diastrophic viewpoint. The physical relations of the Morrison to other formations are described and an attempt is made to visualize the physiographic conditions under which the formation probably developed. It is shown that the Morrison is structurally much more closely related to the over-lying Cretaceous than to the underlying formations and that its sediments were deposited on a graded plain formed mainly by degradation, but in a few places by aggradation. The formation lies with apparent conformity on marine Jurassic, but also overlaps onto a variety of older formations to such an extent as to indicate a long interval of erosion previous to Morrison time.

The sequence of events is pictured as follows: The mountains of Carboniferous time had undergone erosion throughout the Triassic period and the early part of the Jurassic, so that the encroaching sea of Upper Jurassic time found a nearly level plain extending over a large part of the Rocky Mountain region. At or near the close of the Jurassic period a slight uplift expelled this sea from the continent. This uplift, evidenced by the withdrawal of the sea, seems to have been a part of the general post-Jurassic movement which elsewhere is regarded as the close of the Jurassic period. Soon thereafter the interior of North America began to subside and the streams spread out over the graded plain the sediments which constitute the Morrison formation. These accumulated in the shallow basin lately occupied by the Jurassic sea, but also spread beyond its borders over the broad, low-lying peneplain which seems to have extended with little interruption from New Mexico to Montana and from Utah to Kansas. These streams formed the swamps, lagoons and shallow temporary lakes in which lived the huge reptiles of Morrison time. The remarkable uniformity in character and thickness of the sediments is believed to be due to the slow subsidence of a large interior area, a movement that culminated in the formation of the interior basin of the Upper Cretaceous epoch. Later this movement carried the swamp deposits beneath the level of the sea in which were deposited sediments of late Lower Cretaceous age. According to the writer's view, although the character of the sedimentation changes abruptly from the stream deposits of the Morrison to the marine deposits of the Lower Cretaceous, no long period of time intervened between them, and it follows that the Morrison is of Lower Cretaceous age.

The conclusion is reached that the physical character of the Morrison and its relation to contiguous formations indicate that it was deposited on a peneplain soon after the beginning of the Cretaceous subsidence, when the surface was too near sea level for further degradation, but not yet low enough for marine submergence. It is therefore the first sedimentary expression in the Rocky Mountain region

ABSTRACTS: ZOOLOGY

of the order of events that culminated in the occupancy of the interior of North America by sea waters in Cretaceous time. It is a non-marine forerunner of the Cretaceous marine formations and is of Cretaceous age.   W. T. L.

GEOLOGY.—*Eocene glacial deposits in southwestern Colorado.* W. W. Atwood. U. S. Geological Survey Professional Paper 95-B. Pp. 13-26. 1915.

At the northwest base of the San Juan Mountains, not far from the village of Ridgway, Colorado, there is a series of exposures that include a remarkable section of glacial till, which is overlain by formations of Early Tertiary age. At the type locality, where first discovered, the till consists of 80 to 100 feet of material showing all the characters of glacial till, including an abundance of striated pebbles. This is capped by finer material probably also of glacial origin and this in turn by the Telluride conglomerate and the San Juan volcanic tuff, well known to be of Tertiary age. From the facts thus far discovered it is inferred that glaciers of the alpine and possibly also of the piedmont or small ice-sheet types existed in Eocene times in and adjacent to an early generation of San Juan Mountains.   E. S. B.

ZOOLOGY.—*Die Crinoiden der Antarktis.* Austin H. Clark. Deutsche Sudpolar Expedition, XVI, Zoologie, **8**: 103-209, pl. 1-10. May 16, 1915.

This is a complete monograph of the antarctic crinoids, including an historical introduction, systematic discussion, and philosophical conclusions. Full synonymies of the families and genera, as well as of the species, are given, and diagnoses of the species, genera, and higher groups. The families Bourgueticrinidae and Plicatocrinidae and the subfamilies Zenometrinae and Heliometrinae are revised. The origin and relationship of the antarctic fauna is discussed, and the arctic and antarctic faunas are contrasted. The significance of the distribution of antarctic types in its relation to the problem of the circulation of the abyssal water is considered in detail.

One new genus, Eumorphometra, two new subgenera, Anthometra and Florometra, and three new species, *Psathyrometra antarctica, Eumorphometra concinna* and *Ormina occidentalis,* are described.

In the included note by J. Thiele is given a description of *Eulima capensis,* sp. nov., a parasitic gastropod found on *Cominia occidentalis;* and in a note appended, by F. W. Clarke, are given analyses of the skeletons of *Promachocrinus kerguelensis* and *Anthometra adriani.*

A. H. C.

JOURNAL

OF THE

WASHINGTON ACADEMY OF SCIENCES

Vol. V   NOVEMBER 4, 1915   No. 18

CHEMISTRY.—*On some new indicators for the colorimetric determination of hydrogen-ion concentration.*[1] HERBERT A. LUBS and WILLIAM MANSFIELD CLARK, Bureau of Animal Industry.

In the biochemical application of the colorimetric method of determining hydrogen-ion concentrations several difficulties are encountered. The most serious of these are the so-called protein and salt errors and the obscuring effect of the natural colors of the solutions to be tested. All of these hindrances to accurate determinations are encountered to a greater or lesser extent in applying the method to bacterial cultures and culture media. Indeed, the method in its particular application to general bacteriological problems is in a somewhat unsatisfactory condition, and we are, therefore, attempting to simplify and systematize it so that it may be used extensively in general bacteriological work.

Unsatisfactory color changes alone rule out many indicators which, though useful with perfectly clear solutions, are of little or no value in bacteriological media; and, as Sörensen[2] has shown, the great majority of indicators listed in the elaborate tables of Salm, Thiel, and others must be rejected for one reason or another.

[1] From the research laboratory of the Dairy Division, Bureau of Animal Industry. Published by permission of the Secretary of Agriculture.

[2] Biochem. Zeitschr. **21**: 131. 1909; **22**: 352. 1909; Ergebn. d. Physiol., **12**: 393. 1912.

Sörensen has done invaluable service by eliminating from these tables the comparatively useless indicators and in his excellent résumé he has offered a selection of undoubted value. Unfortunately some of these are of little value in bacteriological media and others, from our experience, might be replaced with advantage. The eliminations leave some serious gaps in the series. There are, however, some indicators which have been studied since Sörensen's compilation, a few of which have not been investigated with reference to their applicability for determining hydrogen-ion concentration, and there also remain the possibilities in new syntheses, as Sörensen has suggested.

Walpole[3] in a recent article gives an excellent résumé of the method and suggests some new indicators. Those suggested are either not particularly satisfactory for our purpose or are rather difficult to obtain or prepare.

These considerations have led us to the investigation and compilation herein recorded. A more detailed account of the usefulness of particular indicators, of their protein and salt errors, the determination of their apparent dissociation constants, and our attempts to systematize the method for the general use of the bacteriologist will be reserved for subsequent papers. This paper is to be regarded merely as a preliminary description of our work in this field.

The importance of a simple, accurate, and well-systematized colorimetric method of determining the hydrogen-ion concentrations of bacteriological culture media and cultures has been pointed out in previous papers[4] from this laboratory.

PREPARATION AND PROPERTIES OF INDICATORS OF THE METHYL RED TYPE

Methyl Red, o-Carboxybenzene-azodimethylaniline, $N(CH_3)_2$—C_6H_4—N_2—C_6H_4COOH, was first prepared by Rupp and Loose.[5] Tizard[6] later improved the method of preparation so that almost quantitative yields were obtained. He determined its apparent dissociation constant

---

[3] Biochem. Journ. **8**: 628. 1914.

[4] Journ. Infect. Diseases **17**: 109. 1915; ibid. **17**: 160; Journ. Biol. Chem. **22**: 87. 1915.

[5] Ber. d. deutsch. Chem. Ges. **41**: 3905. 1908.

[6] Trans. Lond. Chem. Soc. **97**: 2477. 1910.

as an acid and found the value, $K = 1.05 \times 10^{-5}$ at 18°. Palitzsch[7] states that the region in which methyl red can be used for colorimetric determination of hydrogen-ion concentration lies between $P_H^+ 4.2$ and $P_H^+ 6.3$, and that in this region a difference of 0.1 in the P_H^+[8] value produces a marked difference in the tint of the indicator. He also determined its so-called protein and salt errors. The range of color extends from yellow on the alkaline side to red on the acid side. The brilliant and sharp changes of methyl red and its utility in the presence of protein and protein cleavage products makes it an excellent indicator for the estimation of the hydrogen-ion concentration of bacteriological media.

It was with the hope of finding an indicator showing color changes at hydrogen-ion concentrations just below those which can be determined by methyl red that we began to synthesize other indicators of this series. In our bacteriological work we found that it was necessary to have an indicator which would give a fairly sharp differentiation between $P_H^+ 6$ and $P_H^+ 6.5$. Para nitrophenol is an excellent indicator for this range in a colorless solution, but unfortunately its color change is of such a nature that it is obscured by the natural color of most bacteriological media.

We found by varying the substituent alkyls in the aniline residue of methyl red that the resulting indicators show but little difference in properties. Their colors vary only in intensity, and the hydrogen-ion concentrations at which the changes occur differ but little. As would be expected, the indicators with two substituent alkyls had a much deeper color than the corresponding monoalkyl derivatives.

INDICATORS OF THE METHYL RED TYPE INVESTIGATED

Monomethyl Red, o-Carboxybenzene-azomonomethylaniline.—A specimen of this material was kindly sent to us by Dr. L. W. Jones. This was recrystallized from alcohol. The nature of the color change was practically the same as that of methyl red but far less intense. Changes occur over the range $P_H^+ 4.25$ to $P_H^+ 6.00$.

Methyl Red, o-Carboxybenzene-azodimethylaniline.—Previously described.

Monoethyl Red, o-Carboxybenzene-azomonoethylaniline.—This indicator was prepared from anthranilic acid and monoethylaniline by the

---

[7] C. R. d. trav. d. Lab. Carls. **10:** 163. 1911.

[8] $P_H^+ = \log \dfrac{1}{C_H}$. For a discussion of the significance and convenience of this symbol see Sorensen, loc. cit.

method of Tizard for the analogous methyl red.   It was recrystallized from alcohol.   Color changes occur over the range P_H^+ 4.25 to P_H^+ 6.00.

Diethyl Red, o-Carboxybenzene-azodiethylaniline.—This substance was prepared from anthranilic acid and diethyl aniline by the method previously described.   It was recrystallized from alcohol.   Its colors are slightly deeper than those of methyl red and the changes occur over the range P_H^+ 4.50 to P_H^+ 6.50.

Monopropyl Red, o-Carboxybenzene-azomonopropylaniline.—This indicator was prepared from anthranilic acid and monopropyl aniline. Color changes are from yellow to red and extend over the range P_H^+ 4.25 to P_H^+ 6.25.

Dipropyl Red, o-Carboxybenzene-azodipropylaniline.—Attempts to prepare this substance in the manner described by Tizard for methyl red were not successful, so the following procedure was adopted: Five grams of anthranilic acid were dissolved in two molecular equivalents of 3N hydrochloric acid.   To the cooled solution was added the necessary amount of sodium nitrite solution.   Starch-potassium-iodide paper was used as the indicator.   The diazotized solution was allowed to stand in ice water for one-half hour and then 6.6 grams of dipropyl aniline dissolved in 150 cc. of alcohol were added.   The mixture was allowed to stand in the ice water for two hours, and then at room temperature over night.   The next morning the bluish purple crystals were filtered off with suction, washed with a little cold alcohol and then with water. The yield, after drying in the air, was about 3 grams.   Color changes are from reddish-violet to yellow and occur over the range P_H^+ 4.50 to P_H^+ 6.50.   They are slightly more intense than in the corresponding diethyl compound.

Dimethyl-α-naphthylamine Red, o-Carboxybenzene-azodimethyl-α-naphthylamine.—Howard and Pope[9] first made this indicator.   Their method of preparation was used and an almost quantitative yield was obtained.   The color changes are extremely brilliant from purple to yellow and occur over the range P_H^+ 4.50 to P_H^+ 6.50.

The phenyl-α-naphthylamine, α-napthylamine, and diphenylamine derivatives of this series were also prepared by Howard and Pope. We investigated the two latter compounds and found that the color changes were not very brilliant and probably would be of little use in bacteriological work.

The color changes of *o*-Carboxybenzene-azodimethyl-α-naphthylamine take place between P_H^+ 5.00 and P_H^+ 6.75.   The changes of the

---

[9] Trans. Lond. Chem. Soc. **99:** 1333.   1911.

diphenylamine compound occur between P_H^+ 4.25 and P_H^+ 5.50.   A cold saturated alcoholic solution of these two indicators was used.   In all other cases a solution of 0.1 gram of indicator in 300 cc. alcohol and 200 cc. distilled water was used.

INDICATORS OF THE SULPHONE-PHTHALEIN TYPE

Phenolsulphonephthalein was first prepared by Remsen and Sohon[10] by the condensation of phenol and the anhydride of *o*-sulphobenzoic acid.   An improved method which has been used in this laboratory is based upon the action of phenol upon the chloride of *o*-sulphobenzoic acid in the presence of anhydrous zinc chloride.   By the old method a large amount of alkali insoluble material is obtained, while by the new method practically none is formed.   An additional advantage of the new method lies in the greater ease with which the starting materials can be prepared.

PHENOLSULPHONE-PHTHALEIN

Preparation.—The starting material was pure saccharin.   From this the ammonium salt of *o*-sulphobenzoic acid was prepared by substantially the same method as described by Remsen and Holmes.[11]   The chloride was prepared from the ammonium salt as described by Remsen and Dohme.[12]   Ten grams of the acid chloride, 15 grams of phenol and 10 grams of freshly fused and pulverized zinc chloride were mixed in a porcelain jar.   As soon as the zinc chloride was added a vigorous evolution of hydrochloric acid gas occurred and the temperature of the reacting mass rose spontaneously to about 55° C., developing a deep red color.   The temperature was raised to 140° C. and held there for six hours.   During the heating the mass was frequently stirred with the thermometer used to indicate the temperature.   The reaction product gradually became more viscous.   When the heating was finished the melt was disintegrated with hot water, boiled for a few minutes and filtered with suction.   After a thorough washing a bright red powder was obtained.   This was then dissolved in strong alkali, the solution filtered and slowly poured into hot dilute hydrochloric acid, with constant stirring.   After boiling for a few minutes the flask containing the sulphonephthalein was allowed to stand for several hours, and then the indicator was filtered off with suction, washed and air dried.   Com-

[10] Amer. Chem. Journ. **20**: 257.   1898.

[11] Amer. Chem. Journ. **25**: 205.   1901.

[12] Amer. Chem. Journ. **11**: 332.   1889.

plete drying can be secured at 120° C.   The indicator obtained by this procedure is quite pure.

Properties.—Levy, Rowntree and Marriot[13] were the first to recognize the excellence of phenolsulphone-phthalein as an indicator for the colorimetric determination of hydrogen-ion concentration. A complete discussion of the theory of color changes of this compound will shortly be published by White and Acree.   The range of color changes is from yellow to reddish-violet and extends from P_H^+ 6.50 to P_H^+ 8.50. Between P_H^+ 7 and P_H^+ 7.50 extremely sharp differentiations can be secured but the indicator can be used with entire satisfaction over the wider range.   A solution of the sodium salt in water is used and such a solution can now be purchased from any of the dealers in chemical supplies.   A 0.01 per cent solution is satisfactory for colorimetric purposes.   Use 4–6 drops.

o-CRESOLSULPHONE-PHTHALEIN

Preparation.—This indicator was also prepared by Remsen and Sohon.[14]   The method of preparation used in this laboratory was, in general, the same as that used for the analogous phenol compound.   Ten grams of o-cresol, 15 grams of the acid chloride and 10 grams of freshly fused and pulverized zinc chloride were heated together for 6 hours at 165°–170°.   The melt was then treated as previously described.   The filtration is much more difficult than in the case of the phenol compound.   Yield about 10 grams.   o-Cresolsulphone-phthalein can be recrystallized from glacial acetic acid.   It is quite soluble in alcohol.

Properties.—This indicator covers practically the same range as phenolsulphone-phthalein.   The color changes are very similar.   On the whole the phenol compound is superior to the cresol compound. The phenol compound can be prepared more easily and shows slightly sharper color changes.   The indicator solution was prepared by dissolving 0.1 gram of indicator in 200 cc. alcohol.   Use 2–4 drops.

THYMOLSULPHONE-PHTHALEIN

Preparation.—Ten grams of the acid chloride, 10 grams of freshly fused and dehydrated zinc chloride and 15 grams of thymol were heated for four hours at 140° C. with frequent stirring.   The reaction mixture must be stirred constantly during the first half hour of the reaction in order to prevent a loss of material from frothing.   The melt was boiled

[13] Archiv. Int. Med. **16**: 38. 1915. (See also Trans. of the Assoc. of Physicians, 1915.)

[14] Amer. Chem. Journ. **20**: 257. 1898.

with water. The dye collected as a black viscous mass at the bottom of the beaker. The water was poured off and the viscous mass which hardened upon cooling was boiled with alcohol to remove the remaining thymol. Upon cooling to room temperature the thymolsulphonephthalein was filtered off as greenish crystals. Yield about 5 grams. These crystals can be recrystallized from alcohol. (1) 0.3288 gram gave 0.1490 gram $BaSO_4$; (2) 0.4224 gram gave 0.2118 gram $BaSO_4$; S. calculated for $C_{27}H_{30}SO_5$, 6.88 per cent; S found (1) 6.21 per cent,[15] (2) 6.88 per cent.

Properties.—The color changes are from yellow to blue and take place between P_H^+ 8 and P_H^+ 9.75. The useful range lies between P_H^+ 8.00 and P_H^+ 9.50. Throughout this range the differentiations are extremely sharp. For colorimetric purposes a dilution of 0.1 gram of indicator in 200 cc. alcohol and 50 cc. water was used. Use 3–6 drops. This indicator covers practically the same range as phenolphthalein, and probably can be substituted for the latter to advantage in many cases. This point will be decided as soon as we have completed our work on the magnitude of the protein and salt errors of these new indicators.

α-NAPHTHOLSULPHONE-PHTHALEIN

Preparation.—Five grams of the acid chloride, 5 grams of freshly fused and dehydrated zinc chloride and 6 grams of α-naphthol were thoroughly mixed. The reaction began at once. A dark green melt was formed. This was heated to 70° with constant stirring and held at this temperature for about ten minutes. Upon longer heating, the dye tends to go over into a substance which is probably an oxidation product and which gives a green color in alkaline solution. The melt was extracted with water to remove the zinc chloride. The residue was then extracted thoroughly with ether in order to remove the excess of naphthol. It was then dissolved in cold alkali and the solution filtered. The indicator was reprecipitated by the addition of strong hydrochloric acid, filtered with suction, washed with water containing hydrochloric acid and air dried. When dry the indicator has a dark green color. Without further purification and after drying at 120° in vacuo, 0.5154 grams gave 0.2345 grams $BaSO_4$; 0.2736 grams gave 0.1239 grams $BaSO_4$. Theoretical for $C_{27}H_{18}SO_5$, 7.06 per cent S. Found (1) 6.24 per cent, (2) 6.21 per cent.

Properties.—The color changes are from yellow to blue over the

---

[15] Incomplete fusion suspected in this case. Further analyses were not made because of limited supply of indicator.

range of P_H^+ 7.50 to P_H^+ 9.00. Very sharp differentiations can be secured over this range. As an indicator solution use 0.1 gram dissolved in 50 cc. alcohol and add 150 cc. distilled water. Use 1–2 drops.

TETRABROM-PHENOLSULPHONE-PHTHALEIN

Preparation.—This compound was prepared as described by White.[16] Two grams of phenolsulphone-phthalein were suspended in 20 cc. of glacial acetic acid and to the suspension were added 10 grams of bromine dissolved in 10 cc. of glacial acetic acid. The flask was allowed to stand, with occasional shaking, for several hours and then the excess of bromine was removed by means of an air current. The precipitate was filtered off with suction, washed with cold acetic acid, recrystallized from the same and air dried.

Properties.—The color changes are from yellow to purple and occur over the range P_H^+ 3.50 to P_H^+ 4.50. The indicator solution was made by dissolving 0.1 gram in 250 cc. alcohol. Use 3–5 drops.

BROMTHYMOL-SULPHONE-PHTHALEIN

Preparation.—This indicator was prepared in the manner described for the analogous phenol compound. It is obtained as yellow granular crystals. We are investigating its chemical constitution and will publish our data shortly.

Properties.—The color changes are from yellow to blue and occur over the range P_H^+ 6.00 to P_H^+ 7.25. As an indicator solution use 0.1 gram dissolved in 250 cc. of alcohol.

Work is now in progress to prepare other new indicators of the sulphonephthalein type. We have already prepared phenol-nitrosulphone-phthalein, but have not purified it sufficiently to give an accurate description of its properties.

The authors take this opportunity to express their gratitude to Dr. L. W. Jones, Dr. S. F. Acree, and Dr. E. C. White for specimens of indicators and to Mr. H. A. B. Dunning for valuable suggestions.

SUMMARY

The following new indicators of the methyl red type have been prepared by us: Monoethyl red, diethyl red, monopropyl red and dipropyl red. Besides these new indicators we have also prepared and investigated the following indicators of the methyl red group which had been

---

[16] White, Disser. Univ. of Wisconsin. 1915.

previously made by others: Monomethyl red, α-naphthylamine red, dimethyl-α-naphthylamine red and diphenylamine red. The well known methyl red had been previously investigated by Palitzsch. Of these indicators the most satisfactory are those containing two substituent alkyls.

Several new indicators of the sulphonephthalein type were prepared; namely, thymolsulphone-phthalein, α-naphtholsulphone-phthalein, and bromthymol-sulphone-phthalein. An improved method of preparation for the sulphone-phthaleins is described.

The hydrogen-ion concentrations at which the color changes of the above indicators occur was determined.

The authors will shortly publish the result of their investigations on the utility of the most satisfactory of the new indicators with particular reference to their salt and protein errors and to their applicability in biochemical investigations.

PHYSICAL CHEMISTRY.—*The solubility of calcite in water in contact with the atmosphere, and its variation with temperature.* ROGER C. WELLS, Geological Survey.[1]

It is well known that even the small amount of carbon dioxide in the atmosphere is sufficient greatly to increase the solubility of calcite in water. Direct experiments on this point at temperatures above 25°C. were made by Kendall,[2] who found the solution to contain calcium equivalent to 46 parts of calcium carbonate per million at 25° and 29 parts at 50°. The partial pressure of carbon dioxide in Kendall's experiments was found by him to be 3.69×10^{-4} atmospheres.

Recently all the data on the solubility of calcite in carbonic acid water have been critically examined by Johnston,[3] and he has calculated the solubility of calcite in water at 16°, in contact with air containing certain small pressures of carbon dioxide, with the results given below.

When Kendall's results are compared with those calculated by Johnston, under similar conditions, the agreement is not as good as one could wish. Moreover, in a paper by Dubois[4] on the

[1] Published with the permission of the Director of the U. S. Geological Survey.

[2] Philos. Mag. Ser. 6, **23**: 973. 1912.

[3] Jour. Am. Chem. Soc. **37**: 2001. 1915.

[4] Proc. Sec. Sci., Amsterdam Academy, **3**: 46. 1901.

CALCULATED SOLUBILITY OF CALCITE IN WATER AT 16°C., IN CONTACT WITH AIR
CONTAINING THE PARTIAL PRESSURE, P, OF CO_2 (JOHNSTON)

P	PARTS $CaCO_3$ PER MILLION	P	PARTS $CaCO_3$ PER MILLION
0.00020	55	0.00040	69
0.00025	59	0.00045	72
0.00030	63	0.00050	75
0.00035	66		

solubility of calcite in natural waters the dependence on temperature is barely mentioned.

Since data at lower temperatures are lacking, and since the variation of the solubility of calcite with temperature is a matter of great importance in geochemistry, I have carried out some new experiments designed especially to show the effect of temperature on the solubility.

The method of working consisted in agitating the solutions under investigation by a current of outdoor air for long intervals. The Jena flasks employed were kept in a thermostat while air was being passed, and, for the experiments at 1°C., they were immersed in a mixture of ice and water in a refrigerator during the whole continuation of the experiments.

The outdoor air used for stirring was filtered through cotton and washed by water. Although the carbon dioxide content of the air is known to be slightly variable,[5] this procedure must have equalized the small variations to a considerable degree. A number of careful determinations of the carbon dioxide content, made at various times, ranged from 3.02 to 3.27 parts in 10,000, with a mean of 3.18 parts. Apparently, then, equilibrium with a normal atmosphere was more nearly approached than it could be by any other simple procedure.

The Joplin calcite used had the following composition: SiO_2 0.09, MnO 0.05, FeO 0.19, CaO 55.80, MgO none, CO_2 (by difference) 43.87, sum 100.00 per cent. As far as determined calcite was the only solid phase involved, but, if a less soluble phase did in fact exist in the mixtures, the solubilities actually found would of course apply to it. The calcium content of the solutions was

[5] Letts and Blake. Sci. Proc. Roy. Dublin Soc. 9: Pt. 2, 107. 1900.

calculated from the result of titrating about 50 cc. with 0.02 N NaHSO$_4$, using methyl orange as indicator. The solutions were slightly acid toward phenolphthalein, thus showing that the calcium was present chiefly as bicarbonate. The results are stated, however, in terms of CaCO$_3$, since that is the solid phase actually dissolved, or the phase that would be again precipitated on evaporation. Table I contains some results obtained at 1°C, when calcite in excess was added to water and air was passed through the solution for an hour or two daily.

TABLE I

CALCITE ADDED TO DISTILLED WATER AT 1°C. AND AIR PASSED DAILY

INTERVAL	PARTS CaCO₃ PER MILLION	INTERVAL	PARTS CaCO₃ PER MILLION
Start	25	22 days	72
1 day	33	27 days	76
2 days	47	30 days	74
3 days	61	32 days	75
11 days	62	34 days	75
14 days	72	50 days	76
18 days	73		

Table II shows how slowly a supersaturated solution, without points of crystallization other than the walls of the flask, loses its excess CO$_2$ and CaCO$_3$ at 1°. The high results of this series are probably due in part to the deposition of a more soluble form of calcium carbonate than calcite and were excluded in drawing the curve below. In Table III are shown results obtained with a similar solution but with considerable powdered calcite present to assist deposition.

TABLE II

AIR PASSED AT 1° THROUGH A SOLUTION CONTAINING CO₂ AND Ca(HCO₃)₂

INTERVAL	PARTS CaCO₃ PER MILLION	INTERVAL	PARTS CaCO₃ PER MILLION
Start	1000	24 days	158
1 day	999	27 days	143
3 days	880	35 days	108
5 days { plentiful crystals	720	40 days	104
		43 days	102
13 days	240	49 days	102
15 days	193	65 days	98

TABLE III

CALCITE ADDED TO A SOLUTION CONTAINING Ca(HCO$_3$)$_2$ AT 1°C. AND AIR PASSED

INTERVAL	PARTS CaCO$_3$ PER MILLION	INTERVAL	PARTS CaCO$_3$ PER MILLION
8 days	119	51 days	88
13 days	111	53 days	87
21 days	98	55 days	83
32 days	94	56 days	83
39 days	90	71 days	86
43 days	90		

Tables IV and V are self-explanatory.   The results of the investigation are summarized by the curve in Figure 1.

TABLE IV

CALCITE ADDED TO DISTILLED WATER AT 30°C. AND AIR PASSED

INTERVAL	PARTS CaCO$_3$ PER MILLION	INTERVAL	PARTS CaCO$_3$ PER MILLION
25 days	58	46 days	57
38 days	53	56 days	55

TABLE V

SOLUBILITIES FOUND AT OTHER TEMPERATURES

TEMPERATURE C.	PARTS CaCO$_3$ PER MILLION	TEMPERATURE C.	PARTS CaCO$_3$ PER MILLION
23°	57	21°	61
22°	57	1°	82
21°	59		

The geochemical conclusion to be drawn from the curve is, that in solutions freely exposed to the atmosphere solid calcium carbonate is considerably more soluble at low temperatures than at higher temperatures.   As, however, there are many possibilities of lag in adjustment of the various equilibria involved, it is doubtless true that conditions of perfect equilibrium are seldom fully attained in nature.

Although it would take too much space to point out all the results in nature, of the variation of the solubility with temperature, one or two applications of the data may be mentioned.

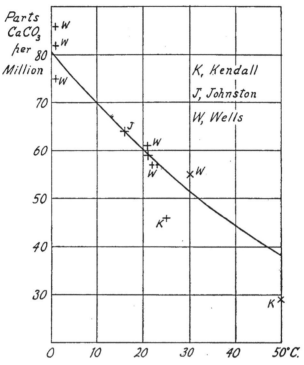

FIG. 1. Solubility of calcite in water in contact with the atmosphere, and its variation with temperature.

The Mississippi River flows, on the average, in a direction of rising temperature. Therefore, if the streams of the North become saturated with calcium carbonate, a considerable amount of it will tend to re-deposit as the river flows southward, merely because of the rise in temperature. The chemical equation is:

$$Ca(HCO_3)_2 = CaCO_3 + CO_2 + H_2O$$

from which it follows that carbon dioxide will be again evolved as the calcium carbonate precipitates. The winds stir the atmosphere so rapidly, in comparison with the movement of the river, that it is useless to look for variations of the carbon dioxide in the atmosphere due to this cause. The water of the Mississippi, however, seems to show clearly the decrease in bicarbonate as it flows southward. Taking the analyses used by Palmer,[6] we have the following data on this point:

Bicarbonate content of Mississippi River water at various localities

LOCALITY	PARTS OF BICARBONATE (HCO$_3$) PER MILLION	EQUIVALENT AMOUNTS OF CaCO$_3$
Minneapolis, Minn..........	188	154
Moline, Ill.................	152	125
Quincy, Ill.................	175	143
Chester, Ill................	174	142
Memphis, Tenn..............	135	111
New Orleans, La............	111	91

The figures in the last column above are not exactly comparable with the solubilities in pure water recorded in this paper on account of the presence of other salts, a varying acidity and a varying calcium ion concentration, but they are believed to illustrate the dependence of the solubility of calcium carbonate on the temperature.

Another application of the varying solubility may be found in the formation of marble from coral. Certain islands in the Philippines, having shores of coral, are found to consist, at fairly shallow depths, of limestone. It may be that the comparatively rapid conversion of coral into limestone is due to the fact that with every fluctuation of temperature, many particles of calcium carbonate alternately dissolve in, and re-deposit from, small amounts of water in the pore space, tending always toward the more stable calcite.

In making analyses of natural waters the temperature at the time of collection should be noted, for, although calcium carbonate may not actually deposit before the analysis can be made, owing to the slowness of the change illustrated by Table II, the question of whether the water was saturated or not when collected would require for its satisfactory answer a knowledge of its temperature.

[6] U. S. Geological Survey Bull. 479, p. 28.

ABSTRACTS

Authors of scientific papers are requested to see that abstracts, preferably prepared and signed by themselves, are forwarded promptly to the editors. Each of the scientific bureaus in Washington has a representative authorized to forward such material to this journal and abstracts of official publications should be transmitted through the representative of the bureau in which they originate. The abstracts should conform in length and general style to those appearing in this issue.

GEOLOGY.—*Some mining districts in northeastern Nevada and northwestern California.* JAMES M. HILL. U. S. Geol. Survey Bull. 594. Pp. 200. 1915.

This report embodies the results of a geologic reconnaissance which had two main objects, (1) to satisfy a present public demand for reliable information, and (2) to gather data which should be of use in preparing at a later time a general report on the geology and ore deposits of Nevada. The report brings out many facts not only of practical but of scientific interest, such as the widespread occurrence of adularia in the veins of northwestern Nevada, the presence of secondary tetrahedrite and wurtzite in the Reese River district, and the presence of selenium in the veins of Aurora.

In the region covered, sedimentary rocks ranging in age from Paleozoic to Mesozoic were noted. These sedimentary rocks, in practically every camp in which they were noted, have been intruded by granitoid rocks ranging from diorites through monzonites, quartz monzonites, and granodiorites, to granites. Their age was not definitely determined, though they cut Jurassic rocks; it is believed, however, that they were all intruded during the late Cretaceous or early Tertiary period of intrusion common to the Sierra Nevada and Great Basin province. Lava flows cover considerable parts of the region visited, particularly along the western border of /Nevada and in northeast California. Farther east, in Lander County, volcanic rocks are less conspicuous.

The ore deposits are grouped as gold-silver deposits, silver-lead deposits, copper deposits, and antimony deposits. Each of these broad groups is further subdivided according to the mineral composition of the ores and their mode of occurrence.

In most of the gold-silver deposits quartz has replaced calcite gangue to some extent, giving a peculiar platy structure to the quartz. With the exception of the veins near Aurora the veins proper carry almost no sulphides although pyrite is found in the altered wall rocks. The gold is all free but usually very finely distributed. At Aurora, besides free gold, the ores carry tetrahedrite, some pyrite and chalcopyrite, and selenium. The nature of the selenium compound is not yet known.

·So far as known all the silver-lead deposits are closely associated with the intrusive quartz monzonite and related rocks and are therefore of late Mesozoic or early Tertiary age. All these veins exhibit marked similarity in the sulphide minerals, though the proportions of one to another differ widely even in the same vein. Antimonial compounds, generally freibergite, are present in practically every vein. Galena, dark sphalerite, pyrite, arsenopyrite, and chalcopyrite are usually fairly abundant.

The copper deposits are associated with quartz monzonite intrusives probably of early Tertiary age. Most of them are of the contact metamorphic type or are replacement deposits in various kinds of sediments near masses of intrusive rock.

Most of the antimony deposits occur in crushed, contorted siliceous shales. The ores consist of white quartz and stibnite, with, in some places, minor quantities of tetrahedrite and galena, showing that they are probably related to the silver-lead mineralization.   E. S. B.

ZOOLOGY.—*A Study of asymmetry, as developed in the genera and families of recent crinoids.* Austin H. Clark. The American Naturalist, **49**: 521–546. 1915.

Among the recent crinoids any wide departure from the normal close approximation to true pentamerous symmetry indicates unfavorable conditions of one or other of two main types, which are not mutually exclusive. These two types are: (1) *Internal unfavorable conditions*, induced by incipient phylogenetical degeneration through type-senescence, as in the Plicatocrinidæ which in the recent seas represent the almost exclusively palæozoic Inadunata; and (2) *External unfavorable conditions*, taking the form of (a) *Phylogenetically excessive cold* which, to cite one example, appears to be the determining factor in the asymmetry of the genus *Promachocrinus*, or (b) *Phylogenetically excessive warmth*, which appears to be the determining factor in the asymmetry of the Comasteridæ.   A. H. C.

JOURNAL

OF THE

WASHINGTON ACADEMY OF SCIENCES

Vol. V   NOVEMBER 19, 1915   No. 19

ELECTRICITY.—*Protection of life and property against lightning.* O. S. PETERS, Bureau of Standards.

This paper is a report of a survey of statistical data relating to life and property hazards from lightning, and describes existing methods of protection against lightning. The field covered does not include electrical power and signal systems. In the course of preparation of the paper an examination was made of the available literature on the subjects of lightning phenomena and protection against lightning, and of the reports of fire marshals and insurance companies. In addition to this a considerable amount of data was obtained from the reports of the Census Bureau, and manufacturers of lightning rods were asked to submit their opinions, and the results of their experiences, as to how a system of lightning rods should be installed. Appendices are included in the complete paper, to be published by the Bureau of Standards, giving rules concerning the installation and maintenance of lightning rods which have in some cases been followed in Germany, England, and the United States, and also rules for first aid treatment in cases of persons injured by lightning.

The chief facts disclosed by the information obtained in the course of the inquiry may be summarized briefly as follows:

1. The property loss by lightning for the entire United States is approximately eight million dollars per year, of which by far the greater part occurs in rural districts.

2. During each year there are approximately 1500 persons affected by lightning stroke in the United States, one-third of this number being killed and the rest subjected to injuries which in many cases are permanent. About nine-tenths of these acci-dents occur in rural districts.

3. Such evidence as is available on the effectiveness of light-ning rods indicates that, taking rods as they come in the gen--eral run of installations, they reduce the fire hazard from light-ning by 80 to 90 per cent in the case of houses, and by as much as 99 per cent in the case of barns. The same is undoubtedly true of other buildings having characteristics similar to those of barns and houses.

4. With regard to the proper metal for lightning rods it may be said that the differences of resistivity of the metals ordinarily available for lightning rods are not great enough to make one metal preferable to another. Resistance to atmospheric and soil corrosion is the chief essential to be considered.

5. Extended metallic masses on or within a building must be made a part of the lightning rod system, with a possible excep-tion, however, in the case of metallic masses within the building which do not come near the roof and are at a distance of ten feet or so from the rods. Gas pipes should be avoided in erect-ing lightning conductors if possible, but if they are so located that it is impossible to keep at a distance of ten feet or more, they should be electrically connected to the rods at several points, connected to earth within the building, and well bonded around the gas meter.

6. The maximum current in a lightning flash may, in some cases, be more than 20,000 amperes.

7. Each flash of lightning consists, in most cases at least, of a number of consecutive discharges along the same path with short time intervals between them. The duration of each of the consecutive discharges is of the order of 1/35000 second. The best obtainable evidence points to the fact that these con-secutive discharges are unidirectional and of steep wave front.

8. The heating effects of a lightning stroke on a rod of ordi-nary size, i.e., a rod weighing about 0.5 kg. per meter, is not

likely to be appreciable except at the place where the stroke enters the rod, or at high resistance joints.

9. Good mechanical construction in a lightning rod system is a prime essential to permanency. Rods are subject to severe strains from wind, snow and ice, thermal expansion and contraction, and, in the event of a stroke of lightning, to electromagnetic stresses, so joints must be strong and the rod securely fastened to the building.

10. The resistance of the earth connection should be made as low as practicable. In practice there is no chance of getting too low a resistance. On the other hand, a resistance which rises above 15 or 20 ohms at any time should be considered as excessively large on account of the potential drop which may possibly be set up in the event of a stroke.

11. When a system of lightning rods is installed aerial terminals with points should be placed at all chimneys, gables, points or other projections toward which a stroke of lightning might be directed. This is necessary because a point cannot be relied upon to protect objects other than that upon which it is placed.

12. Down conductors should be run in such a way that a stroke on any aerial terminal on a structure will have two or more widely separated paths from the foot of the aerial terminal to earth. One path to earth has been found to be unsafe, and more than two are preferable.

13. It has been shown photographically that the path of a lightning discharge may be shifted by the wind as much as 10 meters or more during the period between the initial and final discharge. For this reason it is advisable not to allow too great an expanse of flat roof to be exposed without aerial terminals.

14. The return on an investment in lightning rods may be expected in two ways; in a sense of personal security from lightning, and in actual security to life and property. The property loss from lightning is not sufficient to cause universal protection against lightning to be a paying investment. Protection against lightning is justified as an investment only where risk to human life is involved, or where the property risk is great enough to make protection against lightning more economical than insurance.

15. With regard to personal safety from lightning it may be said that no place to which a person may ordinarily retire can be considered as absolutely safe. The only places which can be considered as closely approximating absolute safety are in a building completely surrounded by a metal network, in a steel frame building, or in an underground chamber. A high degree of safety, however, may be found in a well rodded building; the next degree of safety is undoubtedly to be found in an unprotected house which may be considered as far preferable to the open or to unprotected outbuildings.

BOTANY.—*Notes on Orthopterygium huaucui.* PAUL C. STANDLEY, U. S. National Museum.[1]

In 1907 Mr. W. Botting Hemsley published[2] a very elaborate account of a proposed new family of plants, the Julianiaceae, including two genera, *Juliania* (or *Amphipterygium*) and *Orthopterygium*, the latter being described as new. The family is a very remarkable one in many respects, and for a long time after the description of the first published species, *Juliania adstringens*, in 1843, its proper taxonomic position was unknown. Some authors placed *Juliania* in the Burseraceae or in the Anacardiaceae, while others referred it to the list of "genera incertae sedis." Hemsley, however, demonstrated that while the Julianiaceae bear certain resemblances to the Anacardiaceae, their affinities are rather with the Juglandaceae and Fagaceae.

The genus *Juliania* is an exclusively Mexican group, composed of four species, while *Orthopterygium* consists of a single Peruvian species, *O. huaucui*, the type specimens having been collected by the Wilkes Exploring Expedition "in the vicinity of Yanga, Peru," near Lima.[3] Specimens of the same plant had been collected, however, as early as 1831, on "the sides of the base of the Cuesta of Purruchuca, Province of Canta, Peru," by Mathew.

These two localities were the only ones known to Hemsley when his monograph of the family was prepared. Recently Dr. C. H.

---

[1] Published by permission of the Secretary of the Smithsonian Institution.

[2] Phil. Trans. Roy. Soc., London, Ser. B. **199**: 169–197, pl. 18–24.

[3] A. Gray in Wilkes, U. S. Expl. Exped. **15**: 371. 1854.

T. Townsend, of the U. S. Department of Agriculture, who has spent several years in entomological work in Peru and Ecuador, presented to the National Museum a small collection of plants from western Peru.   Among the specimens are staminate flowers and nearly mature fruit of *Orthopterygium huaucui*.   The fruit agrees perfectly with that of the type collection of the species.

Fig. 1.   *Orthopterygium huaucui* in Chosica Canyon.   The largest individual seen, a pistillate tree with fruits pendent from the branches.

Dr. Gray states that his own material consisted of "two leafless branches . . . . with nothing besides a terminal fascicle of immature, pendent, samaroid fruits."   One of these branches is in the National Herbarium.

Dr. Townsend's specimens come from the general region of the two localities cited above.   They were collected June 6 or 7,

1914, at an altitude of about 1800 meters at Goatherd Camp, Chosica Canyon, in the mountains northwest of the town of Chosica, Peru.   The soil here consists of gravel and rock detritus. Soil and atmospheric humidity are practically nothing in the cool season, which extends from May to December.   At this period the temperature is from 70 to 75°F. during the day, and 60 to 65° at night, the lowest temperature being probably not under 45°.   In the warm season, lasting from January to April, there is a precipitation of perhaps 4 to 6 inches.   The vegetation is very scanty, being confined to 3 species of columnar *Cereus* and a few shrubs and composites in the bed of the canyon.   The animal life, likewise, is limited, only a few arid forms of vertebrates and insects being present.

Orthopterygium forms an extensive patch on a north slope near the top of the bench in the south side of the canyon, being scattered over an area several hundred yards in diameter, many of the trees lying dead on the summit of the northwest exposure of the bench.   The plant is a shrub or small tree, 1 to 2.5 meters high, with spreading, brittle, "fat" twigs and branches having a milky latex.   It was not in leaf the first of June, but the staminate flowers were present, dark red and pendent, as well as the green or reddish, pendent fruits.

The flowers received by the National Herbarium agree in every respect with those illustrated in Hemsley's monograph. The fruits are 6 to 7 cm. long, 11 to 16 mm. wide, and slightly pubescent.   Like those of *Juliania* they are of a very curious structure; the pedicel becomes in age broad and flat and somewhat spongy, and sunken in its apex is borne the involucre which incloses the three flowers.   The whole has the appearance of some samaroid fruit inverted, and the casual observer of the detached fruits might easily take the terminal involucre for a basal point of attachment.

The fruits of Dr. Townsend's specimens are so nearly mature as to show the characters of the seeds, which were not known before.   Of the three ovaries in each involucre only one develops. The seed is pendent, attached laterally near the apex; it is strongly compressed, in outline narrowly ovate-acuminate, tapering gradually from the base to the apex; it is 11 to 12 mm. long, 3.5 mm. broad, and 1.5 mm. thick; the radicle is slender and ascending; the cotyledons are thin and very brittle; the testa is membranous and pale brown.

The illustration showing habit and habitat is from a photograph kindly furnished by Dr. Townsend, who has supplied also the geographic and habital data given above.

TECHNOLOGY.—*Standard zinc-bronze: Relation of microstructure and mechanical properties.* HENRY S. RAWDON, Bureau of Standards.[1]

To complete the study of the mechanical properties of zinc-bronze (Cu 88, Sn 10, Zn 2) as influenced by the method of casting, temperature of pouring, and other varying factors of foundry practice, a detailed study of the micro-structure of a large number of test bars was made. The results show that the method of preparation affects the structure only indirectly by the rate of cooling, amount and distribution of foreign inclusions, etc.

In the cast condition the alloy consists of an aggregate of relatively large crystals, each of which comprises a dendritic matrix consisting of a solid solution of tin (and zinc?) in copper, embedded in which are numerous particles of a hard brittle eutectoid. When stress is applied and continued beyond the "elastic limit," the matrix is plastically deformed while the eutectoid enclosures are shattered and broken transversely across. When broken in the tension test, the bars become wrinkled and roughened in a characteristic manner which is to be attributed to the orientation of the crystal-structure and properties. The examination of a good many broken bars shows that, with few exceptions, when fracture occurs it takes place within the crystals and is not a mere pulling apart and separation of adjacent crystals.

Since the fracture occurs through the crystals, i.e., along cleavage planes, rather than between them, the size of crystals is an important factor in determining the ultimate strength of

[1] To appear in full as a Technologic Paper of the Bureau of Standards.

the tensile bar. The crystals after slow cooling are relatively large and instances were found where the fracture occurred at a point where one crystal extended across the greater portion of a cross-section of the bar and thus determined the mechanical properties of the whole sample. Often, adjacent crystals are very similarly oriented and, mechanically, are practically equivalent to a single crystal. In ordinary sand castings, however, such cases are apparently unavoidable.

Of all possible factors affecting the tensile strength the presence of oxides in the form of pits and films is especially serious. The following illustrates the deleterious effect of such oxide films:

No. of specimens examined.	No. found containing oxide films.	Ultimate tensile strength per sq. in.
13	13	30,000 lbs. or less
12	10	30,000 to 35,000

In test-bars showing a tensile strength above 35,000 pounds per square inch, oxide films were rarely found and then only in small isolated spots.

The presence of oxides of tin and zinc in the form of pits and films may be considered, then, as the predominating factor in the cause of mechanical weakness of cast bronze.

ABSTRACTS

Authors of scientific papers are requested to see that abstracts, preferably prepared and signed by themselves, are forwarded promptly to the editors. Each of the scientific bureaus in Washington has a representative authorized to forward such material to this journal and abstracts of official publications should be transmitted through the representative of the bureau in which they originate. The abstracts should conform in length and general style to those appearing in this issue.

GEOPHYSICS.—*The Earth's magnetism.* L. A. BAUER. Ann. Rep. Smithsonian Institution for 1913, pp. 195–222, 9 pls. 1914. (Smithsonian Inst. Pub. 2281.)

The fourth "Halley Lecture," delivered in the schools of the University of Oxford on May 22, 1913; reprinted, after revision by the author and with additional illustrations, from Bedrock, vol. 2, no. 3, October, 1913, pp. 273–294. The lecture concerns itself especially with Halley's contributions to terrestrial magnetism, to recent advances relating primarily to the mapping of the Earth's magnetic field at any one time, and to the determination of the secular changes. Among the illustrations are a portrait of Halley, a view of the house occupied by Halley while living at Oxford, and a reduced facsimile reproduction of Halley's first chart of the lines of equal magnetic declination as based on his observations in the Atlantic Ocean during the cruises of the *Paramour Pink*, 1698–1700. In the closing paragraph the belief is expressed that a long step forward will have been taken toward the discovery of the *origin* of the Earth's magnetism when once we have found out the causes of its many, and often surprising, variations. As some slight indication of the import the solving of the riddles of the Earth's magnetism may be, Schuster's suggestive remark is recalled that "atmospheric electricity and terrestrial magnetism, treated too long as isolated phenomena, may give us hints on hitherto unknown properties of matter." J. A. F.

GEOLOGY.—*Guide book of the Western United States, Part C. The Santa Fé Route.* N. H. DARTON and others. U. S. Geological Survey Bulletin 613. Pp. 194, maps and illustrations. 1915. (For sale by the Supt. of Public Documents, Washington, D. C. Price $1.)

The average busy American is prone to regard the journey across the Great Plains of the Middle West and the arid stretches of New Mexico and Arizona, as an enforced tedium to be mitigated as far as possible by slumber, magazines, or the "smoker." Only some unusually picturesque feature stirs him to a real interest in his surroundings. Travel for the purpose of understanding the country traversed rather than as a means of getting from city to city is an art less developed here than abroad. The purpose of this guide book of the Santa Fé Route is to make the 1800 miles between Kansas City and Los Angeles interesting and educating to the intelligent traveler, by explaining in non-technical language the meaning of the things that are visible from the car window. Emphasis is placed upon the meaning of the scenic features of the landscape, as is natural in a publication emanating from the Geological Survey, but many features of agricultural or of botanical interest, such as the peculiar floral features of the desert, are also described, and the history of human endeavor in the "winning of the west" receives a just share of attention.

The explanation of such striking natural features as the petrified forest in Arizona, the volcanic cones near Winona, Arizona, and greatest of all, the Grand Canyon, will be particularly welcomed by travelers. Of great human interest are the descriptions and pictures of Hopi and Navajo Indian villages of the "Painted Desert." The journey through some of the less picturesque regions is enlivened by excursions into the geologic past whose gigantic reptiles are pictured from authoritative restorations by Charles R. Knight.   E. S. BASTIN.

GEOLOGY.—*The fractional precipitation of some ore-forming compounds at moderate temperatures.* ROGER C. WELLS. U. S. Geological Survey Bull. 609. Pp. 46. 1915.

The experiments described in this bulletin were made to aid in elucidating the chemistry of ore deposition. They yield as their immediate result the order of solubility of the compounds of each of the classes investigated—sulfides, hydroxides, carbonates, and silicates. The results with the silicates are really those due to hydroxides, since the silicates are so completely hydrolyzed in aqueous solution, but they show that metallic bases are incapable of removing silica from solution completely. The work of Anthon and Schürmann, which covered the sulfides fairly completely, is discussed in order to compare their results with the solubilities and solubility products determined by physicochemical methods. The order of solubility of sulfides obtained from experiments on fractional precipitation agrees better with solubility products calculated from electromotive force measurements than it does with Weigel's results obtained by conductivity determinations. Incidentally, it is shown that the immediate precipitate produced by alkaline- sulfides and copper salts contains a much higher proportion of cuprous sulfide than that formed by hydrogen sulfide in acid solutions. The precipitation series obtained for the hydroxides, beginning with the most insoluble, is as follows: Ferric, aluminium, cupric, zinc, lead, nickel, silver, ferrous, manganous, magnesium, calcium. The series obtained for carbonates, based on results with sodium bicarbonate as precipitant, is: Mercury, lead, cadmium, manganese, silver, ferrous, zinc, calcium, magnesium.

R. C. W.

FORESTRY.—*Value of the big tree contest.* W. H. LAMB. The Journal of Heredity, **6**: 424–428. 1915.

This is a discussion of the scientific value of the prize photograph contest conducted by the American Genetic Association, in which the largest hardwood tree discovered was a sycamore (*Platanus occidentalis*), located at Worthington, Indiana, which measures 42 feet 3 inches in circumference and about 140 feet in height. In this contest the interest of the forester and the dendrologist centered upon the ascertainment of the species reaching the maximum size, the greatest size attained by every species, and upon consideration of the geographic location of notable trees with respect to their natural range. In discussing the contest from this viewpoint, data are presented upon the influence of heredity and environment upon the form and size of trees, on the doctrine of indefinite longevity in trees, and on the scientific and aesthetic value of large specimens. Maps are included showing the natural range and location of the largest individuals of six important timber trees, and attention is called to the desire of the Association for information on the location, life history, and size of notable trees throughout the United States.

W. H. L.

REFERENCES

Under this heading it is proposed to include, by author, title, and citation, references to all scientific papers published in or emanating from Washington. It is requested that authors coöperate with the editors by submitting titles promptly, following the style used below. These references are not intended to replace the more extended abstracts published elsewhere in this JOURNAL.

GEOLOGY

BASTIN, EDSON S. *Ores of Gilpin County, Colorado.* Economic Geology, **10**: 262-291, pl. 12, figs. 40-42. 1915.

BAUER, C. M. *A sketch of the late Tertiary history of the Upper Missouri River.* Jour. Geol. **23**: 52-58, fig. 1. 1915.

BUTLER, B. S. *Geology and ore deposits of the San Francisco and adjacent districts, Utah.* Economic Geology, **9**: 413-434, 529-558, pl. 5, figs. 109-110, 124-129. 1914.

BUTLER, B. S. *Relation of ore deposits to different types of intrusive bodies in Utah.* Economic Geology, **10**: 101-122, figs. 16-19. 1915.

CAPPS, S. R. *Some ellipsoidal lavas on Prince William Sound, Alaska.* Jour. Geol. **23**: 45-51, figs. 1-5. 1915.

CLARKE, F. W. *Analyses of rocks and minerals from the laboratory of the United States Geological Survey, 1880 to 1914.* U. S. Geological Survey Bulletin 591. Pp. 376. 1915.

DILLER, J. S. *The eruptions of Lassen Peak, California.* Bull. Seismological Soc. Amer. **4**: 103-107. 1914. Also, The Mazama, **4**: 54-59, Illustrated. 1914.

FATH, A. E. *Copper deposits in the "Red Beds" of southwestern Oklahoma.* Economic Geology, **10**: 140-150, figs. 22-27. 1915.

FERGUSON, HENRY G. *Pocket deposits of the Klamath Mountains, California.* Economic Geology, **10**: 241-261, pl. 11, figs. 30-39. 1915.

KNOPF, ADOLPH. *Is the boulder batholith a laccolith? Discussion of a paper by A. C. Lawson.* Economic Geology, **9**: 396-402. 1914.

LEE, W. T. *Relation of the Cretaceous formations to the Rocky Mountains in Colorado and New Mexico.* U. S. Geological Survey Professional Paper 95-C, pp. 13-26, pls. 1-4, figs. 2-11. 1915.

LOUGHLIN, G. F. *The oxidized zinc ores of the Tintic district, Utah.* Economic Geology, **9**: 1-19, pls. 1-2, figs. 1-8. 1914.

PALMER, CHASE. *Studies in silver enrichment. Tetranickel-triarsenide, its capacity as a silver precipitant.* Economic Geology, **9**: 664-674. 1914.

POGUE, J. E. *The Cantwell formation. A continental deposit of Tertiary age in the Alaska Range.* Jour. Geol. **23**: 118-128, figs. 1. 1915.

ROGERS, G. S., and LESHER, C. E. *The use of thickness contours in the valuation of lenticular coal beds.* Economic Geology, **9**: 707-729, pls. 16-18. 1914.

SIEBENTHAL, C. E. *Spring deposits at Sulphur Springs, Arkansas.* Economic Geology, **9**: 758-767. 1914,

UMPLEBY, JOSEPH B. *The genesis of the Mackay copper deposits, Idaho.* Economic Geology, **9**: 307–358, figs. 80–89. 1914.

WEGEMANN, C. H. *Anticlinal structure in parts of Cotton and Jefferson Counties, Oklahoma.* U. S. Geological Survey Bulletin 602. Pp. 108, 5 plates. 1915.

ENGINEERING

BABB, C. C., COVERT, C. C., and MATHERS, J. G. *Surface water supply of the north Atlantic coast basins, 1912.* U. S. Geological Survey Water-Supply Paper 321. Pp. 240. 1914.

ELLSWORTH, C. E., and DAVENPORT, R. W. *Surface water supply of the Yukon-Tanana region, Alaska.* U. S. Geological Survey Water-Supply Paper 342. Pp. 343. 1915.

FOLLANSBEE, ROBERT. *Surface water supply of the lower Mississippi River basin.* U. S. Geological Survey Water-Supply Paper 327. Pp. 84. 1914.

FOLLANSBEE, ROBERT, and DEAN, H. J. *Water resources of the Rio Grande basin, 1888-1913,* including *Surface water supply of the western Gulf of Mexico basins, 1913,* by ROBERT FOLLANSBEE, W. W. FOLLETT, and G. A. GRAY. U. S. Geological Survey Water-Supply Paper 358. Pp. 725. 1914.

FOLLANSBEE, ROBERT, and GRAY, G. A. *Surface water supply of lower Mississippi River basin, 1913.* U. S. Geological Survey Water-Supply Paper 357. Pp. 86. 1915.

FOLLANSBEE, ROBERT, PORTER, E. A., and PADGETT, H. D. *Surface water supply of the Colorado River basin, 1912.* U. S. Geological Survey Water-Supply Paper 329. Pp. 238. 1914.

FOLLETT, W. W., FOLLANSBEE, ROBERT, and GRAY, G. A. *Surface water supply of the western Gulf of Mexico basins, 1912.* U. S. Geological Survey Water-Supply Paper 328. Pp. 121. 1914.

HENSHAW, F. F., BALDWIN, G. C., STEVENS, G. C., and FULLER, E. S. *Surface water supply of the north Pacific coast basins, 1911.* U. S. Geological Survey Water-Supply Paper 312. Pp. 706. 1915.

HENSHAW, F. F., and FULLER, E. S. *Surface water supply of the north Pacific drainage basins, Lower Columbia River and Rogue, Umpqua, and Siletz rivers.* U. S. Geological Survey Water-Supply Paper 332-C. Pp. 226. 1914.

HENSHAW, F. F., LEWIS, JOHN H., and McCAUSTLAND, E. J. *Deschutes River, Oregon, and its utilization.* U. S. Geological Survey Water-Supply Paper 344. Pp. 200. 1914.

HENSHAW, F. F., PORTER, E. A., and STEVENS, G. C. *Surface water supply of the Great Basin.* U. S. Geological Survey Water-Supply Paper 330. Pp. 275. 1915.

HORTON, A. H., HALL, W. E., and JACKSON, H. J. *Surface water supply of the Ohio River basin, 1912.* U. S. Geological Survey Water-Supply Paper 323. Pp. 118. 1914.

HORTON, A. H., HOYT, W. G., and JACKSON, H. J. *Surface water supply of the upper Mississippi River and Hudson Bay basins, 1912.* U. S. Geological Survey Water-Supply Paper 325. Pp. 193. 1914.

HORTON, A. H., HALL, W. E. and PETERSON, H. J. *Surface water supply of Ohio River basin, 1913.* U. S. Geological Survey Water-Supply Paper 353. Pp. 264. 1915.

HOYT, W. G., HORTON, A. H. and COVERT, C. C. *Surface water supply of St. Lawrence River basin, 1913.* U. S. Geological Survey Water-Supply Paper 354. Pp. 136. 1915.

LAMB, W. A., FOLLANSBEE, ROBERT, and PADGETT, H. G. *Surface water supply of the Missouri River basin, 1912.* U. S. Geological Survey Water-Supply Paper 326. Pp. 375. 1914.

LAMB, W. A., and FOLLANSBEE, ROBERT. *Surface water supply of Missouri River basin, 1913.* U. S. Geological Survey Water-Supply Paper 356. Pp. 291. 1915.

McGLASHAN, H. D., and STEVENS, G. C. *Surface water supply of the Pacific coast basins in California, 1912.* U. S. Geological Survey Water-Supply Paper 331. Pp. 442. 1914.

MARSHALL, R. B. *Profile surveys in the basin of Clark Fork of Columbia River, Montana-Idaho-Washington.* U. S. Geological Survey Water-Supply Paper 346. Pp. 6. 1914.

MARSHALL, R. B. *Profile surveys in Snake River Basin, Idaho.* U. S. Geological Survey Water-Supply Paper 347. Pp. 12. 1914.

MARSHALL, R. B. *Profile surveys in Hood and Sandy River basins, Oregon.* U. S. Geological Survey Water-Supply Paper 348. Pp. 8. 1914.

MARSHALL, R. B. *Results of spirit leveling in Michigan, 1911 and 1913.* U. S. Geological Survey Bull. 559. Pp. 79. 1915.

MARSHALL, R. B. *Results of spirit leveling in Minnesota, 1897 to 1912, inclusive.* U. S. Geological Survey Bull. 560. Pp. 190. 1915.

MARSHALL, R. B. *Results of spirit leveling in Hawaii, 1910 to 1913, inclusive.* U. S. Geological Survey Bull. 561. Pp. 42. 1914.

MARSHALL, R. B. *Results of spirit leveling in Virginia, 1900 to 1913, inclusive.* U. S. Geological Survey Bull. 562. Pp. 68. 1914.

MARSHALL, R. B. *Results of spirit leveling in Maryland, 1896 to 1911, inclusive.* U. S. Geological Survey Bull. 563. Pp. 80. 1915.

MARSHALL, R. B. *Results of spirit leveling in Colorado, 1896 to 1914, inclusive.* U. S. Geological Survey Bull. 565. Pp. 192. 1915.

MARSHALL, R. B. *Results of spirit leveling in Utah, 1897 to 1914, inclusive.* U. S. Geological Survey Bull. 566. Pp. 77. 1915.

MARSHALL, R. B. *Results of spirit leveling in Idaho, 1896 to 1914, inclusive.* U. S. Geological Survey Bull. 567. Pp. 130. 1915.

MARSHALL, R. B. *Results of spirit leveling in Missouri, 1896 to 1914, inclusive.* U. S. Geological Survey Bull. 568. Pp. 219. 1915.

MARSHALL, R. B. *Results of spirit leveling in Iowa, 1896 to 1913, inclusive.* U. S. Geological Survey Bull. 569. Pp. 126. 1915.

MARSHALL, R. B. *Results of spirit leveling in Wisconsin, 1897 to 1914, inclusive.* U. S. Geological Survey Bull. 570. Pp. 86. 1915.

MARSHALL, R. B. *Results of spirit leveling in Nebraska, 1896 to 1913, inclusive.* U. S. Geological Survey Bull. 572. Pp. 57. 1915.

MARSHALL, R. B. *Results of spirit leveling in Arizona, 1899 to 1915, inclusive.* U. S. Geological Survey Bull. 573. Pp. 123. 1915.

PROCEEDINGS OF THE ACADEMY AND AFFILIATED SOCIETIES

THE PHILOSOPHICAL SOCIETY OF WASHINGTON

The 759th meeting was held at the Cosmos Club, on October 2, 1915. President Eichelberger in the chair, 70 persons present.

Mr. W. F. G. Swann presented a paper on *The normal electric field of the Earth*. The first portion of the paper dealt with the causes responsible for the ionization of the atmosphere. The radio-active material in the air over the sea is not sufficient to account for the ionization observed, but the measured value of the penetrating-radiation is amply sufficient to make up for the deficit. Over the land the active material in the air above is sufficient to account for more than the ionization *ordinarily observed*, so that there is a surplus to account for the existence of a large number of the so-called "Langevin ions."

The second portion of the paper dealt with the maintenance of the Earth's charge. It was shown, on theoretical grounds, that the assumption of a continual return conduction current over some region of the Earth is untenable. Any theory which accounts for the maintenance of the Earth's negative charge by the entrance of negative corpuscles from regions outside the atmosphere, will, in virtue of the known increase of conductivity with altitude, automatically account for the positive charge in the atmosphere.

It was explained that if any theory is adopted in which the negative charge on the Earth comes in some way from the atmosphere, and in which the replenishment is confined to a limited region or time, then, on such a theory it is necessary to assume a state of very high conductivity in the upper atmosphere in order to account for the existence of atmospheric-electric phenomena at places where the replenishment is absent.

The part played by the electrical convection current was considered, and it was explained that any attempt to account for a balance of the conduction current by this agency would result in the conclusion that all atmospheric-electric phenomena should be located within a shell of comparatively small altitude.

The significance of the variation of the vertical conduction current with altitude was discussed, and it was pointed out that such variations indicate a passage of electricity into and out of the volume-elements of the air partly by processes other than conduction. A provisional hypothesis as to a corpuscular emission from the atmosphere was cited, by the help of which such variations in the vertical conduction may be accounted for, and the origin and maintenance of the Earth's charge itself explained.

The paper was discussed by Messrs. OLSHAUSEN, BAUER, HUMPHREYS, and DELLINGER.

Mr. J. W. HUMPHREYS then presented a paper on *Lightning discharges* illustrated with lantern slides. The electric separation essential to the lightning discharge is produced, according to Simpson's well supported theory, by the disruption of rain drops in the air and the transfer of the resulting negative spray to higher altitudes by convection currents. But however produced, when the potential-gradient between different portions of the cloud, or between the cloud and the earth, has anywhere reached the disruptive value, lightning immediately occurs.

When seen at close range lightning appears as a sinuous line or streak of vivid white or, occasionally, pink—sinuous because, presumably, of irregular ionization and consequent irregular conductivity of the atmosphere. Some of these discharges are single, as shown by rotating cameras, and of short duration, while many are multiple, consisting of a number of partial discharges generally of unequal strength and at irregular intervals, but all following the same path, the ionized and therefore conducting path of the first discharge. Occasionally a streak of lightning persists a full second or even longer, gradually fading away, and thus producing, through its end-on and therefore brighter portions, the phenomenon known as beaded or pearl lightning.

Sheet lightning, so often seen in distant cumuli, presumably is only the diffused and reflected light of ordinary streak lightning. The objective reality both of rocket or slow moving lightning and of ball lightning is often doubted, but both have the support of many excellent observers.

It is commonly stated that the lightning discharge consists of many high frequency oscillations. A close examination of the evidence however indicates that it is either unidirectional or else very heavily damped. But little is known of the maximum current strength in a lightning discharge, though there is evidence sufficient, apparently, to show that this may amount to 10,000 amperes, perhaps even 100,000 amperes but that the quantity of electricity is surprisingly small, rarely enough to electrolyze 0.1 cc. of water.

The paper was discussed by Messrs. LITTLEHALES, OLSHAUSEN, AUSTIN, FRAZER, and SWANN.

F. E. WRIGHT, *Secretary pro tem.*

JOURNAL

OF THE

WASHINGTON ACADEMY OF SCIENCES

Vol. V   DECEMBER 4, 1915   No. 20

PETROLOGY.—*The position of the vibration plane of the polarizer in the petrographic microscope.* F. E. WRIGHT, Geophysical Laboratory.

In petrographic microscopes the polarizer is mounted in one of two positions, so that its plane of light transmission is parallel either to the vertical cross-hair or to the horizontal cross-hair of the eyepiece. Certain makers prefer the first position, others the second; but with them the matter seems to be one of long standing habit rather than one of definite reason. It is, therefore, of interest to inquire into the relative merits of the two positions and, if possible, to obtain data which enable us to ascertain definitely which is the better position. In anticipation of the final result it may be stated that for an observer using light from the northern sky, the correct position depends on, and varies with, the time of day at which the observations are made. The evidence on which this unexpected conclusion is based is presented in the following paragraphs.

Of the two positions of the plane of vibration of the polarizer that position is preferable which transmits the most light. In case the light entering the polarizer is strictly non-polarized, the same amount of light is transmitted by the polarizer in either position; under these conditions both positions are equally good. If, however, the incident light be partially polarized, the intensity of illumination varies with the azimuth of the polarizer plane; that position which allows the greater percentage of the polarized light to pass is then obviously the better.

The chief factors which produce partial polarization in the incident light are: (a) polarization by reflection at the surface of the substage reflector; (b) sky polarization.

(a) At first thought it would seem that the first factor is exceedingly important because of the pronounced polarization effect which a plane glass surface produces on reflected rays. The line of vibration for such reflected rays is the normal to the plane of incidence; hence the natural inference is that the preferable position for the plane of vibration of the polarizer is from right to left, parallel to the horizontal cross-hair. But in the case of the silvered mirror we have to do not only with reflection at a glass surface but chiefly with metallic reflection; and for such a surface the percentage intensity of polarization by reflection is in general much less than at a glass surface. Measurements, with a Koenig-Martens polarization photometer, of the relative intensities of the light rays reflected from the substage mirror (metallic reflection) show that the intensity of the rays vibrating normal to the plane of incidence is less than 10 per cent greater than that of the rays vibrating in the plane of incidence; this difference is for practical purposes not of sufficient importance to exclude either position. Unless, therefore, the source of light is distinctly polarized we must conclude that, practically, the one position is as good as the other.

(b) It has been known for nearly a century that much of the light from the sky on a clear day is polarized. Arago, Babinet, and Brewster were the first to discover and to study sky polarization, and since their time many investigators have studied the phenomenon. The literature on the subject is voluminous. The general results of this study so far as it pertains to the present problem are: The light from the different parts of the sky is not uniformly polarized but is at a maximum in the plane polar to the sun; this plane is also the plane of vibration of these polarized rays. The percentage of sky polarization decreases from the polar plane toward, and away from, the sun until the neutral points of no polarization (called Babinet and Arago points and situated about 20° from the sun and its antipoint respectively) are reached; beyond these the sky polarization again increases.

In the early morning and late afternoon the sun is near the horizon on the east or west and the plane of maximum sky polarization is approximately a north-south vertical plane passing through the zenith. The vibration plane of rays contained in this vertical plane and incident on the microscope facing north is parallel to the vertical cross-hair of the microscope. Measurements by H. H. Kimball[1] and others prove that between 50 and 80 per cent of this light is plane-polarized, the actual percentage varying with a number of factors which need not be discussed here. Under these conditions the intensity of the transmitted light, when the plane of the polarizer is in the plane of symmetry of the microscope, is more than twice that when the polarizer is parallel with the horizontal cross-hair.

At noon, on the other hand, the sun is in the south and its polar plane is an inclined plane intersecting the horizon on the east and west. The plane of vibration of the rays from the north incident on the microscope is essentially parallel to the horizontal cross-hair. Under these conditions the most favorable position of the polarizer plane is from right to left or at right angles with the early morning position.

On cloudy and misty days the amount of sky polarization decreases rapidly and is practically negligible. On such days the position of the polarizer plane has little effect on the intensity of the field illumination in the microscope.

If on a clear day the observer wishes to obtain the maximal illumination it is necessary to set the plane of the polarizer parallel to the vertical cross-hair in the early morning or late afternoon and then toward noon to turn it to the horizontal position. But such a procedure is not always convenient as the polarizer is commonly fixed in position; in view of the fact that at noon time there is always an abundance of light from a clear sky while in the early morning and late afternoon the sky illumination is less than half that at noon, the position of the polarizer which favors greater intensity of illumination at early and late

[1] Proc. Third Convention of Weather Bureau Officials, Peoria, Ill. 1904, p. 69. Bull. Mt. Weather Observatory, 1, pt. 2: 38–48. 1908. Ibidem, 3, pt. 2: 113–114. 1910. Jour. Franklin Institute, 171: 333–344. 1911.

hours is to be preferred as the fixed position. In this position the plane of vibration of the rays emerging from the polarizer is parallel with the vertical cross-hair of the eyepiece.

An extended series of tests by the writer with the petrographic microscope corroborates these statements in detail, the general conclusion being that, although either position of the polarizer is permissible, there is a slight practical advantage in having the plane of vibration parallel to the vertical cross-hair.

ENTOMOLOGY.—*A new generic name for the screw-worm fly*. CHARLES H. T. TOWNSEND, Bureau of Entomology.

The screw-worm fly is an insect of much economic importance from both the medical and veterinary standpoints. Its maggots, known as screw-worms, have been repeatedly found to infest diseased nasal sinuses and unguarded sores in man; while they also extensively infest open sores and all cuts, wounds, or other skin abrasions in cattle, horses, mules, sheep, hogs and other stock, as well as dogs and various other animals.

The screw-worm fly was originally published as *Musca macellaria* by Fabricius[1] and Wiedemann.[2] In 1875 Rondani[3] erected the genus *Compsomyia* to include two European and four East Indian species. In 1893 Brauer & Bergenstamm[4] selected *macellaria* as the type of *Compsomyia*, but this can not hold since it is not an originally included species. In 1910 Coquillett[5] designated *Musca dux* Eschscholz as the type of *Compsomyia*, which is evidently valid since there seems to have been no previous designation that can hold.

In 1863 Rondani[6] mentioned *Musca marginalis* Wiedemann, of Africa, as the type of Desvoidy's genus *Chrysomya*;[7] this is not a strictly valid designation, as the name is not originally included or designated in synonymy by Desvoidy, but Coquil-

[1] Syst. Ent. 776. 1775. Syst. Antl. 292. 1805.
[2] Auss. Zw. Ins. 2: 405. 1830.
[3] Ann. Mus. Civ. St. Nat. Genova, 7: 425-427. 1875.
[4] Denkschr. Math.-Nat. Cl. Kais. Akad. Wiss. 60: [91] 179. 1893.
[5] Proc. U. S. Nat. Mus. 37: 526. 1910.
[6] Arch. Zool. Modena, 3: 27. 1863.
[7] Essai Myod. 444. 1830.

lett[8] clinched it in 1910 by designating *regalis* R.D. (= *marginalis* Wd. acc. Bezzi)[9] as the type. A careful comparison of *dux* and *marginalis* shows that they are undoubtedly congeneric, at least so far as can be made out from external characters. Therefore *Compsomyia* apparently becomes a synonym of *Chrysomya*.

Chrysomya is confined to the Old World, while *macellaria* and its congeners are confined to America. The latter are generically distinct on external adult characters from both *dux* and *marginalis* and all the Old World species. *Compsomyia* originally included only Old World species and thus it could not, in any event, have been used for *macellaria*.

Musca macellaria is wrongly cited by Coquillett[10] as the type of *Paralucilia* Brauer & Bergenstamm,[11] by accepting the synonymy of E. Lynch-Arribalzaga,[12] who gives *Calliphora fulvipes* Macquart[13] as a synonym of *macellaria*. This synonymy can not be accepted, since Brauer & Bergenstamm[14] state that *fulvipes* Macquart, for which they erected *Paralucilia*, has the vibrissae close on the oral margin and not constricting the facial plate.

In 1883 Brauer[15] cited the generic name *Callitroga* Schiner MS. as having been applied to *macellaria* and its relatives; and in 1893 Brauer & Bergenstamm[16] state that this name was used in this sense by Schiner in the collection, evidently on labels. The standing of the name *Callitroga* is thus that of a manuscript name cited in synonymy; wherefore it is not validated and hence is not available for use.

It thus appears that there is no generic name in existence that can be used for *macellaria*. It is the purpose of this

[8] Proc. U. S. Nat. Mus. **37**: 523. 1910.

[9] Bull. Soc. Ent. Ital. **39**: 48. 1907.

[10] Proc. U. S. Nat. Mus., **37**: 584. 1910.

[11] Denkschr. Math.-Nat. Cl. Kais. Akad. Wiss. **58**: [87] 391. 1891.

[12] Anales Soc. Cient. Arg. **10**: 71. 1880.

[13] Dipt. Exot. **2**: 3, 132 [289]. 1843.

[14] Synopsis in Denkschr. Math.-Nat. Cl. Kais. Akad. Wiss. **60**: [90–92] 178–180. 1893.

[15] Denkschr. Math.-Nat. Cl. Kais. Akad. Wiss. **47**: 74. 1883.

[16] Denkschr. Math.-Nat. Cl. Kais. Akad. Wiss. **60**: [106] 194. 1893.

paper not only to demonstrate this fact, but also to supply the deficiency.

Cochliomyia Townsend, gen. nov.

Genotype, *Musca macellaria* Fabricius, Syst. Ent. 776. 1775.

Differs from *Chrysomya* R.D. by the epistoma being well elongate, well narrowed by the vibrissal angles, and its plane normally nearly or quite in the vertical. The vibrissae are well removed from the oral margin, normally by a distance equal to twice the length of the second antennal joint. The third vein may be either almost bare or distinctly bristled more than half way to the small crossvein. The parafacials are pubescent. The hind scale of tegulae is not hairy on posterior half, but bare. Antennae not separated at base. The epistomal characters are almost a duplication of those of *Pollenia*.

The generic name has reference to the popular name of the maggot—*screw*-worm.

The genera *Pollenia* and *Cochliomyia* stand removed from all the other Muscidae (syn. Calliphoridae) on the epistomal characters including the constricted facial plate. Other forms having the vibrissae far removed from the oral margin, as *Thelychaeta* B. B. (East Indies) and *Apollenia* Bezzi (Africa), do not have the facial plate strongly constricted, and further differ in having the antennae separated at base. *Chrysomya* R.D. has the plane of epistoma at an angle of about 45° to the vertical, and while the facial plate may be somewhat constricted the epistoma is neither so narrowed nor so elongate as in the present genus; it also has the hind scale of tegulae hairy on posterior half, and the parafacials are practically bare.

The extensive synonymy that has been given by E. Lynch-Arribalzaga for *macellaria*, and quoted by others,[17] cannot be accepted without very careful verification in each case. Certain of the species described are undoubtedly valid. Some of them belong to *Paralucilia* and not to *Cochliomyia*. *Chrysomya wheeleri* Hough, of California, belongs to *Cochliomyia*. The writer has collected a species of *Cochliomyia* in the Andes of Peru which is abundantly distinct from *macellaria* and which occurs at an altitude of over 12,000 feet. He has also taken specimens in Peru that are evidently to be referred to *Paralucilia*, and has seen others from Brazil that belong to the same genus, all closely resembling *macellaria* in the vittate thorax and other superficial characters. Thus it can be seen that much confusion has resulted from the attempts to lump all the names in question.

[17] Williston, Proc. U. S. Nat. Mus. **12**: 203. 1889. Giglio-Tos, Ditt. Mess. IV (Mem. R. Acc. Sc. Torino, ser. 2, **45**), 5-6. 1895. Aldrich, Cat. No. Am. Dipt. 517. 1905.

ABSTRACTS

Authors of scientific papers are requested to see that abstracts, preferably prepared and signed by themselves, are forwarded promptly to the editors. Each of the scientific bureaus in Washington has a representative authorized to forward such material to this journal and abstracts of official publications should be transmitted through the representative of the bureau in which they originate. The abstracts should conform in length and general style to those appearing in this issue.

GEOLOGY.—*Geology and oil resources of the west border of the San Joaquin Valley north of Coalinga, California.* ROBERT ANDERSON and R. W. PACK. U. S. Geological Survey Bulletin 603. Pp. 220, with 15 plates and 5 figures. 1915.

The region described forms the eastern foothills of the Diablo Range, which is the easternmost component of the Coast Ranges in central California. In the higher parts of the range, altered sedimentary and igneous rocks of probable Jurassic age outcrop. Overlying these rocks are thick unmetamorphosed Cretaceous and Tertiary sedimentary formations, with basaltic intrusives and flows in two very small areas. The post-Jurassic sedimentary formations are mainly arkosic sandstones and shales, but there are two persistent shale formations, each over 1000 feet thick, composed largely of the remains of diatoms and foraminifera. One of these formations is of Upper Cretaceous age; the other is probably Oligocene. The Cretaceous rocks all belong to the Chico or Upper Cretaceous phase, and aggregate the astonishing thickness of something over 23,000 feet.

The structure of the region is predominantly monoclinal, forming the eastern flank of the great anticlinal structure that determines the Diablo Range. The regularity of the monoclinal structure is broken, however, by several anticlinal folds that head in the central part of the range and, trending obliquely to it, extend out toward the San Joaquin Valley. Faults are relatively few and only locally dominate the structure.

The petroleum apparently originated in the diatomaceous shales, and at present is found in, or in close association with, the two formations that are composed largely of that material.

The anticlinal folds that trend obliquely to the course of the main range appear to be the chief structural features governing the accumulation of oil. The petroleum has apparently migrated, both vertically, from the organically formed shales into the more porous sandstones that overlie them, and laterally up the dip through the porous beds. Shale lying beneath the broad San Joaquin Valley is believed to have yielded much of the oil now found in the anticlines along the foothills. The oblique folds appear to have a protecting influence upon the concentration of petroleum in the main range, for oil occurs not only along the higher parts of the oblique anticlines but also in the flank of the main range just back of these folds, or in other words in the flanks of the syncline that lies between the oblique anticline and the main range. Oil is not found, however, in the flank of the range where there s no anticlinal fold lying between the main range and the San Joaquin Valley.   R. W. P.

GEOLOGY.—*The phosphate deposits of Florida.* G. C. MATSON. U. S. Geological Survey Bulletin 604. Pp. 101, pl. 17, 2 figs. 1915.

This publication describes the distribution, geology, character, occurrence, origin, age, and consumption of the Florida phosphates. Several pages are devoted to descriptions of methods of preparing the rock for market. A bibliography of Florida phosphates closes the work.

There are several different types of phosphate rock in Florida, but only two of them, rock phosphate and land pebble, are important. In the rock phosphate deposits the phosphate is embedded in a fine-grained matrix and a deposit that will yield 25 per cent of valuable rock is regarded as rich. The river pebble deposits are of fluviatile origin and the fragments of which they are composed show mechanical abrasion. The matrix of the river pebble deposits consists of sand and clay. The land pebble is believed to have been derived secondarily from the underlying phosphatic bed rock.

The deposits are found in sedimentary rocks and with few exceptions are of secondary origin. They are all of Tertiary age and lie in depressions in the surface of lower Oligocene limestones. The land pebble phosphate has been assigned to the Miocene, but may be as late as Early Pliocene. The river pebble deposits are in part Pleistocene and in part Recent. The various theories that have been advanced to explain the origin of the deposits are reviewed at length.

W. C. PHALEN.

PROCEEDINGS OF THE ACADEMY AND AFFILIATED SOCIETIES

THE BOTANICAL SOCIETY OF WASHINGTON

The 104th regular meeting of the Botanical Society of Washington was held at the Cosmos Club on the evening of Tuesday, April 6. 1915. Forty-five members and fifty-three guests were present. The following papers were read:

Prepaleozoic algal deposits: CHARLES D. WALCOTT. Mr. Walcott described the stratigraphic position of the great Prepaleozoic Beltian series of central Montana, which he considered to be of fresh or brackish water origin, in all probability deposited in a great inland lake or lakes covering an area of about 6,000 square miles, and also on river flood plains as sand and gravel, or perhaps as fine dust carried by winds. The formations consist of sandstones, calcareous and siliceous shales, and beds of limestone, the last varying in thickness from a few inches to several thousand feet. The same type of deposits also occurs in the Grand Canyon region of Arizona and extends northward along the main ranges of the Rocky Mountains far into Alberta and British Columbia.

At a horizon approximately 9000 feet below the base of the Cambrian numerous reefs of algal deposits occur at several horizons in the Newland limestone formation of the Beltian in Montana, and isolated concretionary-like forms occur scattered at various levels in the overlying Spokane shales of the Belt Mountains. The algal remains occur in many forms, some of which are surprisingly similar to those of the fresh-water lake and stream blue-green algal deposits of Pennsylvania, New York, Michigan, etc. Others are similar in appearance to the blue-green and green algal deposits of the thermal waters of the Yellowstone National Park.

Mr. Walcott illustrated by lantern slides the various forms of algal deposits as they are found in the Pre-Cambrian rocks and in recent deposits. Photographs of thin sections of both the fossil and recent deposits showed similar chains of cells which are characteristic of the blue green alga. Other photographs illustrated recent bacteria and those associated with the algal remains in the Prepaleozoic of Montana. These included the Micrococci, with both round and oval cells. Some of the sections appear to carry rodlike bacilli.

The algal flora of some Eocene shales: CHARLES A. DAVIS. Extensive beds of petroleum yielding shales of Eocene age occur in northwestern Colorado and westward. They are carbonaceous, and when fresh are dark brown, hard, tough and compact, with a bituminous odor.

So far as observed, they contain no free oil, but yield petroleum on distillation.

By modifying methods of sectioning employed by various investigators in studying coals, the author successfully sectioned these shales by microtome. The sections show an organic detrital rock containing an extensive microscopic flora which includes a large number of perfectly preserved micro-algæ related to blue-green and higher types.

Thirty-five lantern slides showed the various algæ found in these shales.

Algae in the Upper Paleozoic: DAVID WHITE.

The 105th regular meeting of the Botanical Society of Washington was held at the Cosmos Club, Tuesday, May 4, 1915, at 8 p.m. Thirty-three members and four guests were present. Dr. GEORGE R. LYMAN was elected to membership. Dr. CAMILLO SCHNEIDER, general secretary of the Dendrologischen Gesellschaft of Austria-Hungary, was present as a guest of the society. The scientific program was as follows:

The botany of Western Yunnan (China): DR. CAMILLO SCHNEIDER. Dr. Schneider had just returned from a year's journey in the high mountains of western Yunnan. In the region of the upper Yangtze he carried on investigations in botany, zoology and ethnology. He obtained a great number of colored photographs taken from nature (Lumière, autochromes) of which he exhibited 25 with the lantern. These showed most interesting plant types of the high mountains near Li Chiang at an elevation of 10,000 to 17,000 feet. Especially striking was a recently discovered *Primula* (*P. Littoniana*) with a spiked inflorescence which resembles an orchid rather than a *Primula.* The buds are of a dark purple, while the open flowers are lighter colored. A very peculiar plant of biological interest is a new *Saussurea*, which inhabits limestone boulders at about 17,000 feet and has the flowers hidden among the leaves, which are densely hairy and protect them from snow and frost. The virgin forest of the Li Chiang zone consists chiefly of *Pinus Massoninana*, various *Piceas*, *Abies Delavayi*, *Tsuga yunnanensis*, and evergreen oaks, together with many Rhododendrons and numerous other shrubs. The cryptogamic flora is very rich. Dr. Schneider has collected over 3000 different species of phanerogams and ferns.

The genus Endothia: DR. N. E. STEVENS. (To be published in full elsewhere.)

Endothia pigments: DR. LON A. HAWKINS. (To be published in full elsewhere.)

Identification of the teonanacatl, or "sacred mushroom" of the Aztecs, with the narcotic cactus, Lophophora Williamsii, and an account of its ceremonial use in ancient and modern times: MR. W. E. SAFFORD. The early Spanish writers describe certain feasts of the Aztecs in which a narcotic called by them *teonanacatl*, or "sacred mushroom," was used as an intoxicant. Bernardino Sahagun, writing before 1569, states that it was the Chichimeca Indians of the north who first discovered the properties and made use of these "evil mushrooms which intoxicate like wine." Hernández distinguishes them from other mushrooms (*nanacame*, plural of *nanacatl*,) which are used as food, by the distinguishing adjective *teyhuinti*, inebriating, "*quoniam inebrare solent.*" The belief survives that the drug thus used was a mushroom. According to Rémi Siméon, the *teonanacatl* is "une espèce de petit champignon qui a mauvais gout, enivre et cause des hallucinations." (Dict. de la langue Nahuatl, p. 436, 1885.)

Investigations by the author have proved that the drug in question is not a fungus but a small, fleshy, spineless cactus endemic on both sides of the Río Grande in the vicinity of Laredo, Texas, and in the state of Coahuila, ranging southward to the states of Zacatecas, San Luis Potosí, and Querétaro, a region inhabited in ancient times by the tribes called Chichimecas. The drug is prepared in two principal forms: (1) discoid, in which the head of the plant is cut off transversely and, when dried, bears a close resemblance to a mushroom; (2) in longitudinal pieces or irregular fragments, in which the entire plant, including the tap root, is sliced longitudinally into strips like a radish or parsnip, bearing no resemblance whatever to a mushroom, and designated by early writers as *peyotl*, and also as *raiz diabolica*, or "devil's root."

The first to call attention to the ceremonial or religious use of this drug by the Indians of today was Mr. JAMES MOONEY, of the Bureau of American Ethnology, in a paper read before the Anthropological Society of Washington, November 3, 1891. Since the time of Mr. Mooney's observations the use of the drug has spread widely among the Indians of the United States, by whom it is commonly called "mescal button" or "peyote."

Efforts have been made to prevent the Indians from using it, chiefly because it is believed by some of those interested in the Christianizing of the Indians that it has a tendency to make them revert to their primitive condition and to their heathen beliefs. Action was taken in the courts to prosecute a certain Indian for furnishing this drug to the Indians of the Menominee Reservation of Wisconsin on March 15, 1914. It developed that the drug was received by parcel post from the vicinity of Laredo, Texas. In a paper before the Lake Mohonk Conference in October, 1914, affidavits of certain Indians of the Omaha and Winnebago tribes of the Nebraska reservation were read. The evidence showed the existence of a religious organization among the Indians called the "Sacred Peyote Society," the ceremonial meetings of which are remarkably like those of the ancient Mexicans at which the "sacred mushroom" was eaten; and that the physiological effects, as described by those partaking of the drug, were identical with those attributed by the early writers to the *teonanacatl*. The chemical properties of the drug have been studied in Germany and the United States, especially by LEWIN, of Berlin, HEFFTER, of Leipsic, and the late ERVIN E. EWELL, of the Bureau of Chemistry, U. S. Department of Agriculture; and the physiological effects by Drs. D. W. PRENTISS and FRANCIS P. MORGAN, of Washington, D. C.; but it is not possible to give the detailed results of these investigations in the scope of the present paper.

So far as known to the speaker this is the first time the identity of the "sacred mushroom" or "flesh of the gods" with the narcotic cactus known botanically as *Lophophora Williamsii* has been pointed out. That the drug was mistaken for a mushroom by the Aztecs and early Spaniards is not surprising when one bears in mind that the potato (*Solanum tuberosum*) on its introduction into Europe was popularly regarded as a kind of truffle, a fact which is recorded by its German name *Kartoffel*, or *Tartuffel*.

PERLEY SPAULDING, *Corresponding Secretary.*

THE BIOLOGICAL SOCIETY OF WASHINGTON

The 543d meeting of the Biological Society of Washington was held at the Cosmos Club, Saturday, October 23, 1915, at 8 p.m., with President Bartsch in the chair; 85 persons present.

Under the heading Brief Notes, Dr. C. W. STILES recorded observations on blood examinations (cell counts, hemoglobin, etc.) of 600 children, between 6 and 17 years of age, in North Carolina. Dr. Stiles also discussed the International list of generic names of birds.

Under the heading Exhibition of Specimens, Dr. J. N. ROSE showed some interesting examples of humming birds' nests which he had collected in Brazil the past summer.

The first paper of the regular program was by Prof. A. S. HITCHCOCK, *Collecting grasses in the Southwest.* Professor Hitchcock spoke of his trip during the summer in the region from California to Western Texas for the purpose of collecting grasses. At Grand Canyon was found the rare *Stipa arida* Jones. At Ft. Bragg, California, was found *Agrostis breviculmis* Hitchc., known only from this locality and the western coast of South America; it is abundant on the open ground back of the sandy clay cliffs at this point. In a springy place on the side of the cliffs there was a colony of *Phleum alpinum* L. a grass of the high mountains of California; its occurrence at sea level was very unexpected. At various points in northern California occur *Danthonia americana* and *D. californica.* In these species the culms disarticulate near the base at maturity. An examination of the swollen base of the detached culms discloses, hidden beneath the sheath and prophyllum, a cleistogamous spikelet consisting of a single floret. The floret and enclosed caryopsis are much larger than those of the panicle.

Cleveland National Forest, lying east of San Diego, was visited to investigate *Calamagrostis densa* Vasey. This species, known only from the type collection by Orcutt, was provisionally united with *C. kœlerioides* by the speaker (in Jepson, Flora of California, 3:125. 1912), but he is now satisfied that the two are distinct.

An ascent was made of Humphreys Peak of the San Francisco Mountains, near Flagstaff, Arizona. These are the highest mountains in Arizona, the peaks extending above timber line. In the alpine region four species of grasses were found, *Trisetum spicatum, Poa rupicola, Festuca brachyphylla* and *Agropyron scribneri.* Collections were made at several other places of interest: Oracle, about 45 miles north of Tucson, in company with Prof. J. J. Thornber; Big Spring, Alpine, and Del Rio, in western Texas; and the Guadalupe Mountains of southern New Mexico, especially rich in Mexican species. Prof. Hitchcock's paper was discussed by the chair.

The second and last paper of the program was by R. L. GARNER, *African studies: Things in common among men, apes, and other mammals.* Mr. Garner spoke of the courtship, family life, period of infancy, arrival of puberty, instincts, homes, habits, and moral traits of the African anthropoid apes as observed by him in their wild state, during many years of observation in Africa. Among other things he stated that the period of gestation is probably seven months; that the young ape is born with usually 4 teeth present; that twin births are exceedingly rare; that the female becomes sexually mature at from 7 to 9 years, and the male from 1 to 2 years later; that the usual length of life is 20 to 21 years; that their foods are mainly vegetable, but that flesh is an essential part of their diet; that they have no permanent homes, but travel about as nomadic families; that their sleeping position is on their back or side like that of men; that they often make their beds 18 to 25 feet off the ground, but that the young are delivered in a bed on the ground in a well drained place; that sight and particularly hearing are acute, but that smell is not much more developed than in man and that touch is less acute than in man; and that the right of ownership among them is well respected. Mr. Garner concluded by saying he hoped to return to Africa in the near future, and take motion pictures of the great apes.

                                    M. W. LYON, JR., *Recording Secretary.*

THE ANTHROPOLOGICAL SOCIETY OF WASHINGTON

At the 488th meeting held October 13, 1915, at the George Washington Medical School, jointly with the Medical Society of the District of Columbia, Dr. Aleš Hrdlička, Curator in Physical Anthropology, National Museum, delivered an address on *The evolution of man in the light of recent discoveries, and its relation to medicine.* Human evolution is no longer a mere theory but a fixed part of natural history, better documented from day to day by substantial evidence. Its foundations rest upon many and important organic analogies; on actual physical remains of early man and perhaps even some of his predecessors; and on observations of the changes which are at present taking place in man.

The organic analogies are (1) the evidence of evolution in all the better known mammals; (2) the relations of various stages of the embryonic development of man to grades of life represented by some lower vertebrates; (3) resemblances in the mode of conception, the laws of development, in all other vital functions, and in death; (4) similarities between man and other mammals in organs, limbs, and all other physical as well as microscopic parts of the body; (5) close similarities in the chemical constituents of the human body and those of other mammals; and (6) the frequent presence in man of vestiges of or reversions to anatomical features still functional in some lower animals.

The physical evidence of man's evolution consists of a large series of skeletal remains dating from the early Pleistocene to the last prehistoric period. These remains show in general that the farther back we proceed the more primitive are the human features and the more closely they are related to those of the lower primates. This evidence alone is quite conclusive, although there are still, of course, many important gaps in the line of evidence, especially relating to the earlier periods; these however are gradually being filled in.

The historical and recent changes in man show us that his evolution has not as yet been fully accomplished but is still progressing, and that possibly among civilized white men it is progressing more rapidly than it has during most of its course. We see that the higher civilized white man has already in some respects outdistanced others, that he is rapidly diversifying, and that those who can not keep the accelerated pace are being eliminated by nature. Probably the most obvious changes are taking place in his teeth, which are gradually lessening in resistance, in size, and even in numbers—changes which in turn condition weakening and numerous disharmonies in the whole facial structure.

The process of human evolution has close relations to medicine—much closer, in fact, than are commonly appreciated by even the surgeon and physician. Evolution is not only constructive, but eliminative, involving weakening, degeneration, and eventual loss of parts which have become less useful, less functional. The progressive and retrogressive changes are not always harmonious or generally beneficial to the individual, and they bring about many conditions which demand medical or surgical intervention. The process of evolution bears, however, still other relations to medicine. It has prolonged the periods of infancy, childhood, and senility in man, the most dangerous periods of an organism; the assumption of the erect posture had necessarily adverse consequences, which probably have not yet been completely overcome, on the circulatory system and in seriously modifying the abdominal and pelvic drags as well as pressure, especially in pregnancy; it has intensified the sexual functions in man, the results of which are frequently untoward and even dangerous; it has caused an enlargement in the size of the head in the human foetus which necessitated a consequent enlargement of the pelvic cavity, and there are doubtless still disharmonies between the two conditions; it has resulted in greater relative slenderness of bones, even in the skull, rendering them proportionately more liable to injuries; it has brought about greater delicacy of skin, with a consequent less resistance of the body to exposure; it has induced especially a great enlargement of the brain, a process the results of which to this day offer many imperfections; and, finally, while evolution has doubtless improved various immunities in man, it is still very incomplete in this respect, and on the other hand it has evidently led to new dangers and predispositions. There seem to exist some indications that it may in some of the most advanced groups adversely affect the ability of procreation. The evolution of man will continue, and in order that it shall proceed with the least harm and towards the greatest benefit of mankind, it will require the most enlightened and increasingly important help and service from all branches of medicine.

The paper was well illustrated and briefly discussed.

At the 489th meeting of the Society, held October 19, 1915, in the Public Library, Dr. D. S. LAMB, of the Army Medical Museum, read a paper on *The medicine and surgery of the ancient Peruvians,* giving first some account of the country and its people, their history, customs, food, and religion. We have no evidence of hospitals in old Peru. The people are said not to have studied the medicinal properties of their plants, although they well knew the properties of what is called Peruvian bark, used in malarial fevers. Whether syphilis or leprosy occurred among them is doubted. The same may be said of tuberculosis, although some writers, like Ashmead, ascribe the mutilations represented on their pottery to local skin tuberculosis, usually known as *lupus.* These mutilations have also been regarded as resulting from punishments or surgical operations. Three skin diseases are considered peculiar to the ancient Peruvians, the *mirunta,* caused by a worm entering the skin; the *verrugas,* a very fatal disease of a warty character that struck terror into Pizarro's soldiers in 1532; and the *uta.* They had the climatic, dietetic, respiratory, and heart diseases found elsewhere, and from similar causes. Malarial fevers prevailed and were usually of the tertian variety. Smallpox, measles, scarlet fever, and yellow fever were introduced by the Spaniards and their successors. The Peruvians had what seems to have been a typhus called *tabardillo.* Goitre prevailed and was said to be caused by drinking the turbid water from the mountains. They deformed the heads of their infants, very much as did the Chinook Indians of the northwestern United States, by pressure front and back; one tribe is said to do so still. Their injuries were necessarily, for the most part, much the same as now, with the exception of shot wounds and injuries caused in modern industrial occupations. They scarified and let blood, reduced dislocations, used fixation apparatus for fractures as we do, covered open wounds, cut out *pterygiums,* and trepanned the skull. This trepanning was done either directly to relieve disease and injury or simply to let out the demon that caused the trouble.

In discussing Dr. Lamb's paper, Dr. C. L. G. ANDERSON said that the predecessors of the Incas also, the people who built the megaliths at Tiahuanaco and the great fortress at Cuzco, likewise knew much about medicinal herbs. The Indians made infusions, decoctions, powders, and ointments of barks, leaves, berries, roots, and vines. A few remedies were obtained from the mineral kingdom, such as sulphur and salty earths. Certain baths and hot springs were utilized in curing rheumatism and various skin diseases. Garcilaso de la Vega says that the use of drugs was largely prophylactic and that after the disease was well established they left nature to work its cure, merely regulating the diet. The basal idea was to eliminate the evil, whether spirit or substance. Hence, purgatives and venesection were much in vogue, as among all nations.

Throughout tropical America, the wood of the *guayacan* tree, *lignum vitae*, was held to be a specific for the venereal disease called by the Spaniards *las bubas*. Sarsaparilla was said to be the great panacea about Guayaquil. The wonderful drugs, *coca* and *quina-quina*, were peculiar to the Andean regions. The coca was chewed to ward off hunger and fatigue. Quina, later known as Peruvian bark, was the cure for fever. It was introduced into Europe about 1640. Among the common people, old women were herbalists. The new-born babe was bathed in cold water. Usually no midwife was employed. The Peruvians knew of many poisons. Witchcraft and divination were practiced.

Mr. J. N. B. HEWITT spoke of the idea of getting the evil spirit out of the patient as being common to all primitive peoples. In the Iroquois language the expression in case of sickness was "It is biting me," "biting my tooth," or "biting my head," according to the part affected. Dr. E. L. MORGAN, among others who discussed the paper, considered that trepanning probably had its origin in the idea of getting rid of the evil spirit, but was continued as a custom because of the curative results observed in some cases. Dr. LAMB, in response to an inquiry, said that the flattening of the head among the ancient Peruvians as among the Chinook Indians, probably had no effect on the intellect because it was practiced in infancy.

DANIEL FOLKMAR, *Secretary.*

JOURNAL

OF THE

WASHINGTON ACADEMY OF SCIENCES

VOL. V   DECEMBER 19, 1915   No. 21

PHYSICAL CHEMISTRY.—*On a supposed allotropy of copper.*
G. K. BURGESS and I. N. KELLBERG, Bureau of Standards.

Some dilatometric experiments have been carried out recently by Professor Ernst Cohen and W. D. Hulderman[1] which have led them to the conclusion that copper exists in two allotropic (enantiotropic) forms, having a transition point at $71°.7$ C. to $69°.2$ C. under varying conditions of fineness and previous contact with an electrolyte. The copper was in the form of metal chips turned from sticks that had been cast in asbestos from Kahlbaum remelted electrolytic copper. The metal therefore probably contained some cuprous oxide.

Messrs. Cohen and Hulderman also consider the change in the zero value of electrical resistance of copper after heating to 100°C. an *a priori* indication of the probability of allotropic modifications between 0° and 100°C. This phenomenon of shift of zero is, however, common to all metals and is known to be related to the degree of hardness of the metal. It is very persistent, being removed only by complete annealing and freedom from strains.[2]

In Table I are given a comparative series of measurements at 0° and 100° for copper and platinum wire resistance thermometers, wound on the same frame. It will be seen that the plati-

[1] Proc. Amsterdam Acad. **16**: Dec. 27, 1913; **17**: May 30, 1914; Phys. Chemie **87**: 419. 1914.

[2] See for example the behavior of Pt and Pd resistance thermometers, Waidner and Burgess, Scientific Paper No. 124, Bureau of Standards.

num is no more constant in its behavior than the copper, and constancy is attained for both metals after a few heatings to 100°C. If they were now heated to a temperature higher than 100°C., their zeros would again change, and so on.

TABLE I

CONSTANCY OF ZERO RESISTANCE OF PLATINUM AND COPPER

Pt ice	Cu ice	Pt steam	Cu steam
Ohms	*Ohms*	*Ohms*	*Ohms*
3.1600	6.3232		
3.1604	6.3228	4.5222	8.7917
3.1607	6.3212	4.5226	8.7924
3.1612	6.3223	4.5233	8.7920
3.1615	6.3223	4.5233	8.7924
3.1619	6.3221	4.5236	8.7920
3.1620	6.3220	4.5236	8.7922
3.1619	6.3220	4.5237	8.7921
3.1620	6.3221	4.5236	8.7920

Professor Cohen also considers the specific heat experiments of Le Verrier[3]—who found discontinuities at about 360°, 575° and 775°C. from a very limited number of as yet unconfirmed observations—to strengthen his conclusions as to two modifications of copper.

In 1907, Professor Benedicks[4] showed that a supposed allotropic form of copper discovered by Schützenberger[5] was not copper.

In view of the manifest importance of an allotropic phenomenon in copper below 100°, if it really exists, we have executed a series of experiments by an electric resistance method, in the range 0 to 100°C., similar to that described by us for iron,[6] substituting a calorimeter for the furnace.

---

[3] Cohen, Trans. Faraday Soc., May 1915; Le Verrier, Comptes Rendus 114: 907. 1892.

[4] Carl Benedicks, Metallurgie 4: 5, 33. 1907.

[5] Schützenberger, Comptes Rendus 86: 1265. 1878.

[6] Burgess and Kellberg, The Electrical Resistance and Critical Ranges of Pure Iron, Scientific Paper No. 236, Bureau of Standards, and Journ. Wash. Acad. Sci. 4: 436. 1914.

These experiments gave us negative results.   A brief description of the methods used and a summary of the results obtained may, nevertheless, be of some interest.

The copper was in the form of hard drawn wire, of 0.005 cm. diameter by about 35 cm. length, wound, together with a platinum wire of 0.015 cm. diameter, on a mica frame and enclosed within a glass tube.   This was immersed in a completely water-jacketed and electrically-controlled calorimeter[7] the temperature

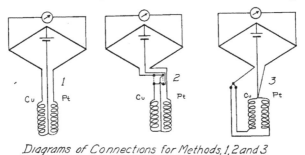

Diagrams of Connections for Methods, 1, 2 and 3

Fig. 1.   Methods of resistance measurement.

of which could be made to vary uniformly at any desired rate between 0° and 95°C.

Three methods of measurement were used, as illustrated in figure 1:

1. The resistance of the platinum and copper coils was measured differentially and simultaneous observations of temperature were taken with a mercury thermometer.   The copper-platinum thermometer was first annealed for 2 hours at 100° and then for 5 hours at 150°C.

2. Using the same copper and platinum coils, a commutator was inserted, as shown in figure 1, which permitted taking alternate readings of the platinum resistance, which then served as a thermometer, and of the platinum-copper resistance difference. In this series of observations the glass container was evacuated, to eliminate extraneous temperature influences caused by convection down the containing tube.

[7] H. C. Dickinson, Bulletin Bureau of Standards **11**: 210.   1915.

3. In a third series, the platinum and copper resistances were measured separately with a common lead and a common battery lead, (as in the observations on iron) and the times taken to 0.1 second on a chronograph. For this series a new length of previously annealed copper wire was used which also received the preliminary alternate heating and cooling shown in Table I.

TABLE II

MEASUREMENTS OF COPPER RESISTANCE

DATE	RATE DEG./SEC.	RANGE DEG. C.	METHOD (SEE FIG. 1) AND REMARKS
Dec. 18, 1914......	0.00414	84.00 – 67.69	1. Differential resistance. Temperature by mercury thermometer
Dec. 18, 1914......	0.00362	20.55 – 85.77	ditto
Dec. 19, 1914.....	0.00516	63.18 – 86.40	ditto
Dec. 19, 1914.....	0.00284	76.69 – 57.08	ditto
Dec. 21, 1914......	0.00096	59.79 – 73.25	ditto
Dec. 22, 1914......	0.00355	26.73 – 54.55	ditto
Sept. 6, 1915......	0.00138	57.2 – 68.2	2. Differential resistance. Temperature by Pt. thermometer. Coils in vacuo
Sept. 6, 1915......	0.00180	67.1 – 58.4	ditto
Sept. 10, 1915......	0.00039	57.2 – 63.8	ditto
Sept. 13, 1915.....	0.00067	56.2 – 68.0	ditto
Sept. 13, 1915.....	0.00160	66.5 – 57.0	ditto
			Heated for 16½ hours at 130°C.
Sept. 14, 1915......	0.00213	72.0 – 59.5	2. Differential resistance. Temperature by Pt. thermometer. Coils in vacuo
Sept. 14, 1915......	0.00058	60.0 – 69.0	ditto
Oct. 22, 1915......	0.00076	62.0 – 73.5	3. Resistance of copper vs. temperature. Temperature by Pt. thermometer
Oct. 23, 1915....	0.00226	72.0 – 59.8	ditto

The thermometer leads were of gold for the third series and of copper for the other two. The Wheatstone bridge used was one specially designed for calorimetric work[8] and, as used, accurate and sensitive to 1 in 500,000. Observations were taken every

[8] Bulletin Bureau of Standards **11**: 571. 1915.

few seconds, often as close together as 0.03°C.   The copper was examined microscopically by Mr. Rawdon and showed a small quantity only of cuprous oxide inclusions, see figure 2.

In Table II is given a list of the ranges over which observations were taken, together with the mean rate of heating or cooling.   Several series were taken in the range 60–70° by the second method, as there were apparent indications, from the observations by the first method, of a possible resistance effect.   This was, however, attributed to convection since it was not constant in position and could be introduced at will by opening a window or door in the

Fig. 2.   Photomicrograph of longitudinal section of copper wire.

laboratory.   In the second and third methods no anomaly could be detected, to at least 1 part in 50,000.   The last series taken

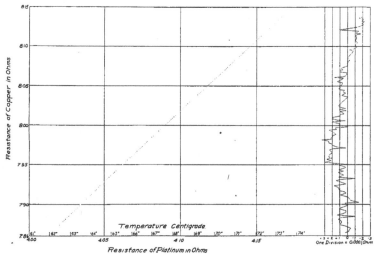

Fig. 3.   Resistance of copper vs. platinum and plot of residuals.

is reproduced in figure 3 in the form of a copper vs. platinum resistance curve and also as a curve of residuals. The plot of residuals was constructed from the platinum-copper resistance curve, using a straight line as reference on cross section paper 165 x 140 cm. The residual plot is slightly curved on account of the slightly different resistance-temperature relations of platinum and copper.

We may, therefore, conclude that an allotropic transformation of copper at about 70°C., postulated by Messrs. Cohen and Hulderman, does not exist; that the resistance of copper in the range of 0° to 100° varies continuously; and that ordinary copper is most probably not in a metastable state.

It may not, perhaps, be out of place to remark in conclusion, that it is extremely regrettable that such a far reaching and disquieting announcement as the metastability at ordinary temperatures of a metal so widely used and extremely important in exact measurements, should be made on the basis of two or three series of very inconclusive measurements.

MEDICAL ZOOLOGY.—*Identification of the stages in the asexual cycle of* Bartonella bacilliformis, *the pathogenic organism of verruga, and their bearing on the etiology and unity of the disease.* CHARLES H. T. TOWNSEND, Bureau of Entomology.

The etiology of the Peruvian disease known as verruga has thus far remained obscure. The writer considers that he has conclusively demonstrated *Phlebotomus verrucarum* Townsend as the vector of this disease, but the true status of the specific organism concerned is as yet undemonstrated. Barton described as "x-bodies" the mature gamete stage of this organism in 1909, discovered by him in 1905 in the erythrocytes of the peripheral blood of verruga cases in the fever phase.[1] Strong et al. have redescribed the same stage under the name *Bartonella bacilliformis*,[2] which they consider to be the specific organism of

---

[1] Crónica Médica (Lima) **26**: 7. 1909.

[2] Journ. Am. Med. Assoc. **61**: 1713-1716. 1913; Rep. First Exped. So. Amer., Harv. Sch. Trop. Med., 32. 1915.

"Oroya fever" (fever phase of verruga), while they consider "verruga peruviana" (eruptive phase of verruga) to be a distinct disease. It is the purpose of the present communication to interpret correctly the stages in the asexual cycle of the pathogenic organism from the findings already published, the significance of which has not yet been fully pointed out. These published findings will be taken up in chronologic order.

In 1911, Darling figured gametes found by him in verruga blood smears from Peru, among which he gives a figure of an erythrocyte filled with minute rods which he terms "young x-bodies," and which will be referred to as Darling's x-bodies.[3] These are the immature gametes of *Bartonella*, shortly after penetration of the erythrocyte.

In September, 1912, Gastiaburú and Rebagliati, working in Lima, Peru, discovered certain "cuerpos" (bodies) in verruga eruption tissue and in liver of verruga patients in the eruptive phase, which they figured and described as *Leishmania*-like.[4] These "cuerpos" are respectively early and maturing schizonts of the *Bartonella* before they have begun to break up into merozoites.

In April, 1913, Mayer, Rocha-Lima and Werner, working in Hamburg, figured and described certain "Zelleinschlüsse" (cell-inclusions) which they found in vascular endothelial cells of the greater part of the verruga nodules examined by them from a case of the disease just arrived from Peru.[5] Their figures 1 to 4 show the cell-inclusions entire, while 5 and 6 show them ruptured. These "Zelleinschlüsse" are evidently to be interpreted as, respectively, maturing *Bartonella* schizonts (1 to 4), and *Bartonella* merozoites which have resulted from the breaking up of schizonts (5 and 6).

In 1915, Strong et al. figured and described certain "spheres" found by them in endothelial cells of spleen and lymphatic nodes of verruga patients in that phase of the disease which they term "Oroya fever," which spheres they state apparently "break up

[3] Proc. Canal Zone Med. Assoc. **4**: 208–209. (No. 6, Case I, right-hand figure.) 1911.

[4] Crónica Médica, **29**: 651. 1912; Journ. Econ. Ent., **6**: 224. 1913.

[5] Münch. Mediz. Wochenschr. **60**: 740. April, 1913.

into a large number of minute elements each of which contains a chromatin granule; these become elongated and finally appear as distinct rods containing at one end a minute particle of chromatin."[6] These "spheres" are obviously an earlier stage of Mayer, Rocha-Lima and Werner's "Zelleinschlüsse;" of this the writer believes there can be no doubt. Figures 1 and 2, plate X, of Strong et al. are early schizonts of the *Bartonella* and the same as Gastiaburú and Rebagliati's eruption "cuerpos;" corresponding more or less nearly to 2a and 3a in Gonder's diagram of the life-cycle of *Lymphohaematocytozoon parvum*,[7] reproduced for purpose of comparison by Strong et al. as figure 1, plate XI. Figure 3, plate X, of Strong et al. corresponds to Mayer, Rocha-Lima and Werner's figures 1 to 4, and to Gastiaburú and Rebagliati's liver "cuerpos;" figures 4, 5, and 7, plate X, represent the elongated stage of the merozoites, somewhat farther advanced than the stage shown in figures 5 and 6 of Mayer et al., though signs of elongation are apparent in the latter's figure 5. Strong et al. add: "If these rod-shaped elements, which have been set free by the rupture of the endothelial cells, are compared with the rods found within red blood-corpuscles lying near, it is seen that they are identical in character. Moreover they are entirely similar to the forms already observed in the blood-cells in the peripheral circulation."[8] These "rods" or "rod-shaped elements," prior to their penetration of the erythrocytes, are to be considered as merely an advanced stage of the merozoites; immediately after entering erythrocytes, and before completing growth, they are to be considered as immature gametes, and are the same as Darling's x-bodies. The work of Strong et al. has thus resulted in establishing a definite connection between Barton's x-bodies, Darling's x-bodies, Gastiaburú and Rebagliati's "cuerpos," and Mayer, Rocha-Lima and Werner's "Zelleinschlüsse," which was hitherto not apparent.

All of these findings appear to indicate conclusively that the *Bartonella* is a protozoan. Several facts, which are easily ex-

[6] Rep. First Exped. So. Amer., Harv. Sch. Trop. Med., 33. 1915.

[7] Journ. Comp. Path. and Ther. **23**: 328. 1910.

[8] Rep. First Exped. So. Amer., Harv. Sch. Trop. Med., 33. 1915.

plicable, have proved stumbling-blocks, however, in interpreting the asexual development of the organism. It has been repeatedly demonstrated that blood containing the *Bartonella* gametes in the erythrocytes fails to originate any symptoms upon injection into healthy animals; that the gametes disappear from the erythrocytes upon the advent of the eruption; that eruption-tissue inoculations produce localized lesions in new tissues without *Bartonella* gametes in the erythrocytes; and that such lesions may be produced successively in series of animals by such inoculations. These and related facts are what induced Strong et al. to consider the fever and eruptive stages of verruga as two distinct pathologic entities.[9] But their finding in "Oroya fever" cases of the schizonts and merozoites, already shown to be characteristic of the eruption tissues, appears to bind inseparably their "Oroya fever" and "verruga peruviana" as phases of one disease. The explanation of the several facts above mentioned will appear below.

It is apparent that the great majority of the *Bartonella* sporozoites introduced by the *Phlebotomus* within the skin of susceptible subjects immediately imbed themselves in the cytoplasm of the vascular endothelial cells at point of inoculation, becoming schizonts, which upon maturing break up into merozoites, these elongating within the unruptured host-cell wall and penetrating such erthrocytes as come in actual and direct contact with the infected cell, whereupon they become immature gametes. The fully formed rods and ovals in the erythrocytes are respectively the mature male and female gametes, which can conjugate only in the *Phlebotomus*. Hence their injection into a healthy warm-blooded animal fails to originate any symptoms of the disease. There appears to be no duplication or repetition of any of the stages, except that the male gametes increase by binary transverse division.

The endothelial cells of the capillaries of the subcutaneous tissues are evidently the chief seat of the above-described schizogonic cycle of the Bartonella, and here is where the erythrocytes become infected.

[9] Ibid., 6, 14, et seq.

The beginning of the fever stage doubtless follows the extensive breaking up of the schizonts in the endothelial cells of the capillaries, and coincides with the extensive penetration of the erythrocytes by the merozoites.

The eruption, which is particularly characterized by a great proliferation of vascular endothelial cells, is the direct result of the extensive asexual multiplication of the Bartonella in the subcutaneous tissues. The proliferation of vascular endothelial cells prevents the erythrocytes from coming in direct contact with cells containing merozoites. Hence the infection of the erythrocytes is cut short, the fever subsides, and the gametes are no longer to be found in the blood. Hence also eruption-tissue inoculations produce no gametes in the erythrocytes of the subject inoculated, for the merozoites contained in such material are obviously unable to come in contact, under proper conditions, with the erythrocytes in the new tissues.

Erythrocytes can evidently become infected only during their slow passage through the capillaries and while in contact through positive chemotropism with a living infected endothelial cell in situ in the capillary wall. Eruption-tissue inoculations are, in a sense, mere transplantations, or grafts, as proved by the fact that the resultant proliferation is strictly localized. They are comparable in behavior to the grafts of carcinoma and other tumors which have been effected within recent years.

The cause which leads to localized proliferation in new tissues following such inoculations appears to be purely mechanical in character, the new proliferation resulting from a specific irritation of the endothelial cells in the capillaries of the new tissues by the proliferated cells thus introduced. Such new proliferation may be successively repeated by inoculation of old proliferated cells into new tissues. This explains the lesions obtained by Strong et al. in twelve series of monkeys, which they considered due to a virus resident in the proliferated tissues used for inoculation.[10] But they were unable to obtain lesions by injection of a filtrate from these tissues;[11] nor were they able to cultivate the virus

[10] Ibid., 122 and table II.
[11] Ibid., 125-127 and table I.

which they supposed to exist.[12] It is further very significant that inoculation of these tissues upon the rabbit's cornea produces no lesion.[13] The lesions produced by these inoculations are toxin-incited, not virus-incited. The original proliferation, incited by a toxin resulting from the metabolism of the organism, possesses a specific chemophysical reaction, transmissible within limits to the new proliferation which it induces.

The sporozoites must also reach the spleen, lymphatic nodes, bone marrow, and liver, as well as the capillaries of the mucous membranes, carried thence by the lymphatic system on their failure to imbed in the subcutaneous tissues. If this happens extensively, internal eruption results. This explains the infarction, necrosis, etc., of the internal organs mentioned, and the articulation and bone pains, so commonly noted in the disease. In most cases the fever and eruptive phases of verruga correspond very faithfully in intensity. When this correspondence is not so marked, antibodies have probably aided in greater degree in cutting short the asexual multiplication of the *Bartonella* in the subcutaneous tissues.

It appears that we are now, for the first time, getting some tangible evidence as to the etiology of verruga. Those familiar with the facts so far known relating to this unique disease will at once see how perfectly they all fit together, now that we interpret the cell-inclusions of the eruption tissues as a part of the schizogonic cycle of *Bartonella*. Thus the unity of verruga appears to be demonstrated by the known stages of its specific organism.

[12] Ibid., 125–126.
[13] Ibid., 130.

ABSTRACTS

Authors of scientific papers are requested to see that abstracts, preferably prepared and signed by themselves, are forwarded promptly to the editors. Each of the scientific bureaus in Washington has a representative authorized to forward such material to this journal and abstracts of official publications should be transmitted through the representative of the bureau in which they originate. The abstracts should conform in length and general style to those appearing in this issue.

GEOPHYSICS.—*General results of the work in atmospheric electricity aboard the "Carnegie," 1909–1914.* L. A. BAUER. Proc. Am. Phil. Soc., **54**: 14–17. 1915.

A paper presented at the annual meeting of the American Philosophical Society at Philadelphia on April 24, 1915. It contains a general account of the progress made by the Department of Terrestrial Magnetism of the Carnegie Institution, in its work in atmospheric electricity aboard the *Carnegie* and at the laboratory in Washington. The Department can now enter actively, with increased facilities, upon participation in another world-wide project, namely, the mapping of the Earth's electric field and the study of its variations at fixed points.

J. A. F.

TERRESTRIAL MAGNETISM.—*Distribution of the magnetic declination in the United States for January 1, 1915, with isogonic chart and secular change tables.* D. L. HAZARD. U. S. Coast and Geodetic Survey Special Publication No. 33, Serial No. 18. 1915.

The general distribution of the magnetic declination in the United States on January 1, 1915, is shown graphically by means of an isogonic chart, on which the lines of equal declination are drawn for each degree. It is based on about 6000 values of the magnetic declination, including about 800 in Canada and 300 in Mexico and the West Indies. In order that the results represented may be used for other dates than the epoch of the chart, tables are given showing the secular change of the magnetic declination at one or more places in each State from 1750 or the date of the earliest observations to 1915. In addition the values of annual change of declination for 1915 are shown graphically on the chart by means of lines of equal annual change. On account of the large number of results available, it was impossible to represent all of the irregularities of distribution by continuous lines, hence the plan was adopted of drawing the lines to represent the general distribution and of entering on the chart isolated abnormal values differing by more than a degree from the normal value for the locality. A disturbed area of some extent, indicated by observations at several places, is represented by a small closed curve. For this reason the lines on this chart appear less irregular than those on the one for 1910 which it supersedes. D. L. H.

GEODESY.—*Application of the theory of least squares to the adjustment of triangulation.* OSCAR S. ADAMS. U. S. Coast and Geodetic Survey, Serial No. 9, Special Publication No. 28. Pp. 220. 1915.

This publication has not been prepared with the idea of displacing the textbooks in dealing with the subject of least squares but of supplementing these in the special field of triangulation. Concrete examples of adjustments are given, ranging in difficulty from some of the easiest to those that are more difficult. A development is given, expressed in the symbolism employed in the office of the Survey at the present time, for the condition equations necessary to effect the closure in geographic positions of a loop. A need for this has been felt for some time past. A method of adjustment by the variation of the geographic coordinates (latitude and longitude) of the various points has been developed and applied to the adjustment of several figures. This is a method which has not heretofore been used in the United States, although something similar is regularly employed in Canada.

At the end of the publication there is given a new development of the formulas for the computation of differences of elevation from the observations of zenith distances. These formulas take into account some of the effects due to the lengths and heights of the lines that were not taken into consideration in the development previously in use in the Coast and Geodetic Survey. O. S. A.

MINERALOGY.—*An arrangement of minerals according to their occurrence.* EDGAR T. WHERRY and SAMUEL G. GORDON. Proc. Acad. Nat. Sci., Philadelphia, **1915**: 426–457. Aug. 24, 1915.

The types of mineral occurrence are classified on the basis of chemical and geological relations, the chief criterion for subdivision being dissimilarity in mineral content. About 800 species of minerals are arranged according to this classification, and an alphabetical index for locating the position of any species is given. E. T. W.

INDEX TO VOLUME V

PROCEEDINGS OF THE ACADEMY AND AFFILIATED SOCIETIES

AUTHOR INDEX

*Abstracts.

·*Abstracts.

$A 1175$

*Abstracts.

*Abstracts.

*Abstracts.

*Abstracts.

*Abstracts.

*Abstracts

*Abstracts.

SUBJECT INDEX

*Abstracts.

*Abstracts.

*Abstracts.

*Abstracts.

---

*Abstracts.

*Abstracts.

*Abstracts.

*Abstracts.

*Abstracts.

Journal of the Washington Academy of Sciences

THE JOURNAL OF THE WASHINGTON ACADEMY OF SCIENCES is a semi-monthly publication and will be sent to subscribers on the fourth and nineteenth of each month, except during the summer, when it will appear on the nineteenth only. The first volume began with the July issue and ended with 1911. Volumes now will correspond to calendar years.

Scope.—The JOURNAL is a medium for the publication of original papers and is a record of scientific work in Washington. It accepts for publication (1) brief papers written or communicated by resident or non-resident members of the Academy; (2) abstracts of current scientific literature published in or emanating from Washington; (3) proceedings and programs of the affiliated societies; and (4) notes of events connected with the scientific life of Washington.

Manuscripts may be sent to any member of the Board of Editors and must be clearly typewritten and in suitable form for printing without essential changes. The editors cannot undertake to do more than correct obvious minor errors. Footnote references should be complete, including year of publication.

Illustrations will be used only when necessary and will be confined to text figures or diagrams of simple character. The editors, at their discretion, may call upon an author to defray the cost of his illustrations, although no charge will be made for printing from a suitable cut supplied with the manuscript.

Proof.—In order to secure prompt publication no proof will be sent to authors unless requested. They are urged to submit their manuscript in final form and the editors will exercise care in seeing that copy is followed.

Authors' Copies and Reprints.—On request the author of an original article will receive ten copies of the number containing his contribution and as many additional copies as he may desire at five cents each. Reprints will be furnished at cost, or approximately as follows:

Reprints without covers, reimposed and re-made ready, saddle wire stitched:

	2 pages	4 pages	8 pages	12 pages	16 pages
25 copies	.55	.60	.65	.75	.90
50 "	.60	.70	.80	.95	$1.10
100 "	.70	.80	.95	$1.10	1.25
additional 100 copies	.20	.40	.60	.80	1.00

100 covers with name of article and author printed on front cover, $2.00. Additional covers, ½ cent each.

As an author may not see proof, his request for extra copies or reprints should reach the editors before his paper goes to press and should preferably be attached to the first page of his manuscript.

The rate of Subscription per volume is.................................$6.00*
Semi-monthly numbers.. .25
Monthly numbers.. .50

Remittances should be made payable to "Washington Academy of Sciences," and addressed to E. W. Parker, Treasurer, Geological Survey, Washington, D. C., to Williams & Wilkins Company, 2419–2421 York Road, Baltimore, Md., or to the European Agents.

European Agents: William Wesley & Son, 28 Essex St., Strand, London, and Mayer and Müller, Prinz Louis-Ferdinand Str., Berlin.

Exchanges.—The JOURNAL does not exchange with other publications.

Missing Numbers will be replaced without charge provided that claim is made within thirty days after date of the following issue.

*Volume I however, from July 19, 1911 to December 19, 1911 will be sent for $3.00. Special rates are given to members of scientific societies affiliated with the Academy.

THE WAVERLY PRESS
BALTIMORE, U. S. A.

Journal of the Washington Academy of Sciences

THE JOURNAL OF THE WASHINGTON ACADEMY OF SCIENCES is a semi-monthly publication and will be sent to subscribers on the fourth and nineteenth of each month, except during the summer, when it will appear on the nineteenth only. The first volume began with the July issue and ended with 1911. Volumes now will correspond to calendar years.

Scope.—The JOURNAL is a medium for the publication of original papers and is a record of scientific work in Washington. It accepts for publication (1) brief papers written or communicated by resident or non-resident members of the Academy; (2) abstracts of current scientific literature published in or emanating from Washington; (3) proceedings and programs of the affiliated societies; and (4) notes of events connected with the scientific life of Washington.

Manuscripts may be sent to any member of the Board of Editors and must be clearly typewritten and in suitable form for printing without essential changes. The editors cannot undertake to do more than correct obvious minor errors. Footnote references should be complete, including year of publication.

Illustrations will be used only when necessary and will be confined to text figures or diagrams of simple character. The editors, at their discretion, may call upon an author to defray the cost of his illustrations, although no charge will be made for printing from a suitable cut supplied with the manuscript.

Proof.—In order to secure prompt publication no proof will be sent to authors unless requested. They are urged to submit their manuscript in final form and the editors will exercise care in seeing that copy is followed.

Authors' Copies and Reprints.—On request the author of an original article will receive ten copies of the number containing his contribution and as many additional copies as he may desire at five cents each. Reprints will be furnished at cost, or approximately as follows:

Reprints without covers, reimposed and re-made ready, saddle wire stitched:

	2 pages	4 pages	8 pages	12 pages	16 pages
25 copies	.55	.60	.65	.75	.90
50 "	.60	.70	.80	.95	$1.10
100 "	.70	.80	.95	$1.10	1.25
additional 100 copies	.20	.40	.60	.80	1.00

100 covers with name of article and author printed on front cover, $2.00. Additional covers, ½ cent each.

As an author may not see proof, his request for extra copies or reprints should reach the editors before his paper goes to press and should preferably be attached to the first page of his manuscript.

The rate of Subscription per volume is.................................$6.00*
    Semi-monthly numbers...25
    Monthly numbers...50

Remittances should be made payable to "Washington Academy of Sciences," and addressed to E. W. Parker, Treasurer, Geological Survey, Washington, D. C., to Williams & Wilkins Company, 2419–2421 York Road, Baltimore, Md., or to the European Agents.

European Agents: William Wesley & Son, 28 Essex St., Strand, London, and Mayer and Müller, Prinz Louis-Ferdinand Str., Berlin.

Exchanges.—The JOURNAL does not exchange with other publications.

Missing Numbers will be replaced without charge provided that claim is made within thirty days after date of the following issue.

*Volume I however, from July 19, 1911 to December 19, 1911 will be sent for $3.00. Special rates are given to members of scientific societies affiliated with the Academy.

THE WAVERLY PRESS

BALTIMORE, U. S. A.

CONTENTS

Journal of the Washington Academy of Sciences

THE JOURNAL OF THE WASHINGTON ACADEMY OF SCIENCES is a semi-monthly publication and will be sent to subscribers on the fourth and nineteenth of each month, except during the summer, when it will appear on the nineteenth only. The first volume began with the July issue and ended with 1911. Volumes now will correspond to calendar years.

Scope.—The JOURNAL is a medium for the publication of original papers and is a record of scientific work in Washington. It accepts for publication (1) brief papers written or communicated by resident or non-resident members of the Academy; (2) abstracts of current scientific literature published in or emanating from Washington; (3) proceedings and programs of the affiliated societies; and (4) notes of events connected with the scientific life of Washington.

Manuscripts may be sent to any member of the Board of Editors and must be clearly typewritten and in suitable form for printing without essential changes. The editors cannot undertake to do more than correct obvious minor errors. Footnote references should be complete, including year of publication.

Illustrations will be used only when necessary and will be confined to text figures or diagrams of simple character. The editors, at their discretion, may call upon an author to defray the cost of his illustrations, although no charge will be made for printing from a suitable cut supplied with the manuscript.

Proof.—In order to secure prompt publication no proof will be sent to authors unless requested. They are urged to submit their manuscript in final form and the editors will exercise care in seeing that copy is followed.

Authors' Copies and Reprints.—**On request** the author of an original article will receive ten copies of the number containing his contribution and as many additional copies as he may desire at five cents each. Reprints will be furnished at cost, or approximately as follows:

Reprints without covers, reimposed and re-made ready, saddle wire stitched:

	2 pages	4 pages	8 pages	12 pages	16 pages
25 copies	.55	.60	.65	.75	.90
50 "	.60	.70	.80	.95	$1.10
100 "	.70	.80	.95	$1.10	1.25
additional 100 copies	.20	.40	.60	.80	1.00

100 covers with name of article and author printed on front cover, $2.00. Additional covers, ½ cent each.

As an author may not see proof, his request for extra copies or reprints should reach the editors before his paper goes to press and should preferably be attached to the first page of his manuscript.

The rate of Subscription per volume is................................$6.00*
    Semi-monthly numbers...25
    Monthly numbers...50

Remittances should be made payable to "Washington Academy of Sciences," and addressed to E. W. Parker, Treasurer, Geological Survey, Washington, D. C., to Williams & Wilkins Company, 2419–2421 York Road, Baltimore, Md., or to the European Agents.

European Agents: William Wesley & Son, 28 Essex St., Strand, London, and Mayer and Müller, Prinz Louis-Ferdinand Str., Berlin.

Exchanges.—The JOURNAL does not exchange with other publications.

Missing Numbers will be replaced without charge provided that claim is made within thirty days after date of the following issue.

*Volume I however, from July 19, 1911 to December 19, 1911 will be sent for $3.00. Special rates are given to members of scientific societies affiliated with the Academy.

Journal of the Washington Academy of Sciences

THE JOURNAL OF THE WASHINGTON ACADEMY OF SCIENCES is a semi-monthly publication and will be sent to subscribers on the fourth and nineteenth of each month, except during the summer, when it will appear on the nineteenth only. The first volume began with the July issue and ended with 1911. Volumes now will correspond to calendar years.

Scope.—The JOURNAL is a medium for the publication of original papers and is a record of scientific work in Washington. It accepts for publication (1) brief papers written or communicated by resident or non-resident members of the Academy; (2) abstracts of current scientific literature published in or emanating from Washington; (3) proceedings and programs of the affiliated societies; and (4) notes of events connected with the scientific life of Washington.

Manuscripts may be sent to any member of the Board of Editors and must be clearly typewritten and in suitable form for printing without essential changes. The editors cannot undertake to do more than correct obvious minor errors. Footnote references should be complete, including year of publication.

Illustrations will be used only when necessary and will be confined to text figures or diagrams of simple character. The editors, at their discretion, may call upon an author to defray the cost of his illustrations, although no charge will be made for printing from a suitable cut supplied with the manuscript.

Proof.—In order to secure prompt publication no proof will be sent to authors unless requested. They are urged to submit their manuscript in final form and the editors will exercise care in seeing that copy is followed.

Authors' Copies and Reprints.—On request the author of an original article will receive ten copies of the number containing his contribution and as many additional copies as he may desire at five cents each. Reprints will be furnished at cost, or approximately as follows:

Reprints without covers, reimposed and re-made ready, saddle wire stitched:

	2 pages	4 pages	8 pages	12 pages	16 pages
25 copies	.55	.60	.65	.75	.90
50 "	.60	.70	.80	.95	$1.10
100 "	.70	.80	.95	$1.10	1.25
additional 100 copies					
	.20	.40	.60	.80	1.00

100 covers with name of article and author printed on front cover, $2.00. Additional covers, ½ cent each.

As an author may not see proof, his request for extra copies or reprints should reach the editors before his paper goes to press and should preferably be attached to the first page of his manuscript.

The rate of Subscription per volume is................................$6.00*
    Semi-monthly numbers.. .25
    Monthly numbers.. .50

Remittances should be made payable to "Washington Academy of Sciences," and addressed to E. W. Parker, Treasurer, Geological Survey, Washington, D. C., to Williams & Wilkins Company, 2419-2421 York Road, Baltimore, Md., or to the European Agents.

European Agents: William Wesley & Son, 28 Essex St., Strand, London, and Mayer and Müller, Prinz Louis-Ferdinand Str., Berlin.

Exchanges.—The JOURNAL does not exchange with other publications.

Missing Numbers will be replaced without charge provided that claim is made within thirty days after date of the following issue.

*Volume I however, from July 19, 1911 to December 19, 1911 will be sent for $3.00. Special rates are given to members of scientific societies affiliated with the Academy.

THE WAVERLY PRESS
BALTIMORE, U. S. A.

CONTENTS

Journal of the Washington Academy of Sciences

THE JOURNAL OF THE WASHINGTON ACADEMY OF SCIENCES is a semi-monthly publication and will be sent to subscribers on the fourth and nineteenth of each month, except during the summer, when it will appear on the nineteenth only. The first volume began with the July issue and ended with 1911. Volumes now will correspond to calendar years.

Scope.—The JOURNAL is a medium for the publication of original papers and is a record of scientific work in Washington. It accepts for publication (1) brief papers written or communicated by resident or non-resident members of the Academy; (2) abstracts of current scientific literature published in or emanating from Washington; (3) proceedings and programs of the affiliated societies; and (4) notes of events connected with the scientific life of Washington.

Manuscripts may be sent to any member of the Board of Editors and must be clearly typewritten and in suitable form for printing without essential changes. The editors cannot undertake to do more than correct obvious minor errors. Footnote references should be complete, including year of publication.

Illustrations will be used only when necessary and will be confined to text figures or diagrams of simple character. The editors, at their discretion, may call upon an author to defray the cost of his illustrations, although no charge will be made for printing from a suitable cut supplied with the manuscript.

Proof.—In order to secure prompt publication no proof will be sent to authors unless requested. They are urged to submit their manuscript in final form and the editors will exercise care in seeing that copy is followed.

Authors' Copies and Reprints.—On request the author of an original article will receive ten copies of the number containing his contribution and as many additional copies as he may desire at five cents each. Reprints will be furnished at cost, or approximately as follows:

Reprints without covers, reimposed and re-made ready, saddle wire stitched:

	2 pages	4 pages	8 pages	12 pages	16 pages
25 copies	.55	.60	.65	.75	.90
50 "	.60	.70	.80	.95	$1.10
100 ".	.70	.80	.95	$1.10	1.25
additional 100 copies	.20	.40	.60	.80	1.00

100 covers with name of article and author printed on front cover, $2.00. Additional covers, ½ cent each.

As an author may not see proof, his request for extra copies or reprints should reach the editors before his paper goes to press and should preferably be attached to the first page of his manuscript.

The rate of Subscription per volume is $6.00*
    Semi-monthly numbers . . . . \ 25
    Monthly numbers . . . . : 50

Remittances should be made payable to "Washington Academy of Sciences," and addressed to E. W. Parker, Treasurer, Geological Survey, Washington, D. C., to Williams & Wilkins Company, 2419-2421 York Road, Baltimore, Md., or to the European Agents.

European Agents: William Wesley & Son, 28 Essex St., Strand, London, and Mayer and Müller, Prinz Louis-Ferdinand Str., Berlin.

Exchanges.—The JOURNAL does not exchange with other publications.

Missing Numbers will be replaced without charge provided that claim is made within thirty days after date of the following issue.

*Volume I however, from July 19, 1911 to December 19, 1911 will be sent for $3.00. Special rates are given to members of scientific societies affiliated with the Academy.

Journal of the Washington Academy of Sciences

THE JOURNAL OF THE WASHINGTON ACADEMY OF SCIENCES is a semi-monthly publication and will be sent to subscribers on the fourth and nineteenth of each month, except during the summer, when it will appear on the nineteenth only. The first volume began with the July issue and ended with 1911. Volumes now will correspond to calendar years.

Scope.—The JOURNAL is a medium for the publication of original papers and is a record of scientific work in Washington. It accepts for publication (1) brief papers written or communicated by resident or non-resident members of the Academy; (2) abstracts of current scientific literature published in or emanating from Washington; (3) proceedings and programs of the affiliated societies; and (4) notes of events connected with the scientific life of Washington.

Manuscripts may be sent to any member of the Board of Editors and must be clearly typewritten and in suitable form for printing without essential changes. The editors cannot undertake to do more than correct obvious minor errors. Footnote references should be complete, including year of publication.

Illustrations will be used only when necessary and will be confined to text figures or diagrams of simple character. The editors, at their discretion, may call upon an author to defray the cost of his illustrations, although no charge will be made for printing from a suitable cut supplied with the manuscript.

Proof.—In order to secure prompt publication no proof will be sent to authors unless requested. They are urged to submit their manuscript in final form and the editors will exercise care in seeing that copy is followed.

Authors' Copies and Reprints.—On request the author of an original article will receive ten copies of the number containing his contribution and as many additional copies as he may desire at five cents each. Reprints will be furnished at cost, or approximately as follows:

Reprints without covers, reimposed and re-made ready, saddle wire stitched:

	2 pages	4 pages	8 pages	12 pages	16 pages
25 copies	.55	.60	.65	.75	.90
50 "	.60	.70	.80	.95	$1.10
100 "	.70	.80	.95	$1.10	1.25
additional 100 copies	.20	.40	.60	.80	1.00

100 covers with name of article and author printed on front cover, $2.00. Additional covers, ½ cent each.

As an author may not see proof, his request for extra copies or reprints should reach the editors before his paper goes to press and should preferably be attached to the first page of his manuscript.

The rate of Subscription per volume is.................................$6.00*
  Semi-monthly numbers...25
  Monthly numbers..50

Remittances should be made payable to "Washington Academy of Sciences," and addressed to E. W. Parker, Treasurer, Geological Survey, Washington, D. C., to Williams & Wilkins Company, 2419–2421 York Road, Baltimore, Md., or to the European Agents.

European Agents: William Wesley & Son, 28 Essex St., Strand, London, and Mayer and Müller, Prinz Louis-Ferdinand Str., Berlin.

Exchanges.—The JOURNAL does not exchange with other publications.

Missing Numbers will be replaced without charge provided that claim is made within thirty days after date of the following issue.

*Volume I however, from July 19, 1911 to December 19, 1911 will be sent for $3.00. Special rates are given to members of scientific societies affiliated with the Academy.

THE WAVERLY PRESS
BALTIMORE, U. S. A.

CONTENTS

Journal of the Washington Academy of Sciences

THE JOURNAL OF THE WASHINGTON ACADEMY OF SCIENCES is a semi-monthly publication and will be sent to subscribers on the fourth and nineteenth of each month, except during the summer, when it will appear on the nineteenth only. The first volume began with the July issue and ended with 1911. Volumes now will correspond to calendar years.

Scope.—The JOURNAL is a medium for the publication of original papers and is a record of scientific work in Washington. It accepts for publication (1) brief papers written or communicated by resident or non-resident members of the Academy; (2) abstracts of current scientific literature published in or emanating from Washington; (3) proceedings and programs of the affiliated societies; and (4) notes of events connected with the scientific life of Washington.

Manuscripts may be sent to any member of the Board of Editors and must be clearly typewritten and in suitable form for printing without essential changes. The editors cannot undertake to do more than correct obvious minor errors. Footnote references should be complete, including year of publication.

Illustrations will be used only when necessary and will be confined to text figures or diagrams of simple character. The editors, at their discretion, may call upon an author to defray the cost of his illustrations, although no charge will be made for printing from a suitable cut supplied with the manuscript.

Proof.—In order to secure prompt publication no proof will be sent to authors unless requested. They are urged to submit their manuscript in final form and the editors will exercise care in seeing that copy is followed.

Authors' Copies and Reprints.—On request the author of an original article will receive ten copies of the number containing his contribution and as many additional copies as he may desire at five cents each. Reprints will be furnished at cost, or approximately as follows:

Reprints without covers, reimposed and re-made ready, saddle wire stitched:

	2 pages	4 pages	8 pages	12 pages	16 pages
25 copies	.55	.60	.65	.75	.90
50 "	.60	.70	.80	.95	$1.10
100 "	.70	.80	.95	$1.10	1.25
additional 100 copies					
	.20	.40	.60	.80	1.00

100 covers with name of article and author printed on front cover, $2.00. Additional covers, ½ cent each.

As an author may not see proof, his request for extra copies or reprints should reach the editors before his paper goes to press and should preferably be attached to the first page of his manuscript.

The rate of Subscription per volume is..................................$6.00*
    Semi-monthly numbers.. .25
    Monthly numbers... .50

Remittances should be made payable to "Washington Academy of Sciences," and addressed to E. W. Parker, Treasurer, Geological Survey, Washington, D. C.; to Williams & Wilkins Company, 2419–2421 York Road, Baltimore, Md., or to the European Agents.

European Agents: William Wesley & Son, 28 Essex St., Strand, London, and Mayer and Müller, Prinz Louis-Ferdinand Str., Berlin.

Exchanges.—The JOURNAL does not exchange with other publications.

Missing Numbers will be replaced without charge provided that claim is made within thirty days after date of the following issue.

*Volume I however, from July 19, 1911 to December 19, 1911 will be sent for $3.00. Special rates are given to members of scientific societies affiliated with the Academy.

THE WAVERLY PRESS
BALTIMORE, U. S. A.

Journal of the Washington Academy of Sciences

THE JOURNAL OF THE WASHINGTON ACADEMY OF SCIENCES is a semi-monthly publication and will be sent to subscribers on the fourth and nineteenth of each month, except during the summer, when it will appear on the nineteenth only. The first volume began with the July issue and ended with 1911. Volumes now will correspond to calendar years.

Scope.—The JOURNAL is a medium for the publication of original papers and is a record of scientific work in Washington. It accepts for publication (1) brief papers written or communicated by resident or non-resident members of the Academy; (2) abstracts of current scientific literature published in or emanating from Washington; (3) proceedings and programs of the affiliated societies; and (4) notes of events connected with the scientific life of Washington.

Manuscripts may be sent to any member of the Board of Editors and must be clearly typewritten and in suitable form for printing without essential changes. The editors cannot undertake to do more than correct obvious minor errors. Footnote references should be complete, including year of publication.

Illustrations will be used only when necessary and will be confined to text figures or diagrams of simple character. The editors, at their discretion, may call upon an author to defray the cost of his illustrations, although no charge will be made for printing from a suitable cut supplied with the manuscript.

Proof.—In order to secure prompt publication no proof will be sent to authors unless requested. They are urged to submit their manuscript in final form and the editors will exercise care in seeing that copy is followed.

Authors' Copies and Reprints.—On request the author of an original article will receive ten copies of the number containing his contribution and as many additional copies as he may desire at five cents each. Reprints will be furnished at cost, or approximately as follows:

Reprints without covers, reimposed and re-made ready, saddle wire stitched:

	2 pages	4 pages	8 pages	12 pages	16 pages
25 copies	.55	.60	.65	.75	.90
50 "	.60	.70	.80	.95	$1.10
100 "	.70	.80	.95	$1.10	1.25
additional 100 copies	.20	.40	.60	.80	1.00

100 covers with name of article and author printed on front cover, $2.00. Additional covers, ½ cent each.

As an author may not see proof, his request for extra copies or reprints should reach the editors before his paper goes to press and should preferably be attached to the first page of his manuscript.

The rate of Subscription per volume is .... $6.00 [*]
    Semi-monthly numbers. .... .25
    Monthly numbers. .... .50

Remittances should be made payable to "Washington Academy of Sciences," and addressed to E. W. Parker, Treasurer, Geological Survey, Washington, D. C., to Williams & Wilkins Company, 2419-2421 York Road, Baltimore, Md., or to the European Agents.

European Agents: William Wesley & Son, 28 Essex St., Strand, London, and Mayer and Müller, Prinz Louis-Ferdinand Str., Berlin.

Exchanges.—The JOURNAL does not exchange with other publications.

Missing Numbers will be replaced without charge provided that claim is made within thirty days after date of the following issue.

[*]Volume I however, from July 19, 1911 to December 19, 1911 will be sent for $3.00. Special rates are given to members of scientific societies affiliated with the Academy.

CONTENTS

Journal of the Washington Academy of Sciences

THE JOURNAL OF THE WASHINGTON ACADEMY OF SCIENCES is a semi-monthly publication and will be sent to subscribers on the fourth and nineteenth of each month, except during the summer, when it will appear on the nineteenth only. The first volume began with the July issue and ended with 1911. Volumes now will correspond to calendar years.

Scope.—The JOURNAL is a medium for the publication of original papers and is a record of scientific work in Washington. It accepts for publication (1) brief papers written or communicated by resident or non-resident members of the Academy; (2) abstracts of current scientific literature published in or emanating from Washington; (3) proceedings and programs of the affiliated societies; and (4) notes of events connected with the scientific life of Washington.

Manuscripts may be sent to any member of the Board of Editors and must be clearly typewritten and in suitable form for printing without essential changes. The editors cannot undertake to do more than correct obvious minor errors. Footnote references should be complete, including year of publication.

Illustrations will be used only when necessary and will be confined to text figures or diagrams of simple character. The editors, at their discretion, may call upon an author to defray the cost of his illustrations, although no charge will be made for printing from a suitable cut supplied with the manuscript.

Proof.—In order to secure prompt publication no proof will be sent to authors unless requested. They are urged to submit their manuscript in final form and the editors will exercise care in seeing that copy is followed.

Authors' Copies and Reprints.—On request the author of an original article will receive ten copies of the number containing his contribution and as many additional copies as he may desire at five cents each. Reprints will be furnished at cost, or approximately as follows:

Reprints without covers, reimposed and re-made ready; saddle wire stitched:

	2 pages	4 pages	8 pages	12 pages	16 pages
25 copies	.55	.60	.65	.75	.90
50 "	.60	.70	.80	.95	$1.10
100 "	.70	.80	.95	$1.10	1.25
additional 100 copies	.20	.40	.60	.80	1.00

100 covers with name of article and author printed on front cover, $2.00. Additional covers, ½ cent each.

As an author may not see proof, his request for extra copies or reprints should reach the editors before his paper goes to press and should preferably be attached to the first page of his manuscript.

The rate of Subscription per volume is..$6.00*
    Semi-monthly numbers... .25
    Monthly numbers... .50

Remittances should be made payable to "Washington Academy of Sciences," and addressed to E. W. Parker, Treasurer, Geological Survey, Washington, D. C., to Williams & Wilkins Company, 2419–2421 York Road, Baltimore, Md., or to the European Agents.

European Agents: William Wesley & Son, 28 Essex St., Strand, London, and Mayer and Müller, Prinz Louis-Ferdinand Str., Berlin.

Exchanges.—The JOURNAL does not exchange with other publications.

Missing Numbers will be replaced without charge provided that claim is made within thirty days after date of the following issue.

*Volume I however, from July 19, 1911 to December 19, 1911 will be sent for $3.00. Special rates are given to members of scientific societies affiliated with the Academy.

THE WAVERLY PRESS
BALTIMORE, U. S. A.

CONTENTS

Journal of the Washington Academy of Sciences

THE JOURNAL OF THE WASHINGTON ACADEMY OF SCIENCES is a semi-monthly publication and will be sent to subscribers on the fourth and nineteenth of each month, except during the summer, when it will appear on the nineteenth only. The first volume began with the July issue and ended with 1911. Volumes now will correspond to calendar years.

Scope.—The JOURNAL is a medium for the publication of original papers and is a record of scientific work in Washington. It accepts for publication (1) brief papers written or communicated by resident or non-resident members of the Academy; (2) abstracts of current scientific literature published in or emanating from Washington; (3) proceedings and programs of the affiliated societies; and (4) notes of events connected with the scientific life of Washington.

Manuscripts may be sent to any member of the Board of Editors and must be clearly typewritten and in suitable form for printing without essential changes. The editors cannot undertake to do more than correct obvious minor errors. Footnote references should be complete, including year of publication.

Illustrations will be used only when necessary and will be confined to text figures or diagrams of simple character. The editors, at their discretion, may call upon an author to defray the cost of his illustrations, although no charge will be made for printing from a suitable cut supplied with the manuscript.

Proof.—In order to secure prompt publication no proof will be sent to authors unless requested. They are urged to submit their manuscript in final form and the editors will exercise care in seeing that copy is followed.

Authors' Copies and Reprints.—On request the author of an original article will receive ten copies of the number containing his contribution and as many additional copies as he may desire at five cents each. Reprints will be furnished at cost, or approximately as follows:

Reprints without covers, reimposed and re-made ready, saddle wire stitched:

	2 pages	4 pages	8 pages	12 pages	16 pages
25 copies	.55	.60	.65	.75	.90
50 "	.60	.70	.80	.95	$1.10
100 "	.70	.80	.95	$1.10	1.25
additional 100 copies	.20	.40	.60	.80	1.00

100 covers with name of article and author printed on front cover, $2.00. Additional covers, ½ cent each.

As an author may not see proof, his request for extra copies or reprints should reach the editors before his paper goes to press and should preferably be attached to the first page of his manuscript.

The rate of Subscription per volume is	$6.00*
Semi-monthly numbers	.25
Monthly numbers	.50

Remittances should be made payable to "Washington Academy of Sciences," and addressed to E. W. Parker, Treasurer, Geological Survey, Washington, D. C., to Williams & Wilkins Company, 2419–2421 York Road, Baltimore, Md., or to the European Agents.

European Agents: William Wesley & Son, 28 Essex St., Strand, London, and Mayer and Müller, Prinz Louis-Ferdinand Str., Berlin.

Exchanges.—The JOURNAL does not exchange with other publications.

Missing Numbers will be replaced without charge provided that claim is made within thirty days after date of the following issue.

*Volume I however, from July 19, 1911 to December 19, 1911 will be sent for $3.00. Special rates are given to members of scientific societies affiliated with the Academy.

CONTENTS

Journal of the Washington Academy of Sciences

THE JOURNAL OF THE WASHINGTON ACADEMY OF SCIENCES is a semi-monthly publication and will be sent to subscribers on the fourth and nine-teenth of each month, except during the summer, when it will appear on the nine-teenth only. The first volume began with the July issue and ended with 1911. Volumes now will correspond to calendar years.

Scope.—The JOURNAL is a medium for the publication of original papers and is a record of scientific work in Washington. It accepts for publication (1) brief papers written or communicated by resident or non-resident members of the Academy; (2) abstracts of current scientific literature published in or emanating from Washington; (3) proceedings and programs of the affiliated societies; and (4) notes of events connected with the scientific life of Washington.

Manuscripts may be sent to any member of the Board of Editors and must be clearly typewritten and in suitable form for printing without essential changes. The editors cannot undertake to do more than correct obvious minor errors. Footnote references should be complete, including year of publication.

Illustrations will be used only when necessary and will be confined to text figures or diagrams of simple character. The editors, at their discretion, may call upon an author to defray the cost of his illustrations, although no charge will be made for printing from a suitable cut supplied with the manuscript.

Proof.—In order to secure prompt publication no proof will be sent to authors unless requested. They are urged to submit their manuscript in final form and the editors will exercise care in seeing that copy is followed.

Authors' Copies and Reprints.—On request the author of an original article will receive ten copies of the number containing his contribution and as many addi-tional copies as he may desire at five cents each. Reprints will be furnished at cost, or approximately as follows:

Reprints without covers, reimposed and re-made ready, saddle wire stitched:

	2 pages	4 pages	8 pages	12 pages	16 pages
25 copies	.55	.60	.65	.75	.90
50 "	.60	.70	.80	.95	$1.10
100 "	.70	.80	.95	$1.10	1.25
additional 100 copies	.20	.40	.60	.80	1.00

100 covers with name of article and author printed on front cover, $2.00. Additional covers, ½ cent each.

As an author may not see proof, his request for extra copies or reprints should reach the editors before his paper goes to press and should preferably be attached to the first page of his manuscript.

The rate of Subscription per volume is.......................................$6.00*
   Semi-monthly numbers..25
   Monthly numbers..50

Remittances should be made payable to "Washington Academy of Sciences," and addressed to William Bowie, Treasurer, Coast and Geodetic Survey, Washing-ton, D. C., to Williams & Wilkins Company, 2419–2421 York Road, Baltimore, Md., or to the European Agents.

European Agents: William Wesley & Son, 28 Essex St., Strand, London, and Mayer and Müller, Prinz Louis-Ferdinand Str., Berlin.

Exchanges.—The JOURNAL does not exchange with other publications.

Missing Numbers will be replaced without charge provided that claim is made within thirty days after date of the following issue.

*Volume I however, from July 19, 1911 to December 19, 1911 will be sent for $3.00. Special rates are given to members of scientific societies affiliated with the Academy.

THE WAVERLY PRESS
BALTIMORE, U. S. A.

CONTENTS

Journal of the Washington Academy of Sciences

This JOURNAL, the official organ of the Washington Academy of Sciences, aims to present a brief record of current scientific work in Washington. To this end it publishes: (1) short original papers, written or communicated by members of the Academy; (2) a complete list of references to current scientific articles published in or emanating from Washington; (3) short abstracts of certain of these articles; (4) proceedings and programs of meetings of the Academy and affiliated Societies; (5) notes of events connected with the scientific life of Washington. The JOURNAL is issued semi-monthly, on the fourth and nineteenth of each month, except during the summer when it appears on the nineteenth only. Volumes correspond to calendar years. Prompt publication is an essential feature; a manuscript reaching the editors on the fifth or the twentieth of the month will ordinarily appear, on request from the author, in the next issue of the JOURNAL.

Manuscripts may be sent to any member of the Board of Editors; they should be clearly typewritten and in suitable form for printing without essential changes. The editors cannot undertake to do more than correct obvious minor errors. References should appear only as footnotes and should include year of publication.

Illustrations will be used only when necessary and will be confined to text figures or diagrams of simple character. The editors, at their discretion, may call upon an author to defray the cost of his illustrations, although no charge will be made for printing from a suitable cut supplied with the manuscript.

Proof.—In order to facilitate prompt publication no proof will be sent to authors unless requested. It is urged that manuscript be submitted in final form; the editors will exercise due care in seeing that copy is followed.

Authors' Copies and Reprints.—On request the author of an original article will receive ten copies of the number containing his contribution and as many additional copies as he may desire at five cents each. Reprints will be furnished at the following schedule of prices:

	4 pp.	8 pp.	12 pp.	16 pp.
50 copies	$1.05	$1.90	$2.85	$3.70
100 copies	1.25	2.30	3.45	4.50
Additional copies, per 100	.40	.80	1.20	1.50

Covers bearing the name of the author and title of the article, with inclusive pagination and date of issue, will be $1.50 for the first 100. Additional covers $.50 per 100.

As an author may not see proof, his request for extra copies or reprints should invariably be attached to the first page of his manuscript.

The rate of Subscription per volume is.............................. $6.00*
   Semi-monthly numbers....................................... .25
   Monthly numbers.. .50

Remittances should be made payable to "Washington Academy of Sciences," and addressed to William Bowie, Treasurer, Coast and Geodetic Survey, Washington, D. C., to Williams & Wilkins Company, 2419–2421 Greenmount Ave., Baltimore, Md., or to the European Agents.

European Agents: William Wesley & Son, 28 Essex St., Strand, London, and Mayer and Müller, Prinz Louis-Ferdinand Str., Berlin.

Exchanges.—The JOURNAL does not exchange with other publications.

Missing Numbers will be replaced without charge, provided that claim is made within thirty days after date of the following issue.

* Volume I, however, from July 19, 1911 to December 19, 1911, will be sent for $3.00. Special rates are given to members of scientific societies affiliated with the Academy.

THE WAVERLY PRESS
BALTIMORE, U, S. A.

CONTENTS

Journal of the Washington Academy of Sciences

This JOURNAL, the official organ of the Washington Academy of Sciences, aims to present a brief record of current scientific work in Washington. To this end it publishes: (1) short original papers, written or communicated by members of the Academy; (2) a complete list of references to current scientific articles published in or emanating from Washington; (3) short abstracts of certain of these articles; (4) proceedings and programs of meetings of the Academy and affiliated Societies; (5) notes of events connected with the scientific life of Washington. The JOURNAL is issued semi-monthly, on the fourth and nineteenth of each month, except during the summer when it appears on the nineteenth only. Volumes correspond to calendar years. Prompt publication is an essential feature; a manuscript reaching the editors on the fifth or the twentieth of the month will ordinarily appear, on request from the author, in the next issue of the JOURNAL.

Manuscripts may be sent to any member of the Board of Editors; they should be clearly typewritten and in suitable form for printing without essential changes. The editors cannot undertake to do more than correct obvious minor errors. References should appear only as footnotes and should include year of publication.

Illustrations will be used only when necessary and will be confined to text figures or diagrams of simple character. The editors, at their discretion, may call upon an author to defray the cost of his illustrations, although no charge will be made for printing from a suitable cut supplied with the manuscript.

Proof.—In order to facilitate prompt publication no proof will be sent to authors unless requested. It is urged that manuscript be submitted in final form; the editors will exercise due care in seeing that copy is followed.

Authors' Copies and Reprints.—On request the author of an original article will receive ten copies of the number containing his contribution and as many additional copies as he may desire at five cents each. Reprints will be furnished at the following schedule of prices:

	4 pp.	8 pp.	12 pp.	16 pp.
50 copies	$1.05	$1.90	$2.85	$3.70
100 copies	1.25	2.30	3.45	4.50
Additional copies, per 100	.40	.80	1.20	1.50

Covers bearing the name of the author and title of the article, with inclusive pagination and date of issue, will be $1.50 for the first 100. Additional covers $.50 per 100.

As an author may not see proof, his request for extra copies or reprints should invariably be attached to the first page of his manuscript.

The rate of Subscription per volume is	$6.00*
Semi-monthly numbers	.25
Monthly numbers	.50

Remittances should be made payable to "Washington Academy of Sciences," and addressed to William Bowie, Treasurer, Coast and Geodetic Survey, Washington, D. C., to Williams & Wilkins Company, 2419–2421 Greenmount Ave., Baltimore, Md., or to the European Agents.

European Agents: William Wesley & Son, 28 Essex St., Strand, London, and Mayer and Müller, Prinz Louis-Ferdinand Str., Berlin.

Exchanges.—The JOURNAL does not exchange with other publications.

Missing Numbers will be replaced without charge, provided that claim is made within thirty days after date of the following issue.

* Volume I, however, from July 19, 1911 to December 19, 1911, will be sent for $3.00. Special rates are given to members of scientific societies affiliated with the Academy.

THE WAVERLY PRESS
BALTIMORE, U. S. A.

CONTENTS

Journal of the Washington Academy of Sciences

This JOURNAL, the official organ of the Washington Academy of Sciences, aims to present a brief record of current scientific work in Washington. To this end it publishes: (1) short original papers, written or communicated by members of the Academy; (2) a complete list of references to current scientific articles published in or emanating from Washington; (3) short abstracts of certain of these articles; (4) proceedings and programs of meetings of the Academy and affiliated Societies; (5) notes of events connected with the scientific life of Washington. The JOURNAL is issued semi-monthly, on the fourth and nineteenth of each month, except during the summer when it appears on the nineteenth only. Volumes correspond to calendar years. Prompt publication is an essential feature; a manuscript reaching the editors on the fifth or the twentieth of the month will ordinarily appear, on request from the author, in the next issue of the JOURNAL.

Manuscripts may be sent to any member of the Board of Editors; they should be clearly typewritten and in suitable form for printing without essential changes. The editors cannot undertake to do more than correct obvious minor errors. References should appear only as footnotes and should include year of publication.

Illustrations will be used only when necessary and will be confined to text figures or diagrams of simple character. The editors, at their discretion, may call upon an author to defray the cost of his illustrations, although no charge will be made for printing from a suitable cut supplied with the manuscript.

Proof.—In order to facilitate prompt publication no proof will be sent to authors unless requested. It is urged that manuscript be submitted in final form; the editors will exercise due care in seeing that copy is followed.

Authors' Copies and Reprints.—On request the author of an original article will receive ten copies of the number containing his contribution and as many additional copies as he may desire at five cents each. Reprints will be furnished at the following schedule of prices:

	4 pp.	3 pp.	12 pp.	16 pp.
50 copies	$1.05	$1.90	$2.85	$3.70
100 copies	1.25	2.30	3.45	4.50
Additional copies, per 100	.40	.80	1.20	1.50

Covers bearing the name of the author and title of the article, with inclusive pagination and date of issue, will be $1.50 for the first 100. Additional covers $.50 per 100.

As an author may not see proof, his request for extra copies or reprints should invariably be attached to the first page of his manuscript.

The rate of Subscription per volume is $6.00*
    Semi-monthly numbers .... .25
    Monthly numbers .... .50

Remittances should be made payable to "Washington Academy of Sciences," and addressed to William Bowie, Treasurer, Coast and Geodetic Survey, Washington, D. C., to Williams & Wilkins Company, 2419–2421 Greenmount Ave., Baltimore, Md., or to the European Agents.

European Agents: William Wesley & Son, 28 Essex St., Strand, London, and Mayer and Müller, Prinz Louis-Ferdinand Str., Berlin.

Exchanges.—The JOURNAL does not exchange with other publications.

Missing Numbers will be replaced without charge, provided that claim is made within thirty days after date of the following issue.

* Volume I, however, from July 19, 1911 to December 19, 1911, will be sent for $3.00. Special rates are given to members of scientific societies affiliated with the Academy.

THE WAVERLY PRESS
BALTIMORE, U. S. A.

CONTENTS

Journal of the Washington Academy of Sciences

This JOURNAL, the official organ of the Washington Academy of Sciences, aims to present a brief record of current scientific work in Washington. To this end it publishes: (1) short original papers, written or communicated by members of the Academy; (2) a complete list of references to current scientific articles published in or emanating from Washington; (3) short abstracts of certain of these articles; (4) proceedings and programs of meetings of the Academy and affiliated Societies; (5) notes of events connected with the scientific life of Washington. The JOURNAL is issued semi-monthly, on the fourth and nineteenth of each month, except during the summer when it appears on the nineteenth only. Volumes correspond to calendar years. Prompt publication is an essential feature; a manuscript reaching the editors on the fifth or the twentieth of the month will ordinarily appear, on request from the author, in the next issue of the JOURNAL.

Manuscripts may be sent to any member of the Board of Editors; they should be clearly typewritten and in suitable form for printing without essential changes. The editors cannot undertake to do more than correct obvious minor errors. References should appear only as footnotes and should include year of publication.

Illustrations will be used only when necessary and will be confined to text figures or diagrams of simple character. The editors, at their discretion, may call upon an author to defray the cost of his illustrations, although no charge will be made for printing from a suitable cut supplied with the manuscript.

Proof.—In order to facilitate prompt publication no proof will be sent to authors unless requested. It is urged that manuscript be submitted in final form; the editors will exercise due care in seeing that copy is followed.

Authors' Copies and Reprints.—On request the author of an original article will receive ten copies of the number containing his contribution and as many additional copies as he may desire at five cents each. Reprints will be furnished at the following schedule of prices:

	4 pp.	8 pp.	12 pp.	16 pp.
50 copies	$1.05	$1.90	$2.85	$3.70
100 copies	1.25	2.30	3.45	4.50
Additional copies, per 100	.40	.80	1.20	1.50

Covers bearing the name of the author and title of the article, with inclusive pagination and date of issue, will be $1.50 for the first 100. Additional covers $.50 per 100.

As an author may not see proof, his request for extra copies or reprints should invariably be attached to the first page of his manuscript.

The rate of Subscription per volume is $6.00*
　Semi-monthly numbers .... .25
　Monthly numbers .... .50

Remittances should be made payable to "Washington Academy of Sciences," and addressed to William Bowie, Treasurer, Coast and Geodetic Survey, Washington, D. C., to Williams & Wilkins Company, 2419–2421 Greenmount Ave., Baltimore, Md., or to the European Agents.

European Agents: William Wesley & Son, 28 Essex St., Strand, London, and Mayer and Müller, Prinz Louis-Ferdinand Str., Berlin.

Exchanges.—The JOURNAL does not exchange with other publications.

Missing Numbers will be replaced without charge, provided that claim is made within thirty days after date of the following issue.

* Volume I, however, from July 19, 1911 to December 19, 1911, will be sent for $3.00. Special rates are given to members of scientific societies affiliated with the Academy.

THE WAVERLY PRESS
BALTIMORE, U. S. A.

CONTENTS

Journal of the Washington Academy of Sciences

This JOURNAL, the official organ of the Washington Academy of Sciences, aims to present a brief record of current scientific work in Washington. To this end it publishes: (1) short original papers, written or communicated by members of the Academy; (2) a complete list of references to current scientific articles published in or emanating from Washington; (3) short abstracts of certain of these articles; (4) proceedings and programs of meetings of the Academy and affiliated Societies; (5) notes of events connected with the scientific life of Washington. The JOURNAL is issued semi-monthly, on the fourth and nineteenth of each month, except during the summer when it appears on the nineteenth only. Volumes correspond to calendar years. Prompt publication is an essential feature; a manuscript reaching the editors on the fifth or the twentieth of the month will ordinarily appear, on request from the author, in the next issue of the JOURNAL.

Manuscripts may be sent to any member of the Board of Editors; they should be clearly typewritten and in suitable form for printing without essential changes. The editors cannot undertake to do more than correct obvious minor errors. References should appear only as footnotes and should include year of publication.

Illustrations will be used only when necessary and will be confined to text figures or diagrams of simple character. The editors, at their discretion, may call upon an author to defray the cost of his illustrations, although no charge will be made for printing from a suitable cut supplied with the manuscript.

Proof.—In order to facilitate prompt publication no proof will be sent to authors unless requested. It is urged that manuscript be submitted in final form; the editors will exercise due care in seeing that copy is followed.

Authors' Copies and Reprints.—On request the author of an original article will receive gratis ten copies of the number containing his contribution and as many additional copies as he may desire at five cents each. Reprints will be furnished at the following schedule of prices

	4 pp.	8 pp.	12 pp.	16 pp.
50 copies	$1.05	$1.90	$2.85	$3.70
100 copies	1.25	2.30	3.45	4.50
Additional copies, per 100	.40	.80	1.20	1.50

Covers bearing the name of the author and title of the article, with inclusive pagination and date of issue, will be $1.50 for the first 100. Additional covers $.50 per 100.

As an author may not see proof, his request for extra copies or reprints should invariably be attached to the first page of his manuscript.

The rate of Subscription per volume is	$6.00*
Semi-monthly numbers	.25
Monthly numbers	.50

Remittances should be made payable to "Washington Academy of Sciences," and addressed to William Bowie, Treasurer, Coast and Geodetic Survey, Washington, D. C., to Williams & Wilkins Company, 2419-2421 Greenmount Ave., Baltimore, Md., or to the European Agents.

European Agents: William Wesley & Son, 28 Essex St., Strand, London, and Mayer and Müller, Prinz Louis-Ferdinand Str., Berlin.

Exchanges.—The JOURNAL does not exchange with other publications.

Missing Numbers will be replaced without charge, provided that claim is made within thirty days after date of the following issue.

* Volume I, however, from July 19, 1911 to December 19, 1911, will be sent for $3.00. Special rates are given to members of scientific societies affiliated with the Academy.

THE WAVERLY PRESS
BALTIMORE, U. S. A.

Journal of the Washington Academy of Sciences

This JOURNAL, the official organ of the Washington Academy of Sciences, aims to present a brief record of current scientific work in Washington. To this end it publishes: (1) short original papers, written or communicated by members of the Academy; (2) a complete list of references to current scientific articles published in or emanating from Washington; (3) short abstracts of certain of these articles; (4) proceedings and programs of meetings of the Academy and affiliated Societies; (5) notes of events connected with the scientific life of Washington. The JOURNAL is issued semi-monthly, on the fourth and nineteenth of each month, except during the summer when it appears on the nineteenth only. Volumes correspond to calendar years. Prompt publication is an essential feature; a manuscript reaching the editors on the fifth or the twentieth of the month will ordinarily appear, on request from the author, in the next issue of the JOURNAL.

Manuscripts may be sent to any member of the Board of Editors; they should be clearly typewritten and in suitable form for printing without essential changes. The editors cannot undertake to do more than correct obvious minor errors. References should appear only as footnotes and should include year of publication.

Illustrations will be used only when necessary and will be confined to text figures or diagrams of simple character. The editors, at their discretion, may call upon an author to defray the cost of his illustrations, although no charge will be made for printing from a suitable cut supplied with the manuscript.

Proof.—In order to facilitate prompt publication no proof will be sent to authors unless requested. It is urged that manuscript be submitted in final form; the editors will exercise due care in seeing that copy is followed.

Authors' Copies and Reprints.—On request the author of an original article will receive gratis ten copies of the number containing his contribution and as many additional copies as he may desire at five cents each. Reprints will be furnished at the following schedule of prices:

	4 pp.	8 pp.	12 pp.	16 pp.
50 copies	$1.05	$1.90	$2.85	$3.70
100 copies	1.25	2.30	3.45	4.50
Additional copies, per 100	.40	.80	1.20	1.50

Covers bearing the name of the author and title of the article, with inclusive pagination and date of issue, will be $1.50 for the first 100. Additional covers $.50 per 100.

As an author may not see proof, his request for extra copies or reprints should invariably be attached to the first page of his manuscript.

The rate of Subscription per volume is $6.00*
    Semi-monthly numbers .... .25
    Monthly numbers .... .50

Remittances should be made payable to "Washington Academy of Sciences," and addressed to William Bowie, Treasurer, Coast and Geodetic Survey, Washington, D. C., to Williams & Wilkins Company, 2419-2421 Greenmount Ave., Baltimore, Md., or to the European Agents.

European Agents: William Wesley & Son, 28 Essex St., Strand, London, and Mayer and Müller, Prinz Louis-Ferdinand Str., Berlin.

Exchanges.—The JOURNAL does not exchange with other publications.

Missing Numbers will be replaced without charge, provided that claim is made within thirty days after date of the following issue.

* Volume I, however, from July 19, 1911 to December 19, 1911, will be sent for $3.00. Special rates are given to members of scientific societies affiliated with the Academy.

THE WAVERLY PRESS
BALTIMORE, U. S. A.

Journal of the Washington Academy of Sciences

This JOURNAL, the official organ of the Washington Academy of Sciences, aims to present a brief record of current scientific work in Washington. To this end it publishes: (1) short original papers, written or communicated by members of the Academy; (2) a complete list of references to current scientific articles published in or emanating from Washington; (3) short abstracts of certain of these articles; (4) proceedings and programs of meetings of the Academy and affiliated Societies; (5) notes of events connected with the scientific life of Washington. The JOURNAL is issued semi-monthly. on the fourth and nineteenth of each month, except during the summer when it appears on the nineteenth only. Volumes correspond to calendar years. Prompt publication is an essential feature; a manuscript reaching the editors on the fifth or the twentieth of the month will ordinarily appear, on request from the author, in the next issue of the JOURNAL.

Manuscripts may be sent to any member of the Board of Editors; they should be clearly typewritten and in suitable form for printing without essential changes. The editors cannot undertake to do more than correct obvious minor errors. References should appear only as footnotes and should include year of publication.

Illustrations will be used only when necessary and will be confined to text figures or diagrams of simple character. The editors, at their discretion, may call upon an author to defray the cost of his illustrations, although no charge will be made for printing from a suitable cut supplied with the manuscript.

Proof.—In order to facilitate prompt publication no proof will be sent to authors unless requested. It is urged that manuscript be submitted in final form; the editors will exercise due care in seeing that copy is followed.

Authors' Copies and Reprints.—On request the author of an original article will receive gratis ten copies of the number containing his contribution and as many additional copies as he may desire at five cents each. Reprints will be furnished at the following schedule of prices:

	4 pp.	8 pp.	12 pp.	16 pp.
50 copies	$1.05	$1 90	$2 85	$3.70
100 copies	1.25	2.30	3.45	4.50
Additional copies, per 100.	.40	.80	1.20	1.50

Covers bearing the name of the author and title of the article, with inclusive pagination and date of issue, will be $1.50 for the first 100. Additional covers $.50 per 100.

As an author may not see proof, his request for extra copies or reprints should invariably be attached to the first page of his manuscript.

The rate of Subscription per volume is $6.00*
    Semi-monthly numbers .... .25
    Monthly numbers .... .50

Remittances should be made payable to "Washington Academy of Sciences," and addressed to William Bowie, Treasurer, Coast and Geodetic Survey, Washington, D. C., to Williams & Wilkins Company, 2419-2421 Greenmount Ave., Baltimore, Md., or to the European Agents,

European Agents: William Wesley & Son, 28 Essex St., Strand, London, and Mayer and Müller, Prinz Louis-Ferdinand Str., Berlin.

Exchanges.—The JOURNAL does not exchange with other publications.

Missing Numbers will be replaced without charge, provided that claim is made within thirty days after date of the following issue.

* Volume I, however, from July 19, 1911 to December 19, 1911, will be sent for $3.00. Special rates are given to members of scientific societies affiliated with the Academy.

THE WAVERLY PRESS
BALTIMORE, U. S. A.

Journal of the Washington Academy of Sciences

This JOURNAL, the official organ of the Washington Academy of Sciences, aims to present a brief record of current scientific work in Washington. To this end it publishes: (1) short original papers, written or communicated by members of the Academy; (2) a complete list of references to current scientific articles published in or emanating from Washington; (3) short abstracts of certain of these articles; (4) proceedings and programs of meetings of the Academy and affiliated Societies; (5) notes of events connected with the scientific life of Washington. The JOURNAL is issued semi-monthly, on the fourth and nineteenth of each month, except during the summer when it appears on the nineteenth only. Volumes correspond to calendar years. Prompt publication is an essential feature; a manuscript reaching the editors on the fifth or the twentieth of the month will ordinarily appear, on request from the author, in the next issue of the JOURNAL.

Manuscripts may be sent to any member of the Board of Editors; they should be clearly typewritten and in suitable form for printing without essential changes. The editors cannot undertake to do more than correct obvious minor errors. References should appear only as footnotes and should include year of publication.

Illustrations will be used only when necessary and will be confined to text figures or diagrams of simple character. The editors, at their discretion, may call upon an author to defray the cost of his illustrations, although no charge will be made for printing from a suitable cut supplied with the manuscript.

Proof.—In order to facilitate prompt publication no proof will be sent to authors unless requested. It is urged that manuscript be submitted in final form; the editors will exercise due care in seeing that copy is followed.

Authors' Copies and Reprints.—On request the author of an original article will receive gratis ten copies of the number containing his contribution and as many additional copies as he may desire at five cents each. Reprints will be furnished at the following schedule of prices:

	4 pp.	8 pp.	12 pp.	16 pp.
50 copies	$1.05	$1.90	$2.85	$3.70
100 copies	1.25	2.30	3.45	4.50
Additional copies, per 100	.40	.80	1.20	1.50

Covers bearing the name of the author and title of the article, with inclusive pagination and date of issue, will be $1.50 for the first 100. Additional covers $.50 per 100.

As an author may not see proof, his request for extra copies or reprints should invariably be attached to the first page of his manuscript.

The rate of Subscription per volume is $6.00*
    Semi-monthly numbers .... .25
    Monthly numbers .... .50

Remittances should be made payable to "Washington Academy of Sciences," and addressed to William Bowie, Treasurer, Coast and Geodetic Survey, Washington, D. C., to Williams & Wilkins Company, 2419–2421 Greenmount Ave., Baltimore, Md., or to the European Agents.

European Agents: William Wesley & Son, 28 Essex St., Strand, London, and Mayer and Müller, Prinz Louis-Ferdinand Str., Berlin.

Exchanges.—The JOURNAL does not exchange with other publications.

Missing Numbers will be replaced without charge, provided that claim is made within thirty days after date of the following issue.

* Volume I, however, from July 19, 1911 to December 19, 1911, will be sent for $3.00. Special rates are given to members of scientific societies affiliated with the Academy.

THE WAVERLY PRESS
BALTIMORE, U. S. A.

CONTENTS

Journal of the Washington Academy of Sciences

This JOURNAL, the official organ of the Washington Academy of Sciences, aims to present a brief record of current scientific work in Washington. To this end it publishes: (1) short original papers, written or communicated by members of the Academy; (2) a complete list of references to current scientific articles published in or emanating from Washington; (3) short abstracts of certain of these articles; (4) proceedings and programs of meetings of the Academy and affiliated Societies; (5) notes of events connected with the scientific life of Washington. The JOURNAL is issued semi-monthly, on the fourth and nineteenth of each month, except during the summer when it appears on the nineteenth only. Volumes correspond to calendar years. Prompt publication is an essential feature; a manuscript reaching the editors on the fifth or the twentieth of the month will ordinarily appear, on request from the author, in the next issue of the JOURNAL.

Manuscripts may be sent to any member of the Board of Editors; they should be clearly typewritten and in suitable form for printing without essential changes. The editors cannot undertake to do more than correct obvious minor errors. References should appear only as footnotes and should include year of publication.

Illustrations will be used only when necessary and will be confined to text figures or diagrams of simple character. The editors, at their discretion, may call upon an author to defray the cost of his illustrations, although no charge will be made for printing from a suitable cut supplied with the manuscript.

Proof.—In order to facilitate prompt publication no proof will be sent to authors unless requested. It is urged that manuscript be submitted in final form; the editors will exercise due care in seeing that copy is followed.

Authors' Copies and Reprints.—On request the author of an original article will receive gratis ten copies of the number containing his contribution and as many additional copies as he may desire at five cents each. Reprints will be furnished at the following schedule of prices:

	4 pp.	8 pp.	12 pp.	16 pp.
50 copies	$1.05	$1.90	$2.85	$3.70
100 copies	1.25	2.30	3.45	4.50
Additional copies, per 100	.40	.80	1.20	1.50

Covers bearing the name of the author and title of the article, with inclusive pagination and date of issue, will be $1.50 for the first 100. Additional covers $.50 per 100.

As an author may not see proof, his request for extra copies or reprints should invariably be attached to the first page of his manuscript.

The rate of Subscription per volume is $6.00*
   Semi-monthly numbers .... .25
   Monthly numbers .... .50

Remittances should be made payable to "Washington Academy of Sciences," and addressed to William Bowie, Treasurer, Coast and Geodetic Survey, Washington, D. C., to Williams & Wilkins Company, 2419–2421 Greenmount Ave., Baltimore, Md,, or to the European Agents.

European Agents: William Wesley & Son, 28 Essex St., Strand, London, and Mayer and Müller, Prinz Louis-Ferdinand Str., Berlin.

Exchanges.—The JOURNAL does not exchange with other publications.

Missing Numbers will be replaced without charge, provided that claim is made within thirty days after date of the following issue.

* Volume I, however, from July 19, 1911 to December 19, 1911, will be sent for $3.00. Special rates are given to members of scientific societies affiliated with the Academy.

THE WAVERLY PRESS
BALTIMORE, U. S. A.

CONTENTS

Journal of the Washington Academy of Sciences

This JOURNAL, the official organ of the Washington Academy of Sciences, aims to present a brief record of current scientific work in Washington. To this end it publishes: (1) short original papers, written or communicated by members of the Academy; (2) a complete list of references to current scientific articles published in or emanating from Washington; (3) short abstracts of certain of these articles; (4) proceedings and programs of meetings of the Academy and affiliated Societies; (5) notes of events connected with the scientific life of Washington. The JOURNAL is issued semi-monthly, on the fourth and nineteenth of each month, except during the summer when it appears on the nineteenth only. Volumes correspond to calendar years. Prompt publication is an essential feature; a manuscript reaching the editors on the fifth or the twentieth of the month will ordinarily appear, on request from the author, in the next issue of the JOURNAL.

Manuscripts may be sent to any member of the Board of Editors; they should be clearly typewritten and in suitable form for printing without essential changes. The editors cannot undertake to do more than correct obvious minor errors. References should appear only as footnotes and should include year of publication.

Illustrations will be used only when necessary and will be confined to text figures or diagrams of simple character. The editors, at their discretion, may call upon an author to defray the cost of his illustrations, although no charge will be made for printing from a suitable cut supplied with the manuscript.

Proof.—In order to facilitate prompt publication no proof will be sent to authors unless requested. It is urged that manuscript be submitted in final form; the editors will exercise due care in seeing that copy is followed.

Authors' Copies and Reprints.—On request the author of an original article will receive gratis ten copies of the number containing his contribution and as many additional copies as he may desire at five cents each. Reprints will be furnished at the following schedule of prices:

	4 pp.	8 pp.	12 pp.	16 pp.
50 copies	$1.05	$1.90	$2.85	$3.70
100 copies	1.25	2.30	3.45	4.50
Additional copies, per 100	.40	.80	1.20	1.50

Covers bearing the name of the author and title of the article, with inclusive pagination and date of issue, will be $1.50 for the first 100. Additional covers $.50 per 100.

As an author may not see proof, his request for extra copies or reprints should invariably be attached to the first page of his manuscript.

The rate of Subscription per volume is	$6.00*
Semi-monthly numbers	.25
Monthly numbers	.50

Remittances should be made payable to "Washington Academy of Sciences," and addressed to William Bowie, Treasurer, Coast and Geodetic Survey, Washington, D. C., to Williams & Wilkins Company, 2419-2421 Greenmount Ave., Baltimore, Md., or to the European Agents.

European Agents: William Wesley & Son, 28 Essex St., Strand, London, and Mayer and Müller, Prinz Louis-Ferdinand Str., Berlin.

Exchanges.—The JOURNAL does not exchange with other publications.

Missing Numbers will be replaced without charge, provided that claim is made within thirty days after date of the following issue.

* Volume I, however, from July 19, 1911 to December 19, 1911, will be sent for $3.00. Special rates are given to members of scientific societies affiliated with the Academy.

THE WAVERLY PRESS
BALTIMORE, U. S. A.

CONTENTS

Lightning Source UK Ltd.
Milton Keynes UK
UKHW022016210119
335961UK00017B/1496/P